MW00395925

Medallic Portraits of

Washington

2nd Ed.

Russell Rulau and George Fuld

In consultation with Q. David Bowers

© 1999 by
Krause Publications, Inc.

All rights reserved. No portion of this publication may be reproduced or transmitted in any form or by any
means, electronic or mechanical, including photocopy, recording, or any information storage and retrieval
system, without permission in writing from the publisher, except by a reviewer who may quote brief
passages in a critical article or review to be printed in a magazine or newspaper, or electronically
transmitted on radio or television.

Published by

**krause
publications**

700 E. State Street • Iola, WI 54990-0001
Telephone: 715/445-2214

Please call or write for our free catalog of numismatic publications.
Our toll-free number to place an order or obtain a free catalog is 800-258-0929
or please use our regular business telephone 715-445-2214
for editorial comment and further information.

Library of Congress Catalog Number: 98-87365
ISBN: 0-87341-681-3

Printed in the United States of America

Reverse painting on glass. The Pater Patriae (Father of his Country) is mourned by Columbia and a weeping soldier. By an unknown painter. (Metropolitan Museum of Art)

Chapter Outline

INTRODUCTION

When William Spohn Baker's book *Medallic Portraits of Washington* made its appearance in 1885, the collecting of Washingtonia was one of the high spots of American numismatics. In the 114 years since the publication of Baker, collector interest in the series fell to a low point about 1940, and as recently as 1950 Washington pieces were selling for less than they did in 1860!

There has been a massive and continuing renewal of interest on the part of Americans in the numismatics of the Father of his Country, however, urged along by the 1965 reprint-revision of the Baker work by Dr. George J. Fuld; the American Bicentennial observances in 1976; the sale of the John Work Garrett holdings of Washingtonia in 1980; the delightful appearance of the 250th birthday commemorative half dollar for George Washington in 1982, and our own First (Centennial) Edition of this catalog in 1985.

Baker's pioneering catalog appeared in 1885 and was reasonably complete up to that time, but thousands of worthy Washington pieces have appeared since then, and only our 1985 catalog (long since out of print) attempted to link these together with pricing, copious footnotes and new illustrations for the novice and advanced collector. The centennial of the Constitution, 1887; centennial of Washington's inauguration, 1889; centennial of his death, 1899; sesquicentennial of U.S. independence, 1926; bicentennial of his birth, 1932, and the 250th anniversary of Washington's birth, 1982 - were all occasions in which the Father of his Country was enshrined anew in gleaming metal.

Baker, who listed everything he knew of through about 1883 when his manuscript was finished, did not have to contend with legal tender coins bearing Washington's portrait. The Washington "colonials" (actually early Republic token coinage) and a number of patterns were as close as the world had come in that day to placing Washington's effigy on a spendable coin.

The year 1900 called forth the erection of a monument in Paris to Washington's aide, Marquis de Lafayette, and Washington and Lafayette were shown jugate on the obverse of the Lafayette dollar, America's first coin to depict any of its presidents. (Interestingly, two foreigners, Christopher Columbus in 1892-93 and Queen Isabella in 1893, were the first actual persons to be portrayed on U.S. coins, the Columbian half dollar and Isabella quarter.)

George Washington appears on pitifully few different types of legal tender coins. In America they are the 1900 Lafayette dollar, 1926 Sesquicentennial half dollar, George Washington 1982 half dollar, the three 1991 Mount Rushmore coins, and the Washington quarter. The quarter dollar trade coin, issued with every year date but 1933 and 1975 through 1998, is the saving

grace. Hundreds of millions of these small coins have passed through the hands of four generations of Americans and others around the globe since 1932 and the face (as modeled by Houdon) of the Pater Patriae is remarkably well known.

America will be gracing the reverse of the Washington quarter with images from the 50 states of the Union, so 50 new designs will be keeping his effigy fresh and meaningful for years to come. America will also issue a 1999 $5 gold coin to honor the 200th anniversary of his death.

Of foreign nations only a few have seen fit to grace their coinage with Washington's portrait. The Isle of Man and the Turks and Caicos Islands, both British dependencies, took this first step in 1976 and other foreign coins have also been issued since.

A greatly useful reference on Washingtonia appeared in 1949, Susan H. Douglas' "The George Washington Medals of 1889", as part of *The Numismatist* that year.

A very popular monograph, Wayte Raymond's *The Early Medals of Washington*, appeared in 1941 to boost the flagging fortunes of Washington medal collecting. The well illustrated monograph covers the important early struck medals from 1776 through 1834 - ignoring the engraved Indian Peace medals.

The present volume is a complete revision of Baker, with listings added from Douglas' work, Francis Prucha's catalog of Indian Peace medals, and other major literary works by Hansen, Melvin Fuld, Collins, Levine, Hume and many others. The section on Early Republic token coinage has been completely redone from our 1985 edition, though following Baker's original arrangement. The section on pattern pieces has been enlarged, as have the sections on 19th and 20th century store cards. A greatly expanded 1932 Bicentennial chapter is included.

What to include and what to exclude? The choice has been arbitrary because no single work could include everything. We trust we have included that which is important, especially before World War II.

Russell Rulau and
George Fuld
December, 1998

RARITY SCALE

The rarity of Washington medals is at best an estimate based on our experience, auction records, etc. We have examined numerous collections as well as having inventories on many more.

In the 1965 reprint and revision of Baker published by Krause Publications under the editorship of Dr. George Fuld, rarity ratings were assigned to almost all the original Baker pieces, and these ratings have now stood the test of 34 years of exposure to experts, specialists and other users of the catalog. So we feel a certain confidence in advancing them again.

The rarity scale used is a 1 (common) to 10 (unique) scale adapted from that proposed by Dr. W. H. Sheldon in Penny Whimsy and used so successfully in the Fulds' books on Civil War tokens. The scale is based on the number of pieces known, as follows:

Rarity	Estimated Number Existing
1	Over 4,000 (Common)
2	2,000 to 4,000
3	500 to 1,999
4	200 to 499
5	75 to 199
6	20 to 74
7	10 to 19
8	5 to 9
9	2 to 4
10	Unique (1 only)

DRAWN BY B. TROTT.   ENGRAVED BY C. GOBRECHT.

GEORGE WASHINGTON.

Portrait of George Washington drawn by B. Trott and engraved by Christian Gobrecht (1785-1844), the third engraver of the U.S. Mint. Gobrecht became assistant engraver in 1836 and chief engraver in 1840. Based on the 1796 Gilbert Stuart portrait.

PREFACE

Washington medals form a considerable portion of that great monument which love and gratitude have so steadily built in memory of the services and virtues of the man who is often termed "the foremost man in American History."

While some may rank Abraham Lincoln - or another - above the Pater Patriae (Father of his Country), none will dispute the point that - were it not for George Washington - there might well not have been a United States of America.

The medallic form of expression has lost much of its historic significance and fitness, but thanks to the 1885 work of W.S. Baker there at least was begun a systematic arrangement of the pieces, so that the medallic history of Washington could be viewed and comprehended. Partial lists before Baker (and since) only bewilder the student and collector.

Baker's words about the medallic portraiture in his 1885 opus are as germane today as they were a century ago, and so we repeat them here:

"All of the original portraits of Washington, commencing with that by Charles Willson Peale painted in 1772 and ending with the one by Saint Memin in 1798, possess either on account of faithfulness of representation, artistic excellence, or historical connection, an engrossing interest.

"Of these the Du Simitiere (1779), Joseph Wright (1790), and Gilbert Stuart (1796) have been introduced on medals, none of which, excellent as they may be in other respects, are of that positive character demanded by the requirements of medallic portraiture.

"The Houdon bust, however, seems to meet fully the demand. Modeled from a cast taken from the face at Mount Vernon in October, 1785, and used for the first time on the Washington Before Boston medal (see Chapter 4), it has not only come to be recognized as the medallic type, but also as the standard portrait of Washington.

"No other representation of the features of the hero and statesman, which has come down to us from either painter or sculptor, conveys to the mind of the observer a fuller sense of individuality, strength of character, and dignity of purpose. Its truthfulness to nature cannot reasonably be doubted, and an examination of the portrait by Robert Edge Pine painted a few months earlier, and that by Edward Savage five years later in date, both of which possess similar characteristics, will convince the most skeptical.

"The painting by Pine, the work of a finished artist, has always been classed as an admirable portrait, and the latter - although claiming no artistic excellence - certainly leaves the impression of being a faithful portrayal of an individual.

"Of the other portraits noticed, the Du Simitiere is best known, from its being found on the coins (Colonial coins), while the profile by Wright - drawn and etched in 1790 - quite as interesting and available, is but little known, the representation thus far with one or two exceptions being anything but good translations."

There have, of course, been a large number of medals portraying Washington issued in the century since Baker wrote these words, but only a few totally new renditions of Washington portraiture have appeared within the confines of the round coin or medal.

A few notable departures from the Houdon-Stuart-Wright-Du Simitiere group of portraiture motifs may be mentioned. A notable new representation of George Washington appears on the 1939 American Numismatic Society medal (see Chapter 31), and an innovative spinoff of the Stuart effigy on Elizabeth Jones' 1982 George Washington half dollar (see chapter 1).

It needs but a glance at the chapter titles to reveal how the name of George Washington is associated in the minds of a people with all their diversified interests, pursuits and enterprises. Setting aside those directly referring to his own history, civil and military, the memorials of his death, eulogistic inscriptions and quotations from his pen (which comprise the Washington Medals proper), the catalog will be found to contain almost every subject, national, local and personal, which has arisen in the two centuries since his death in 1799.

Whenever benevolence is to be awakened, patriotism aroused, emulation excited, temperance inculcated, industry stimulated, monuments erected, or events celebrated, the mind of the medallic designer seems to turn at once to the Pater Patriae, and the resultant medal must, of course, bear his effigy or at least call upon his name.

Interesingly, George Washington has apparently never been satirized on a medallic work. All medals show nothing but respect - though the workmanship on some of them is execrable and thus may be said to show some sort of indirect lack of respect.

In his own preface to the 1885 opus, which he dated at Philadelphia Nov. 1, 1884, Baker expressed gratitude to U.S. Mint engravers William H. Key and George T. Morgan and to private medalist George Hampden Lovett of New York for important technical information gathered for his catalog.

The present authors express gratitude to all those researchers of the past, and those of the present, who are named on the Contributors' page.

A few words in closing. Are Washington medals and their collecting a thing of the past? Hardly. Every day we see new evidence of massive interest in this subject, and it continues growing. Hardly a first-class numismatic auction catalog has been produced in the 1990's without its section on Washingtonia, and a good number of catalogs and fixed price listings have been dominated by assemblages of Washingtonia. The upcoming 1999 multipart sale of the giant collection formed by Dr. Irving N. Schuster may set records not seen since the Garrett, Norweb, Collins, Magriel and Brand (1985) sales occurred.

Collectors and dealers who have access to the First Edition of this work (1985) may be amazed to see that a good number of Washington pieces have doubled or trebled in price in just 14 years. The pricing quoted herein is not imaginary; it is a compilation of auction and private treaty sales. A list of public sales on which many prices are based may be found herein.

This maxim holds true: The brightest spot in medal collecting is Washingtonia. It exceeds all other categories by a league.

W.S. Baker's collection is still largely intact. It is held at Historical Society of Pennsylvania at Philadelphia.

Houdon's bust of Washington, modeled from a cast taken off his face itself in Oct., 1785, is the best model for medallic art. Washington in his prime stood 6 feet 3 inches tall and weighed a well-muscled 220 pounds. Here he is 53 years old.

Contributors to this Edition

David Thomason Alexander
Frederick Borgmann
Paul Bosco
Q. David Bowers
Kenneth E. Bressett
Gregory G. Brunk
Catherine Bullowa-Moore
Carl W.A. Carlson
John Cheramy
William Christensen
Elvira Clain-Stefanelli
Courtney L. Coffing
George Cuhaj
Richard W. Doty
L.B. Fauver
D.L. Fennimore
John J. Ford Jr.
Cora Lee Gilliland
Philip Greenslet
Dick Grinolds
David C. Harper
Rich Hartzog
Steve Hayden

Jimmie Hayes
Leon Hendrickson
David H. Hirsch
Michael Hodder
Everett Hull
D. Wayne Johnson
Robert W. Julian
Donald Kagin
Charles E. Kirtley
Paul Koppenhaver
Kurt R. Krueger
H. Joseph Levine
Dana Linett
Deborah Rae McDonald
Bob Moffatt
Su Nadin-Davis
Eric P. Newman
John M. Pack
Donald N. Partrick
Derek Charles Pobjoy
Francis P. Prucha
Edwin V. Quagliana
William Russell Raiford

Jeff Rock
Reigh L. Roelofs
Jerome Schaeper
David W. Schaetzle
David Schenkman
Irving L. Schuster
David R. Sear
Russell Sears
Arlie R. Slabaugh
Bob Slawsky
Henry Spangenberger
Harvey Stack
Alan M. Stahl
Stephen Tanenbaum
Don Taxay
Barry Tayman
Robert A. Vlack
L.W. Vosloh
Alan V. Weinberg
R.B. White
Robert Wilhite
Michael Brand Zeddies

American Numismatic Association
American Numismatic Society
Amos Press Inc.
Bowers & Merena Galleries
British Museum
Civil War Token Society
Massachusetts Historical Society
Mount Vernon Association

Presidential Coin & Antique Co.
Smithsonian Institution
Society of the Cincinnati
Stack's Inc.
Token and Medal Society
Winterthur Museum
Wisconsin Historical Society

Gratitude to those who Explored this Pathway Earlier

Edgar H. Adams
Charles E. Anthon
William Sumner Appleton
William Spohn Baker
Bauman L. Belden
Charles Wyllys Betts
Frederick C. C. Boyd
William Leggett Bramhall
Virgil Michael Brand
Walter Breen
Charles Ira Bushnell
M.W. Brown
Edward Cogan
Jack Collins
Charles G. Colver
Sylvester S. Crosby

Richard Dalton
J. Doyle DeWitt
Susan H. Douglas
John W. Dunn
Thomas L. Elder
Jules Fonrobert
Leonard Forrer
Sarah E. Freeman
Melvin Fuld
George Ganter
John Work Garrett
T. Harrison Garrett
Homer A. Hall
Samuel H. Hamer
Paul Hamm
Harvey L. Hansen

Edgar Erskine Hume
Byron Johnson
Richard D. Kenney
Joseph Lepczyk
Harry M. Lessin
Joseph N.T. Levick
Gaylor Lipscomb
J.F. Loubat
Lyman Haynes Low
John McCoy
Herbert I. Melnick
William T. R. Marvin
Ralph "Curly" Mitchell
Paul Patterson
William A. Pettit
Richard Picker

Wayte Raymond
John L. Roper
Augustus B. Sage
Max M. Schwartz
James Ross Snowden
Elizabeth C. Steinle
Horatio Robinson Storer
Malcolm Storer
Georg F. Ulex-Hamburg
Roy C. Van Ormer
Adolf Weyl
W.W. C. Wilson
Stewart P. Witham
Isaac F. Wood
Farran Zerbe

Top: a French clock, gilded bronze
Above: a Liverpool pottery teapot
Right: Chinese export porcelain jug

AUCTION CATALOGS REFERRED TO

Atlantic	Exonumia auction for Atlantic Rarities Expo, July 29, 1995 by Presidential Coin & Antique Co.
Auction 60	Exonumia auction, June 21, 1996, by Presidential Coin & AntiqueCo.
Auction 61	Exonumia auction, Nov. 16, 1996, by Presidential Coin & Antique Co.
Auction 62	Exonumia auction, May 16, 1997, by Presidential Coin & Antique Co.
Brand	Virgil M. Brand collection of Masonic Mark pennies, March 25-26,1985, by Bowers & Merena Galleries. Contains the largest assemblage of Masonic lodge tokens ever offered.
Bullowa-Lessin	Harry M. Lessin collection, Sept. 19, 1984, by Catherine E. Bullowa
Clark	Dr. Glenn M. Clark collection, Feb. 17-18, 1984, by Herbert I. Melnick Inc.
Coin Galleries	Washington collection sale, July 18, 1995, by Coin Galleries division of Stack's Inc.
Collins	Frederick C. C. Boyd collection, fixed price list, 1991, by Jack Collins
Colonial	Colonial Coins and Medals fixed price list, 1990, by Stack's Inc.
Dreyfuss	David W. Dreyfuss collection, Apr. 12, 1986, by Bowers & Merena Galleries and Presidential Coin & Antique Co., jointly.
Early American	Mail bid auction, June 8, 1996, by Early American Numismatic Auctions Inc.
Fred-Ward	Rogers Fred and Peter Ward collections, Nov. 13-14, 1995, by Bowers & Merena Galleries. Contains extensive offering of U.S. Assay Commission medals.
Ganter I	George Ganter collection, June 25, 1994, by Presidential Coin & Antique Co.
Ganter II	George Ganter collection, Nov. 19, 1994, by Presidential Coin & Antique Co.
Garden State	Exonumia auction for Garden State numismatic convention, May 16, 1997, by Presidential Coin & Antique Co.
Garrett IV	John Work Garrett collection of Johns Hopkins University, March 25-26, 1981, by Bowers & Ruddy Galleries.
Great Eastern	Great Eastern collection, June 24, 1989, by Presidential Coin & Antique Co.
Hartzog	World Exonumia sale, Sept. 4, 1984, by Rich Hartzog
Historical	American Historical Medals fixed price list, 1991, by Stack's Inc.
Kirtley 64	Exonumia mail bid sale, Dec. 4, 1990, by Charles E. Kirtley
Kirtley NYCII	Exonumia auction, March 23, 1991, by Charles E. Kirtley
Kirtley 144	Exonumia mail bid sale, May 6, 1997, by Charles E. Kirtley. Contains large offering of unpublished medals and 1907-12 store cards.
Kirtley 158	Exonumia mail bid sale, March 31, 1998, by Charles E. Kirtley. Contents similar to sale 144
Krueger	Summer Americana & Exonumia sale, Aug. 1983, by Kurt R. Krueger
Landmark	Four landmark collections (Hagle, Griner, Rudduck, Bebee), March 27-31, 1989, by Bowers & Merena Galleries
Magriel	Paul Magriel collection, June 25, 1988, by Presidential Coin & Antique Co.
McSorley	Charles McSorley collection and other properties, Nov. 15, 1997, by Presidential Coin & Antique Co.
Middendorf	Ambassador J. William Middendorf collection, Dec. 8, 1990, by Presidential Coin & Antique Co.
Norweb	Norweb family collections, Oct. 12-13, 1987, by Bowers & Merena Galleries
Patterson	Dr. Paul Patterson collection, Dec. 8, 1986, by Presidential Coin & Antique Co.
Picker	Richard Picker collection, Oct. 24, 1984, by Stack's Inc.
Roper	John L. Roper collection, Dec. 8, 1983, by Stack's Inc.
Scott	Stanley Scott collection, 1976, by Bowers & Ruddy Galleries
Sebring-Garbe	Thomas Sebring and Gunther Garbe collections, March 21-23, 1996, by Bowers & Merena Galleries
Slawsky	Exonumia mail bid sale, March 30, 1995, by Bob Slawsky. Encased silver Washington quarters.
Springfield	Springfield Library and Museum Association collection, Dec. 15-18, 1981, by Bowers & Merena Galleries
Stack-Collins	Jack Collins collection, April 30, 1996, by Stack's Inc.
Steinberg	Gil Steinberg collection, Oct. 17, 1989, by Stack's Inc.
Witham	Stewart Witham and Sansoucy collections, Sept. 14-15, by Bowers & Merena Galleries.

METALS

Aluminum	pure aluminum, silvery ##
A&S	aluminum ring around silver center
Brass	copper-zinc alloy, yellowish
B&S	brass ring around silver center
Bronze	copper-tin alloy, brownish
Red Bronze	bronzed copper, reddish to mahogany coloration vv
Yellow Bronze	copper-tin alloy, yellowish ww
Celluloid	translucent cc
Copper	pure copper, reddish
Cupronickel	copper-nickel alloy*
Fiber	composition, color stated
Galvanized iron	zinc on iron, grayish
German Silver	copper-nickel-zinc alloy*
Gold	pure gold to gold-copper alloy
Goldine	gilt brass alloy
Iron	pure iron, grayish, magnetic
Lead	pure lead, dark grayish +
Nickel	pure nickel, silvery, magnetic*
N&S	nickel ring around silver center
Pewter	copper-tin alloy, dark gray
Silver	pure silver to silver-copper alloy
Steel	iron alloy, silvery, magnetic
Tin	pure tin***
Vulcanite	hardened rubber ++
White Metal	lead-tin alloy, grayish-white +
Zinc	pure zinc, grayish

* It is frequently difficult to tell nickel and its principal alloys apart. New, they all resemble silver and look much alike. Pure nickel is magnetic; only a small amount of impurity removes the magnetic quality. Cupronickel resists tarnish, while German silver (also called nickel silver or argentan) tarnishes in air much like silver. Nickel and its alloys were used sparingly on Washington medals, but frequently on tokens and coins.

** The best pewters are made of 90% tin and 10% copper, but in the 19th century antimony and bismuth partly replaced copper. All pewters look much alike. They have a hard surface and possess sheen.

*** Pure tin is seldom used in medal manufacture. Old catalogs refer to "tin" pieces; what is meant is generally silvered white metal, a silver-gilt-surfaced lead-tin alloy of great beauty until well worn.

cc Introduced into U.S. manufacture in 1869. Flammable.

vv Red bronze in 19th century U.S. Mint parlance is actually bronzed-surface copper which tones to a rich mahogany color. True bronzes are also red if minimal amounts of tin (or zinc) are used as hardener.

ww Yellow bronze includes the U.S. Mint 20th century matte surface bronze used for medals on sale to the public. It is attractive when new, but discolors badly when exposed to many forms of airborne or surface contaminants.

+ Lead and white metal pieces have a unique quality: they will not "ring" when sounded with a solid metal piece. Silver, gold, brass and other solid-metal alloys will ring, each with its own bell-like tone.

Very few medals, tokens or patterns were made of aluminum prior to 1890. It was too expensive, and too scarce, for such use. Its price dropped to $1.50 a pound in 1891 and to 75 cents in 1893 and became plentiful for medallic use.

++ Vulcanite was used sparingly in the U.S. in the 1860's onward.

NOTE: The U.S. Mint used primarily .999 fine gold and .999 fine silver for its medal production. unlike its coins which were .900 fine in both cases. British medalists also preferred pure metal, but used coin standards (.9167 fine gold and .925 fine silver) on occasion. Continental European precious metal standards ranged from .800 upward on silver, and .585 upward on gold. The .585 fine gold (14-Karat) was also an American standard for pieces produced by goldsmiths and jewelers.

When a slash (/) is used to connect metals in descriptions, e.g. Silver/Copper, the reader may assume the piece is plated unless otherwise described. Gilt (gold colored) and Silver-Gilt (Silver colored) surfaces were common on medals and tokens before alloys such as goldene or anodyzed aluminum were introduced.

ABBREVIATIONS

A & S	aluminum ring around silver coin		Maj.	Major
abt	about		Maj. Gen.	Major General
Adm.	Admiral		Md. TAMS	Maryland Token & Medal Society
alum	aluminum		Mex.	Mexican
ANA	American Numismatic Association		MHS	Massachusetts Historical Society
ANS	American Numismatic Society		mi.	miles
AU	about uncirculated		mil.	military, militia
AVA	American Vecturist Association		mm	millimeters
B & M	Bowers & Merena Galleries		ms.	manuscript
B & R	Bowers & Ruddy Galleries		N & S	nickel ring around silver coin
B & S	brass ring around silver coin		N/Br	nickel-plated brass
BM	British Museum		no.	number
Br	brass		N/Steel	nickel-plated steel
Brit.	British		obv.	obverse
Brs	brass		oct.	octagonal
Brz	bronze		PCAC	Presidential Coin & Antique Co.
Bs	brass		PF	proof
Bz	bronze		P-L	prooflike
circ.	circulated, circulation		pl.	plated
CN	cupronickel		pop.	population
co.	company		poss.	possibly
Co.	County		prob.	probably
Col.	Colonel		procl.	proclamation
coll.	collection		prov.	province
Cop	copper		R	rarity (rating)
Capt.	Captain		r.	right
ctmk	countermark		rect.	rectangular
ctsp	counterstamp		rev.	reverse
CW	Civil War		Rev.	Revoutionary (War)
CWT	Civil War token		R-F	Rulau-Fuld (game counters)
CWTS	Civil War Token Society		Rv:	reverse
dept.	department		scal	scalloped
diff.	different, differing		Scrc	scarce
EAT	Early American token		S/Br	silvered brass
EF	extremely fine		S/Brass	silvered brass
Eng.	England, English		S/Cop	silvered copper
ex-	out of (collection)		silv.	silver
F	fine		Smithson.	Smithsonian Institution
Fcg	facing		Span. -Am.	Spanish-American
Fr	fair		sq	square
G	good		svd	silvered
G/Brz	gilt bronze		S/WM	silvered white metal
G/Cop	gilt copper		TAMS	Token and Medal Society
Gen.	General		TOGN	Tokens of the Gay Nineties
G/WM	gilt white metal		trian	triangular
GS	German silver		Unc	uncirculated
hex	hexagonal		USMT	U.S. Merchant token
HT	Hard Times		USTT	U.S. Trade token
HTT	Hard Times token		VF	very fine
in.	inches		VG	very good
inst.	institution		vulc.	vulcanite
irreg.	irregular		w/	with
K-M	Krause-Mishler		WM	white metal
l.	left		w/o	without
Lt. Col.	Lieutenant Colonel		Y	Yeoman
Lt. Gen.	Lieutenant General		Yeo	Yeoman
ltr	letter		Z	zinc

A Few Medallic Terms...

Base	Lower portion of a shield
Border	Ornamentation near rim of a medal
Cartouche	A closed shape, generally not a straight-line geometric pattern like a rectangle or square
Chief	Upper portion of a shield
Courant	Rearing on hind legs (horse, unicorn)
Crest	Ornamentation atop a shield
Displayed	Facing, wings spread (eagle)
Edge	That portion of the medal which is neither obverse nor reverse (do not confuse with Rim!)
Electrotype	Generally copper copy made as a shell from original; electrotypes always have a joint line on edge, sometimes well hidden
Exergue	That portion of a medal below a ground line or straight line below main devices
Field	Smooth part of flan, below devices & letters
Flan	Disc on which medal is struck
Incuse	Punched into surface
Intaglio	Opposite side of relief face, on embossed pieces (mirror image, sunken)
Laureate	Laurel wreath on head
Mantled	Wearing a mantle
Mantling	Devices behind a shield
Nude	Naked (bust)
Passant	Passing
Passant Gardant	Passing, head turned toward viewer
Planchet	Synonymous with Flan
Rampant	Rearing on hind legs (lion, bear, etc.)
Relief	Height of devices & lettering above the field
Rim	Outermost part of a medal's face (do not confuse with Edge!)
Supporters	Figures on either side of a shield
Three-quarters (or 3/4)	Facing, head turned one-quarter to a side
Wreath	Generally an open-topped pair of crossed branches

Framed lithographs in color of Martha and George Washington, in 4 by 4 3/4-inch size, made circa 1908. Frames are plaster of paris. (Courtesy Charles E. Kirtley)

DESIGNERS OF WASHINGTON MEDALS

NOTE: The original Baker numbers of 1885 have been extensively supplemented and rearranged, and thus do not necessarily follow in numerical sequence. This guide to engravers, minters and producers thus may be used as an index to the Baker numbering system, to ease in locating by page number.

Baker	Engraver/Medalist	Maker	Publisher/Distributor	Page
47-47ZA	Pierre S. DuVivier	Paris Mint		56-57
48-48H	Pierre S. DuVivier	Paris Mint		57-58
48J	Pierre S. DuVivier	Paris Mint	Horace Binney	58
49	Pierre S. DuVivier	Philadelphia Mint		59
49B-49C	Pierre S. DuVivier/Charles E. Barber	Philadelphia Mint		59
49G-49J	Pierre S. DuVivier	Paris Mint		60
49M	Crowned SR	(European)		60
49CA		Philadelphia Mint		60
50-50L		Robert Lovett Jr.		61
51-51A		Robert Lovett Jr.		61
52-52G		Robert Lovett Jr.		61
52R-52S		Whitehead & Hoag		61
52U				61
52W		Whitehead & Hoag	So. Boston	61
53-53A	Charles C. Wright			62
53F	Charles C. Wright	George Segebaden		62
53G-53M	Charles C. Wright			62
54-54A	John Reich	Philadelphia Mint	Joseph Sansom	62
55-55G	John H. Henning	(England)		63
56-56C	James Adams Bolen			63
57	John Reich	Philadelphia Mint	Joseph Sansom	64
58-58C	John Reich	Philadelphia Mint	Joseph Sansom	64
61-61C	Samuel Brooks		Jacques Manly & Co.	65
62-62B	Samuel Brooks		W. S. Lincoln & Son	65-66
63-63B	Selig Baumgarten		Reed & Brady	66
64-64C	Selig Baumgarten	Jacob Gminder	George Massamore	66
65	Joseph Wright	Twigg		66
66	Thomas Wyon			67
67-67A	Thomas Wyon			67
70-70P	Thomas Halliday			67
70S-70T	Thomas Halliday	Thomason & Jones		67-68
71-71B	John Reich		Joseph Sansom	68
72-72B	John Reich	Philadelphia Mint		68
72F	John Reich			68
72M-72P	John Reich	Philadelphia Mint		68
73-73C	John Reich		S.H.&H. Chapman	68
74-74D	Charles C. Wright	Wright & Bale		69
75-75C	Charles C. Wright			69
A75				69
76-76D	Charles C. Wright			69
77-77E	George H. Lovett		Alfred S. Robinson	69
A77	Script B	MM monogram		69
78-78D		(Paris, France)	Voltaire (Arouet)	70
79-79D	James Sharpless ?	John Westwood ?		70
80-80B	John Westwood	(England)		71
81-81B	John Westwood	(England)		71
82	John Westwood	(England)		71
83	H. (Henning ?)	John Westwood		71
84-84A	H.	John Westwood		71
85-85B	Thomas Webb		Daniel Eccleston	72
86		C. Wyllys Betts		72
87		C. Wyllys Betts		72
88-88D	Joseph H. Merriam			73
89-89C	John B. Gardiner		Ramsey McCoy	72
90-90A	John B. Gardiner		Ramsey McCoy	72
91-91F	William Kneass	Philadelphia Mint		73
A91		Philadelphia Mint		73
92-92B	James A. Bolen			73
93-93A	James A. Bolen		A. R. McCoy	73
94-94F		William H. Key		73
95-95C				74
96-96C	Charles C. Wright			74

Baker	Engraver/Medalist	Maker	Publisher/Distributor	Page
E96-E96Q	Charles C. Wright		Charles Ira Bushnell	74
97-97C	George H. Lovett			75
98-98M	George H. Lovett			75
99	Frederick B. Smith			75
100-100C	Charles C. Wright		Charles I. Bushnell	75
100M				75
101-101C	Charles C. Wright		Charles I. Bushnell	75
102-102C	Charles C. Wright		Charles I Bushnell	75
103-103C	Charles C. Wright		Charles I. Bushnell	76
A103-A103C	Charles C. Wright		Charles I. Bushnell	76
104-104C	Charles C. Wright		Charles I. Bushnell	76
A104-A104C	Charles C.Wright		Charles I. Bushnell	76
105	Charles C. Wright		Charles I. Bushnell	76
106-109C	Robert Lovett Jr.		Charles I. Bushnell	76
110	Frederick B. Smith			106
111	Frederick B. Smith	Smith & Hartmann		106
112	Frederick B. Smith	Smith & Horst		106
113-113G		George H. Lovett		108
114-114D		George H. Lovett		108
114G		George H. Lovett	Augustus B. Sage	108
115-116C		George H. Lovett		108
117-117B	Frederick B. Smith	Smith & Hartmann		107
118-118B	Charles C. Wright	Smith & Hartmann		106
119-119A	Frederick B. Smith	Smith & Hartmann		107
119B	Frederick B. Smith	Smith & Horst		107
120	Frederick B. Smith	Smith & Hartmann		108
121	Frederick B. Smith	Smith & Horst		108
122-122V		Joseph H. Merriam		108-109
123				109
124-128B		George H. Lovett		109
R128-S128	J. Crutchett	Mt. Vernon Factory		110-111
T128	Abraham Demarest	Mt. Vernon Factory	J. Crutchett	112
129		(England)		117
B129				117
130-130B	John R. A. Bacon	Paris Mint	Amedee Durand	117
131-131A	Mathias N. M. Vivier	Paris Mint	Amedee Durand	117
132-132A	Mathias N. M. Vivier	Paris Mint	Amedee Durand	117
133-133B	Charles C. Wright	Smith & Hartmann		118
134-134B	Frederick B. Smith	Smith & Hartmann		118
135-135D	Robert Lovett Jr.			118-119
136-136G	Robert Lovett Jr.		Edward Cogan	119
137-144A		George H. Lovett		119-120
145-150A		George H. Lovett		120
151-154C	Charles C. Wright		Charles I. Bushnell	120-121
A154				121
155-155B	Anthony C. Paquet	Philadelphia Mint		121
156-156C	Anthony C. Paquet	Philadelphia Mint		121
B156				121
157-157A	William H. Key			121
158-158C		Bale & Smith		121-122
158M-158N	Bale & Smith	George H. Lovett		122
159-159C	Bale & Smith	George H. Lovett		122
B159	Frederick Koch			122
B159A-B159B	Frederick Koch	Paul Franklin		122
160-160H			Philadelphia silversmiths	123
161			Philadelphia tinsmiths	123
162	Godfrey Conradt		Phila Cordwainers	123
163	Thomas			123
163F				124
164-164A	Dudley A. Tyng		Nicholas Pearce	113
165-165C	Dudley A. Tyng	Jacob Perkins		113
166-166C	Dudley A. Tyng	Jacob Perkins		113
167		Jacob Perkins		114
168				114
169-169X		Jacob Perkins		114
170-170A	Conrad H. Kuchler	Boulton & Watt		77
171-171A	Conrad H. Kuchler	Boulton & Watt		77
172-172A	Conrad H. Kuchler	Boulton & Watt		78
173		(England ?)		78
173M-173Q		(Nebraska)		78-79
173R		B. Mead	Pierre Chouteau	79

Baker	Engraver/Medalist	Maker	Publisher/Distributor	Page
173V	Anthony C. Paquet	Philadelphia Mint		80
174-174A				80
174F-174FA			Buffalo Hist. Soc.	81
174G-174K	Thomas Wyon			81
174L-174LA		Philadelphia Mint		81
174M-174P				83-86
174Q-174S	Joseph Richardson Jr.			86-89
174T	Joseph Loring			89
174U	Joseph Richardson Jr.			90
174V-174Y				90-91
F174				88
175-179A		George H. Lovett		92
180-180B		Robert Lovett Jr. ?		92
181-186A		George H. Lovett		92-93
187-194A		George H. Lovett		93-94
195-195B		George H. Lovett		94
H195-H195A				94
J195-J195B				94
L195				94
196-196S	Emile Rogat/Valentin M. Borrel		Cercle Britannique	95
197-197C	Charles C. Wright	Wright & Bale		95
198-198G	Charles C. Wright			95
199-199F				96
200-200B	Robert Lovett Jr.	George H. Lovett	Isaac F. Wood	96
A200	John Flanagan	Medallic Art Co.	Lafayette Friends	96
L200	Maurice Delannoy	Paris Mint	Expo. Coloniale	96
M200	Gaston Lavrillier	Paris Art	Amer. Legion	96
M200B	Gaston Lavrillier	Paris Art		96
201-201C		James Bale		97
202-202B		James Bale		97
203-203B	Charles C. Wright	Wright & Bale		97
H203-H203A				97
204-204B		Joseph H. Merriam		97
205-206B		George H. Lovett		97
A206-C206		(France)		98
E206-E206B		Mexico City Mint	Mexico govt.	98
207-207C	Charles C. Wright	Key		98
208-209B		Robert Lovett Jr.		98-99
H209-H209A				99
210-211C		Key		99
212-212C	Bale & Smith	Robert Lovett Jr.		99
213-213C	Bale & Smith	Robert Lovett Jr.		99
214-214B		Joseph H. Merriam		99
215		Joseph H. Merriam		99
216-216F		George H. Lovett		100
217-217A		William H. Key		100
218	Robert Lovett Jr.	William H. Key		100
219-219C		William H. Key		100
220		Key		100
H220	J. Aumiller	E. K.		100
HA220	Caetani / Z. Nowicki	AIFT ?	Polish-Am Num	100
J220	Christian Gobrecht/Robert Lovett Jr.	Robert Lovett Jr.		100
221-221F	William H. Bridgens			101
221K		William H. Bridgens		101
222		James A. Bolen		101
223-223S	Anthony C. Paquet	Philadelphia Mint		101
224-224A	Anthony C. Paquet	Philadelphia Mint		101
225-225A		Robert Lovett Jr.		101
226-227D		Robert Lovett Jr.		101-102
228-228B	Bale & Smith	Robert Lovett Jr.		102
229-229C		Robert Lovett Jr.		102
230	Frederick B. Smith			102
231-231A	John Marr	Mossin & Marr		102
232-232A	John B. Gardiner	Key		102
233-233A	Joseph H. Merriam	James A. Bolen		102
234-234A	Joseph H. Merriam	James A. Bolen		102
235-240C		William H. Key		102-103
A240		William H. Key		103
241	Charles C. Wright	William H. Key		103
242-242A	Charles C. Wright/Anthony C. Paquet	William H. Key		103
243	Charles C. Wright	William H. Key		103

Baker	Engraver/Medalist	Maker	Publisher/Distributor	Page
244				103
245-245X	Anthony C. Paquet/Charles E. Barber	Philadelphia Mint		103
246-246A	Anthony C. Paquet/Charles E. Barber	Philadelphia Mint		104
247-247C	George, H. Lovett	Scovill Mfg. Co.	William L. Bramhall	104
248-248H				104
249-249B		William H. Key		104
250-250D		William H. Key		104
251-251A		George H. Lovett		104
252-252C	Anthony C. Paquet	Philadelphia Mint		104
253-253B		Philadelphia Mint	George B. Soley	105
254-254B	F. C. Key			105
255-256A				105
256X	Anthony C. Paquet/George T. Morgan	Philadelphia Mint		105
257-257B		James A. Bolen		125
258-258C		James A. Bolen	Phila Union League	125
259-259C		James A. Bolen		125
260-263F		George H. Lovett		126
264-264G		Robert Lovett Jr.		126
A264		Robert Lovett Jr.		126
265-267S				127
268-268M		Robert Lovett Jr.	Edward Cogan	127
269-270A		Robert Lovett Jr.		128
A270		Robert Lovett Jr.		128
271-271C		George H. Lovett		128
272-272C		Davis (Birmingham)	Joseph Davis ?	128
273		Davis (Birmingham)		128
274-274D	F. C. Key			128
275-275C		George H. Lovett		128-129
276-276A		George H. Lovett	Augustus B. Sage	129
P276		George H. Lovett	Augustus B. Sage	129
277-278F		George H. Lovett		129
279-279U	Anthony C. Paquet	Philadelphia Mint		129-130
280-280A				130
281	Charles C. Wright			130
282-282F				130
283				134
284-284A		George H. Lovett		134
285		George H. Lovett		134
286-286D	Giuseppe Longhi	William H. Key	Sigmund K. Harzfeld	135
287-287F	Giuseppe Longhi	William H. Key	Sigmund K. Harzfeld	135
A287	A. E. Gale	(England)	Anglo-Am. Comm.	135
C287			Keyser family	136
D287-D287D	Pierre S. DuVivier	Paris Mint		136
D287F-D287G	Pierre S. DuVivier	Philadelphia Mint		137
288-288D	Pierre E. du Simitiere	Peter Getz ?		138
289-289S		George H. Lovett		138-139
290	Anthony C. Morin	George H. Lovett		139
291	Charles C. Wright	George H. Lovett		139
292-292E	Rudolph Laubenheimer			139
293-293C		George H. Lovett		140
294-295		Joseph H. Merriam		140
296-297B		George H. Lovett		140
M297-M297E			Wash. Lodge 59	140
N297			Roxbury Lodge	141
0297-0297A		August C. Frank	Grand Lodge Pa.	141
0-297F	Donald DeLue	Medallic Art Co.	Grand Lodge Pa.	141
0-297G	Donald DeLue	Medallic Art Co.	Grand Lodge Pa.	141
PA297		August C. Frank	Philo Lodge 444	142
P297-S297G				146-147
T297-T297A		George H. Lovett		147
T297C-T297P				147-148
U297-U297A		George H. Lovett		148
U297F-U297K		(Minneapolis)		148
V297-Z297				148
ZA297				148
298-298B		George H. Lovett	Isaac F. Wood	146
299-299D	Pierre S. DuVivier		George B. Soley	142
300-301E	Anthony C. Paquet			142
301J	F. C. Key ?			142
302-303C		William H. Key	Sigmund K. Harzfeld	142-143
304-304D		George H. Lovett	Isaac F. Wood	143

Baker	Engraver/Medalist	Maker	Publisher/Distributor	Page
305-305K				143
306-306B		George H. Lovett	Isaac F. Wood	143
307-308A		George H. Lovett		144
309		George H. Lovett	Isaac F. Wood	144
310-310A		George H. Lovett	Lake City Lodge	144
A310			Pittsburgh Jr OUAM	144
C310			Sta. Barbara Masons	144
E310		Dieges & Clust	Pleasantville 886	144
G310			Chicago 45 RAM	145
311-314	Charles Cushing Wright		Charles I. Bushnell	145
B314-B314A	Casa Baron	(Mexico)	Cuernavaca Ldg 23	145
C314				145
D314			Tampa Consistory	145
315-319F		George H. Lovett		149
S319-S319A	Charles Osborne/Lea Ahlborn	Stockholm Mint	Amer. Num. Soc.	150
T319		Medallic Art Co.	N.Y. Stock Exch.	150
320-320B				152
321-322C		George H. Lovett	Isaac F. Wood	152
M322				152
N322				152
0322				153
P322	'T' monogram			153
Q322-S322				153-154
323-323E		George H. Lovett		153
324-324D		Robert Lovett Jr.		153
B324-B324A	Bechtel of Trenton			155
C324-C324B				155-156
D324				156
E324				156
M324				155
N324				155
Q324				156
S324-S324A	Peter L. Krider	August C. Frank	Soc. Cincinnati	154
T324-T324A				154
U324-U324E	George T. Morgan			154
U324J				155
V324				156
X324	Ralph J. Menconi	Medallic Art Co.	Capitol Hist. Soc.	156
Y324				157
Z324	John LaVelle	Medallic Art Co.	J. G. Graham/Bkln Plaza Assn	157
325-325D	Anthony C. Paquet	Philadelphia Mint		157
326-326B	Anthony C. Paquet	Philadelphia Mint		157
327	John Reich	Philadelphia Mint	Wash. Benevolent	158
328-328D		Robert Lovett Sr.	Wash. Temperance	158
329-329B		Robert Lovett Sr.	Wash. Temperance	158
330-330A			Wash. Temperance	158
331			Wash. Temperance	158
332-332D		James Bale		158-159
333		James Bale		159
334				159
335	Solomon Schmidt			159
336-336C		Robert Lovett Jr.	O.U.A.M.	159
337-337A		Key	Joseph N. T. Levick	260
338-338D			Wash Chowder Club	159
339-339C	William H. Key	Philadelphia Mint	Lancaster A&M Soc.	159-160
339D	William H. Key		Lancaster A&M Soc.	160
A339	A. Glickman/R. Adelman	(Israel)	B'nai B'rith	160
340-340A	Charles C. Wright		Union Agric. Soc.	160
341-341 B		Robert Lovett Sr.	Mech. Literary Assn.	160
R341-X341			P.O. Sons of Amer.	162
Y341		L.F. Grammes	P.O. Sons of Amer.	163
Z341			Ladies Loyal Leag.	163
342-342F	Francis N. Mitchell	Philadelphia Mint	Metro. Mech. Inst.	163
343-343A		Robert Lovett Jr.	American Institute	163
344	James B. Longacre	Philadelphia Mint	Washington College	163
345	James B. Longacre	Philadelphia Mint	Wash. & Lee Univ.	164
Q345		Dieges & Clust	N. Y. American	164
R345		Whitehead & Hoag	N.Y. American	164
R345M		Whitehead & Hoag	Pittsburgh Press	164
S345	Pierre C. L'Enfant	(Court jewelers, Paris)	Soc. Cincinnati	164
S345R	Pierre C. L'Enfant	Bailey Banks Biddle	Soc. Cincinnati	165

Baker	Engraver/Medalist	Maker	Publisher/Distributor	Page
S345T	Pierre C. L'Enfant	(New Hampshire)		165
T345	Charles E. Barber	Philadelphia Mint	Soc. Cincinnati	167
U345	Pierre C. L'Enfant	Whitehead & Hoag	Soc. Cincinnati	167
V345-V345A	Pierre C. L'Enfant	Victor D. Brenner		167-168
W345	George T. Morgan	Philadelphia Mint	Soc. Cincinnati	168
X345		Robbins Co.	Soc. Cincinnati	168
Y345		Bailey Banks Biddle	Soc. Cincinnati	169
346	Anthony C. Paquet	Philadelphia Mint	West Point	169
S346		Grand Army Rep.		169
347-347B	Charles E. Barber	Philadelphia Mint	US Assay Comm	169
A347	Charles E. Barber	Philadelphia Mint		169
348	Charles E. Barber	Philadelphia Mint	US Assay Comm	169
A348	Charles E. Barber	Philadelphia Mint	US Assay Comm	170
B348		Philadelphia Mint	US Assay Comm	170
C348	DuVivier / ?	Philadelphia Mint	US Assay Comm	171
D348		Philadelphia Mint	US Assay Comm	171
E348		Philadelphia Mint	US Assay Comm	170
F348	Laura Gardin Fraser/John R. Sinnock	Philadelphia Mint	US Assay Comm	171
349		Davis (Birmingham)	Joseph Davis ?	171
350		Davis (Birmingham)		171
351		Davis (Birmingham)		171
352-352C		George H. Lovett		172
353		Davis (Birmingham)		171
354		William H. Key		171
355		Robert Lovett Jr.		172
356-356B	Robert Lovett Senior			172
A356			Daughters Rev.	172
B356			Daughters Rev.	172
E356-E356B	Anton Scharff	Joseph Christelbauer	Hall of Fame	173
F356-F356A	G. W. Carter	Medallic Art Co.	Hall of Fame	173
357	Anthony C. Morin			173
358-358K		Ludwig C. Lauer		242
359	Anthony C. Paquet		1st Regt. Inf.	173
360-360A		Philadelphia Mint	Phila. Rifle Club	173
A360-C360		Joseph K. Davison	Engineers Club	174
361-361B	Anthony C. Morin/Anthony C. Paquet			175
362-362G			NY Sanitary Fair	175
363-363B	Anthony C. Paquet		Great Cent. Fair	175
364-364D			Nantucket Sanit.	176
365-365A		James A. Bolen	Soldiers Fair	176
366	James A. Bolen	A. R. McCoy		176
367				176
368-368C		Robert Lovett Jr.	Bailey & Co.	177
369-369C		William H. Key	Isaac F. Wood	177
370-370C		Robert Lovett Jr.		177
371-371C		George H. Lovett		177
372-372B	Anthony C. Paquet	George H. Lovett		178
373-374B		George H. Lovett		178
375-375A	Charles E. Barber		Bethany School	178
376-376A		Robert Lovett Jr.		178
377-377E	Anthony C. Paquet			178
378-378A	Anthony C. Paquet			179
F378	Charles E. Barber		Intl Med Congress	179
G378		James Murdock	Ohio Valley Expo	179
K378	C. B. Millefiori	C. Orsini		179
P378				180
379-379D		Robert Lovett Jr.		181
380-380A		William H. Key		181
381	W. H. Bridgens	William H. Key		181
382-382A	W. H. Bridgens	William H. Key		181
383-383C		William H. Key	Isaac F. Wood ?	181
384-384E	George H. Lovett	Scovill Mfg. Co.	William L. Bramhall	267
385-385A	Benjamin C. True			182
386				182
387		Peter H. Jacobus		182
388-388A	Abraham Demarest	George H. Lovett		183
389-389C		George H. Lovett		183
390-391G		George H. Lovett		183
392-392B		William H. Key		183
393		(England)		184
A393		Carl Stubenrauch		184

Baker	Engraver/Medalist	Maker	Publisher/Distributor	Page
394-394G		George B. Soley		184
395-396J	Anthony C. Paquet	William H. Key		184
C396-C396B				184
397-397C		William H. Key	John H. Diehl	185
398				185
399		James A. Bolen		185
400-403F	Anthony C. Paquet	William H. Key		185
404-405D		George B. Soley		186
406-406A	John F. W. Dorman	U.S. Mfg. Co.		186
407		(France)		186
408-408C		George H. Lovett		186
409-409B		Francis X. Koehler		186
410-410A	C. F. Mohrig	Albert Kuner		187
411-412B		George H. Lovett	Isaac F. Wood	187
413-418B		George H. Lovett		187-188
A418		George H. Lovett		188
419-419C	Anthony C. Paquet			188
420-420A	Anthony C. Paquet	George H. Lovett		188
421-421J				188-189
A421	Francois Anger	Paris Mint		189
B421	Magdeleine Mocquot	Paris Mint		189
F421-F421B	Albin Polasek	U.S. Mint**	SesquiExpo	189
		** Mint equipment at Expo grounds		
422-422M	Smith & Hartmann	Smith & Horst		190
423		Smith & Horst		190
423M	Frederick B. Smith	Smith & Horst		190
424-424A		Robert Lovett Jr.		191
425-425C		Robert Lovett Jr.		191
426-426B	H. Ohlrik	F. Schmahlfeld	V. Christesen	191
427-427B	H. Ohlrik	F. Schmahlfeld	V. Christesen	191
428-428B	R. Laubenheimer			192
429		(Germany)		192
430-432C		(Germany)		192
A432				192
433-433C		George B. Soley		192
434-434C		George B. Soley		192
435-435B		George H. Lovett		193
A435	Francois Anger	Paris Mint		193
B435	Magdeleine Mocquot	Paris Mint		193
436-439C		George H. Lovett	Isaac F. Wood	194
440-448N		George H. Lovett		194-196
B448	S. Swett/John Lavelle	Medallic Art Co.	Bkln Bridge Assn	196
449-449R	William E. Barber	Philadelphia Mint		196
450-450A				197
451-451 B		William H. Key	Sigmund K. Harzfeld	197
452-452C		Peter L. Krider		197
C452				197
E452				197
453-453C	George T. Morgan			197-198
454-454B	George T. Morgan		Pennsylvania State	198
A454		Medallic Art Co.	Grand Lodge Va.	198
E454	Edgar E. Hume/A. Baqueville	Paris Mint	Va Soc Cincinnati	198
F454				199
J454		(Berlin)		199
K454	Pierre Turin	Paris Mint		199
M454				200
455-455M		Robert Lovett Jr.		200
456-456C		George H. Lovett		200
R456-R456A	Abraham Demarest			134
S456				200
457-457H	George T. Morgan	John H. Diehl		200
458-458A	George T. Morgan	John H. Diehl		200
459-459B	Charles C. Wright/Anthony C. Paquet	Warner & Bro.		201
460-460B	Anthony C. Paquet			201
461		Robert Lovett Jr.		201
462-462A				201
463-463B		William H. Key		201
464-464E		George B. Soley		201
A464	J.D.L.	a.	Longines Symph	202
A464A	W.	a.	Longines Symph	202
AA464	J. D. L.	a.	Longines Symph	202

Baker	Engraver/Medalist	Maker	Publisher/Distributor	Page
AC464	A.M.		Wiftnauer PMG	202
B464		Franklin Mint	Natl Commem Soc	202
610-613				248
614		Davis (Birmingham)		248
617		C. Wyllys Betts	New Haven Num.	248
A617			Intl Assn Prof Num	160
AA617		Robbins Co.		161
B617			Am Israel Numis	161
C617			Morgenstern Found.	161
E617			Amer. Num. Assn.	161
K617			Amer. Num. Assn.	161
618		Joseph H. Merriam		248
619				249
620-620B				249
621-621A	Robert Lovett Jr.			249
624-625		William H. Key		249
627-631		George H. Lovett		249
639-639M		George H. Lovett	Isaac F. Wood	249
640-640A		George H. Lovett.	Isaac F. Wood	249
641-641A		Robert Lovett Jr.		250
642		George H. Lovett		250
M642	Robert Lovett Jr.		Thomas L. Elder	250
N642		Childs & Co. ?		250
643-646	Charles C. Wright		Charles I. Bushnell	250
647-647B				250
648		Kettle & Sons		250
649-649A	Louisa Lander			251
M649				251
N649				251
650-650B		William H. Key		251
651-651A		George B. Soley		251
C651	G. H.			251
M651				251
N651				251
M652				251
N652		Robert Lovett Jr.		251
P652				252
653				252
654-654B				252
A654-B654	(Philadelphia)	Robert Bashlow		252
660				255
675				252
676			Freedoms Foundn	253
A676-A676A	Philip Nathan		Freedoms Foundn	253
677				254
678-678A	Francois Anger	Paris Mint		254
B678-B678A			Amer Wheelmen	257
C678				255
CA678		Bailey Banks Biddle		254
D678			Sons Amer. Rev.	255
E678		Whitehead & Hoag		255
E678C				254
EA678		Robbins Co.	Sons Amer. Rev.	256
EB678		Whitehead & Hoag		256
EC678		Medallic Art Co.		256
F678	John Eyerman	Bailey Banks Biddle		256
G678				257
H678				257
J678				257
K678-K678B		(European ?)		257
L678-L678A			NY Police Reserve	258
M678				258
N678			Univ. Postal Union	258
P678		(Milwaukee ?)	Wash. Artillery Co.	258
Q678		Childs & Co.		259
682				259
683		Franklin Mint		259
900-900C	Laura Gardin Fraser	Philadelphia Mint	Bicent. Commission	222
901-901 B	Laura G. Fraser	Bailey Banks Biddle	Bicent. Commission	222
901C	Laura G. Fraser	Philadelphia Mint		223
902		Philadelphia Mint		224

Baker	Engraver/Medalist	Maker	Publisher/Distributor	Page
903-903A	Lucien Bazor	Paris Mint		224
A903		Whitehead & Hoag		224
904		Mayer & Wilhelm		225
A904-A904A		F. H. Noble Co.		225
C904				225
D904				225
E904				225
F904	Fraser	Medallic Art Co.		225
G904				226
J904				226
K904				226
L904-L904A		Medallic Art Co.		226
M904				226
N904				226
Q904-Q904C		A. Kahn Inc.		226
R904		Dieges & Clust		227
905		Bastian Bros.	Fredericksburgh	227
906		Whitehead & Hoag	Fredericksburgh	227
A906		Robbins Co.	Fredericksburgh	227
907		Robbins Co.	Masonic Memorial	227
907A		Whitehead & Hoag	Masonic Memorial	227
A907		Robbins Co.	Masonic Memorial	227
908		Whitehead & Hoag	Masonic Memorial	227
A908		Grammes Co.	Masonic Memorial	227
909		Whitehead & Hoag	Yorktown Ch. 304	228
A909			Masonic Memorial	228
B909		Bailey Banks Biddle	Masonic Memorial	228
910		Bastian Bros.	Sharon Elks Home	228
911		Whitehead & Hoag	Knights Pythias	228
A911			Eaton Rotary	228
C911	L. B. Bauer ?		Philippine Masons	228
912		Bastian Bros.	Fort Necessity	229
A912		Bastian Bros.	Friendship Fire	229
913			Virginia Firemen	229
914		Bastian Bros.		229
915		Bastian Bros.	P.O.S. of A.	230
A915		Bastian Bros.	N.J. P.O.S. of A.	230
B915			Pa. P.O. S. of A	230
C915		Bastian Bros.	Richmond Blues	230
916-916A		Bastian Bros.		230
918-919		Bastian Bros.		230-231
A919-A919A				231
B919		Bastian Bros.		231
D919			City Appleton	231
F919		Whitehead & Hoag	Daughters Rev.	231
G919-K919		Bastian Bros.	Repub Natl Conv	231
M919		Greenduck Co.	Chicago Comm.	233
N919-Q919		Greenduck Co.		233
920		Bastian Bros.	St. Paul Church	233
921		Bastian Bros.	Eagles Conv.	233
A921	Literary Digest			233
922		Robbins Co.	Rhode Island	233
923		Robbins Co.	Rhode Island	233
924-924A		Robbins Co.	Rhode Island	233
925-925D		Whitehead & Hoag		234
926-926C		Whitehead & Hoag		234
0926				234
927		Whitehead & Hoag	Eastern States	234
928		Whitehead & Hoag	I.O. Foresters	234
929		Whitehead & Hoag		234
929F		Whitehead & Hoag	City New York	235
930		Amer. Tree Assn.		235
B930				235
931-931B	Janowsky		Sculpture Sales Assn.	235
932		Whitehead & Hoag		235
A933				236
C933		Greenduck Co.	Ku Klux Klan	235
E933		Grammes Co.	Grammes Co.	236
934		Whitehead & Hoag	American Legion	236
934A		Robbins Co.	American Legion	236
934C		Bastian Bros.	American Legion	236

Baker	Engraver/Medalist	Maker	Publisher/Distributor	Page
934D		Whitehead & Hoag	American Legion	236
934G		Bastian Bros.	American Legion	236
935		Whitehead & Hoag	Vets Forgn Wars	236
936-936B		Whitehead & Hoag		237
A936-A936A		Whitehead & Hoag		237
C936		Whitehead & Hoag	Pulaski Celebn.	237
937-937B		Whitehead & Hoag	Chicago Military	237
939		Bastian Bros.	Macungie Bo	237
940-940A		F. H. Noble Co.	City Green Bay	237
945	Harry Rapp/Aug. Frank	August C. Frank Co.	Detroit Coin Club	238
946			City of Buffalo	238
947-947B		Whitehead & Hoag	NY Bicent Comm	238
948		Whitehead & Hoag	Mass. School	238
1000				243
1000R				243
1001				243
1002				243
1003-1003C				243-244
1003R		J. R. Gaunt & Sons		244
1003S				244
1004				244
A1004	Adam Pietz			244
1005-1007				244
1009-1009A				244
1010-1010A				244
1010R				244
1011				244
1012				244
1013-1013A				244
1014				244
1015				244
1016-1023				245
post 1023		George W. Will		245
post 1023		Blakslee Barns		245
A1023				245
1024				245
1030-1032C				245-246
1036-1042				246
1050-1053AC				246
1053-1053B				246
1054				246
1056				246
1057				246
1058-1059		Robert Bashlow		246
1800-1800A				203
1803				203
1804				203
1805				203
A1805				203
E1805	E. A. Kretschman			203
1806				204
1807		Medallic Art Co.		204
1808				204
1809-1809D	Marcel Jovine	Medallic Art Co.	Capitol Hist. Soc.	204
1810	George T. Morgan			204
1811	Ernest Schroeder	Franklin Mint	Intl. Num. Agency	204
1812	Ronald Hower	Franklin Mint	Great Moments	204
1825		Philadelphia Mint	Wash Mon Assn	219
1826		Philadelphia Mint	Wash Mon Assn	219
1828		Philadelphia Mint	Wash Mon Assn	219
1829-1829A		Philadelphia Mint	Wash Mon Assn	219
1831-1831A		Robert Sneider Co.	Mt. Vernon	219
B1831		Robert Sneider Co.		219
1832-1833		Robert Sneider Co.		220
1835		Robert Sneider Co.		220
1836-1836A			Alexa-Wash Lodge	220
1837			Alexa-Wash Lodge	220
1840-1841		William H. Key		220
1845				220
3000-3000A	Albert Stewart	Medallic Art Co.	Amer. Num. Soc.	239
3001				239

Baker	Engraver/Medalist	Maker	Publisher/Distributor	Page
3002		Etched Products Corp.		239
3004-3004A		Etched Products Corp.		239
3005-3005A		Whitehead & Hoag	Poland govt	239
3006				239
3007				239
Y-1	Key		G. Arnaud	297
Y-2			No Penn Rptr	297
Y-3				298
Y-5	Timothy Keith			298
Y-6				298
Y-7		(Russia)		299
Y-7A				299
Y-8		(England)		299
Y-9	Brevete			299
Y-10			G. Flack	299
Y-11-11A		Medallic Art Co.	Square Deal Prod	299
Y-12			Grand Army Rep.	300
Y-13				300
Y-16-18	Frank Gasparro		Bowers & Merena	300
Y-20	August C. Frank	Aug. C. Frank Co.	John Wanamaker	301
Y-21	Alexander M. Greig	Franklin Mint	Postmasters Amer	301
Y-25		Robbins Co.	Page Academy	301
Y-26	L.		Liberty Lobby	301
Y-27	Richard Lantz	Medallic Art Co.		301
Y-28	R. W. J. / C. W. W.	Medallic Art Co.		301
Y-100			Wash. Assn. N.J.	302
Y-105	U. C. H. ?		Wash. Legion 3	302
Y-110		Tiffany & Co.	Continental Guard	302
Y-112		C. G. Braxmar	Kn. Templar 33	303
Y-113			Essex Stamp Club	303
Y-115-115A			U.S. Postal Service	303
Y-116	Rudolph Freund	Medallic Art Co.		303
Y-117	Anthony Jones	Franklin Mint		303
Y-125		Hamilton Mint		303
Y-200	Kell A. Peale		Soc. Colonial Wars	303
Y-210	Stephan Schwartz			303
Y-215		S.		304
Y-220				304
Y230-230A				304
Y-240	R. Ostrander Smith	Willian Inc.		305
Y-241		Progressive Brass Co.		306
Y-242				307
Y-243	Howard Chandler Christy			307
Y-244	L. W.			307
Y-245				307
Y-246	Laura Gardin Fraser	Medallic Art Co.		307
Y-247	Aphse Foquet	(France)		307
Y-248-248A	G. P. Kato			308
Y249	G. P. Kato			308
Y-250	C. Luini			308

Chapter 1

OFFICIAL COINAGE OF THE UNITED STATES AND OTHER NATIONS

UNITED STATES

WASHINGTON QUARTER DOLLAR

Struck 1932-1998

Baker	Date(s)	Metal	Size	EF	Unc	Proof
C-1	1932	Silver	24.3mm	1.75	2.25	4.50
	'34-64					

Washington head left, LIBERTY above, IN GOD WE / TRUST at left, date below. Rv: Stylized spread eagle, UNITED STATES OF AMERICA / E PLURIBUS / UNUM above, QUARTER DOLLAR below. Reeded edge. Mintmarks appear below bow of the wreath on reverse. Silver fineness: .900. Gross weight: 6.25 grams. Occurs with no mintmark (Philadelphia), D (Denver) and S (San Francisco)

Baker	Date(s)	Metal	Size	EF	Unc	Proof
C-2	'65-67	CN-clad Copper	24.3mm	—	.85	—

As- C-1, but struck in cupronickel-clad copper. Gross weight: 5.67 grams. Mintmarks same as C-1.

Baker	Date(s)	Metal	Size	EF	Unc	Proof
C-3	'68-74	CN-clad Copper	24.3mm	—	.50	1.50
	'77-98					

As C-2, but mintmark now appears on obverse, to right of the tying of Washington's long hair. Gross weight: 5.67 grams. Mintmarks: P (Philadelphia), D (Denver), S (San Francisco), no mark (Philadelphia 1968-1979).

The Washington quarter was originally introduced in 1932 to commemorate the bicentennial of birth of George Washington, 1732-1932. The Standing Liberty quarter had last been struck in 1930. Though introduced for commemorative purposes, the Washington quarter was struck in 1932 in 6.2 million copies and entered circulation. No quarters were minted in 1933, but 35.4 million were minted in 1934. None were minted bearing the 1975 date.

Bicentennial Reverse

Baker	Date(s)	Metal	Size	EF	Unc	Proof
C-4	1976	CN-clad Copper	24.3mm	—	.50	1.25

Obverse as C-3, Rv: Continental drummer at right, facing three-quarters left, torch of liberty within circle of 13 stars to his left, E PLURIBUS / UNUM beneath it. Around: UNITED STATES OF AMERICA / QUARTER DOLLAR. Reeded edge. Gross weight: 5.67 grams. Occurs with mintmarks D (Denver), S (San Francisco), and no mark (Philadelphia).

Baker	Date	Metal	Size	EF	Unc	Proof
C-5	1976	Silver	24.3mm	—	2.25	3.00

As C-4, but struck in an .800 fine silver-clad base silver (.210 fine) core. Reeded edge. Overall silver fineness: .400. Gross weight: 5.75 grams. Occurs only with mintmark S (San Francisco).

The Bicentennial reverse quarters were struck during 1975-1976 but all bear the 1976 date. The circulating coins mark the 200th anniversary of independence of the United States, 1776-1976.

The Washington quarter was designed by John Flanagan. The special Bicentennial reverse was designed by Jack L. Ahr.

States of the Union Reverses

Under the new Coinage Act of 1997, the Washington quarter dollar will honor each of the States of the Union, in their order of admission to the Union. The governors and legislatures of each state shall select the design, which must then go through a federal approval process before being struck. All the coins shall circulate freely, replacing the present Spread Eagle design for the years 1999-2008.

The U.S. Mint will strike five different designs per year until all 50 states are represented. If, during the interim 10-year period additional states are admitted to the Union (e.g. Puerto Rico or Marianas Islands), Congress would have to decide whether the program would be extended to an 11th year. The Washington quarter obverse will also be redesigned (see Chapter 3).

The roster of the first 15 states to be honored (in order) follows:

1999: Delaware, Pennsylvania, New Jersey, Georgia, Connecticut.

2000: Massachusetts, Maryland, South Carolina, New Hampshire, Virginia

2001: New York, North Carolina, Rhode Island, Vermont, Kentucky.

Several adopted designs are shown at the end of Chapter 3, Pattern Coins.

SESQUICENTENNIAL HALF DOLLAR

Struck 1926

Baker	Date	Metal	Size	VF	EF	Unc
C-6	1926	Silver	30.6mm	—	55.00	140.

Jugate busts of George Washington and Calvin Coolidge face right, * LIBERTY * above, UNITED.STATES.OF.AMERICA below. Rv: Liberty Bell at center divides 1776-1926. Around, on circular frame: SESQUICENTENNIAL OF AMERICAN INDEPENDENCE /.HALF DOLLAR. Reeded edge. Silver fineness: .900. Gross weight: 12.5 grams. Occurs with no mintmark (Philadelphia) only.

Designed by John R. Sinnock, the chief engraver of the United States. This is a commemorative half dollar, struck in 141,120 copies to mark the 150th anniversary of American independence. Premiums were used to help finance an International Fair held in Philadelphia to mark the sesquicentennial observances.

GEORGE WASHINGTON HALF DOLLAR

Struck 1482

Baker	Date	Metal	Size	EF	Unc	Proof
C-7	1982	Silver	30.6mm	—	5.25	5.25

Equestrian demi-figure of George Washington and his horse facing, heads turned three-quarters left. GEORGE WASHINGTON above, LIBERTY to left, mintmarks at right, 250TH ANNIVERSARY OF BIRTH. 1982 below. Rv: Eastern facade of Mount Vernon at center. UNITED STATES OF AMERICA / IN GOD WE TRUST above, eagle with shield on breast and HALF DOLLAR below. Reeded edge. Silver fineness: .900. Gross weight: 12.5 grams. Occurs with D (Denver) and S (San Francisco) mintmarks..

Designed by Elizabeth Jones, chief sculptor-engraver of the United States. This coin won the first-ever Coin of the Year top honors from Krause Publications, presented in Washington, D.C. in 1984 for the year 1982. This is a commemorative half dollar, struck in 2,210,458 Unc. and 4,894,044 Proof copies to mark the 250th birth anniversary of Washington, 1732-1982. It was the first commemorative half dollar struck since 1954.

MOUNT RUSHMORE HALF DOLLAR

Struck 1991

Baker	Date	Metal	Size	AU	Unc	Proof
C-A7	1991	CN -clad	30.6mm	—	14.00	13.00

Mount Rushmore National Memorial in South Dakota is shown radiate. The facing heads carved in the rock by Gutzon Borglum are (from left): George Washington, Thomas Jefferson, Theodore Roosevelt and Abraham Lincoln. IN GOD / WE TRUST and 1991 are below monument. Around all: LIBERTY / MOUNT RUSHMORE. Rv: Bison left. Around: UNITED STATES OF AMERICA / GOLDEN / ANNIVERSARY / E PLURIBUS UNUM / .HALF DOLLAR. The reverse rim is completely encircled with stars. Reeded edge. Gross weight: 11.34 grams. Occurs with P (Philadelphia) and S (San Francisco) mintmarks on reverse.

Obverse design by Marcel Jovine and reverse by T. James Ferrell, U.S. Mint sculptor-engraver. This coin and its companion silver dollar and gold $5 piece commemorate the 50th anniversary of dedication of Mount Rushmore National Memorial. Struck in 133, 139 Unc. and 738,419 Proof.

LAFAYETTE DOLLAR

Struck 1900

Baker	Date	Metal	Size	VF	EF	Unc
C-8	1900	Silver	38.1mm	—	275.	1,500.

Jugate heads right of Washington and Lafayette, UNITED. STATES. OF. AMERICA above, *LAFAYETTE. DOLLAR* below. Rv: Equestrian statue of Gen. Lafayette in Paris at center, ERECTED. BY. THE. YOUTH. OF. THE. UNITED. STATES. IN. HONOR. OF. GEN. LAFAYETTE around, * PARIS * 1900 * below. Reeded edge. Silver fineness: .900. Gross weight: 26.73 grams. Occurs only with no mintmark (Philadelphia).

Designed by Charles E. Barber, then chief engraver of the United States. This is the first commemorative dollar issued by the U.S. and the first U.S. coin of the realm to bear Washington's portrait. It marks the erection in Paris of a monument to Lafayette, a hero of the American Revolution. Proceeds aided the Lafayette Memorial Commission.

Struck in 36,026 specimens.

MOUNT RUSHMORE DOLLAR

Baker	Date	Metal	Size	AU	Unc	Proof
C-9	1991	Silver	38.1mm	—	30.00	30.00

Mount Rushmore memorial, not radiate. Around: LIBERTY / GOLDEN ANNIVERSARY / MOUNT RUSHMORE NATIONAL MEMORIAL / (laurel sprays tied by bow) / (tiny) MHS . CYM at lower right. Rv: Outline map of U.S. on which is superimposed U.S. seal in radiate circle. Around: UNITED STATES OF AMERICA / E . PLURIBUS . UNUM / ONE DOLLAR. Tiny FG under left end of map. Reeded edge. Silver fineness: .900. Gross weight: 26.73 grams. Occurs with D (Denver) and S (San Francisco) mintmarks on reverse.

Obverse design by Marika Somogyi and reverse by Frank Gasparro, then retired chief engraver of the U.S. Mint. Mintages were 172,754 Unc. and 753,257 Proof.

RUSHMORE $5 GOLD COIN

Baker	Date	Metal	Size	AU	Unc	Proof
C-A9	1991	Gold	21.6mm	—	140.	140.

American eagle from left swoops toward tiny, distant Rushmore memorial, six stars form right border. At right: LIBERTY / 1991. Rv: In fancy script at center: Mount / Rushmore / National / Memorial, tiny RL and CWC below. Around all: UNITED STATES OF AMERICA / . FIVE DOLLARS . E PLURIBUS UNUM . Reeded edge. Gold fineness: .900. Gross weight: 8.359 grams. Occurs with W (West Point) mintmark on reverse.

Obverse design by John Mercanti of the Mint staff, reverse designed by Robert Lamb, then engraved by William Cousins of the Mint staff. Mintages were 31,959 Unc. and 111,991 Proof. Surcharge from sale of the three Rushmore coins was divided between the Treasury Dept. and the Mount Rushmore National Memorial Society of Black Hills, S.D.

The workmanship on all three coins is competent, but only the dollar obverse and $5 obverse merit an artistic salute. Gutzon Borglum earlier had carved the Stone Mountain Battlefield Memorial in Georgia, but his enduring lifetime achievement was his Rushmore salute to the four presidents he felt were America's greatest.

ANTIGUA & BARBUDA

Baker	Date	Metal	Size	VF	EF	Proof
C-10	1982	Silver	38.6mm	—	—	45.00

Coats of Arms. Around: ANTIGUA & BARBUDA INDEPENDENCE NOVEMBER 1981 / 1982 / 30 DOLLARS. Rv: Three Continental army soldiers firing cannon left, flag in background. Around: 1732 GEORGE WASHINGTON 1982 / YORKTOWN 1781. Gross weight 31.1 grams. Silver fineness: .500. Mintage: 1200. (KM2; Collins 1)

Baker	Date	Metal	Size	VF	EF	Proof
C-11	1982	Silver	38.6mm	—	—	50.00

Obverse as C10. Rv: Washington stands in large rowboat with dignitaries and oarsmen, doffing his hat to crowd on pier in background. Around: 1732 GEORGE WASHINGTON 1982 . INAUGURATION 1789. Weight 31.1 gram. Silver fineness .500. Mintage: 1125. (KM3; Collins 2

Baker	Date	Metal	Size	VF	EF	Proof
C-A11	1982	Silver	38.6mm	—	—	60.00

Obverse as C-10. Rv: Full length military figure of Washington leaning against his horse, trail and hills in background. Around: 1732 GEORGE WASHINGTON 1782 / VERPLANCK'S POINT 1790. Weight 31.1 grams. Silver fineness: .500. Mintage: 675 pieces. (KM4; Collins 3)

The Antigua-Barbuda series honors the 250th birthday of George Washington by the small Leeward Islands nation made up of Antigua, Barbuda and Redonda, which became independent Nov. 1, 1981. The queen of England remains head of state. The coins were struck at the Royal Mint, Llantrisant, Great Britain.

HAITI

BATTLE OF SAVANNAH

Struck 1974-76

Baker	Date	Metal	Size	EF	Unc	Proof
C-12	1974,1975,1976	Silver	30mm	—	6.00	12.50

Soldiers and cannon charge left on central panel,, REPUBLIQUE D'HAITI / 1775-1975 / BICENTENAIRE DES U.S.A. above, "SAVANNAH" / BICENTENNIAL OF U.S.A. below. Rv: Haitian arms across center, LIBERTE EGALITE FRATERNITE above, 25 / GOURDES / 1974 (or 1976) below. To left of the 25 is an oval containing a mintmark. Reeded edge. Fineness of silver: .925. Gross weight: 8.38 grams. (KM 112.1).

Baker	Date	Metal	Size	EF	Unc	Proof
C-13	1974	Silver	30mm	—	8.00	—

As last, but country name at top of obverse changed to: BICENTENAIRE DES U.S.A./ 1776-1976. Rv: As C-12. Reeded edge. Silver fineness: .925. Weight 8.38 grams. (KM 112.2)

Baker	Date	Metal	Size	VF	EF	Proof
C-14	1974, 1975	Gold	32mm	—	200.	275.

Similar to C-10, but change in metallic composition, and denomination is 1000 / GOURDES / 1974. Reeded edge. Fineness of gold: .900. Gross weight: 13 grams. (KM 118.1)..

These Haitian coins commemorate the Bicentenial of the U.S. and the 200th anniversary of the Second Battle of Savannah (1779), in which Haitian troops under the French participated. Gen. Kazimierz Pulaski, Sgt. William Jasper and 800 French and Americans were casualties, and another 120 taken prisoner in the disastrous assault on Octorber 9, 1779. The commemoratives do not have a direct bearing on George Washington. All were struck at Argor Mint, Chiasso, Switzerland.

MINTAGE FIGURES:

C-12	1974 Unc.	25,000
	1974 Proof	600
	1975 Proof	?
	1976 Proof	10,000
C-13	1974 Unc.	25,000
C-14	1974 Unc.	3,040
	1974 Proof	480
	1975 Proof	?

ISLE OF MAN

INDEPENDENCE BICENTENARY

Struck 1976

Baker	Date	Metal	Size	EF	Unc	Proof
C-15	1976	CN	38.6mm	1.25	2.50	—

Coroneted bust of Elizabeth II right, ISLE OF MAN ELIZABETH II around, 1976 below. Rv: Washington bust in civil dress left, BICENTENARY OF AMERICAN INDEPENDENCE around. . ONE CROWN . below. Reeded edge. Gross weight: 28.28 grams. Occurs only with mintmark PM (Pobjoy). Mintage: 50,000. (KM37).

Baker	Date	Metal	Size	EF	Unc	Proof
C-15A	1976	Silver	38.6mm	—	8.00	10.00

Same as C-15, but change in metallic composition. Reeded edge. Fineness of silver: .925. Gross weight: 28.28 grams. Occurs only with mintmark PM (Pobjoy). Mintage: Unc not known; Proof 30,000. (KM 37a)

Baker	Date	Metal	Size	EF	Unc	Proof
C-15B	1976	Silverclad	38.6mm	—	8.00	

Same as C-15, but change in metallic composition. Reeded edge. Overall fineness of silver:?. Gross weight: 28.28 grams. Mintage not known.

Baker	Date	Metal	Size	EF	Unc	Proof
C-15C	1976	Gold	38.6mm	—	—	Unique

Same as C-15. Reeded edge. Only 1 struck.

Baker	Date	Metal	Size	EF	Unc	Proof
C-15D	1976	Platinum	38.6mm	—	—	Rare

Same as C15. Reeded edge. Only 6 struck.

These crowns (25-pence pieces) mark the Bicentennial of the United States. The obverse design is by Arnold Machin, and the reverse design by Leslie Lindsay after the Houdon portrait of Washington. Mintage statistics: Copper-nickel, circulation strike: 50,000. CN, diamond finish Unc.:?. Silver, Unc.?, Silver, proof: 30,000. Silverclad:?. Gold, proof: 1. Platinum, proof: 6.

CONSTITUTION BICENTENARY

Crown (25 Pence)

Baker	Date	Metal	Size	EF	Unc	Proof
C-16	1987	CN	38.6mm	—	4.00	7.50

Crowned bust right. Wide raised border around with incuse legend: ELIZABETH II. ISLE OF MAN. 1987. Rv: Upper portion of Statue of Liberty separates 1787 -- 1987, surrounded by facing busts of 11 leading Americans. Clockwise (from 12 o'clock): Ronald Reagan, Thomas Jefferson, Benjamin Franklin, George Washington, James Monroe, Abraham Lincoln, Ulysses S. Grant, Theodore Roosevelt, Franklin D. Roosevelt, Dwight Eisenhower and John F. Kennedy. Wide raised border around all with incuse legend: BICENTENARY OF AMERICA'S CONSTITUTION / 1 / ** CROWN **. Reeded edge. Mintage not known. (KM 176; Collins 7)

Baker	Date	Metal	Size	EF	Unc	Proof
C16A	1987	Palladium	38.6mm	—	—	350.

As C-16. struck in .999 fine palladium. Weight 31.1 grams (one troy ounce). Reeded edge. Authorized mintage 28,000, but a lesser number actually struck to advance order. (KM 176a)

Baker	Date	Metal	Size	EF	Unc	Proof
C-16B	1987	Platinum	38.6mm	—	—	800.

As C-16, struck in .995 fine platinum. Weight 31.1 grams. Thin planchet. Reeded edge. Authorized mintage 1000 but a much smaller number actually struck to advance order. (KM 176b)

5 Crowns (125 Pence)

Baker	Date	Metal	Size	EF	Unc	Proof
C-17	1987	Silver	65.1mm	—	—	65.00

As C-16 in larger size, with small FINE SILVER 5 OUNCES added under busts at 6 o'clock. Struck in .999 fine silver; weight 155.6 grams. Reeded edge. Mintage: 12,000. (KM 177)

10 C6owns (250 Pence)

Baker	Date	Metal	Size	EF	Unc	Proof
C-18	1987	Silver	75.1mm	—	—	125.

As C-17 in larger size, inscription FINE SILVER 10 OUNCES. Struck in .999 fine silver; weight 311.04 grams. Reeded edge. Mintage 9000. (KM 188; Collins 6)

C-16 thru C-18 struck at Pobjoy Mint, Sutton, England. Obverse design modified from Raphael Maklouf official Commonwealth effigy. Tiny mintmark PM under truncation of monarch's bust. The basic design motif was inspired by the Boulton 1797 Cartwheel copper twopence and penny coins, with sunken center field, wide plain border with incuse lettering. Reverse design under control of Pobjoy chief engraver Robert Nicholas.

Elizabeth II reigns as Lord of Man, not queen, on the Irish Sea British dependency. Since 1765, when Man was purchased by George III from the Duke of Atholl, the island has been a direct crown possession, though fully self-governing through its 1000-year-old Tynwald (parliament, founded by Norse freebooters in 979). Great Britain provides only foreign affairs and defense services for the Manx government.

INAUGURATION BICENTENARY

Crown (25 Pence)

Baker	Date	Metal	Size	EF	Unc	Proof
C-19	1989	CN	38.6mm	—	2.75	9.00

Obverse as C-16, but dated 1989. Rv: Washington standing left in boat with oarsmen and soldiers, CROSSING THE DELAWARE / 1778 above, 1 in exergue. On raised border in incuse legend: BICENTENARY OF GEORGE WASHINGTON'S PRESIDENTIAL INAUGURATION / (Manx shield) CROWN (Manx shield). Reeded edge. Weight 28.28 grams. Mintage not known. (KM 246; Collins 9)

Baker	Date	Metal	Size	EF	Unc	Proof
C19A	1989	Silver	38.6mm	—	—	35.00

As C-19, struck in sterling (.925 fine) silver. Weight 28.28 grams. Reeded edge. Mintage not known. (KM 246a; Collins 8)

Baker	Date	Metal	Size	EF	Unc	Proof
C20	1989	CN	38.6mm	—	2.75	9.00

Obverse as C-19. Rv: Washington bust facing 1/4 left, numeral 1 superimposed over collar. Border as on C-19. Reeded edge. Mintage not known. (KM 247; Collins 11)

Baker	Date	Metal	Size	EF	Unc	Proof
C20A	1989	Silver	38.6mm	—	—	35.00

As C-20, struck in .925 fine silver. Reeded edge. Mintage not revealed. (KM 247a; Collins 10)

Baker	Date	Metal	Size	EF	Unc	Proof
C-21	1989	CN	38.6mm	—	2.75	9.00

Obverse as C-19. Rv: Washington bust in oval frame facing 1/4 right, protective eagle at top, scroll below, numeral 1 under scroll. Border as on C-19. Reeded edge. Mintage not known. (KM 248; Collins 13)

Baker	Date	Metal	Size	EF	Unc	Proof
C-21A	1989	Silver	38.6mm	—	—	35.00

As C-21, struck in .925 fine silver. Reeded edge. Mintage not revealed. (KM 248a; Collins 12)

Baker	Date	Metal	Size	EF	Unc	Proof
C-22	1989	CN	38.6mm	—	2.75	9.00

Obverse as C-19. Rv: Half length bust of Washington facing, taking the oath, eight flags behind him, numeral 1 below. Border as on C-19. Reeded edge. Mintage not known. (KM 249; Collins 15)

Baker	Date	Metal	Size	EF	Unc	Proof
C-22A	1989	Silver	38.6mm	—	—	35.00

As C-22, struck in .925 fine silver. Reeded edge. Mintage not revealed. (KM 249a; Collins 14)

Baker C-19 thru C22A struck at Pobjoy Mint, Sutton, England. Tiny mintmark PM appears under truncation of monarch's bust.

The Isle of Man's preoccupation with George Washington in the 1976, 1987 and 1989 issues stems in part from historical and in part from commercial considerations. Martha Washington's first husband's family (Custis) had Manx heritage.

While the 1976 issues were aimed at the U.S. marketplace, they were distributed worldwide and somewhat difficult to obtain.

The 1987 and 1989 issues were aimed at and principally distributed in the United States. The cupronickel BU crowns sold widely at $4 to $6 each. Baker C-17 and C-18 are recognized by the Standard Catalog of World Coins (1999 edition) only as bullion coin issues. All 1976, 1987 and 1989 cupronickel crowns were fully legal tender, having been paid out at face value by commercial banks on the I.O.M. for short periods after issuance.

While legal tender, the crown is far too large a coin for normal circulation, the largest-diameter coin seen in trade on the island being the 7-sided 30mm CN 50-pence coin, and the somewhat smaller round virenium 2-pound piece. All I.O.M. commemorative coins tend to be hoarded by the island's 70,000 permanent residents, 350,000 summer residents and the large tourist influx. This was at least the situation when your author Russ Rulau visited the island four times in the 1987-1992 period.

Martha Washington (1732-1802), nee Dandridge, married at 17 Daniel Parke Custis, by whom she had four children. Two died in infancy. Custis died 1759, one of Virginia's wealthiest planters. She married George Washington Jan. 6, 1959. They had no children, but raised the younger two children of her son, who had died.

MILLENIUM 2000

Crown

Baker	Date	Metal	Size	EF	Unc	Proof
C-45	1998	CN	38.6mm	—	13.00	—

Crowned bust of Elizabeth II right, tiny RDM on truncation, small PM under truncation. Around: ELIZABETH II ISLE OF MAN . 1998. Rv: Eight men gathered to sign the Declaration of Independence, based on Jonathan Trumbull's painting. Above: AMERICAN INDEPENDENCE / 2/ooo. Below: 1 CROWN. Reeded edge.

Baker	Date	Metal	Size	EF	Unc	Proof
C-45A	1998	Silver	38.6mm	—	35.00	—

As C-45, struck in sterling (.925 fine) silver. Reeded edge. Mintage limited to 10,000 pieces.

1/5 Crown

Baker	Date	Metal	Size	EF	Unc	Proof
C-46	1998	Gold	22mm	—	—	75.00

As C-45, but 1/5 CROWN on reverse. Weight 6.22 grams (1/5 troy ounce). Struck in pure (.9999 fine) gold. Reeded edge. Mintage limited to 2,000 pieces.

The 1998 Millenium 2000 series of coins salutes the greatest events of the Second Millenium of the Christian era, as selected by the staff of Pobjoy Mint Ltd., Kingswood, Surrey, England. These coins were released by the mint in June, 1998, as one of four designs in the lengthy series, the other three designs being the French Revolution 1789; the Renaissance (Quattrocento in Italian), and the Reformation of the church in 1517.

Struck at Pobjoy Mint, official minters to the Isle of Man government since 1971. Obverse effigy by Raphael D. Maklouf, as modified at the mint.

The cupronickel crown (25-pence) was placed in circulation in the Isle of Man briefly at face value. The silver and gold specimens were sold only at premiums to collectors and others.

LESOTHO

Baker	Date	Metal	Size	VF	EF	Proof
C-30	1982	Silver	38.6mm	—	—	18.50

Coat of arms. Around: KINGDOM OF LESOTHO / 10 MALOTI. Rv: Periwigged military bust left. Around: 1732 GEORGE WASHINGTON 1982 / FIRST U.S. PRESIDENT. Gross weight 31.1 grams. Silver fineness: .500. Mintage: 7355. (KM 40; Collins 16)

Baker	Date	Metal	Size	VF	EF	Proof
C-31	1982	Silver	38.6mm	—	—	20.00

Obverse as C-30. Rv: Washington in military greatcoat kneeling in prayer, tress and house in background. Around: 1732 GEORGE WASHINGTON 1982 / VALLEY FORGE. Weight 31.1 grams. Silver fineness: .500. Mintage: 4200. (KM 41; Collins 17)

Baker	Date	Metal	Size	VF	EF	Proof
C-32	1982	Silver	38.6mm	—	—	18.50

Obverse as C-30. Rv: Washington crossing the Delaware. Around: 1732 GEORGE WASHINGTON 1982 / CROSSING THE DELAWARE. Weight 31.1 grams. Silver fineness: .500. Mintage: About 15,000. (KM 42; Collins 18)

Lesotho became an independent kingdom under Moshoeshoe II on Oct. 4, 1966. It had been the British protectorate of Basutoland prior to that. The nation honored Washington's 250th birth anniversary with this issue, struck at Great Britain's Royal Mint, Llantrisant, Wales.

TURKS AND CAICOS ISLANDS

U.S. BICENTENNIAL

Struck 1976

Baker	Date	Metal	Size	EF	Unc	Proof
C-40	1976	Silver	46mm	20.00	22.50	25.00

Elizabeth II bust with coronet to right, ELIZABETH II D .G. REGINA around, 1976 below. Rv: Two oval medallions at center, containing busts facing each other of George III and Washington, with KING / GEORGE III under left bust and GEORGE / WASHINGTON under right. Small Union Jack and Stars and Stripes flags above the medallions separate 17 - 76. Below, between medallions: 20 / CROWNS / crossed, draped flags. All this within a circle of stars. Outside the circle: TURKS AND CAICOS ISLANDS / * BICENTENNIAL OF THE UNITED STATES *. Lettered edged. Silver fineness: .925. Gross weight: 38.8 grams. No mintmark. (KM 13)

Baker	Date	Metal	Size	EF	Unc	Proof
C-41	1976	Gold	21mm	50.00	100.	90.00

As C-14, but change in metallic composition and size, and reverse reads: 50 / CROWNS. Lettered edge. Gold fineness: .500. Gross weight: 8.958 grams. No mintmark. (KM 15)

Mintage figures: 20-crowns Unc., 5,022; 20-crowns proof, 4,474; 50-crowns Unc., 905; 50-crowns proof, 2,421. Both coins salute the United States Bicentennial, 1776-1976, and have the distinction of being the only coins ever struck showing the two 18th century enemies, George III and George Washington, on a single legal tender piece.

The Turks and Caicos Islands are a crown colony of Great Britain, having been a British possession since 1678. They were made a separate crown colony in 1962. Four main islands make up most of the colony's 166 square miles, located just east of the Bahamas chain and north of Haiti.

Struck at Royal Mint, Llantrisant, Wales.

OTHER COINS

There are three other series of modern coins which refer in the broadest sense to the life and times of Washington, issued by the Netherlands Antilles, Netherlands and by Nicaragua. Neither series portrays Washington or mentions him in any way.

In 1976 the Netherlands Antilles issued two coins to celebrate the Bicentennial of the United States - a 25-gulden coin in .925 fine silver (Y-15) and an octagonal 200-gulden piece in .900 fine gold (Y-16).

Then in 1982 the Netherlands Antilles issued a 50-gulden coin (Y-28) in .925 fine silver honoring the 200th anniversary of Dutch-American friendship. The 1976 issues portray Queen Juliana and the 18th century vessel Andrew Doria, while the 1982 issue portrays Queen Beatrix and Peter Stuyvesant. The 1976 coins bear the FM mintmark (Franklin Mint), but the 1982 coins have no mintmark (Utrecht).

In 1982 the Netherlands issued a 50-gulden coin struck in .925 fine silver to honor the 200th anniversary of Dutch-American friendship, Y-74, without mintmark (Utrecht). In addition, two pieces were struck in gold as presentation items. The coins depict Queen Beatrix, a lion and an eagle.

Nicaragua in 1975 issued three coins to recognize the Bicentennial of the United States. These were Y-32, 100-cordobas, .925 fine silver; Y-35, 1,000-cordobas, .900 fine gold, and Y-36, 2,000-cordobas, .900 fine gold. Each bears the triangular arms of Nicaragua on obverse. The 100 and 2,000-cordoba pieces depict Betsy Ross sewing the American flag and Neil Armstrong planting the flag on the moon, while the 1,000-cordoba coin depicts the Liberty Bell. All these pieces were distributed by Italcambio of Milan and Caracas.

EARLY REPUBLIC COINS

Included in this chapter are all those pieces considered Washington Colonial coins and tokens, whether they were struck for circulation in the 18th century or for any reasons later. An attempt has been made to "date" all the issues to their first appearance, where their appearance differs from the date they bear.

We have also placed the struck copies of historic importance in this chapter, mingled with the pieces they imitate though clearly labeled as copies. Also included are a number of die trials and patterns for Washington coinage, and restrikes, forgeries, fantasies and electrotypes.

Insofar as possible, we have stayed with William S. Baker's original 1885 scheme of listing in this section — chronologically by the date on the piece. The Baker numbers have become sacrosanct within our beloved hobby in this regard. However, we have rearranged the section somewhat — placing together at the beginning all cents, halfpennies and pennies, including those copper medalets which seem to belong in this category. Generally the cents and halfpennies range in size from 27 to 30 millimeters, the pennies larger — in the 33 to 34mm range.

Following the cent-penny segment, other denominations follow — half cent, half dollar and dollar.

The terminology is newer in some cases (e.g. the use of "center-grained" instead of "engrailed" when describing edges; using the denomination "decad" or the mint-location Harper's coachhouse; and substituting "draped" for "mantled" in describing Washington's bust).

Coinage with a portrait of George Washington has been ac-cepted as part of the early American coinage, although none had any official status. Some Washington pieces did circulate in England, and others were in use as currency in the United States as late as the 1850's. The first to appear was the Georgius Triumpho copper token of 1783. Four types dated 1783 were struck only after 1815. There is one piece dated 1784; three of the Confederatio-Immune Columbia series of 1785-86, some being dated; American-made Peter Getz half dollars dated 1792; and finally a group of English commercial tokens dated 1791, 1792, 1793 and 1795.

Many new varieties are included herein, some published for the first time in a general-use catalog. All data included is accurate to the best of our knowledge and based upon the latest research by authors such as Eric Newman, Walter Breen, Robert Vlack, Don Taxay, Michael Hodder, Richard Doty, Robert Hoge and James Spilman. Due to crudeness in striking methods, listed sizes in millimeters and weights in grains may not match all specimens.

Another novelty in connection with this chapter is a table of the known or suspected medalists, diesinkers, makers and publishers of most of the pieces listed, keyed by Baker number.

"WA" numbers cited in this chapter are those assigned by Dr. George Fuld, one of your co-authors, in the 94-page monograph "Coinage Featuring George Washington" presented at American Numismatic Society's "COAC95" on October 28, 1995. This was published in 1996 by ANS as a non-covered offprint and as part of the COAC95 hardbound book.

DESIGNERS AND MINTERS OF WASHINGTON COLONIALS

Baker No.	Medalist/Diesinker	Maker	Publisher/Distributor
1-1A	—	(Birmingham)	James Kean (distr.)
2-2B	Thomas W. Ingram	Soho Mint	—
2C	—	William Lutwyche	
3-3B	Thomas W. Ingram	W.J. Taylor	W.S. Lincoln
3C-F	—	W.J. Taylor	—
3M	—	W.J. Taylor	—
3X-3Y	Thomas W. Ingram	Medallic Art Co.	Stack's Inc.
4-4B	Edward Savage*	Thomas W. Ingram	Edward Thomason
5-5A	Edward Savage*	Thomas W. Ingram	—
6-6A	Thomas Halliday	Edward Thomason	—
7	—	(England)	—
8	—	(America)	—
9	—	Thomas Wyon	—
10	Thomas Wyon	Walter Mould	—
11	—	Thomas Wyon	—
11F-11G	—	Julius Guttag	
12	James F. Atlee	—	Matthias Ogden?
13-13C	James F. Atlee	—	Matthias Ogden?
13J-13K	Joseph Merriam	—	Alfred S. Robinson
14-14U	George H. Lovett	—	Alfred S. Robinson
15	John G. Hancock	Obadiah Westwood	Alex Walker & Thomas Ketland
15AA	John G. Hancock	Lewis Pingo	Walker & Ketland
15E-15J	—	Obadiah Westwood	
16-16F	John G. Hancock	Obadiah Westwood	Walker & Ketland
17-17A	John G. Hancock	Obadiah Westwood	Walker & Ketland
18-18A	John G. Hancock	Obadiah Westwood	Daniel Eccleston
19-19C	John G. Hancock	Obadiah Westwood	—
20-20B	John G. Hancock	Obadiah Westwood	—
21-21B	—	—	—
22	John G. Hancock	Obadiah Westwood	—
22B-22F	John G. Hancock	—	Albert Collis

22M	John G. Hancock	Obadiah Westwood	—
23	Peter Getz	Harper's coachhouse	—
24-24C	Peter Getz	Harper's coachhouse	—
25-25D	Peter Getz	Harper's coachhouse	—
25E	—		—
25K-25N	—	John S. Warner	William Idler
26	—		—
27	—	Edwin Bishop	—
28-28A	—		—
29-29D	Thomas Wyon	James Good or Peter Kempson	—
29AA	Thomas Wyon	James Good or Peter Kempson	—
30-30D	Thomas Wyon	Peter Kempson & Son	—
30E-30F	Thomas Wyon	Peter Kempson & Son	—
31-31C	Arnold, Dixon and Mainwaring	William Lutwyche	Matthew Denton or Thomas Prattent
31M	Arnodl, Dixon and Mainwaring	William Lutwyche	Matthew Denton or Thomas Prattent
31P	Arnold, Dixon and Mainwaring	William Lutwyche	Matthew Denton
32-32A	—	Peter Kempson & Son	—
32E	—	Peter Kempson & Son	—
33	—		—
33A	Jacob Perkins		—
34-34A	—	William Lutwyche	—
35	—		—
36	—		—
59-59A	John G. Hancock	Obadiah Westwood	—
60-60B	John G. Hancock	Soho Mint	—
68-68B	Thomas Wyon	Peter Kempson	—
69-69B	Thomas Wyon	Peter Kempson	—
X-1	—	Paul Revere ?	—
X-2, 2A	George H. Lovett	—	Alfred F. Robinson

* Portraitist

WASHINGTON & INDEPENDENCE SERIES

"UNITY STATES" CENT

Struck about 1820

Baker	Date	Metal	Size	VG	VF	EF
1	1783	Copper	28.2mm	75.00	200.	400.

Laureate, mantled bust left, WASHINGTON & INDEPENDENCE around, 1783 below. Rv: ONE/CENT within olive wreath, bow at bottom. UNITY STATES OF AMERICA around, 1/100 below. Plain edge. Rarity 1. (Garrett 1693; Picker 297; WA. NC. 1783.1). Weight 120 grains.

Supposedly James Kean of Philadelphia distributed the "Unity States" pieces in America.

1A	1783	Copper	28.2mm	Ex. Rare

Obverse as 1, reverse as on regular U.S. cents. Wreath has 16 leaves on left, 19 right, triple leaf at F. (WA. NC. 1783.2; Vlack 27-X; Breen 1187). Probably Rarity 8, but only one piece located, in Harmer-Rooke Dec. 5, 1972 sale, lot 128, bought by James King.

DRAPED BUST

Struck about 1820

Baker	Date	Metal	Size	F	VF	EF
2	1783	Copper	28.3mm	75.00	175.	375.

Similar to 1, but different die. Small periods flanking date. Signature I in toga folds above 3 of date. Rv: Liberty seated left, olive branch in extended right hand, staff with Phrygian cap supported by the left hand. UNITED STATES around, exergue blank. Plain edge. Rarity 1. (Garrett 1694; Picker 298; WA. NC. 1783.3). Weight 115 grains.

The I = Thomas Wells Ingram.

2A	1783	Copper	27mm	Unique	—	—

As 2, but overstruck on token of I. WALKER, FLIMBY PARK COLLIERY of England, Davis-Waters 70. Undertype struck circa 1815. Plain edge. (WA. NC. 1783.3.o; Schulman Apr. 3, 1959 sale, lot 1173, ex-Winsor, Mills, Brand, Fuld, MHS). Current location not known.

2B	1783	Copper	29mm	—	—	1400

Similar to 2, but head larger and mantling is better defined. Exergue line on reverse is wavy, not straight. Plain edge. Rarity 7. (WA. NC. 1783.7)

Enlarged

2C   1783   Copper   28mm   Ex. Rare   —   —

Similar to 2, but error INDEPEDENCE. Button on drapery. (Probably struck by William Lutwyche of Birmingham). (New Netherlands 488; WA-NC. 1783.23). Rarity 8.

Struck in 1860

Baker	Date	Metal	Size	—	EF	Proof
3	1783	Copper	28.4mm	—	—	600.

Similar to 2, but struck from reworked dies by W.S. Lincoln in London, England. Letters are heavier, date is larger. Center-grained edge. Rarity 1. Weight 140 grains. (Garrett 1695; Picker 299; WA.NC. 1783.7)

3A	1783	Silver	29mm	—	—	1000.

As 3. Center-grained edge. Rarity 5. (Roper 362; WA. NC. 1783.7a). 50-100 struck.

3B	1783	Gold	29mm	—	—	Rare

As 3. Center-grained edge. Only 2 struck. (WA. NC. 1783.7b). Current location not known. Chapman 1907 sale; Colonial Newsletter for Oct. 1960.

Struck in 1851

3C   1783   Copper   29mm   —   —   500.

Similar to Baker 2B. Plain edge restrike by W.J. Taylor in London. Rarity 5. (WA. NC. 1783.6)

3D   1783   Copper   29mm   Very Rare

As 3C but Corded edge. Rarity 8. (WA. NC. 1783.6a; Vlack 14-J)

3E   1783   Bz/Cop   29mm   —   —

As 3C but in Bronzed Copper. Rarity 6. (WA. NC. 1783.6b. Bz; Vlack 14-J)

3F   1783   Silver   29mm   —   —   Ex. Rare

As 3C. (WA. NC. 1783.6c. Ag; Vlack 14-J).

3M   1851   Copper   28.3mm   —   —   650.

Obverse as reverse of 3C. Rv: Kangaroo standing right, MELBOURNE. around. In exergue: W.J. TAYLOR, MEDALLIST / TO THE GREAT / EXHIBITION / 1851. Rarity 4. Plain edge. (WA. NC. 1783.M1)

Struck 1988

Baker	Date	Metal	Size	VF	EF	UNC
3X	1985	Bronze	28.3mm	—	—	30.00

Obverse as Baker 3. Rv: COMMEMORATING OUR FIRST / Large script 50 with scroll across reading: YEARS OF PUBLIC AUCTION SALES / Stack's (script) / 1935-1985 / 123 WEST 57TH STREET NEW YORK N.Y. 10019

The original dies of 1818-20, first used by W.S. Lincoln in 1860, were preserved. In 1950 James Kelly, who had obtained them from Burdette G. Johnson, sold them to collector Ruder of Ohio, later of Florida. When Ruder's collection was dispersed, Stack's Inc. had transfer dies made from them and struck advertising tokens from the latter. The striking occured ca. 1988. The original dies were then donated in Ruder's name to the Smithsonian Institution. The die work and striking were done by Medallic Art Co., Danbury, Conn.

3Y	1985	Bronze	28.3mm	—	—	30.00

Obverse as Baker 3 reverse. Rv: As Baker 3X.

Both silver and gold versions of 3X and 3Y were prepared for presentation purposes.

LARGE MILITARY BUST

Struck about 1820

Baker	Date	Metal	Size	F	VF	EF
4	1783	Copper	28mm	70.00	150.	350.

Laureate, uniformed bust left, WASHINGTON & INDEPENDENCE around, .1783. below. Point of bust close to W. Rv: Similar to reverse of Baker 2, but staff is held almost upright. In tiny letters under exergue line are T.W.I. at left and E.S. at right. Plain edge. Rarity 1. (Garrett 1696; Breen 1203; WA.NC. 1783.10 thru 18). Weight 116.8 grains.

T.W.I. = Thomas Wells Ingram, maker, Birmingham, England.
E.S. = Edward Savage, painter, Philadelphia (1761-1817).
Note: There are 9 die varieties of Baker 4. Large bust.

The portrait on Baker 4 is actually that of the Duke of Wellington! Thomason simply borrowed the punch used for the Canadian Wellington tokens, Breton 987, Charlton 222-224. Thomas Halliday created the obverse dies, Ingram the reverse, and Sir Edward Thomason struck them.

For collectors interested in the 9 die varieties of Baker 4 and the 2 varieties of Baker 4A, see the special table following Baker 6B.

SMALL MILITARY BUST

Struck about 1820

Baker	Date	Metal	Size	F	VF	EF
4A	1783	Copper	28mm	75.00	175.	400.

Similar to 4, but smaller bust. Point of bust farther from W. Plain edge. Rarity 2. Weight 122.8 grains. (Picker 301; WA. NC. 1783.8; Vlack 1-A)

Baker	Date	Metal	Size	F	VF	EF
4B	1783	Copper	29mm	100.	275.	600.

As 4A. Center-grained edge. Rarity 3. Weight 120.8 grains. (Picker 302; WA. NC. 1783.8a)

DRAPED BUST WITH BUTTON

Struck about 1820

Baker	Date	Metal	Size	F	VF	EF
5	1783	Copper	28mm	125.	300.	550.

Obverse similar to 2. Button on drapery at neck. Rv: Similar to 2, but T.W.I. and E.S. under exergue line. Large Liberty. Plain edge. Rarity 5. Four die varieties, all very similar. (Crosby 284; WA.NC. 1783.19 thru 22)

"DOUBLE HEAD" CENT

Struck 1815-20

Baker	Date	Metal	Size	F	VF	EF
6	ND	Copper	27.8mm	90.00	200.	450.

Small laureate, military bust left, WASHINGTON around, elongated 8-pointed star below. Rv: Similar bust left, ONE CENT around, similar star below. Plain edge. Rarity 1. Possibly 50,000 struck. (Garrett 1698; WA.NC. 1783.24)

Baker	Date	Metal	Size	F	VF	EF
6A	ND	Copper	27.8mm	—	—	Unique

As 6, but center-grained edge. (N.Y. Public Library sale, 1981, lot 2105). 124 grains. One specimen known. (WA.NC. 1783.24a)

Baker	Date	Metal	Size	F	VF	EF
6B	ND	Copper	28.5mm	—	—	Very Rare

Similar to 6, with flat rims, larger flan. Rv: As 6, but ornament under bust rotated slightly. (WA.NC.1785.25)

BAKER 4A (SMALL) AND 4 (LARGE)

MILITARY BUST OBVERSE DIE TABULATION

Obv. Die	Bust	Position of Washington	Point of Wreath	Upright of 7	Position of A	Characteristic of C	I of Independence	Distinctive Features
1	small	well in front of bust	close to base of I	right base defective	C defective at top			Long crossbar on G, beads fine and close
1a	small	well in front of bust		spur to left at top right	space between beads			Base points of W connected by die break
2	large	under bust	close but not touch base of I	slightly right of bead	to space between beads	defective at top	bead slightly left of center	
3	large	under bust	touches left base of I	points at a bead	to space between beads	defective at top		
4	large	under bust	heavily touch left base of I	between beads	to left side of bead		bead slightly left of center	heavy die breaks, rim between and 3, along bottom of NGTON
5	large	under bust	close, not touch left base of I	to a bead	slight right space between bead	defective at top	slight left of center, double cut other lower left bottom	left crossbar of W defective; straight top to 3, die breaks
6	large	under bust	close, not touching base of I	to a bead	to space between beads		recut, base of other I shows left bottom	weakly struck at CE top of 3 has wavy surface, die breaks
7	large	under bust	point touches left base of I	to a bead	slightly left of a bead	defective at top	bead left of its center	left serif of W is defective, many die breaks
8	large	under bust	touches left base of I	to a bead	to space between beads	defective at top	bead slightly left of its center	left serif of W is defective, weakly struck at ON, die breaks
9	large	under bust	close, not touch base of I	slightly right of bead	to space between beads	defective at top	bead at its center lower serif of second E double cut	weakly struck at ON, die breaks
10	large	under bust	touch extreme left base of I	to space between beads	slightly to right of bead		bead slightly to right of center	left serif of W defective

NOTE: Die numbers were assigned by Robert Vlack.

GEORGIUS TRIUMPHO CENT

("TRIUMPHANT GEORGE")

Struck 1783-84

Baker	Date	Metal	Size	VG	VF	EF
7	1783	Copper	28.5mm	75.00	300.	700.

Laureate, undraped bust right, GEORGIVS TRIUMPHO. around. Rv: Goddess of Liberty left, behind framework of 13 bars, fleur-de-lis at each corner. Olive branch and staff in her hands. VOCE POPOLI around, 1783 below. Plain edge. Weight 110 to 135 grains. Rarity 3. (Garrett 1699; Vlack 30-Z; WA.1783.1)

The portrait resembles George III far more than George Washington, but authorities consider this a token intended to commemorate the successful termination of the Revolutionary War. United States independence was formally recognized by the Treaty of Paris in September, 1783. The term VOCE POPOLI = "voice of the people."

According to Robert Vlack (see Bibliography), these pieces first circulated in Georgia, then later in Virginia and Florida. Because of the George III-like bust, many were reportedly destroyed or mutilated, and some others sent to Jamaica for currency use. However, this assertion seems to have no basis of support; we reject it.

Researcher Paul Bosco adds this about Baker 7: "The portrait imitates the George III Irish halfpenny. Reverse is the standard Britannia design of the English coppers, but here the lower part of the seated figure is satirically imprisoned in a cage of 13 bars (the 13 American colonies) held together in the corners by four fleur-de-lis (France). It is certainly a Bungtown halfpenny, and is listed as such by Atkins, number 232.

"Although Bungtowns were struck as late as 1795, I suspect this one appeared when the events were fresher, making this the first numismatic reference to Washington."

He added, "Garrett (number 1699) stated some New Jersey cents were overstruck on these, so they were available (in the U.S.) 1788-89...Certainly these first circulated in England or Ireland."

Many auction sales offer one or two of these pieces. Stack's Inc. "Colonial Coins & Medals" fixed price listing of 1990 offered no less than six pieces, all illustrated. Two were in EF at $675 and $625; three in VF at $225, $200 and $150, and one in F/VF at $150.

WASHINGTON THE GREAT

Baker	Date	Metal	Size	VG	F	EF
8	(17)84	Copper	29mm	3600.	14,850.	—

Ugly head right. Around: WASHINGTON. THE. GREAT. D. G. Rv: Chain of 13 linked rings, each bearing initials of one of the 13 original states. In central space: 84. Plain edge. Only 3 or 4 specimens known. (Appleton 48; Garrett 1700; Roper 369; WA.1784.1)

| 8E | (17)84 | WM | 29mm | — | — | — |

All white metal pieces but one are cast imitations. The genuine piece = Wood-Petry-Ellsworth-Garrett. Weight 125.5 grains. (Breen 1186; WA.1784.1.WM)

| 8F | (17)84 | Silver | 27mm | — | — | — |

Many electrotype copies exist. Gould-Fuld-Partrick specimen. (WA.FA.1784.1)

Originals of Baker 8 are in the Smithsonian Institution and Massachusetts Historical Society collections. These may be of American origin.

All known specimens of 8F are electrotypes. No genuine specimens are known.

GEN. WASHINGTON SERIES

CONFEDERATIO CENT OR "DECAD"

Baker	Date	Metal	Size	VG	F	EF
9	1785	Copper	29mm	7000.	9000.	15,000.

Military bust right, GEN. WASHINGTON. around. Rv: Cluster of 13 stars at center of glory of 24 groups of rays. CONFEDERATIO around. .1785. below. Plain edge. (Appleton 12; Breen 4-D/1125; Garrett 1331; WA.1785.1). 6 or 7 specimens known.

| 10 | 1786 | Copper | 29mm | — | — | Ex. Rare |

Obverse as 9. Rv: Eagle displayed, shield on its breast, 13 stars around its head. * E. PLURIBUS UNUM. around, 1786 below. Plain edge. One known specimen in MHS collection, the other Prann-Kagin. 2 specimens known. (WA.1786.1)

Baker	Date	Metal	Size	VG	F	EF
11	ND	Copper	29mm	—	—	50,000.

Obverse as 9. Rv: U.S. shield at center, * E * PLURIBUS * UNUM * around. Plain edge. Known specimens in Garrett, Boyd and Fuld collections (the latter ex-Parsons). 3 known. (Crosby 1165; Garrett 1980 sale)

The Haseltine specimen sold in 1883 to Lorin G. Parmelee for an incredible $620, then the highest price ever paid for a Washington piece. All of the Gen. Washington series tokens are listed in Yeoman's Red Book under States, not under Washington.

Forgeries

| 11F | ND | Gold | 22mm | — | — | 2 Known? |

Crude forgery of Baker 11. This is struck over U.S. $5 gold piece. (WA.FA.1786.2.Au.o)

| 11G | ND | Silver | 27mm | — | — | Unique? |

As 11F. (Boyd-Fuld-Picker). This is struck over a 1917 Canadian quarter!! (WA.FA.1786.2.Ag.o)

Note: A "decad" was a suggested name for the 1/100th of a Spanish dollar.

Baker 11G was made in early 1920's by Julius Guttag. He may also have made 11F.

NON VI VIRTUTE PIECES

Baker	Date	Metal	Size	G	F	VF
12	ND	Copper	29mm	—	—	Unique

Bust in civil dress right, NON VI VIRTUTE VICI. around. Rv: Similar to reverse of 11, shield smaller. Plain edge. (Garrett coll., ex-Parmelee; WA.1786.5)

Probably a contemporary counterfeit of Machin Mills.

Baker	Date	Metal	Size	G	F	VF
13	1786	Copper	28mm	3000.	6000.	10,000.

Obverse as 12, but in finer style. Rv: Seated Liberty right, scales of justice in extended left hand, right supporting staff with Phrygian cap atop. NEO - EBORACENSIS. around, 1786 in exergue. Plain edge. Rarity 6. About 25 specimens known. (Scott C247; Eliasberg sale 56; WA.1786.3)

Neo-Eboracensis = New York. The dies were cut by James F. Atlee in 1786 before his association with the Machin's Mill mint in Newburgh, N.Y. the next year. Atlee also cut the dies for Baker 13C.

Baker	Date	Metal	Size	VG	VF	EF
13C	1786	Copper	29mm	—	—	Very Rare

Similar to 13 but both dies are finer in style. Staff holds a flag as well as a Phrygian cap and the head of Washington is larger. Plain edge. Only 2 known. (Scott C246; WA.1786.4; Parmelee 450)

Probably a contemporary counterfeit.

ROBINSON COPIES

Struck in 1861

Baker	Date	Metal	Size	VF	EF	Unc
13J	ND	Copper	28mm	—	—	75.00

Bust of George Clinton right, NON VI VIRTUTE VICI around. Tiny MERRIAM under left end of truncation. Rv: Defiant eagle right on U.S. shield, E * PLURIBUS * UNUM around, EXCELSIOR below. Plain edge. Only 54 struck. (WA.FA.nd.1)

Baker	Date	Metal	Size	VF	EF	Unc
13K	ND	Silver	28mm	—	—	200.

As 13J. Plain edge. Only 6 struck. (WA.FA.nd.1a.Ag)

Baker 13J and 13K were published by Alfred S. Robinson of Hartford, Conn. The dies were cut by Joseph Merriam, Boston, Mass. These struck copies intended to depict Governor George Clinton of New York but were clearly modeled after the 1786 products which supposedly portray Washington and thus are included here.

The motto "Non Vi Virtute Vici" translates "I conquered not by force (but) by manhood." It seems apt for Washington.

DeWitt notes, "It is interesting to observe that Merriam signed the piece so that it could not be mistaken for an original, and Robinson took pains to describe it in his sale lists as 'George Clinton Medalet.' His reason for so doing arose from the fact that the bust was a copy of the Clinton bust on the George Clinton cent issued in New York in 1787, rather than the bust on the Non Vi Virtute cent which was intended to represent Washington. Robinson stated that six copies were struck in silver and fifty-four in copper and the dies destroyed.

ROBINSON'S FANTASY

Struck about 1863

Baker	Date	Metal	Size	VF	EF	Unc
14	1789	Copper	32mm	—	115.	200.

Military bust left, GEORGE WASHINGTON PRESIDENT around, 1789 below. Rv: Scrawny eagle displayed, shield on its breast with six vertical stripes on it. Plain edge. (Garrett 1743; D&H Middlesex 242; Rulau-E Non 15; WA.FA.1789.1)

Baker	Date	Metal	Size	VF	EF	Unc
14B	1789	Silver	32mm	—	—	300.

As 14. Plain edge. (R.B. White coll.; WA.FA.1789.1a.Ag)

Baker	Date	Metal	Size	VF	EF	Unc
14T	1789	Lead	32mm	—	—	Unique

Intaglio of the obverse. Lead hub trial.

Baker	Date	Metal	Size	VF	EF	Unc
14U	ND	Lead	32mm	—	—	Unique

Intaglio of the reverse. Lead hub trial. (WA.FA.1789.1b.Pb)

Alfred S. Robinson (1836-1876) of Hartford, Conn. published these pieces about 1863. George Hampden Lovett of New York City cut the dies.

An EF specimen of 14 fetched $115.50 in the PCAC May 16, 1997 sale, lot 109.

PRESIDENT — EAGLE SERIES

LARGE EAGLE CENT

Baker	Date	Metal	Size	F	EF	Unc
15	1791	Copper	30mm	300.	700.	1800.

Military bust left, WASHINGTON PRESIDENT around, 1791 below. Rv: Large eagle displayed, shield on its breast. ONE CENT above. Edge lettered: UNITED STATES OF AMERICA.X. (D&H Middlesex 1049; Rulau-E Non 18; Breen 1206; WA.1791.1). About 2,000 struck. Rarity 2. Weight 196 grains.

Edgar Adams in 1907 reported that Baker 15 existed in gold, but this is not known today. Gilt copper specimens are known.

A plain edge copper piece is reported.

LARGE EAGLE DIE TRIALS

Baker	Date	Metal	Size	F	EF	Unc
15E	1791	Copper	30mm	—	—	Unique

Unfinished die trial, ONE CENT missing. Edge: BERSHAM BRADLEY WILLEY SNEDSHILL. In ANS collection. (WA.1791.P7)

SMALL EAGLE CENT

Baker	Date	Metal	Size	F	EF	Unc
16	1791	Copper	30mm	285.	700.	2000.

Obverse as 15, but no date under bust. Rv: Small eagle displayed, eight stars and an arch of clouds around its head. ONE CENT above, 1791 below. Edge lettered: UNITED STATES OF AMERICA .X. (D&H Middlesex 1050; Rulau-E Non 19; WA.1791.2). Rarity 3.

| 16A | 1791 | Brass | 30mm | — | — | 2 Known |

As 16. (Garrett 1706 and ex-Fuld collections; WA.1791.2a)

| 16B | 1791 | Copper | 30mm | — | — | 5 Known |

As 16, but edge lettered: PAYABLE AT MACCLESFIELD LIVERPOOL OR CONGLETON. (Breen 1218; WA.1791.2a)

Type of 16, edge lettered PAYABLE AT THE WAREHOUSE OF THOS. WORSWICK & SONS (D&H Middlesex 1050a; Atkins Wash. 174a), probably does not exist.

SMALL EAGLE DIE TRIALS

| 16E | ND | Copper | 29mm | — | — | Unique |

Die trial of obverse, no buttons on coat. Edge as 16B, MACCLESFIELD etc. (Crosby 299; WA.1791.P10)

| 16F | ND | Copper | 29mm | — | — | Unique |

As 16E, but edge is lettered: PAYABLE AT THE WAREHOUSE OF THOS. & ALEXR. HUTCHISON. (Garrett 1707; WA.1791.P9)

Baker numbers 15 and 16 supposedly were ordered from Westwood's mint in Birmingham by W. and Alex Walker of Birmingham, and distributed in America by Thomas Ketland & Sons of Philadelphia.

LIVERPOOL HALFPENNY

Baker	Date	Metal	Size	F	VF	Unc
17	1791	Copper	29mm	725.	1600.	4800.

Obverse as 15. Rv: Ship sailing right, two crossed oak branches below. Around: LIVERPOOL HALFPENNY. Edge lettered: PAYABLE IN ANGLESEY LONDON OR LIVERPOOL .X. (At least 25 specimens known; Rarity 6). (WA.1791.3)

| 15F | ND | Copper | 30mm | — | — | Unique? |

Die trial of reverse die; opposite side blank. (Garrett 1702; WA.1791.P2)

Baker	Date	Metal	Size	F	VF	Unc
15G	ND	Copper	28mm	—	—	Unique

Die trial of reverse die. (Garrett 1701; WA.1791.P1)

| 15H | ND | Copper | 27mm | — | — | Unique |

Unfinished die trial of reverse die, ONE CENT missing. (Garrett 1703; WA.1791.P3)

| 15J | 1791 | Copper | 32.3mm | — | — | Unique |

Obverse as 15, struck on large flan of thin (1mm) character, cancelled by roller. Rv: Large eagle trial. Weight 127.5 grains. Ex-Hepner, Tralins, A.M. Kagin. (WA.1791.P5)

GEORGE III — LARGE EAGLE MULING

| 15AA | ND | Copper | 31mm | — | — | 6000. |

Laureate draped bust left, GEORGIVS III DEI GRATIA around. Rv: Similar to reverse of 15, but dentilated rim. Plain edge. (Realized $2100 in New Netherlands Dec. 3-4, 1968 sale). Unique. (WA.1791.P6)

17A	1791	WM	29mm	—	—	Unique

As 17, but reverse from different die. (Norweb coll., ex-NNC, H. Schulman 1951, Mehl, Futter; WA.1791.P11.WM)

19A	ND	Copper	30mm	—	—	Unique?

Obverse similar to 19, but I.G. HANCOCK. F. in place of date under head. Rv: Blank. Edge lettered: MACCLESFIELD. Die trial of obverse by its maker, John Gregory Hancock Sr. of Birmingham, England. (WA.1792.P1)

SHIP HALFPENNY

Baker	Date	Metal	Size	F	VF	Unc
18	1793	Copper	30.7mm	160.	350.	1100.

Obverse as 16. Rv: Ship sailing right, HALFPENNY around, 1793 on panel below. Edge as 17 (ANGLESEY etc.). Rarity 3. (D&H Middlesex 1051; Rulau-E Non 20; Garrett 1709; WA.1793.2.1)

A plain edge variety realized $770 in the Roper sale. (WA.1793.2.1a)

19C	ND	WM	29.5mm	—	—	Unique

Similar to 19, but beaded rim on obverse, and no date. PRESEDENT is the spelling at right. Rv: Blank. Die trial of obverse. Fuld collection, ex Schulman. (WA.1792.P2)

All Roman head pieces were designed by Hancock and issued by Obadiah Westwood.

Walter Breen calls the Roman head pieces "Hancock's Revenge" in his 1984 opus on half cents of the U.S. He says "This is a satirical piece — 'Hancock's Revenge' — privately distributed by John Gregory Hancock on behalf of Obadiah Westwood, lampooning Washington's objections to portrait coinage as 'monarchical,' in revenge for G.W.'s having killed contract coinage proposals. Supposedly 12 are known. I have examined seven different ones, all in copper with the same edge, together with the Merkin-Picker uniface trial with I.G. HANCOCK F. instead of date, and Dr. George Fuld's white metal trial piece from a rejected obverse with beaded borders and spelling error PRESEDENT."

He adds, "The old story that the 12 known of these came from a packet of British tokens consigned to Jeremiah Colburn (1858-63) makes sense in one context too; very likely these 12 (plus perhaps a few held out by the maker) were the only ones ever coined."

Numbers 19A and 19C were stolen from Richard Picker at 1971 ANA convention and never recovered.

George Fuld says about 20 specimens of Baker 19 are known, of which 5 are in museum collections.

18A	1793	Brass	30mm	—	—	Unique?

As 18. Rarity 9. (Bushnell sale, lot 1256; Garrett 1710; WA.1793.2.1.BR)

Baker 18 was designed by John Gregory Hancock Sr., Birmingham, England, who also designed coins 15, 16, 17 and 19. The Washington likeness on all these coins is excellent. It is believed that 15 and 16 were intended as patterns for a coinage which never eventuated.

ROMAN HEAD CENTS

Baker	Date	Metal	Size	—	EF	Proof
19	1792	Copper	30mm	—	8000.	15,000.

"Roman" head right, WASHINGTON. PRESIDENT. around, 1792 below. Rv: Eagle displayed, shield on its breast, six stars around head. CENT above. Edge lettered: UNITED STATES OF AMERICA .X.X.X. Rarity 6. About 20 specimens are known, all but one in proof. Weight 198.5 grains. (Picker 309; WA.1792.3)

AMERICAN ARMIES CENTS

Struck circa 1792

Baker	Date	Metal	Size	VG	F	
22	1789	Copper	31mm	1100.	2200.	400

Uniformed bust left, GEO. WASHINGTON BORN VIRGINIA FEB. 1732. Rv: * / GENERAL / OF THE / AMERICAN ARMIES / 1775 / RESIGNED / 1783 / PRESIDENT / OF THE / UNITED STATES / 17 Plain rim. Plain edge. The 1 of 1775 points to I of AMERICAN. (R Book). About 40-50 known.

Struck in 1959

Baker	Date	Metal	Size	VF	EF	Unc
22B	1789	Copper	33mm	—	—	45.00

Restrike of obverse die of Baker 60 with dentilated rim. Reverse is blank. Plain edge. 5019 struck. (WA.NC.1792.2)

Baker	Date	Metal	Size	VF	EF	Unc
22C	1789	Silver	33mm	—	—	85.00

As 22B. Only 22 struck. (WA.NC.1792.2a.Ag)

Baker	Date	Metal	Size	VF	EF	Unc
22D	1789	Lead	33mm	—	—	Rare

As 22B. Only about 3 struck. Die trials. (WA.NC.1792.2b.Pb)

Baker	Date	Metal	Size	VF	EF	Unc
22E	1789	Gold	33mm	—	—	800.

As 22B. Only 7 struck. (WA.NC.1792.2c.Au)

Baker	Date	Metal	Size	VF	EF	Unc
22F	1789	Platinum	33mm	—	—	Unique

As 22B. Only 1 struck. (WA.NC.1792.2d.Pt)

Albert Collis of Newburyport, Mass., bought the original obverse die in 1959 (for about $5,000) from a descendant of Jacob Perkins. Perkins had obtained the die in 1818-19 at the Obadiah Westwood minting facility in England. Later, the die was donated to the American Numismatic Society museum.

Specialist R. B. White of Sheldonville, Mass., told the authors about 1984: "About 1970 I saw the remains of the Albert Collis estate. There were die trials of this obverse (22B) in copper, silver and lead, and also in copper and lead on large, odd-shaped planchets."

Jack Collins in 1991 sold a partial obverse brockage in copper, 33.35mm, for $65 (Collins 46 in BU). He also sold an obverse strike on a clipped copper planchet of 36.9mm for $65 (Collins 47 in BU).

Struck after 1792

Baker	Date	Metal	Size	F	VF	EF
22M	1789	Copper	30mm	2500.	4000.	—

Obverse as 22. Rv: Large eagle displayed with shield on breast, 13 stars above. Only 3 pieces reported. Rare muling of Armies cent obverse with Large Eagle reverse. Plain edge. (Breen 1236; Newcomer 2772; Holland 852; MHS collection is VG, 173 grains; WA.1792.7)

Baker	Date	Metal	Size	F	VF	Unc
60	1789	Copper	31mm	2200.	4000.	—

Obverse similar to 22, but with dentilated rim. Rv: As 22 reverse. Plain edge. Rarity 6. Weight 166.6 grains. (Picker 322; WA.1792.9)

Baker	Date	Metal	Size	F	VF	Unc
60A	1789	Silver	31mm	5200.	—	—

As 60. Plain edge. Only 5 known. (Roper 402; WA.1792.9.Ag)

Baker	Date	Metal	Size	F	VF	Unc
60B	1789	Silver	31mm	—	—	—

As 60. Lettered edge. Rarity 9. (WA.1792.9a.Ag)

Baker	Date	Metal	Size	VG	F	VF
59	1792	Copper	31mm	1300.	4000.	5500.

Similar to 16E but date 1792 added under head. The 1 of 1775 points to C of AMERICAN. Rv: As 60 reverse. Plain edge. Rarity 8. Only about 15 pieces known. Weight 185.1 grains. (Picker 321; WA.1792.6)

Baker	Date	Metal	Size	VG	F	VF
59A	1792	Copper	31mm	—	—	Ex. Rare

As 59. Edge lettered: UNITED STATES OF AMERICA. Only 3 known. (Appleton 30; WA.1792.6a)

All the American Armies pieces were designed by John Gregory Hancock Sr. and struck by Obadiah Westwood in England.

A Fine specimen of Baker 60 brought a rarefied $2750 in a Stack's Inc. 1990 sale catalog.

GRATE HALFPENNIES
LARGE BUTTONS

Baker	Date	Metal	Size	VF	EF	Unc
29	1795	Copper	28.2mm	180.	450.	950.

Uniformed bust right, large buttons on coat. Around: G. WASHINGTON. THE FIRM FRIEND TO PEACE & HUMANITY *. Rv: Open fireplace, grate showing, LONDON / 1795 below. Around: PAYABLE BY CLARK & HARRIS 13. WORMWOOD ST.
BISHOPSGATE. Edge lettered: PAYABLE AT LONDON LIVERPOOL OR BRISTOL. (D&H Middlesex 283; Atkins Middlesex 201; Rulau-E Non 10). About 10 known. (WA.1795.5b)

Baker	Date	Metal	Size	VF	EF	Unc
29AA	1795	Copper	28.2mm	125.	275.	650.

As 29, but with diagonally reeded edge. Weight 140-145 grains. Several hundred pieces known; Rarity 1. (D&H Middlesex 283a; Breen 1271; WA.1795.5)

Baker	Date	Metal	Size	VF	EF	Unc
29A	1795	Brass	28.2mm	—	—	Unique

As 29. (Bushnell 1263; WA.1795.5.BR)

| 29B | 1795 | Copper | 28.2mm | 160. | 450. | 875. |

As 29. Diagonally reeded (right) edge. D&H Middlesex 283a; Atkins Middlesex 201a; Rulau-E Non 11; WA.1795.5a)

Seven specimens of Baker 29B (one BU one Unc, four AU and one EF) were offered in Stack's 1990 Colonial price catalog!

SMALL BUTTONS

| 29D | 1795 | Copper | 28.2mm | 300. | 500. | 900. |

As 29, but small buttons on coat. Diagonally reeded (right) edge. Rarity 3. (D&H Middlesex 283b; Atkins Middlesex 201b: Rulau-E Non 12; WA.1795.6)

The Grate cents — acutally halfpennies — Baker 29 to 29D, were designed by Thomas Wyon and struck by James Good, both in Birmingham, England. They were intended for English circulation, but have always been collected as part of the American Colonial series.

LIBERTY AND SECURITY SERIES

Struck 1795

Baker	Date	Metal	Size	F	VF	Unc
30	ND	Copper	33mm	175.	300.	2000.

Uniformed bust left, GEORGE WASHINGTON. around. Rv: Spade-shaped shield, divided per pale, seven pales in gules (red) in dexter, 15 mullets (stars) in sinister. The crest is a scrawny eagle displayed, clutching olive branch and three arrows. Around: LIBERTY AND SECURITY. Edge lettered: AN ASYLUM FOR THE OPPRESS'D OF ALL NATIONS :: : :: (D&H Middlesex 243; Atkins Middlesex 42; Rulau-E Non 1; WA.1795.2) Rarity 2.

| 30A | ND | Copper | 33mm | — | — | — |

As 30. Plain edge. Rarity 9. (WA.1795.2b)

| 30C | ND | Brass | 33mm | — | — | Unique? |

As 30. (Sold in April, 1863; WA.1795.2a.BR)

| 30D | ND | Fire Gilt/ Copper | 33mm | 500. | 800. | 3000. |

As 30. (About 9 known) (WA.1795.2c)

| 30E | ND | Copper | 34mm | 300. | 800. | 2500. |

As 20, but engine turning around each rim. (12 specimens known; Garrett specimen illustrated; WA.1795.2d)

| 30F | ND | Copper | 33mm | — | — | Unique |

Reverse of 30 with Conder antislavery obverse (D&H 233) with AM I NOT A MAN AND A BROTHER. Only specimen known ANS, ex-Norweb, Baldwin. WA.1795.M3

Baker	Date	Metal	Size	F	VF	EF
31	1795	Copper	29.4mm	100.	205.	400.

Uniformed bust right, GEORGE WASHINGTON around. Rv: As 30, but point of shield divides 17 - 95. Edge lettered: PAYABLE AT LONDON LIVERPOOL OR BRISTOL. Rarity 2. (D&H Middlesex 1052a; Atkins Middlesex 176a; Rulau-E Non 3: Garrett 1727; WA.1795.1)

| 31A | 1795 | Copper | 29mm | 200. | 400. | 975. |

As 31. Edge lettered: AN ASYLUM FOR THE OPPRESS'D OF ALL NATIONS. (D&H Middlesex 1052b; Atkins Middlesex 176b; Rulau-E Non 4; WA.1795.1a). At least 15 known.

| 31B | 1795 | Copper | 29mm | 110. | 220. | 550. |

As 31. Edge lettered: BIRMINGHAM, REDRUTH & SWANSEA. (Rarity 5) (WA.1795-1b)

| 31C | 1795 | Copper | 27mm | 110. | 215. | 500. |

As 31. Plain edge. (Bushnell 1260; WA.1795.1c). About 30 known.

Baker	Date	Metal	Size	F	VF	Unc
31M	1795	Copper	29.3mm	110.	200.	300.

Figure of Hope standing, leaning on an anchor. Around: .IRISH HALF-PENNY. / 1795. Rv: As reverse of 31. Edge lettered: PAYABLE AT LONDON LIVERPOOL OR BRISTOL. (D&H Dublin 9; Atkins Dublin 8; Rulau-E Non 8; Garrett 1729; WA.1795.M1)

Baker	Date	Metal	Size	VG	F	EF
31P	1795	Copper	29mm	—	—	Ex. Rare

Figure of Fame flying left, blowing a trumpet. FOR. THE. CONVE-NIENCE. OF. THE PUBLIC around, .1794. below. Rv: As reverse of 31. Plain edge. (D&H Cork 13; Atkins Cork 12; Rulau-E Non 7; WA.1795.M2)

According to Thomas Sharp (see Bibliography), the issuer of the "Cork mules" was Matthew Denton, a coin dealer of West Smithfield, London. In this instance—Baker 31P—Denton apparently had the mulings struck by William Lutwyche of Birmingham. Arthur Waters says Lutwyche also struck 31M.

Denton or Thomas Prattent, another West Smithfield coin dealer, may have been responsible for Baker 31 as well. If so, they copied the military bust device of Thomas Wyon, whose Washington portrait on the Grate cents (Baker 29) served as the model.

All the Liberty and Security tokens were apparently made for sale in America as well as in England. Some may have been struck by Peter Kempson & Son in Birmingham—Breen says all the pennies were.

Baker	Date	Metal	Size	F	VF	Unc
32	1795	Copper	33mm	2000.	4500.	Ex. Rare

Similar to Baker 31 in larger size; the bust has been redrawn and has a differing truncation. Single dentilated border around rim. Edge lettered as 31A (AN ASYLUM). (D&H Middlesex 244; Atkins MIddlesex 43; Rulau-E Non 2; WA.1795.4) About 8 specimens known.

| 32A | 1795 | Copper | 33mm | — | — | Unique |

As 32. Plain edge. Rarity 10. (Aston collection)

| 32E | ND | WM | 33mm | | — | 2 Known |

Large head right, field completely filled with rays from head. Rv: As reverse of 30 (no date). In Norweb and Picker collections. Now in ANS. (WA.1795.3.WM)

Baker 32E may not be contemporary with the 1795 issues. Discovered ca. 1952. Picker specimen ex-New Netherlands 1952, Fuld 1968.

NORTH WALES HALFPENNIES

Struck about 1795

Baker	Date	Metal	Size	G	F	VF
34	ND	Brass	27mm	90.00	235.	—

Uniformed bust left, GEORGEIVS WASHINGTON around. Rv: Crowned harp, 6-pointed star at either side of base. Around: NORTH WALES. Plain edge. Thin flan. Weight varies, 91 to 97.5 grains. Rarity 4. (Breen 1294-1295; WA.1795.7)

| 34A | ND | Copper | 27mm | 475. | 1250. | 1800. |

As 34. Edge lettered: PAYABLE IN LANCASTER LONDON OR BRISTOL. 139 to 154 grains. (Crosby sale 310). There are 6 or 7 known specimens. (Roper 397; Breen 1296; WA.1795.7a)

Struck about 1795

| 35 | ND | Brass | 27.3mm | 1100. | 3500. | — |

Similar to 34, but 2 stars at each side of harp's base. Plain edge. 108 grains. (Crosby 309). 7 or 8 specimens known. (Breen 1298; WA.1795.8)

| 36 | ND | Copper | 28mm | — | — | Unique |

Similar to 34 but bust faces right. Head is different, and there is a star at each side of the crown. Plain edge. (Snowden 101). This piece has not been located in a collection. (WA.1795.9)

Baker 34 thru 36 are probably bungtown evasion halfpence; all are crudely made. Lutwyche apparently made 34 and 34A.

Baker 35 is so rare that a Poor specimen fetched $418 in the PCAC May 15, 1997 sale, lot 115! Bare outlines visible to attribute it as 35.

REPUB. AMERI PIECES

Baker	Date	Metal	Size	F	EF	Unc
68	1796	Bronze	33mm	175.	425.	600.

Bust right, WYON on truncation, GEORGE WASHINGTON around, 1796 below. Rv: Caduceus, crossed cannon and fasces, and scroll within central circle. Three concentric lines of text around: GENL. OF THE AMERICAN ARMIES RESIGND. THE COMMD. 1783: / ELECD. PRESIDENT OF THE UNITED STATES 1789 + / RESIGNED THE PRESIDENCY 1796 +. Plain edge. Rarity 5. (D&H Middlesex 245; Rulau-E Non 22; Raymond 5; WA.1796.2)

| 68A | 1796 | WM | 33mm | — | — | Rare |

As 68. Plain edge. Rarity 7. (WA.1796.2b.WM)

| 68B | 1796 | Bronze | 33mm | — | 1500. | — |

As 68. Edge lettered: PAYABLE IN LONDON LIVERPOOL OR ANGLESEY. Rarity 9. (Chapman 1914 sale, lot 607; WA.1796.2a)

A specimen of 68A in white metal offered in PCAC No. 61 Nov. 1996 sale, lot 139, is the only specimen in this metal traced in last 50 years.

Struck 1870

| 69 | 1799 | Bronze | 33mm | 175. | 425. | 600. |

Similar to 68, but obverse legend: GEORGE WASHINGTON / BORN FEB. 11. 1732. DIED DC. 21. 1799. Plain edge. Rarity 5. (WA.1800.1)

| 69A | 1799 | WM | 33mm | 175. | 425. | 600. |

As 69. Plain edge. Rarity 5. (D&H 245 bis; WA.1800.1b.WM)

| 69B | 1799 | Copper | 35.8mm | — | — | Ex. Rare |

Baker 69 overstruck on a Cartwheel penny of Great Britain, 1797, 3mm thick. Plain edge. (WA.1800.1a; Breen 1279; Garrett 1759)

The collection of Dr. I.N. Schuster contains a copper (not bronze) specimen of Baker 69.

All these pieces, as Baker judged in 1885, are more medallic than token-like. Yet the Wyon connection, the size, the lettered edges, etc., induce us to place them here under Colonial and Early Republic coins and tokens. They are all of penny size.

Dalton and Hamer did the same in listing two of these pieces (Baker 68 and Baker 69A).

These pieces are the size of a Soho Mint penny, and one specimen (69B) is known overstruck on a 1797 Cartwheel penny. Robert Vlack and Walter Breen also attributed these as Washington Colonials.

NON DEPENDENS STATUS

Baker	Date	Metal	Size	VG	F	EF
X-1	1778	Copper	29mm	—	—	3 Known

Cuirassed bust of a man right, NON. DEPEN-DENS. STATUS around. Rv: Seated is youth in headband and feathered skirt to left, holding branch in right hand and leaning on oval shield with left. (The shield is blue, divided in diagonal quarters by sword and flagstaff. In each diamond-shaped quarter is a fleur de lis.) AMER ICA around, 1778 in exergue. Plain edge. (R.B. White coll.)

ROBINSON COPIES

Struck about 1863

| X-2 | 1778 | Copper | 28mm | — | — | 175. |

Similar to original, but from new dies. Single exergue line. Plain edge.

| X-2A | 1778 | Copper | 28mm | — | — | 125. |

As X-2, but small word COPY under bust.

| X-3 | 1778 | Silver | 28mm | — | — | 6 Struck |

As X-2. Plain edge.

Published here is the possible original from which Alfred S. Robinson commissioned George Hampden Lovett to prepare his 1862-63 copies. It was discovered by R. Byron White of Rhode Island about 1971. It and its mates are retouched and retooled copies.

The history of the Non Dependens Status pieces is shrouded in mystery. Sylvester Crosby included it in his 1874 work, but remarked "origin and history unknown."

Just who is depicted—if indeed it is an actual person — and why, remain unanswered. It does get across the message that in 1778 America's status was not that of a dependency.

White writes: "Robinson made his copy (X-2) from the drawing in Dickinson. Norton (Norton's Literary Letter No. 2, 1858) says that the original, which is hand carved, was supposed to be one of the many pattern pieces engraved and designed by Paul Revere.

"Woodward sold the original twice; sale 4, Finotti, 11/11/1862 $70 (in the same sale a Higley realized $50, silver center cent $52.50 and 1793 half cent in EF $4) and sale, 88, 6/26/1886, to E. Cogan for Mrs. Judge Paige.

"I am now quite sure that the profile is that of Samuel Adams, the Firebrand of the Revolution. The hair style fits and the profile is very close including the high (balding) forehead. See Copley's picture."

The portrait is not that of George Washington!

WASHINGTON HALF CENT

FANTASIES

Made about 1853

Baker	Date	Metal	Size	F	VF	EF
27	1793	Copper	23mm	—	—	3 Known

Uniformed bust right, LIBERTY above, 1793 below. Rv: HALF / CENT within laurel wreath, UNITED STATES OF AMERICA around, 1/200 below. Edge lettered: TWO HUNDRED FOR A DOLLAR. (Snowden 39; Bushnell 1254; WA.NC.1793.1)

Edwin Bishop, of 9 Dutch Street, New York, made this fabrication by brazing the obverse shell to a genuine 1793 half cent of the U.S. They are joined skillfully. Bishop's collection was sold by W. Elliott Woodward, Dec. 17, 1863. One known copy is in the Smithsonian Institute, another in the Massachusetts Historical Society; the third was in the hands of a minor N.Y. dealer, according to R.B. White.

For a full explanation4 see Walter Breen's 1984 book on half cents, pages 80-83.

| 27F | ND | Copper | 23mm | — | — | 2 Known |

Washington head left, continuous oak wreath surrounding. Rv: Similar to reverse of 27; this is the reverse of an 1806 U.S. half cent. Plain edge. (Fuld COAC95 pg.245)

Baker 27F is an electrotype imitation of a supposed coin. See Breen's 1984 half cent opus, page 275.

WASHINGTON HALF DOLLARS

13 STARS

Baker	Date	Metal	Size	VG	F	EF
20	1792	Silver	31.5mm	—	—	—

Uniformed bust left, WASHINGTON PRESIDENT around, 1792 below. Rv: Large eagle displayed, shield on its breast, ribbon on its beak reading: UNUM E PLURIBUS. There are 13 stars above the eagle's head, 12 in an arc and one above its eye. Edge lettered: UNITED STATES OF AMERICA —X. Weight 168.5 grains. (Probably 4 or 5 known). (Breen 1231; WA.1792.4c.Ag)

				VG	F	EF
20A	1792	Silver	31.5mm	—	—	—

As 20. Plain edge. (Probably 3 or 4 known). (Breen 1232; WA.1792.4b.Ag)

20B	1792	Gold	31.5mm	—	—	Unique

As 20. (Eric P. Newman coll., ex-Lorin Parmelee and M.I. Cohen; Breen 1233; WA.1792.4d.Au)

21	1792	Copper	31mm	—	—	Ex. Rare

As 20. Edge lettered as 20. (About 5 to 6 known). (WA.1792.4a)

21A	1792	Copper	31mm	—	—	—

As 20. Plain edge. (About 6 to 7 known). (WA.1792.4)

21B	1792	Copper	31mm	—	—	Unique

Similar to 20, 13 stars above eagle, but obverse die has T of PRESI-DENT under shoulder. Lettered edge as 20. (Breen 1228; WA.1792.5)

NO STARS

Baker	Date	Metal	Size	VG	F	EF
23	1792	Silver	35mm	—	—	16,500.

Military bust left, G. WASHINGTON. PRESIDENT. I. around. 1792 below. Rv: Large eagle displayed, shield on its breast. UNITED STATES OF AMERICA around. (Bushnell 1253; Garrett 1713). Unique. (WA.1792.2.Ag)

The only known specimen, ex-Lorin G. Parmelee and Johns Hopkins University, has a pedigree dating back to 1831. It fetched $16,500 in the 1981 Garrett sale (EF condition).

The dies were cut by Peter Getz (1768-1804) of Lancaster, P. Getz also cut the dies for Baker 24 and 25. The pieces were struck at Harper's coachhouse in Philadelphia, on 6th Street.

Harper was a sawmaker at the corner of 6th and Cherry, whose cellar housed the U.S. Mint's machinery in 1792 before the first mint building was occupied. According to Dr. J. Hewitt Judd, Harper's was also the place of striking of the 1500 to 2000 1792-dated half dimes (Adams-Woodin 4; Judd 7).

The coinage presses for the mint, made in England, arrived at the mint Sept. 21, 1792, but no coins were actually struck at the mint until Dec. 18, 1792, so late September or early October, 1792, seems the likeliest time for the Harper's minting facility striking.

24	1792	Silver	35mm	—	—	—

Obverse as 23. Rv: Small eagle displayed, shield on its breast, 51 stars around its head. .UNITED STATES OF AMERICA. around. Plain edge. (Garrett 1714; WA.1792.1e.Ag). About 15 known.

24A	1792	Silver	35mm	—	—	3 Known

As 24. Edge has circles and squares. (Norweb coll. and MHS coll., ex-Appleton; Witham coll.; WA.1792.1g.Ag)

24B	1792	Silver	35mm	—	—	Unique

As 24. Edge has vine and bars. (Zabriskie 104; ex-Raymond; WA.1792.1h.Ag)

24C	1792	Silver	35.5mm	—	40,000.	—

As 20, but overstruck on foreign silver coin, e.g. England 1679 half crown, 218.4 grains; France 1/2 ecu of 1726-40 type, Craig 41, 214.1 grains; Spanish-American 4-reales. 3 pcs. known. (Breen 1349; Gadoury 313; Garrett IV 1714; Stack's March 18, 1993 sale, lot 2007; WA.1792.1f.Ag.o)

The overstrike on the France demi-ecu is in Alan V. Weinberg coll.

Enlargement of Baker 24, Garrett 1714, WA.1792.1e.Ag

Baker	Date	Metal	Size	VG	F	EF
25	1792	Copper	32mm	3250.	5000.	—

As 24. Plain edge. About 30 pieces known. Weight 220 to 273 grains. (Picker 310; Garrett 1715; WA.1792.1)

Baker	Date	Metal	Size	VG	F	EF
25A	1792	Copper	36mm	—	—	8000.

As 24. Plain edge. 7 to 9 known.

Baker	Date	Metal	Size	VG	F	EF
25D	1792	Copper	36mm	—	5000.	—

As 25. Edge has circles and squares. (Garrett 1716; WA.1792.1c; Breen 1357)

Baker	Date	Metal	Size	VG	F	EF
25E	1792	Copper	35mm	—	20.00	30.00

Imitation. (Garrett 1717)

Enlargement

Baker	Date	Metal	Size	VG	F	EF
25G	1792	Copper	36mm	—	—	3000.

Baker 25D with circles and squares edge, but with initials engraved around Washington's bust. All lettering is open, with strong serifs. Initials read: I.M.W. A.W. S.W. (Curtis R. Paxman coll., lot 173)

Collector Homer A. Hall of Seymour, Texas purchased this piece in 1927 as a VF-EF specimen of Baker 25D. (Crosby pp. 357-358) and reported it to the authors Aug. 20, 1985, soon after he'd purchased a copy of the 1985 edition of this catalog. Hall says he had the piece authenticated as genuine by Baylor University staff and Dr. Morse, curator at Mount Vernon. He stated that the initials seemed to have a "family" provenance since all ended in W.

After nearly 40 years of ownership, during which time he conducted such research as he could, he concluded that the piece may well have arrived in Texas via Lewis Washington, a relative of George Washington. Lewis Washington, son of Samuel Washington, arrived in Texas 1831 with his fourth wife, Anne Steptoe Washington. Hall consulted Washington family trees at Mount Vernon. His conclusion, completely unsupported of course, is that the initials stood for Lewis M., Anne and Samuel Washington.

IDLER COPIES

Struck about 1860

Baker	Date	Metal	Size	VF	EF	Unc
25K	1792	Silver	35mm	—	—	375.

Struck copy of Baker 24 by William Idler of Philadelphia. The word COPY is at left of the eagle's tail on some copies but has been removed from the die on others (as on illustration above). On other pieces COPY has been tooled from the struck specimen. Some recognizable points on the struck copies: Uppermost star on reverse points at E (points between T-E on original); end of 2 in date points up (points down on original). Weight about 123.5 to 157.5 grains for copies. Plain edge. (WA.FA.1792.1c.Ag)

Baker	Date	Metal	Size	VF	EF	Unc
25L	1792	WM	35mm	—	—	125.

As 25K. Some specimens are known silver-plated after striking. (WA.FA.1792.1b.WM)

Struck about 1860

Baker	Date	Metal	Size	VF	EF	Unc
25M	1792	Copper	35mm	—	—	135.

As 25K. Weight about 135 grains.

NOTE: On the Idler copies, the '1' of the date is actually a 'J' which makes differentiation from some originals even easier — though they bear only superficial resemblance to originals.

Baker	Date	Metal	Size	VF	EF	Unc
25N	1792	Brass	35mm	—	—	125.

As 25K. Scarcest metal. (WA.FA.1792.1a.Br)

Coin dealer William Idler of 111 No. 9th St., Philadelphia from 1858 on, commissioned medalist John S. Warner of Philadelphia to strike 25K through 25N. He also muled both dies with his own store cards; these may be found cataloged under STORE CARDS in this volume.

FONROBERT COPY

Baker	Date	Metal	Size	F	VF	EF
26	1792	Silver	35mm	—	—	Unique

General imitation of Baker 23, but from completely different dies. Obverse reads PRESIDENTI. instead of PRESIDENT.I. and face is fleshier. Eagle is drawn differently. (Anthon Part V, 407; Garrett 1718; Fonrobert 6103; WA.NC.1792.1)

This piece may be a contemporary counterfeit. It was sold in Berlin, Germany in 1878 as part of the gigantic Jules Fonrobert collection to Charles E. Anthon of New York, then went to T. Harrison Garrett and the Johns Hopkins Univ. collection and eventually was sold in 1981 by Bowers & Ruddy Galleries.

WASHINGTON DOLLARS

Struck about 1859-64

Baker	Date	Metal	Size	VG	F	EF
28	1794	Silver	41mm	—	—	Unique?

Uniformed bust left, WASHINGTON PRESIDENT 1794 around. Rv: Eagle standing within wreath of olive branches. UNITED STATES OF AMERICA around. (Appleton 33; WA.NC.1794.1a.Ag)

28A   1794   Copper   41mm   —   —   2 Known

As 28. (Norweb coll., ex-Holden, McCoy 2461; WA.NC.1794.1)

33   1796   Silver   40mm   —   —   Unique

Uniformed bust left, WASHINGTON PRESIDENT around, 1796 below — all within beaded circle from which rays reach toward rim. Rv: Similar to reverse of Baker 25 within broad dentilated (rayed) border. (Snowden XI,43; ANA sale 1962; Kagin sale 1975; WA.1796.1.Ag)

Baker 33, the H. Drumheller specimen of 1861, is actually a medal. See Fuld and Newman in *Numismatic Scrapbook Magazine* for Nov., 1961, pages 2882-2885. The half dollar-size dies are struck over a Mexico 8-reales circa 1772-1808.

Baker 33 also appeared as lot 31 in B&M Sept. 1989 sale, and lot 41 in Collins 1996 listing.

33A   (1799)   Silver   41mm   —   —   Ex. Rare

The so-called Perkins dollar, bust of Washington in center from hub of Perkins funeral medal. Surrounded by engine turning, WASHINGTON above.

Known copies are a thin shell, with reverse intaglio of obverse. Solid piece was known, lost by registered mail when mailed by Wayte Raymond to F.C.C. Boyd about 1955 — never recovered. One exhibited by H.O. Granberg at ANS, 1914. Judd page 265, P-5067. Not a colonial coin, but it may be a private pattern issue.

PATTERN COINS

Several proposals were made in England and in America to place Washington's likeness on coinage during his presidency but these came to naught because the first president felt it was too "monarchical" for such portraiture.

A number of the pieces in the preceding chapter were apparently private British patterns for a Washington portrait cent, most notably the Large Eagle and Small Eagle cents of 1791 by Obadiah Westwood's minting facility in Birmingham (Baker 15 and 16), and the Roman head pieces, Baker 19, are supposedly satirical reminders of the fit of pique Westwood and his engraver, Hancock, had after President Washington had rejected the idea. (The Roman head pieces show Washington as a Roman emperor.)

During the president's tenure the only American pattern to honor him is the so-called "G.W.Pt." Birch cent of 1792, which may be a U.S. Mint product but may have been engraved in England.

Long after Washington's death, the U.S. Mint did consider coinage with his portrait. The 1863-dated pattern 2-cent coins and 1866-dated pattern nickel 5-cent coins attest to these proposals.

The U.S. Mint Director, James Pollock, preferred the U.S. shield obverse for the 2-cent piece to the design of Washington's head. In his letter of Dec. 8, 1862 to Secretary of the Treasury Salmon P. Chase, he wrote: "I prefer the 'shield and arrows' to the 'head of Washington,' on the obverse of the coin. Secretary Chase approved Pollock's recommendations and the 2-cent coin was authorized in the Act of April 22, 1864.

It was a long time later, in 1900, before Washington finally made it onto an American coin, and then it was only a commemorative dollar seen by few people, the Lafayette Dollar.

The first trade coin came in 1932, the Washington quarter, and it is still with us.

The Washington pattern series is extremely complex, especially with the 1866-69 5-cent issues due to extensive restriking outside the mint. The 2-cent pieces were not restruck, although some pieces were made in moderate quantities. The 5-cent series with IN GOD WE TRUST and UNITED STATES OF AMERICA, denoted as dies 1 and 2 by Fuld were extensively muled with both 5-cent reverse plus a half eagle pair and with a 5-cent style resembling the 3-cent nickel. The 3-cent nickel style 5-cent pattern is dated 1867, with two types listed by Judd and Pollock.

The major difference between the dies is that one has an incuse star on the coronet (Judd 568, P-637). There is another die without the star on the coronet (Judd 566, P-627). As far as we can ascertain only one die, with the star, was muled with Washington dies. This is contrary to other published references which list the no star type but no actual specimens or photographs of this type have been observed in the past 20 years. Thus, the no star type will not be listed in this reference.

This series of related restrikes is completely detailed by G.J. Fuld, "A Related series of U.S. Pattern Restrikes" in *The Numismatist,* May 1998. Actually, examples of the two Washington head dies 1 and 2 were in the possession of the Boston Numismatic Society up to 1958. After some modern restriking, both dies were seized and destroyed by the Secret Service.

The 1863 2-cent patterns and the 5-cent patterns which bear dates of 1866, 1867 and 1869, are the work of James B. Longacre of the U.S. Mint at Philadelphia.

The pattern $5 gold pieces of 1866 bearing Washington's portrait were made outside the Mint, muling genuine Washington dies from 5-cent patterns with the regular dies of the $5 piece (minus the reverse motto).

Forty years later the U.S. Mint experimented with a Washington trade coinage, which accounts for the 1909-1910 pattern 5-cent pieces bearing his effigy. Again, the idea failed to result in coinage.

One of the keenest descriptions for patterns recorded in the literature is that given by Patterson DuBois in "The Pattern Piece," *American Journal of Numismatics* for January 1883:

"Open for me your cabinet of Patterns, and I open for you a record, which, but for these half-forgotten witnesses, would have disappeared under the finger of Time. Read to me their catalogue, and I read to you, in part, at least, the story of an escape from the impracticable schemes of visionaries and hobbyists — a tale of national deliverance from minted evil.

These are to be enjoyed as bygones, though there linger a fear for the spark that still smoulders under the ashes. Laws have been framed for them, words have warred over them. Now, only these live to tell the tale of what 'might have been;' only these remind us of what has been weighed, measured and set aside among the things that are not appropriate, not convenient, in short, that are not wanted."

'G.W.PT.' CENT

OF AMERICA. / G* W. PT. Plain edge. Unique. (Garrett 2350; WA.1792.11.WM). Weight 104.5 grains.

G* W. PT. = George Washington, President.

This pattern piece realized $90,000 in the Garrett sale in 1981. It may have been engraved by Robert Birch, who made the famous "Birch cent" of 1792 (similar to the G.W.Pt. piece above except that Liberty's hair is longer and the numeral 1/100 replaces the G.W.Pt. and it is in copper), but the catalogers of the Garrett sale felt it may have been engraved and struck in England and then sent to America where it was rejected, probably by President Washington. It precedes the copper "Birch cent" pattern of 1792, in all probability.

The piece was obtained by Garrett from Henry Chapman's Jan. 16, 1915 sale and is now in a Long Island collection. Earlier than Garrett it had appeared in a Sotheby, Wilkinson & Hodge sale.

Don Taxay says one B. Birch of Philadelphia may have been the engraver. Carl W. A. Carlson named William Russell Birch of England.

Baker	Date	Metal	Size	F	VF	Unc
P-37	1792	WM	32mm	—	125,000.	—

Loose kinky hair Liberty bust right, 1792 under bust. Around: * LIBERTY PARENT OF SCIENCE & INDUSTRY. Rv: ONE / CENT within beaded central circle, all within circular laurel wreath. Around: UNITED STATES

Illustration enlarged

Baker	Date	Metal	Size	VF	EF	Unc
38	1863	Bronze	23mm	—	—	2500.

Obverse as 37. Rv: 2 / CENTS within wheat wreath as on 37, but CENTS curves in a gentle upward arc, while on 37 CENTS curves around the lower portion of 2. UNITED STATES OF AMERICA around. Plain edge. Rarity 7. (Adams-Woodin 408; Judd 309; P-374)

Baker	Date	Metal	Size	VF	EF	Unc
38A	1863	CN	23mm	—	—	2750.

As 38. Plain edge. Rarity 7. (Adams-Woodin 410; Judd 311; P-375)

Baker	Date	Metal	Size	VF	EF	Unc
38B	1863	Aluminum	23mm	—	—	3000.

As 38. Plain edge. Rarity 8. (Adams-Woodin 409; Judd 310; P-376)

The Act of April 22, 1864, which changed the composition of the cent from cupronickel to bronze also provided for a bronze 2-cent piece, 23 millimeters in diameter and weighing 96 grains — but without the effigy of George Washington. The first 2-cent coins appeared in 1864 using a U.S. shield obverse and a reverse almost identical to that on Baker 38.

FIVE-CENT PATTERNS

Baker 39

Baker 39 enlarged

Baker	Date	Metal	Size	VF	EF	Proof
39	1866	Nickel	20.5mm	—	—	—

Undraped bust right, IN GOD WE TRUST around, 1866 below. Rv: 5 within circle of 13 6-pointed stars, UNITED STATES OF AMERICA around, CENTS below. Plain edge. Rarity 9. Magnetic. (Judd 476; P-566)

Baker	Date	Metal	Size	VF	EF	Proof
39A	1866	WM	20.5mm	—	—	2500.

As 39. Plain edge. Rarity 8. (Judd 479; P-567). 3 known specimens.

Baker	Date	Metal	Size	VF	EF	Proof
39B	1866	Copper	20.5mm	—	—	—

As 39. Plain edge. Rarity 9. (Judd 477)

The illustrated specimen, a white metal piece (Baker 39A), was struck without a collar causing its rim to split much as a die splasher would do.

TWO-CENT PATTERNS

Baker	Date	Metal	Size	VF	EF	Proof
37	1863	Bronze	23mm	—	—	2000.

Undraped bust right, GOD AND OUR COUNTRY above, * 1863 * below. Rv: 2 / CENTS within wheat wreath tied by a band, UNITED STATES OF AMERICA around. Plain edge. Rarity 4. (Adams-Woodin 404; Judd 305; P-370)

Baker	Date	Metal	Size	VF	EF	Proof
37A	1863	CN	23mm	—	—	3000.

As 37. Plain edge. Rarity 7. (Adams-Woodin 403; Judd 306; P-371)

Baker	Date	Metal	Size	VF	EF	Proof
37B	1863	Aluminum	23mm	—	—	2500.

As 37. Plain edge. Rarity 8. (Adams-Woodin 406; Judd 308; P-373)

Baker	Date	Metal	Size	VF	EF	Proof
37C	1863	Oroide	23mm	—	—	2500.

As 37. Plain edge. Rarity 8. (Judd 307; P-2500)

Baker 37B represents one very early use of aluminum by the United States Mint. In 1863 it was very expensive. In 1859 the only aluminum refinery in the world, in France, sold the metal at $17 a pound but had been able to produce only 60 pounds of the pure metal. During the 1860's and 1870's the price rose gradually to $2 an ounce — twice the price of silver at the time. Only after the electrolytic process of refining aluminum from bauxite was introduced in November, 1888, did aluminum drop dramatically in value, to 75 cents a pound by 1893.

Many of these pattern pieces were struck outside the mint about 1870 from genuine mint dies obtained by J.J. Mickley, the well known collector. The government seized dies about 1876, but two remained in the Boston Numismatic Society cabinet, from which they were seized by the U.S. Secret Service about 1954. A breakdown of Mint and non-Mint strikes is at the end of this chapter.

Baker	Date	Metal	Size			
39C	1866	Brass	20.5mm	—	—	—

As 39. Plain edge. Rarity 9. (Judd 478; P-568)

This particular group of patterns was not listed by Adams & Woodin in 1913, though reported by Baker in 1885. They have been reported in Judd's editions of 1959 and 1962, however. They are also listed by Pollock, given in this section as "P" numbers.

Baker	Date	Metal	Size	VF	EF	Proof
40	1866	Nickel	20.5mm	—	—	2000.

Obverse as 39. Rv: 5 within a circle made up of 13 6-pointed stars and 13 rays, UNITED STATES OF AMERICA around, . CENTS . below. Plain edge. Rarity 6. (Adams-Woodin 551; Judd 473; P-564)

| 40A | 1866 | Copper | 20.5mm | — | — | 2000. |

As 40. Plain edge. Rarity 8. (Adams-Woodin 552; Judd 474; P-565)

| 40B | 1866 | Bronze | 20.5mm | — | — | 2000. |

As 40. Plain edge. Rarity 8. (Adams-Woodin 553; Judd 475; P-567)

The Act of May 16, 1866, provided for a cupronickel (75% copper and 25% nickel) 5-cent coin measuring 20.5 millimeters and weighing 77-16/100 grains — again without Washington's portrait. The 1866 Shield nickels used a U.S. shield similar to that on the 2-cent coins introduced in 1864, and used the identical reverse of Baker 40 for the trade coin.

Baker	Date	Metal	Size	VF	EF	Proof
41	1866	Nickel	20.5mm	—	—	500.

Obverse as 39. Rv: 5 within laurel wreath tied by a bow. The numeral 5 is short and squat (see illustration). Around: UNITED STATES OF AMERICA. Plain edge. Rarity 7. (Adams-Woodin 543; Judd 464; P-558)

| 41A | 1866 | Copper | 20.5mm | — | — | 2000. |

As 41. Plain edge. Rarity 7. (Adams-Woodin 544; Judd 465; P-559)

| 41B | 1866 | Bronze | 20.5mm | — | — | 2000. |

As 41. Plain edge. Rarity 7. (Judd 466; Adams-Woodin 544; P-559)

| 41C | 1866 | Silver | 20.5mm | — | — | — |

Obverse as 41. Rv: As reverse of 45. Plain edge. Rarity 9. (Judd 466a; P-555 not verified)

| 41F | 1866 | Nickel | 20.5mm | — | — | 2000. |

Obverse as 41. Rv: As reverse of 41, but numeral 5 is taller and thinner (see illustration). Plain edge. Rarity 8. (Judd 467; Adams-Woodin 545; P-560)

| 41G | 1866 | Copper | 20.5mm | — | — | 1500. |

As 41F. Plain edge. Rarity 7. (Judd 468; P-561)

| 41H | 1866 | Bronze | 20.5mm | — | — | 1500. |

As 41F. Plain edge. Rarity 7. (Judd 469; P-561)

Baker	Date	Metal	Size	VF	EF	Proo
42	1866	Nickel	20.5mm	—	—	2500.

Obverse as 39. Rv:5 within olive wreath tied by a bow. UNITED STATES OF AMERICA around. Plain edge. Rarity 6. (Adams-Woodin 548; Judd 470; P-562)

| 42A | 1866 | Copper | 20.5mm | — | — | 2500. |

As 42. Plain edge. Rarity 7. (Adams-Woodin 550; Judd 471; P-563)

| 42B | 1866 | Bronze | 20.5mm | — | — | 2500. |

As 42. Plain edge. Rarity 7. (Judd 472; P-563)

Enlargement

Baker	Date	Metal	Size	VF	EF	Unc
P-42	1867/6	WM	20.5mm	—	—	3000.

Obverse of 39. Rv: Coronet Liberty head left, star on coronet, head left, UNITED STATES OF AMERICA around 1867 below (similar to design adopted in 1865 for 3-cent cupronickel coins issued by U.S. Mint). Plain edge. Judd 580; P-636 (with correct reverse); Judd 585; P-645. Rarity 9.

| P-42A | 1867/6 | Silver | 20.5mm | — | — | Ex. Rare |

J-579; P-634 (with correct reverse); and P-644A. Rarity 8.

Enlargement

Baker	Date	Metal	Size	VF	EF	Unc
Q-42	1869	Nickel	20.5mm	—	—	Unique

Obverse as 39. Rv: Similar to reverse of P-42, but date is now 1869 (The enlargement below clearly shows the LIBERTY and 5-pointed star on the coronet.) Plain edge. Rarity 9. (Not listed in Adams-Woodin or Judd; ex-Garrett; P-767)

Baker	Date	Metal	Size	VF	EF	Proof
43	1866	Nickel	20.5mm	—	—	5000.

Undraped bust right (larger and bolder than that on 39), GOD AND OUR COUNTRY around, 1866 below. Rv: Small 5 within olive wreath tied by a bow, UNITED STATES OF AMERICA around. Plain edge. Rarity 8. (Adams-Woodin 555; Judd 483; P-573)

| 43A | 1866 | Copper | 20.5mm | — | — | 4000. |

As 43. Plain edge. Rarity 8. (Adams-Woodin 556; Judd 484; P-574)

| 43B | 1866 | Bronze | 20.5mm | — | — | 4000. |

As 43. Plain edge. Rarity 8. (Judd 485; P-574)

| 44 | 1866 | Nickel | 20.5mm | — | — | 3500. |

Obverse as 43, but larger bust. Rv: Tall 5 within laurel wreath tied by a bow, UNITED STATES OF AMERICA around. Plain edge. Rarity 7. (Adams-Woodin 554; Judd 481; P-571)

| 44A | 1866 | Copper | 20.5mm | — | — | 2500. |

As 44. Plain edge. Rarity 8. (Judd 482; P-572)

Baker	Date	Metal	Size	VF	EF	Proof
45	1866	Nickel	20.5mm	—	—	3500.

Undraped bust right, UNITED STATES OF AMERICA around, 1866 below. Rv: 5 / CENTS within laurel wreath tied by a bow, IN GOD WE TRUST above. Plain edge. Rarity 6. Magnetic. (Adams-Woodin 541; Judd 461; P-535)

| 45A | 1866 | CN | 20.5mm | — | — | 3000. |

As 45. Plain edge. Rarity 8. (Judd 463; P-537)

| 45B | 1866 | Copper | 20.5mm | — | — | 3000. |

As 45. Plain edge. Rarity 7. (Adams-Woodin 542; Judd 462; P-536)

Baker	Date	Metal	Size	VF	EF	Unc
46	1866	Nickel	20.5mm	—	—	2500.

Obverse as 45. Rv: 5 within a circle of 13 6-pointed stars, UNITED STATES OF AMERICA around, . CENTS . below. Plain edge. Rarity 8. (Judd 516; P-543)

| 46A | 1866 | Copper | 20.5mm | — | — | 1500. |

As 46. Plain edge. Rarity 8. (Judd 517; P-544)

| 46B | 1866 | Lead | 20.5mm | — | — | 2000. |

As 46. Plain edge. Rarity 8. (Judd 520; P-536)

Baker	Date	Metal	Size	VF	EF	Unc
46C	1866	Brass	20.5mm	—	—	—

As 46. Plain edge. Rarity 8. (Judd 519; P-546)

| 46D | 1866 | Silver | 20.5mm | — | — | — |

As 46. Plain edge. Rarity 8. (Judd 518; P-545)

Greatly enlarged

| 46E | 1866 | CN | 20.5mm | — | — | Unique |

As 46, but struck over an 1867 Shield nickel. Plain edge. Rarity 10. (Not in Judd or Adams-Woodin; P-543A)

The existence of Baker 46E, proves the pattern dies were used after the date they bear, 1866, though apparently without mint sanction. Discovered by George Fuld at 1952 ANA convention, ex-Lenox Lohr. Sold in Crouch collection, by Superior Stamp & Coin Co., later Brannigan.

Baker	Date	Metal	Size	VF	EF	Unc
P-46	1866	WM	20.5mm	—	—	3000.

Obverse as 46. Rv: As obverse of 39. Plain edge. Rarity 8. (Judd 524)

| P-46A | 1866 | Copper | 20.5mm | — | — | 1000. |

As P-46. Plain edge. Rarity 8. (Judd 522)

| P-46B | 1866 | Brass | 20.5mm | — | — | 3500. |

As P-46. Plain edge. Rarity 7. (Judd 523)

| P-46C | 1866 | Silver | 20.5mm | — | — | 3500. |

As 46. Plain edge. Rarity 9. (Judd 521)

| Q-46 | 1866 | WM | 20.5mm | — | — | 4000. |

Obverse as 46. Rv: Same (obverse of 46). Plain edge. Rarity 9. (Judd 526)

| Q-46A | 1866 | Copper | 20.5mm | — | — | 4000. |

As Q-46. Plain edge. Rarity 9. (Judd 525)

Baker	Date	Metal	Size	VF	EF	Unc
R-46	1867/6	WM	20.5mm	—	—	Ex. Rare

Obverse of 46, reverse P-42 with star on coronet. (Judd 584, P-645). Rarity 9.

Baker	Date	Metal	Size	VF	EF	Unc
R-46A	1867/6	Nickel	20.5mm			

Judd 580; P-635 (with correct reverse); not in Judd; P-644. Rarity 9.

Baker	Date	Metal	Size	VF	EF	Unc
A-39	1909	Nickel	20.5mm	—	Unique	—

Military bust right, ******* LIBERTY ******* around, 1909 below- Rv: 5 / CENTS within laurel wreath with opening at 7 o'clock, UNITED STATES OF AMERICA around, . E PLURIBUS UNUM . below. Plain edge. Rarity 10. (Adams-Woodin 1745; Judd 1782; P-2017)

Baker	Date	Metal	Size	VF	EF	Unc
A-39B	1909	Nickel	20.5mm	—	Unique	—

Obverse as A-39 but smaller date numerals. Rv: As reverse of A-39. Plain edge. Rarity 10. (Adams-Woodin 1746; Judd 1783; P-2018)

Baker	Date	Metal	Size	VF	EF	Unc
A-39D	1909	Nickel	20.5mm	—	Unique	—

Obverse as A-39 (large date), but around is: ************* LIBERTY. Rv: As reverse of A-39. Plain edge. Rarity 10. (Adams-Woodin 1747; Judd 1784; P-2019)

Baker	Date	Metal	Size	VF	EF	Unc
B-39	1909	Nickel	20.5mm	—	Unique	—

Obverse as A-39 (large date), but around: L**I**B**E**R**T**Y*. Rv: As reverse of A-39. Plain edge. Rarity 10. (Adams-Woodin 1748; Judd 1785; P-2020)

Baker	Date	Metal	Size	VF	EF	Unc
C-39	1909	Nickel	20.5mm	—	Unique	—

Large civil bust left, LIBERTY along upper right rim, 1909 at lower left. Rv: As reverse of A-39. Plain edge. Rarity 10. (Adams-Woodin 1750; Judd 1786; P-2021)

Baker	Date	Metal	Size	VF	EF	Unc
D-39	1909	Nickel	20.5mm	—	2 Known	—

Obverse as C-39, but date is in different style of numerals with long-tailed 9's. Rv: Large outline 5 across which is CENTS, within untied laurel branches. Above: UNITED STATES OF AMERICA / E PLURIBUS UNUM. Plain edge. Rarity 9. (Adams-Woodin 1751; Judd 1787; P-2022)

Baker	Date	Metal	Size	VF	EF	Unc
E-39	1910	Nickel	20.5mm	—	2 Known	—

Large civil bust left, LIBERTY 1910 around. Rv: As reverse of D-39 with added line of text along lower rim: IN GOD WE TRUST. Plain edge. Rarity 9. (Adams-Woodin 1752; Judd 1788; P-2023)

FIVE-DOLLAR PATTERNS

Baker	Date	Metal	Size	VF	EF	Unc
T-46	1866	WM	22mm	—	Unique	—

Obverse as Baker 39 (IN GOD WE TRUST). Rv: Eagle displayed with shield on its breast, UNITED STATES OF AMERICA around, .FIVE D. .below (reverse of regular $5 gold piece, without the motto). Plain edge. Rarity 10. (Judd 545; P-6240)

Baker	Date	Metal	Size	VF	EF	Unc
U-46	1866	WM	22mm	—		1150.

Obverse as Baker 45 (UNITED STATESOF AMERICA). Rv: As reverse of T-46. Plain edge. Rarity 10. (Judd 547; P-6245)

Baker U-46 in AU has sold in public auctions 1962, 1977 and 1983, the last time realizing $1150.

Both T-46 and U-46 are crude work, private pattern fantasies and not U.S. Mint work.

WASHINGTON QUARTER MODELS

Though no pattern coins resulted from the work, there were models prepared of designs which did not become a reality. Through the courtesy of the late John W. Dunn of Norman, Okla., two of these are illustrated herewith.

Illustration reduced

Baker	Date	Metal	Size	—	—	Value
Model 1	1932	Plaster	310mm	—	—	—

Head right (an adaptation of the Houdon bust), LIBERTY above partly obscured by Washington's head, IN GOD / WE / TRUST to left, 1932 to right. Rv: Eagle displayed, head turned right, three arrows and a branch in its talons, 13 stars in two arcs above eagle's head. Above: UNITED STATES OF AMERICA. Below: E PLURIBUS UNUM / QUARTER DOLLAR.

Model 2	1932	Plaster	302mm	—	—	—

Uniformed bust right, the high uniform collar above a line drawn to the point of the chin. LIBERTY above, partly obscured by the head. At left: In / God We / Trust (in upper and lower case letters). At right: 1932. Rv: Blank.

Model 2 by James Earle Fraser.

Also shown below are three sketches for the obverse of the Washington quarter, each with uniformed bust to left. None of these designs was acceptable to the mint. The sketches do closely resemble the 1 1/2 and 3-inch official Mint medals made by Fraser.

The Washington quarter itself was designed by John Flannagan, a New York sculptor.

Model 3	1932	Plaster	?mm	—	—	—

Bare head right, IN / GOD WE / TRUST to right of neck, LIBERTY / ****** 1932 ****** around. Rv: Eagle perched left on a fasces, UNITED STATES OF AMERICA / E PLURIBUS UNUM above, .QUARTER DOLLAR. below.

Model 3 is by U.S. Mint engraver Adam Pietz. A plaster of this reverse is in the collection of the American Numismatic Association museum. (Photo courtesy Kenneth E. Bressett)

MINT AND NON-MINT PRODUCTS

It is the opinion of the authors that many of the foregoing Pattern coins of the United States were struck outside the U.S. Mint, using genuine Mint dies, probably about 1870, utilizing the dies obtained by J.J. Mickley, the well-known collector with close friends inside the Mint.

It is our belief the following tabulation distinguishes Mint-struck from non-Mint struck products.

MINT STRUCK. Baker types 37, 38, 41, 41F, 42, 43, 44, 45, A-39 thru E-39.

STRUCK OUTSIDE THE MINT. Baker types 39, 40, P-42, Q-42, 46A thru 46E, P-46 thru 46E, Q-46, R-46, R-46A, T-46, U-46.

MINT DRAWINGS FOR 1999 DELAWARE HALF DOLLARS

Four reverse designs were submitted to Delaware's governor and legislature for consideration. One of them, with modifications, becomes the first 1999 "States" quarter. Note that the Washington obverse design has also been altered from that introduced in 1932!

WASHINGTON QUARTER SKETCHES FOR 1999

WASHINGTON QUARTER OBVERSE

Shown below are the United States Mint-revised obverse for the Washington quarter to be issued in 1999 and through 2008, or later. Tiny initials JF and WC appear on the truncation of the bust, for original designer John Flanagan and Mint sculptor-engraver William Cousins. The obverse model was exhibited first at the U.S. Mint booth at the 1998 American Numismatic Association convention in Portland, Oregon, August 5 to 9. Mintmarks P, S and D will appear behind Washington's neck.

Also shown are the approved sketches submitted by the governor of the first five states to be honored on the new "States Series" Washington quarters, which are to replace the eagle reverse design 1999-2008. Delaware's quarter is being released first as it was the first state to ratify the Constitution in 1787.

The other 1999 releases will be for the states of New Jersey, Pennsylvania, Georgia, and Connecticut. All 1999-2008 quarters will be released into circulation and the Mint plans collector versions as well.

Delaware, the "first state," honors **Caesar Rodney**, who conducted a midnight ride to Philadelphia to cast the deciding vote in favor of the Declaration of Independence.

Pennsylvania, the Keystone State, chose **"Commonwealth,"** the statue atop the dome of the Pennsylvania capitol, as well as a keystone against an outline map of the state.

The famed **Georgia peach** on an outline map of the state is surrounded by its scroll motto and sprays.

Connecticut's best-known state symbol, the **Charter Oak**, graces that state's quarter design.

Washington crosses the Delaware to fight the Battle of Trenton on **New Jersey's** quarter dollar. The Christmas attack is often called the turning point in the Revolutionary War.

GRADE HEADINGS

Three grade (condition) columns appear in this catalog. Coins and tokens, which circulate, are graded down to VG (Very Good), but medals, which do not circulate, usually are graded no less than VF (Very Fine). Other abbreviations used are F (Fine), EF (Extremely Fine), AU (About Uncirculated), Unc (Uncirculated), and P-L (Prooflike). Proof is spelled out.

Chapter 4

WASHINGTON BEFORE BOSTON

NOTE: On some of the Paris Mint restrikes of these medals over the years, a symbol and a word for the metallic content are incused on the edge. This edge-marking enables the collector to attribute his piece to a particular era (remembering that the symbols occasionally were used after they should have been.) The most commonly encountered metal words are: OR (gold), AR-GENT (silver), CUIVRE (copper) and BRONZE (bronze).

The French "marques et differents" (privy marks) are those of either the mint director or chief engraver. In the table below, we list all such marks used from 1800 on, without implying that all were used on edges of Washington Before Boston medals.

Paris Mint Director Privy Marks		Paris Chief Engraver Privy Marks	
Cock	1798-1821	Horse head	1816-24
Anchor	1822-31	T in script	1824-30
Antique lamp	1832-41	Star	1830-42
Anchor with C	1841-42	Dog head	1843-55
Prow of ship	1843-45	Anchor	1855-79
Pointing hand	1846-60	Anchor with bar	1879
Bee	1860-79	Fasces	1880-96
Cornucopia	1880-98, 1901	Torch	1896-1930
NONE	1897-1920	Wing	1931-58
		Owl	1958-74
		Fish	1974-

Stahl (see Bibliography) says gold and silver restrikes date only from 1832 and copper only from 1841. He also says that only Mint Director marks were used, but Engraver Marks have been used since at least 1931. Actual examination of more edge-marked specimens must be made before conclusions can be finally drawn.

Original, struck 1790

Baker	Date	Metal	Size	VF	EF	Unc
47	1776	Gold	68mm	—	Ex. Rare	—

Undraped Washington bust right, DU VIVIER / PARIS. F. in two lines under bust. Around: GEORGIO WASHINGTON SVPREMO DVCI EXERCITVVM ADSERTORI LIBERTATIS. Below: COMITIA AMERICANA. Rv: Washington and staff officers, mounted, on an eminence at left, watch Boston being evacuated by the British, with American troops in middle ground waiting to take possession. Two cannon and a fort at right, on one cannon is: DUVIV. Above: HOSTIBUS PRIMO FUGATIS. In exergue: BOSTONIUM RECUPERATUM / XVII. MARTII / MDCCLXXVI. Plain edge. (One struck at Paris and presented to Gen. Washington on March 21, 1790; now in collection Boston Public Library.) 2 pieces known.

Baker	Date	Metal	Size	VF	EF	Unc
47A	1776	Silver	68.8mm	—	20,000.	—

As 47. Plain edge. (Gen. Washington's 'hope chest' copy now in Massachusetts Historical Society.) 5 pieces known.

Specimens now known: MHS ex-Daniel Webster; private Rhode Island Collection, ex-Peru, 1961, George Fuld, Richard Picker, John Ford, Jr.; John Ford, Jr. ex-Paris 1967; private Massachusetts collection, ex-Rossa & Tannenbaum, privately in New York; Presidential Middendorf sale, December 8, 1990, lot 32 at $17,500 ex. & Dreyfuss Sale, Dr. Paul Patterson, unnamed source in England.

PHOTO COURTESY MASSACHUSETTS HISTORICAL SOCIETY, BOSTON.

Baker	Date	Metal	Size	VF	EF	Unc
47B	1776	Bronze	68.8mm	—	1700.	2100.

As 47. Plain edge. Only 20 to 30 known. Rim 5.5mm thick. Weight 2409 grains. (Fuld coll., Norweb coll., Parsons 1914 sale; Julian MI-1; Stack's Jan. 14-15, 1998 sale, lot 60.). Rarity 6.

An EF-AU specimen of 47B made $1705 in the PCAC May 16, 1997 sale, lot 116. Another choice AU was offered at $2250 in the 1991 Collins sale.

The gold specimen presented by Congress to Gen. Washington remained in a collateral branch of his family until the winter of 1876, when it was purchased for $5,000 by 50 citizens of Boston and presented to the city. The trustees of the Boston Public Library were selected as its custodian and it has remained there since.

A second specimen, worn, appeared at the Chicago Coin Fair in the late 1980's, with William Christensen acting as agent. Rulau and others examined it visually; it appeared genuine.

One silver specimen was presented to Washington by the French government and was owned subsequently by Daniel Webster. A later owner, Peter Harvey, donated it April 16, 1874 to the Massachusetts Historical Society. Four other specimens are known.

On all originals, four legs of a horse appear under the belly of Washington's horse.

NOTE: Caution! There are five distinct restrikes of the Washington Before Boston medal! The illustration in Wayte Raymond's *The Early Medals of Washington* (Raymond 1) is actually a restrike, for example.

Any collector considering the purchase of a Washington Before Boston medal touted as an original, or even an early restrike, should first read George Fuld's "The Washington Before Boston Medal" in the TAMS Journal for Sept.-Dec., 1963, which provides complete descriptions, illustrations and tips for the collector and dealer.

On all originals, the O in PRIMO is perfectly round; on all restrikes it is oval to varying degrees. There are periods after XVII. and MDCCLXXVII. The last I of MARTII is under the R of RECUPERATUM. But, not all round O's are original!

Baker	Date	Metal	Size	VF	EF	Unc
47Z	1276	Copper	69mm	—	—	Unique

Solid strike in Copper of Baker 47 with error date MCCLXXVI. (J.J. Ford collection)

47ZA	1276	White Metal	69mm	—	—	Unique

Reverse die trial. (Norweb)

**First restrike
Paris, 1820**

Die trials

Baker	Date	Metal	Size	VF	EF	Unc
47X	ND	WM	69mm	—	—	—

Obverse similar to 47. Line above COMITIA AMERICANA. Rv: Blank, but covered with paper disc on which are four partially illegible lines of black type: ... ETHIS DE .../... ORDRE DE .../... SEPH VEYTA .../... UIS, C ... Plain edge. Rejected dies. (Garrett 1744; Norweb)

47Y	1776	WM	69mm	—	—	—

Obverse as reverse of 47. Rv: Blank. Plain edge. Unique. (Garrett 1744)

Baker	Date	Metal	Size	VF	EF	Unc
48	1776	Red Bronze	68.4mm	—	950.	—

Similar to 47. Differences: O in PRIMO is slightly oval. Second I of MARTII is under second E of RECUPERATUM. NOTE: Edges are plain, just as 47, minus markings. Rarity 8. (Raymond 1; Collins 53)

48A   1776   Lead   68mm   —   —   —

On all first restrikes, four horse's legs show under Washington's horse.

48H   1776   Golden Bronze 68mm   —   —   —

As 48F. Edge marking: (Cornucopia) BRONZE. Rarity 3. This type struck at Paris about 1890. These usually show a die break over HOST of HOSTIBUS.

Edges

Silver	Bronze

Second restrike
Paris, 1835-1880

Baker	Date	Metal	Size	VF	EF	Unc
48F	1776	Silver	68.5mm		500.	900.

Similar to 47. Differences: Only 3 horse's legs show under Washington's horse. O in PRIMO slightly oval. Second I in MARTII under second R of RECUPERATUM, but no periods after XVII or MDCCLXXVI in exergue. Word ARGENT incused on edge, after privy mark. About 15 or more known. Weight 150.32 grams. (ANS, Fuld, Kagin ex-Magriel, Norweb)

48G	1776	Dark Bronze	68mm	165.	275.	—

As 48F. Edge marking: CUIVRE after privy mark. Over 100 specimens known, Rarity 4. This type first struck about 1835. (Magriel 228)

Known silver markings: **(Pointing hand) ARGENT** = 1846-60; **(Bee) ARGENT** = 1860-79; **(Cornucopia) 2 ARGENT** = 1880-?

Before Boston with Wreath

Struck 1888

Baker	Date	Metal	Size	VF	EF	Unc
B48J	1776	Silver	69mm	—	1500.	—

Obv. of Baker 47-8, with defined die break in right field. Rv: A fully formed wreath all around, engraved in center. MARIE SORCHAN / HORACE BINNEY / 19 AVRIL 1888. Paris Mint edgemark of cornucopia and ARGENT. First and only appearance in PCAC #62 11/97, lot 249. Binney had illustrious connections and possibly accounts for this special issuance by the French Mint.

Cataloger H. Joseph Levine describes the medal in his 1997 auction catalog as "proof, with light hairlines," adding that the Paris Mint used "the die used . . . to strike the original Washington Before Boston medal." A large die lump is in front of

Washington's chin and other die rust "matches that seen on original specimens" (Baker 47B).

This is the only known instance where the French Mint muled the WBB obverse with another reverse, indicating the Binney and Sorchan families must have had enormous influence with the French government. The Horace Binney named on the medal (Horace Binney III) was grandson of Horace Binney Sr., renowned Philadelphia lawyer who in 1807-1814 prepared six volumes of Pennsylvania Supreme Court decisions, served a term in Congress, and died 1875 at age of 95. Horace Binney Jr., also a lawyer, was president of the Sanitary Commission and founder of the Union League, dying in 1870. Marie Sorchan is a French name, but we have learned nothing of her family.

The medal is housed in a light brown leather presentation box with applied BS monogram (Binney-Sorchan) mounted at top, and blue 1elvet interior.

Fourth restrike
Philadelphia, 1890-1910

Baker	Date	Metal	Size	EF	Unc	Proof
49B	1776	Dark Bronze	68mm	—	175.	625.

Similar to 47 (4 horse's legs under belly of Washington's horse). Plain edge. Only 4 known (Fuld 2, Norweb, Kagin ex-Magriel; Julian MI-1). Rarity 7.

The dies for 49B were cut by Charles Barber after the 1863 gunmetal dies had failed.

Third restrike
Philadelphia, 1863-1889

Baker	Date	Metal	Size	VF	EF	Unc
49	1776	Dark Bronze	67.9mm	—	220.	450.

Similar to 48F (3 horse's legs show). Differences: Edge is plain, without markings. The differences between 48G and 49 are minor! Several hundred struck. Rarity 4.

Struck from transfer dies using a French bronze original medal via gunmetal blocks. There is some detail loss from the French dies.

Baker	Date	Metal	Size	VF	EF	Unc
49C	1776	Yellow Bronze	68.2mm	—	—	16.00

Similar to 49C, but struck in the U.S. Mint's "late bronze" and still available at modest cost from the Mint. Plain edge. Rarity 1.

| 49J | 1776 | Golden Bronze 68mm | — | — | 18.00 |

As 49G, but on edge: Wing, BRONZE. Rarity 1. This type still available at modest cost from Paris Mint.

Reported edge markings: **(Wing)** BRONZE = 1931-58; **(Owl)** BRONZE = 1958-74; **(Fish)** BRONZE = 1974-on.

Contemporary cast
Circa 1830's

Note Hall Marks on edge (Unidentified to date).

Edges

| First Type (@1910) | Second type (after 1930) |

Fifth restrike
Paris, 1910-on

| 49G | 1776 | Silver | 68mm | — | — | 50.00 |

Similar to 47 (4 horse's legs under Washington's horse). Difference: ARGENT and wing incused in edge. This restrike since 1958 has been available from the Paris Mint.

| 49AG | 1776 | Silver | 68.6mm | — | 200. | — |

As 49G, but cornucopia and ARGENT on edge. Made circa 1920. (PCAC May 16, 1997 sale, lot 121)

| 49H | 1776 | Golden Bronze 68mm | — | — | 35.00 |

As 49G, but on edge: Cornucopia, BRONZE and FRANCE. Rarity 3.

Baker	Date	Metal	Size	VF	EF	Unc
49M	1776	Silver	67mm	—	—	—

Cast silver imitation made in Europe from a Second Restrike specimen. Edge markings: 800, Crowned SR and Crown, in three separate depressions. (Raymond coll, ex-Fuld; ANS 1919, ex-Bland)

The Washington Before Boston medal has always been considered the most important of the Washington medals, because it was the first authorized by the Continental Congress and it first used the Houdon profile on the general, considering the best.

Following the Battle of Bunker Hill (June 17, 1775), George Washington of Virginia took command of the Continental Army of about 17,000 men encamped around Boston on July 2. The siege of Boston, held by 6,500 British under Major Gen. Thomas Gage, began in earnest. Gage was recalled in October, and Major Gen. William Howe replaced him. British reinforcements arrived in January, 1776, bolstering the force to 12,000. But in March Howe decided to abandon Boston and pursue a campaign in New York, and the 12,000 British troops evacuated on March 17, 1776 - Boston and Massachusetts were free of the British for the rest of the Revolutionary War.

On March 25, 1776, Congress passed a resolution authorizing a letter of thanks and a special gold medal for the commander-in-chief. They appointed a committee for this purpose — John Adams, John Jay and Stephen Hopkins. This committee was immortalized in metal on the resultant medal by the words COMITIA AMERICANA on the obverse — "American Committee" representing the Continental Congress.

The dies for the medal were executed at Paris by Pierre Simon Benjamin DuVivier, an eminent engraver, some time after May of 1786. The French artist Nicolas Marie Gatteaux drew the designs in 1785. DuVivier used for the Washington bust on the piece the bust modeled by Jean Antoine Houdon, the French sculptor, which had been executed from life in October, 1785 at Mount Vernon, Va. Houdon brought his work back to Paris in January, 1786. The gold medal for presentation to Washington was struck at the Paris Mint, as were a few impressions later in silver and in a dark red bronze.

The gold medal was presented to Washington by Thomas Jefferson on March 21, 1790. He also received at the same time a silver specimen as part of the 11-piece silver Comitia Americana set struck at the Paris Mint. Other battles are commemorated on the other 10 medals authorized by Congress.

Struck 1974-1976

Baker	Date	Metal	Size	EF	AU	Unc
49CA	1776	Pewter	38.1mm	—	—	6.00

Reduced size facsimile of 49C, struck in antique finished pewter. This was part of a 15-piece set of U.S. historical medals struck by Philadelphia Mint for the nation's bicentennial. (Collins 58). Rarity 2.

SIEGE OF BOSTON MEDALETS

Struck 1859

Baker	Date	Metal	Size	VF	EF	Proof
50	1776	Silver	31.6mm	—	—	165.

Equestrian figure of Washington in uniform, on an eminence, head facing; in the distance a city, to the right an American encampment; to the left a battery. Around: GEO. WASHINGTON. 1776. Rv: Within olive wreath connected at top by drum, flags and arms: SIEGE OF BOSTON 1775-6 in three lines. Under the wreath: LOVETT'S SERIES NO. 2. PHILADA: Reeded edge. Rarity 5.

50A	1776	Copper	31.6mm	—	—	60.00

As 50. Reeded edge. Also known in bronze, reeded edge.

50B	1776	Brass	31mm	—	—	60.00

As 50. Reeded edge.

50C	1776	WM	31mm	—	—	60.00

As 50. Reeded edge.

50D	1776	WM	31mm	—	—	60.00

As 50. Plain edge.

Baker	Date	Metal	Size	VF	EF	Unc
50J	1776	Copper	31mm	—	—	25.00

Similar to 50, but obverse legend erased on die, and LOVETT'S SERIES NO. 2 PHILADA also erased on die. Parts of the erased words show. Plain edge.

50K	1776	Brass	31mm	—	—	25.00

As 50J. Plain edge.

50L	1776	WM	31mm	—	—	25.00

As 50J. Plain edge.

The dies were in existence until early 1880's, then destroyed. All struck by Robert Lovett Jr. of Philadelphia. Lovett also created the mulings which follow, Baker 51 and 52.

First muling

51	1776	Silver	31.7mm	—	85.00	150.

Obverse as 50. Rv: Roman-mantled Washington bust right, GEORGE WASHINGTON around. Reeded edge. Rarity 8. (Collins 61)

51A	1776	Copper	31mm	—	—	80.00

As 51. Reeded edge. Rarity 7.

Second muling

Baker	Date	Metal	Size	VF	EF	Unc
52	1776	Copper	31.9mm	—	—	45.00

Obverse as 50. Rv: Undraped Washington bust right, LOVETT on truncation and R.L. under bust. Around: GEORGE WASHINGTON / * SECURITY *. Reeded edge. Rarity 5.

52A	1776	Copper	31.9mm	—	—	50.00

As 52. Plain edge. Rarity 6.

Third muling

52F	1776	Silver	31mm	—	—	250.

Obverse as 50. Rv: As obverse of Baker 136. (Undraped bust right, LOVETT on truncation). Reeded edge. Rarity 8.

52G	1776	Copper	31mm	—	—	100.

As 52F. Reeded edge. (Elizabeth Steinle coll., So. Charleston, W. Va.)

EVACUATION DAY 125TH ANNIVERSARY

Struck 1901

Baker	Date	Metal	Size	VF	EF	Unc
52R	1901	Bronze	38mm	11.00	20.00	60.00

Obverse is a reproduction of the Washington Before Boston medal. Rv: Oak wreath open at top encloses: SOUVENIR / 125TH / ANNIVERSARY / EVACUATION DAY / BOSTON, MASS. / 1901. At bottom, in tiny letters: W. & H. CO. NEWARK N.J. Plain edge. Rarity 2. (Hibler-Kappen 131; Collins 64)

52S	1901	Pewter	38mm	—	37.00	—

As 52R. (Coin Galleries July 18, 1995 sale, lot 50)

Whitehead and Hoag Co. prepared these dollar-sized souvenirs. Evacuation Day occurred on March 17, 1776 when the British abandoned Boston to Washington's army. The souvenirs were given to school children; many were carried as pocket pieces and they are often encountered worn. Choice BU specimens are quite scarce.

A small hoard of worn specimens, mostly VF, came onto the numismatic market in 1983.

EVACUATION DAY 250TH ANNIVERSARY

Baker	Date	Metal	Size	VF	EF	Unc
52U	1976	Brass	38mm	—	—	10.00

Reproduction of Washington before Boston medal obverse. Rv: Within wreath: 250th / ANNIVERSARY/ EVACUATION DAY / BOSTON, MASS. / 1976. (H.J. Levine report)

MALCOLM E. NICHOLS

Baker	Date	Metal	Size	VF	EF	Unc
52W	1935	Gilt/Bz	38mm	—	17.50	25.00

Reproduction of Washington before Boston medal, but MARTII is misspelled MARTN. Rv: Within wreath in ten lines: PRESENTED / TO HONORABLE / MALCOLM E. / NICHOLS / BY HIS / SOUTH BOSTON / FRIENDS / Nov. 26, 1935 / MOUNT / WASHINGTON. Along lower rim: (tiny) WHITEHEAD-HOAG. Plain edge. (Roelofs coll.; H.J. Levine report)

This unpublished medal is probably scarce. Its purpose has not been determined.

DECLARATION OF INDEPENDENCE

SIGNING CEREMONY

Struck about 1854

Baker	Date	Metal	Size	VF	EF	Unc
53	1776	Bronze	91mm	—	5000.	8000.

Undraped bust left, C. C. WRIGHT. D & F on truncation. GEORGE WASHINGTON around. Rv: Across center is medallic representation of Jonathan Trumbull's painting of the Declaration of Independence of 1776. DECLARATION/OF above, INDEPENDENCE/JULY 4TH. 1776./ (tiny) C. C. WRIGHT. FECIT. Plain edge. Rarity 8. 5 or 6 known. (Raymond 42; Wilson 874; Stack's 1991 catalog, lot 133)

| 53A | 1776 | White Metal | 91mm | — | Unique | |

As 53. Plain edge. (Raymond 42; Bushnell 1273)

| 53F | 1776 | Copper | 94mm | — | — | 400. |

Electrotype copy, by George Segebaden about 1880. Very deceptive, but eminently collectible. (Magriel sale; Collins 65; Hirsch coll.)

The dies were cut by Charles Cushing Wright of New York a few years before his death, which occurred on June 7, 1854, at age 58. Wright was the best die engraver this country produced in its early years.

The massive medallion is considered Wright's masterwork.

An EF-AU specimen of Baker 53F fetched $363 in the May 16, 1997 PCAC sale, lot 122. A choice Unc. specimen was offered but withdrawn in the Stack's Collins sale of 1996.

The David Hirsch specimen of 53F, bid in at $308, measures 94mm in diameter.

Baker	Date	Metal	Size	VF	EF	Unc
53G	1776	Silver	91mm	—	Unique	—

Obverse: Constitution. Rv: As reverse of Baker 53. (Garrett IV sale; B&M Leidman 1986 sale, lot 4126)

| 53H | 1776 | Bronze | 91mm | — | Unique | — |

As 53G. Plain edge. (See Wilson 875; published by Fuld 1981; now in an eastern collection)

| 53J | 1776 | Bronze | 91mm | — | — | 150. |

Electrotype copy of 53G. A number are known.

Made 1851

| 53M | 1776 | Copper | 90mm | — | — | 300. |

Electrotype. Obverse. Same as reverse of Baker 53. Rv: A facsimile of all 59 signatories from John Hancock to Button Gwinett. (PCAC 60, June 1996 sale, lot 157; Magriel sale)

AMERICAN BEAVER

Struck 1807

Baker	Date	Metal	Size	VF	EF	UNC
54	1776	Silver	40mm	—	2 or 3 known	

Jugate busts left of Benjamin Franklin and George Washington, R. on truncation. Rv: The American beaver gnaws at trunk of overshadowing English oak, symbolizing destruction of British authority in the American colonies. In exergue: 1776. Plain edge. (Raymond 14)

| 54A | 1776 | Bronze | 40mm | — | — | 900. | 1100. |

As 54. Plain edge. (Raymond 14; Julian CM-4; Stack Collins 57)

John Reich, assistant U.S. Mint engraver, cut the reverse die in November, 1807. Previously, in 1805, he had used the obverse die in his Peace of 1783 medal (Baker 58). Before striking Baker 54, however, he cut another die showing Franklin alone on obverse, pairing it with the Beaver reverse. These Franklin medals were originally presented Dec. 1, 1807 to two survivors of the Congress of 1776, George Clymer and Dr. Benjamin Rush. The Franklin medal is not cataloged here.

All the Beaver medals were published by Joseph Sansom of Philadelphia and struck at the U.S. Mint.

OBVERSE AND REVERSE

The term Obverse refers to the "heads" or "face" side of a piece. Where there is a human head or bust, this is easy to determine, but where there is no head, the side with the "principal device" is the Obverse. The opposite side is the Reverse. In some cases determining Obverse and Reverse must be arbitrary, especially where a head is on each side.

Each piece also has a third side, the Edge, which is described as Reeded, Plain, Lettered, etc. The term Rim is not the edge, but the periphery of one face or another.

AMERICAN EAGLE

Struck 1834

Baker	Date	Metal	Size	VF	EF	Unc.
55	1834	WM	50mm	700.	1500.	1800.

Military bust left, J.H.H. below. Around, in three concentric rings: G. WASHINGTON ELC. 1789 SERVD. 8 YEARS J. ADAMS EL. 1797, 4 Y.T. JEFFERSON EL. 1801 8 Y. J. MADISON EL. 1809 8 Y. J. MONROE EL. 1817 8 Y. J. Q. ADAMS EL. 1825 4 Y. A. JACKSON EL. 1829 LAFAYETTE APOINTED MAJ. GEN. OF THE U.S. ARMY 1777 DIED MAY 20, 1834. Rv: Eagle flying, in its talons a U.S. shield and a scroll lettered: ALL MEN ARE / CREATED EQUAL / JULY 4, 1776. Above: INDEPENDENCE ***, below: **** *1834*** **. Plain edge. (Raymond 39; Stack's 1991 price catalog, lot 134; Stack Collins 58)

55A	1834	WM	50mm	—	850.	1000.

As 55. Engrailed edge.

55B	1834	Bronze	50mm	—	Unique	—

As 55. (Fuld coll.)

55G	1846	WM	50mm	—	—	—

As 55, but dated 1846. (MHS coll.)

It is believed that these were struck in England; engraved by John H. Henning (1771-1861), who also engraved an Abraham Lincoln medal much later.

LIBERTAS AMERICANA

Struck about 1874

Baker	Date	Metal	Size	VF	EF	Unc
56	1776	Silver	25mm	—	Rare	150.

Bust in Roman mantle right, BOLEN beneath. WASHINGTON around. Rv: Copy of Libertas Americana medal, BOLEN on truncation. Plain edge.

56A	1776	Bronze	25mm	—	Rare	75.00

As 56. Plain edge.

56B	1776	Brass	25mm	—	Rare	75.00

As 56. Plain edge.

56C	1776	WM	25mm	—	Rare	75.00

As 56. Plain edge.

Dies cut by James Adams Bolen, Springfield, Mass. These are mulings of two Bolen dies. The Washington die had been used in 1864 for Soldiers' Fair tokens of Springfield (which see in Russell Rulau's *U.S. Trade Tokens 1866-1889*).

PEACE OF 1783

SANSOM MEDALS

Struck 1805

Baker	Date	Metal	Size	VF	EF	Proof
57	1783	Silver	40mm	—	—	—

Military bust left, R. on truncation. Around: G. WASHINGTON C.C.A.U.S. Rv: Eagle with lightning bolts in its talons, descending on a section of the globe marked UNITED STATES. At top: 1783. Plain edge. (Raymond 15; Garrett 1751; Julian CM-6). Only 5 known: Norweb; Spink & Son sale; John J. Ford; PHS; Garrett sale.

C.C.A.U.S. = Commander in Chief, Armies of the United States.

John Reich, assistant engraver at the U.S. Mint, cut the dies for Joseph Sansom of Philadelphia, the medal's publisher.

This medal was advertised in *The United States Gazette,* Philadelphia, for Dec. 28, 1805, as follows:

"A medal worthy of the illustrious Washington has been executed in Philadelphia by a German artist (John Reich) upon the designs of a person of taste, under the inspection of the Director of the Mint, the librarian of the Philosophical Society, and other gentlemen of professional ability or acknowledged judgement...

Proof impressions in gold and silver are now submitted to public examination at the book store of John Conrad & Co. where subscriptions will be received for the same. In gold 50 Dollars Silver at 5."

John Reich, born in Germany as Jacob Reich came to America and served as an assistant engraver at the United States Mint in Philadelphia. His works include the half dollar and half eagle of 1807 as well as several important medals.

The "person of taste" was Joseph Sansom, a well-known Philadelphia merchant. Other Sansom-sponsored medals include Baker-54, 58, and 71. All were struck at the U.S. Mint.

Struck 1808

Baker	Date	Metal	Size	VF	EF	Proof
58	1783	Silver	40mm	—	—	—

Jugate busts of Benjamin Franklin and George Washington left, R. on truncation. Rv: As reverse of 57. Plain edge. (Raymond 16; Garrett 1752; Betts 617; Julian CM-5). Only 2 known.

58A	1783	Bronze	41mm	—	800.	1100

As 58. Plain edge. (Raymond 16; Garrett 1753; Julian CM-5; Betts 617)

58B	1783	Lead	44mm	—	Unique	—

As 58. Plain edge. (Fuld coll.)

58C	1783	WM	40mm	—	—	—

As 58. Plain edge. (B&M Witham 1992 sale, lot 2108)

Publisher: Joseph Sansom. Engraver: John Reich.

MILITARY AND CIVIL CAREER

MANLY MEDALS

First obverse, 1790

Baker	Date	Metal	Size	VF	EF	Unc
61	1790	Silver	48mm	—	6000.	—

Uniformed bust left, BROOKS F. on truncation. GEO. WASHINGTON BORN VIRGINIA. around, FEB. 11. / 1732 below. Rv: * / GENERAL / OF THE / AMERICAN ARMIES 1775 / RESIGNED, / 1783. PRESIDENT / OF THE / UNITED STATES / 1789. / (small) J. MANLY & C. 1790. Plain edge. (Raymond 3; Garrett 1754). Only 5 known.

61A	1790	WM	48mm	—	3000.	—

As 61. (Raymond 3; Garrett 1755). 8 or 10 known.

61B	1790	Bronze	48mm	—	900.	3000.

As 61. Rarity 6. (Raymond 3)

61C	1790	Gold	48mm	—	—	Unique

As 61. (Raymond 3). The only specimen is in the MHS collection, ex-William Sumner Appleton.

Second obverse

Struck ca. 1850-1858

Baker	Date	Metal	Size	VF	EF	Unc
62	1790	Silver	49mm	—	—	4500.

Same bust as 61, but differing lettering, with S. B. F. on truncation. GEO. WASHINGTON NATUS VIRGINIA BP. WM. C. around, 11 FEB. O.S. / 1732 below. Rv: As reverse of 61; from new dies. Plain edge. (Raymond 4)

62A	1790	WM	49mm	—	—	—

As 62. Only 2 known.

Cast copy of early vintage

Baker	Date	Metal	Size	EF	AU	Unc
65F	1789	WM	36mm	—	—	—

Excellent cast copy of Baker 65. Porosity may be seen by examination with at least a 10-power microscope. (Kirtley June 16, 1998 sale, lot B027, ex-Jack Collins coll.)

Charles Kirtley confirmed to the authors that this cast copy has been known for a number of years. It may date to the 19th century.

WASHINGTON OF VIRGINIA

Originals, struck 1860

Baker	Date	Metal	Size	VF	EF	Unc
63	1789	Copper	34mm	—	Unique	—

Uniformed bust right, GEORGE WASHINGTON OF VIRGINIA around. Rv: Pyramid of 15 cannon balls above crossed swords at center. Legend around in two concentric circles: GENL OF THE AMERICAN ARMIES 1775 RESIGNED THE COMMAND 1783. / ELECT. PRESIDENT OF THE UNITED STATES 1789. Plain edge. (Appleton 16)

63A	1789	Brass	34mm	—	Unique	—

As 63.(Bushnell 1282)

| 63B | 1789 | Lead | 34mm | — | Unique | — |

As 63,(Per Massamore)

Restrikes, 1883

Baker	Date	Metal	Size	EF	Unc	P-L
64	1789	Gold	34mm	—	Unique	

As 63. Thick planchet. Plain edge. Weight 67.7 grams. (Garrett 1756) Only 1 struck, for T. Harrison Garrett.

| 64A | 1789 | Silver | 34mm | — | 375. | 700. |

As 63.21 struck. Weight: 27 dwt.

| 64B | 1789 | Copper | 34mm | — | 300. | |

As 63. 21 struck. 5mm thick!

| 64C | 1789 | Brass | 34mm | — | 300. | |

As 63. 21 struck.

It was once supposed that Baker 63 was struck by someone who attempted to imitate an earlier issue. However, the portrait seems to be copied from no particula

---

| 62B | 1790 | Bronze | 49mm | — | 550. | 750. |

As 62. Rarity 5. Raymond 4; Collins 68)

WM. C. = Westmoreland County, Washington's birthplace. O. S. = Old Style (calendar).

The first American-made Washington medal. It was designed by Samuel Brooks, a Philadelphia goldsmith and seal-cutter, and published by Jacques Manly of Philadelphia. The aged Washington portrait may have been inspired by Joseph Wright, who executed a portrait of Washington from life in 1784.

On March 3, 1790, *The Pennsylvania Packet and Daily Advertiser* offered these medals for sale. The portrait was described as being "a strong and expressive likeness and worthy of the attention of the citizens of the United States of America." Prices were given as $1 for a medal in "fine white metal, to resemble silver" (tin), $2 for a "fine gold-colored medal" (presumably bronze), and $4 for a "fine silver medal." It was noted that gold impressions were available at a price "in proportion to weight."

London coin dealer W. S. Lincoln & Son apparently first offered Baker 62 and 62B in 1858, at 25 shillings for 62 and 5 shillings for 62B. These were high prices for the times.

TWIGG MEDAL

Struck circa 1790

Baker	Date	Metal	Size	F	EF	Unc
65	1789	WM	35.7mm	—	400.	900.

Uniformed bust right, TWIGG on truncation. Around: GEORGE WASHINGTON. Rv: In nine lines: GENERAL OF THE AMERICAN ARMIES. 1775. RESIGN'D THE COMMAND. 1783. ELECTED PRESIDENT OF THE UNITED STATES. 1789. Plain edge. 167.5 grains. (Raymond 10; Stack's Inc. Jan. 1998 auction, lot 220)

Twigg engraved this medal from a sketch by Joseph Wright, made of George Washington from life while he attended New York's Trinity Church.

Twigg has not been identified even though 200 years have elapsed. Even the indefatigable Leonard Forrer was unable to pin him down.

A Mrs. Dupalais Twigg, born in Philadelphia in 1805, has been suggested as a possible relation (assuming Twigg was an American).

earlier style. The medal, once considered to be very early, actually was prepared in archaic style in Baltimore about 1860, according to Dr. George Massamore, a dentist of that city who had as a sideline a dealership in rare coins. Around 1860, Messrs. Reed and Brady, proprietors of the Old Curiosity Shop, located at the corner of Saratoga and Eutaw streets in Baltimore, conceived the idea. Brady designed the piece, and the engraving was done by Selig Baumgarten, a German who came to Baltimore in 1852. Only three impressions are believed to originally have been taken, one each in copper, brass, and lead. These pieces are listed as Baker-63.

In 1882 Dr. George Massamore acquired the dies. In January 1883, 64 additional impressions were struck for him by Jacob Gminder. Twenty-one each were struck in silver, copper, and brass. T. Harrison Garrett, who was one of Massamore's clients, learned of the project and specifically commissioned a gold striking.

Baker 64C in choice Unc. Realized $574.75 in the 1996 Stack Collins sale, lot 66.

WYON, PRESIDENCY RESIGNED

Baker	Date	Metal	Size	F	EF	Unc
66	1797	WM	37mm	—	575.	800.

Uniformed bust left, WYON on truncation. Around: GEORGE WASHINGTON. Rv: In nine lines: GENERAL OF THE AMERICAN ARMIES. 1775. RESIGND THE COMMAND 1783 ELECTED PRESIDENT OF THE UNITED STATES 1789. RE-ELECTED, 1793. RESIGN'D. 1797. Plain edge. (Raymond 11; Coin Galleries July 18, 1995 sale, lot 26)

WYON, RESUMED COMMAND

67	1798	WM	39mm	—	—	—

Uniformed bust left, T. WYON on truncation. Around: GEORGE WASHINGTON DIED 14. DECEMBER 1799. AGED 68. Rv: In 12 lines: GENERAL / OF THE AMERICAN / ARMIES 1775. / RESIGN'D THE COMMAND 1783. / ELECTED PRESIDENT OF / THE UNITED STATES 1789. / RE-ELECTED 1793. / RESIGN'D 1797. / RESUMED THE / COMMAND OF / THE ARMIES / 1798. Plain edge. (Raymond 12). Only 4 specimens known.

67A	1798	WM	39mm	—	2 Known	—

Similar to 67, but differing obverse. For particulars, see *Lake Erie Exonumist Bulletin*, 1964 number 1, page 5.

The four specimens of Baker 67 are in the Smithsonian Institution; Norweb coll., PHS coll.; ex-W.S. Baker; and Johns Hopkins Univ. coll., the latter sold in 1981 (Garrett 1758). The 67A Specimen was in George Fuld coll., now in Smithsonian Institution (ex-Wayte Raymond, W.W.C. Wilson).

The dies were cut by Thomas Wyon of Birmingham, England.

HALLIDAY MEDAL

Struck 1816

Baker	Date	Metal	Size	VF	EF	Proof
70	1797	WM	55mm	—	1200.	—

Bust in civil dress right, HALLIDAY. S. on truncation. Around: GEORGE WASHINGTON PRESIDENT OF THE UNITED STATES. Rv: Pedestal with U.S. shield on right side. Over the pedestal is thrown a fringed cloth, on which lay a crossed sword and fasces bound by an olive wreath. Around: COMMISSION RESIGNED: PRESIDENCY RELINQUISHED. In exergue: 1797. Plain edge. (Raymond 20; Garrett 1760). About 10 specimens known, of which 2 (including Garrett specimen illustrated) have engine turned rims.

70A	1797	WM	55mm	—	Unique	—

As 70. Reeded edge. (Norweb collection)

70B	1797	Silver	55mm	—	Unique	—

As 70. Plain edge. (Crosby 351; Wood 2400 a.). Specimen in J.J. Ford (ex-Fuld) collection. The former Magriel specimen is a forgery.

70C	1797	Bronze	54mm	—	900.	1250.

As 70. Plain edge. Rarity 7. (Coin Galleries July 18, 1995 sale, lot 58)

Of this medal, Baker says: "The most important medal in this group [pertaining to his military and civil career] from an artistic point of view, and as recording two of the most significant acts of Washington, is the 'Commission Resigned, Presidency Relinquished,' No. 70, executed about the beginning of the century by Thomas Halliday, a celebrated die engraver of Birmingham, England. The head is probably after Stuart, and both the obverse and reverse are engraved in the very best manner. We are not informed as to whether it was produced at the instance of an English admirer of Washington, or was merely an undertaking of the artist."

Baker	Date	Metal	Size	VF	EF	Proof
70P	ND	**	55mm	—	Rare	—

** Gutta Percha specimen. As Baker 70. Rv: Blank. Plain edge. (Stewart Witham coll.)

70S	ND	WM	55mm	—	Rare	—

Obverse as 70, with rims lower. The rim is the "engine" variety, with XXXXX denticles, on both sides of the medal. Rv: Napoleon medal by Sir Edward Thomason. Plain edge. (Witham coll.)

Baker 70S was struck by Thomason & Jones after dies by Halliday, according to Stewart Witham, the late North Canton, Ohio researcher.

Baker	Date	Metal	Size			
70T	ND	WM	55mm	—	Rare	—

Similar to 70S, but rims are made up of three parallel wavy lines each above the other. Plain edge. (Witham coll.)

SANSOM MEDAL

Original dies, 1807

Baker	Date	Metal	Size	EF	Unc	Proof
71	1797	Silver	40.7mm	600.	900.	—

Bust in civil dress left, R. on truncation. Around: G. WASHINGTON PRES. UNIT. STA. Rv: Pedestal device similar to that on Baker 70. COMMISS. RESIGNED: PRESIDENCY RELINQ. Around, 1797 in exergue. Plain edge. (Raymond 17). 6 or 7 known.

Baker	Date	Metal	Size	EF	Unc	Proof
71A	1797	Bronze	40.7mm	250.	450.	—

As 71.Plain edge. (Raymond 17; Garrett 1761). 12 to 15 known.

Baker	Date	Metal	Size	EF	Unc	Proof
71B	1797	WM	40.7mm	200.	400.	625.

As 71. Plain edge. (Raymond 17). A proof of this appeared in the PCAC sale of May 14, 1983. A brilliant proof fetched $623 in the Coin Galleries July 18, 1995 auction, lot 59. Rarity 7.

Baker	Date	Metal	Size			
71C	1797	WM	40.7mm	—	—	—

As 71B, but Reeded edge. (PCAC July 1995 sale, lot 232)

The original Sansom dies inspired the Halliday medal, Baker 70. The Sansom pieces were designed by John Reich, whose initial appears on the truncation. They were published by Joseph Sansom of Philadelphia.

This is the fourth in the series of Sansom medals issued in 1807 in Philadelphia. Specimens from the original reverse die were produced in exceedingly limited quantities. (Later the reverse die was redone, and the letters of the second issue have slightly different spacing.) The very rare original reverse can be distinguished by the abbreviation RELINQ, with the Q very close to the horizontal line on the exergue of the pedestal.

Robert Julian in his work on U.S. Mint medals shows that the Halliday medals, Baker 70, were copied from Baker 71.

Mint dies, 1859

Baker	Date	Metal	Size	VF	EF	Proof
72	1797	Silver	40.8mm	—	450.	600

Similar to 71. Obverse restruck from original dies. Reverse made through hubs taken from original dies. The 'Q' of RELINQ is farther from the line. Plain edge. (Raymond 18; Garrett 1762). Only 57 struck. Made at the U.S. Mint in Philadelphia beginning in 1859.

Baker	Date	Metal	Size			
72A	1797	Red Bronze	40.8mm	—	—	300

As 72. Plain edge. Only 308 were struck. Rarity 5. (Made 1859 to 1870's)

Baker	Date	Metal	Size			
72B	1797	Brass	40.8mm	—	—	—

As 72. Plain edge. (Lot 2007A in Dr. Glenn Clark sale of Feb. 17-18 1984). Unique. This piece could be 72M.

Baker	Date	Metal	Size			
72F	1797	S/WM	40.8mm	—	35.00	—

Silver-plated white metal cast copy of 72. (Kirtley 1991 fixed price Washingtonia list)

Baker	Date	Metal	Size			
72M	1797	Golden Bronze	39.6mm	—	—	20.00

As 72. Plain edge. (Still being offered for sale by the U.S. Mint in 1984 first struck 1920's).

NOTE: During the 1860s interest in Washington pieces was at an all-time high. The Washington cabinet at the Philadelphia Mint, inaugurated at that time, featured prize coins, tokens, and medals gathered by the curators and was considered to be the finest exhibit outranking in interest the many rarities of regular and classic coinage on display.

Baker	Date	Metal	Size	VF	EF	Unc
72P	1797	Copper/WM	41mm	—	—	75.00

As 72, but struck from rusted dies on a copper-plated white metal blank. Plain edge. Rarity 9. May be a counterfeit.

Baker 72P, not listed by Baker, Fuld, or Robert Julian, appeared in the Rich Hartzog sale of Aug. 14, 1982, lot 433.

Third dies, 1879

Baker	Date	Metal	Size	VF	EF	Proof
73	1797	Silver	47mm	—	—	—

Reproduction of 71 through hubs, but conveyed to a larger die. Plain edge. (Raymond 19). The dies were in the possession of Joseph Mickley and are still in private hands, in good shape. (George Fuld say the silver specimens he has seen are not genuine)

Baker	Date	Metal	Size	VF	EF	Proof
73A	1797	Bronze	47mm	—	185.	250

As 73. Plain edge.

Baker	Date	Metal	Size	VF	EF	Proof
73B	1797	WM	47mm	—	75.00	110

As 73. Plain edge.

Baker	Date	Metal	Size	VF	EF	Proof
73C	1797	Copper	47mm	—	85.00	110

As 73. Plain edge. (Garrett 1764)

Of this issue Baker notes: "a reproduction through the same hubs as mentioned in the preceding note, but conveyed to a larger die. The letters are also larger and not especially made, as in the former case, to imitate the originals. On the reverse the floor of the pedestal has not been tooled out to the edge as in the other, the hub not transferring that portion of the design."

The brothers S. H. and H. Chapman made these copy medals (Baker 73 to 73C) for sale in 1879. Their advertisement in the American Journal of Numismatics, volume 13, number 4 (1879) states: "WASHINGTON MEDAL. Just issued from our dies, the large Richardson (commonly called the large Sansom) Washington Medal. Size 29. Prices: Bronze Proofs $1.00. White Metal Proofs 50 cents each."

The Chapman connection was uncovered by H. Joseph Levine in his Presidential Coin & Antique Co. sale of May 14, 1983, lot 153.

NOTE: Occasionally choice Washingtonia is ignored in current auction sales. This happened in the Charles Kirtley sale of Dec. 5, 1995, when only 9 of 76 lots received bids. Unbidden were, among others, Baker 72A, 75A, 78B, 91B, 91D, 113B, 113G, 135C, 160F (3 pieces), 325C, 348 (!), R-456, 458A, and Douglas 10, 14, 17 (2 pieces), 47 (2 pieces) and 51D (!).

WRIGHT & BALE MEDALS

First reverse, 1832

Baker	Date	Metal	Size	VF	EF	Unc
74	1799	Silver	45mm	—	V. Rare	—

Head left, W. FT. below neck line, GEORGE WASHINGTON around. Along bottom edge, in tiny letters: WRIGHT & BALE. Rv: BORN FEB. 22D. 1732 / CHOSEN COMMANDR. IN / CHIEF, JULY 1776 / CHOSEN PREST. 1789 / DIED DECR. 14 1799 / AGED 68 YEARS in six lines, all within oak wreath tied with bow at bottom. Plain edge. (Raymond 36)

Baker	Date	Metal	Size	VF	EF	Unc
74A	1799	WM	45mm	275.	V. Rare	—

As 74. Plain edge.

Baker	Date	Metal	Size	VF	EF	Unc
74B	ND	Silver	45mm	—	—	—

Obverse as 74. Reverse has wreath but no inscription within. (Bushnell 1338)

Baker	Date	Metal	Size	VF	EF	Unc
74C	ND	Bronze	45mm	—	Unique	—

Obverse as 74. Rv: Blank. Plain edge. (Bushnell 1339). Ex-Brand, Fuld, Picker.

Baker	Date	Metal	Size	VF	EF	Unc
74D	ND	Lead ?	45mm	—	Unique	—

Obverse similar to 74. Rv: Blank. Plain edge. (Fuld coll., ex-Bushnell 1335)

Second reverse, 1834

Baker	Date	Metal	Size	VF	EF	Unc
75	1799	Silver	45mm	—	V. Rare	—

Obverse as 74. Rv: Similar to 74, but letters have different spacing and wreath is different. Plain edge. Rarity 8. (Raymond 37).

Baker	Date	Metal	Size	VF	EF	Unc
75A	1799	Bronze	45mm	—	225.	350.

As 75. Plain edge. Rarity 7. (Raymond 37; Garrett 1765)

Baker	Date	Metal	Size	VF	EF	Unc
75B	1799	WM	45mm	—	250.	300.

As 75. Plain edge.

Baker	Date	Metal	Size	VF	EF	Unc
75C	ND	WM	45mm	—	250.	350.

Obverse as 75. Rv: Blank. Plain edge. (PCAC July 1998 sale, lot 187, $341 in AU)

The obverse die of 75 to 75C has the names WRIGHT & BALE partly tooled off. The partnership broke up before October, 1833. Charles Cushing Wright and James Bale were in partnership May 1829 until late 1833. Wright may have executed 75 alone.

In the PCAC 1987 Great Western sale, a holed specimen of Baker 74A fetched $105. An AU specimen of Baker 75A realized $357 in a 1995 Coin Galleries sale.

SURVEYED NATURAL BRIDGE

Virginia

Baker	Date	Metal	Size	EF	AU	Unc
A75	ND	Bronze	32mm	8.00	11.00	13.00

Bust right, GEORGE WASHINGTON below. Rv: View of bridge. Around: SOUVENIR / OF / NATURAL / BRIDGE / VIRGINIA / SURVEYED BY / GEORGE WASHINGTON. (Kirtley May 1997 sale, lot AD 144; realized $11 in AU)

Unpublished modern medal, one of the few Washington pieces to stress his early career as a surveyor of Lord Fairfax' lands and on his own account from 1749 (at age 17).

In the summer of 1749, Washington was appointed official surveyor for Culpeper County, Va. and through 1751 he surveyed many frontier areas for their landowners. In 1753 he was appointed adjutant with the rank of major for one of Virginia's military districts, ending at 21 his surveying and mathematical interests.

GEN. OF THE AMERICAN ARMIES

Struck ca. 1850-1860

Baker	Date	Metal	Size	VF	EF	Unc
76	1799	Silver	19mm	—	50.00	80.00

Bust in civil dress three-quarters left, BORN FEB. 22 1732. above, DIED DEC. 14 1799. below. Rv: In seven lines: GEN. OF THE AMERICAN ARMIES 1775. RESIGD. THE COMD. 1783. ELECTED PREST. U.S. 1789. Plain edge.

Baker	Date	Metal	Size	VF	EF	Unc
76A	1799	Copper	19mm	—	40.00	60.00

As 76. Plain edge. Rarity 5.

Baker	Date	Metal	Size	VF	EF	Unc
76B	1799	Bronze	18mm	—	50.00	75.00

As 76. Plain edge. Rarity 5.

Baker	Date	Metal	Size	VF	EF	Unc
76C	1799	Brass	19mm	—	40.00	60.00

As 76. Plain edge.

Baker	Date	Metal	Size	VF	EF	Unc
76D	1799	WM	18mm	—	40.00	62.50

As 76. Plain edge. Rarity 5.

The obverse die (Fuld Civil War die 1134) has been muled with Civil War tokens and other pieces until at least 1876. Baker says the dies were destroyed in the 1880's. The dies were cut by Charles Cushing Wright of New York City, who died in 1854.
Baker 76A is known on thick planchet, $70 in Unc.

ROBINSON'S MEDALET

Struck 1860's

Baker	Date	Metal	Size	VF	EF	Unc
77	1799	Gold	33mm	—	Unique	—

Uniformed bust left. Around: GEORGE WASHINGTON, FIRST IN WAR, FIRST IN PEACE; the whole surrounded by border of scrollwork and alternate eagles and stars. Rv: Nine-line legend. Plain edge. (Norweb coll.)

Baker	Date	Metal	Size	VF	EF	Unc
77A	1799	Silver	33mm	—	—	150.

As 77. Plain edge.

Baker	Date	Metal	Size	VF	EF	Unc
77B	1799	Copper	33mm	—	—	75.00

As 77. Plain edge.

Baker	Date	Metal	Size	VF	EF	Unc
77C	1799	Brass	34mm	—	—	75.00

As 77. Plain edge. Rarity 7.

Baker	Date	Metal	Size	VF	EF	Unc
77D	1799	WM	33mm	—	—	75.00

As 77. Plain edge. (PCAC Magriel sale, lot 378)

Baker	Date	Metal	Size	VF	EF	Unc
77E	1799	Nickel	33mm	—	—	125.

As 77. Plain edge. (Fuld coll.)

Baker	Date	Metal	Size	VF	EF	Unc
77F	1799	Bronze	33mm	—	—	75.00

As 77. Plain edge.

Published by Alfred S. Robinson of Hartford, Conn., and dies cut by George Hampden Lovett of New York.

In 1995, Stack's Inc. reported the diameter of 77B and 77C to be 33.8mm.

COMMANDER, CONTINENTAL ARMY

Baker	Date	Metal	Size	EF	AU	Proof
A77	1975	Silver*	39mm	—	—	22.50

* Sterling silver (.925 fine), brilliant proof finish.

Full length military figure standing, facing, sword and scroll in his hands. Large script B on raised boss below. Around: GEORGE WASHINGTON COMMANDER IN CHIEF / OF THE CONTINENTAL ARMY. JULY 3,1775. Rv: General Washington mounted, before large body of troops, all headed right. In exergue: UNDER WASHINGTON'S INSPIRATIONAL / LEADERSHIP THE CONTINENTAL FORCES BECAME COGENT / WARRIORS OF FREEDOM. Plain edge, marked: ABCS STERLING (monogram MM in rectangle) (P in square) (75 in square) 0872 (or another serial number). (H. J. Levine report)

The phrase " cogent warriors of freedom" had not been used elsewhere to our knowledge, so must have sprung from the fertile imagination of the designer of this medal. They may not rank with Jack Daniel's "mellowed drop by drop" but the legends on this piece, overall, make up in part for its lack of medallic artistry.

EULOGISTIC INSCRIPTIONS

VOLTAIRE MEDAL

Struck 1778

Baker	Date	Metal	Size	VF	EF	Unc
78	ND	Silver	41mm	—	1200.	1500.

Head right. Around: GE. WASHINGTON ER. GENERAL OF THE CON- TINL. ARMY IN AMERICA. Rv: Radiant military trophy (cannon, mortar, cannon balls, drum, trumpet and flags). Around: WASHIN. REUNIT PAR UN RARE ASSEMBLAGE, LES TALENS DU GUERRIER & LES VERTUS DU SAGE. Plain edge. Only 4 specimens known: Imperial Mu- seum, Vienna; MHS, ex-Appleton; Garrett coll.; Fuld-Noreb.

78A	ND	Silver	41mm	—	Unique	—

As 78, but thick flan. Plain edge. (Dr. I. N. Schuster coll.)

78B	ND	Bronze	41mm	200.	400.	600.

As 78. Plain edge. 3mm thick. (Raymond 29; Stack's 1991 catalog, lot 140)

78C	ND	S/Bronze	41mm	—	Rare	—

As 78A, but silvered before striking. Plain edge. (Dr. I. N. Schuster coll.)

78D	ND	WM	41mm	—	—	—

As 78. Plain edge. (Fewsmith sale 1578)

Reportedly struck in Paris by order of Voltaire. (According to the journal and letters of Samuel Curwen, an American in England 1775-1783; entry of April 20, 1778.) The portrait is imaginary and this piece is the earliest medal ever struck for George Washington.

Some authorities believe the imaginary portrait is based on the features of Brit- ish humanitarian Jeremy Bentham.

Voltaire was the pen name of author Francois Marie Arouet (1694-1778). Vol- taire visited Paris in 1778 after an absence of 34 years, being received with tremen- dous enthusiasm. He died the same year, aged 84. Voltaire's writings critical of French institutions had forced him to live much of his life in exile in Switzerland, Prussia, England, etc.

The French reverse translates: "Washington combines in a single union the tal- ents of a warrior and the virtues of a philosopher."

Baker 78B is known struck over England 1797 Cartwheel twopence; 3 or 4 known. It is also known on a 5mm thick plain flan (Schuster coll.).

HERO OF FREEDOM

Baker	Date	Metal	Size	VF	EF	Pro
79	1800	Silver	38mm	—	—	–

Bust in civil dress right. Around: GEORGE WASHINGTON OB: 14 DE CR. 1799 AE: 68. Rv: Within oak and olive wreath: THE HERO / C FREEDOM / THE PRIDE OF / HIS COUNTRY / AND ORNAMENT / C HUMAN / NATURE / 1800 / .in nine lines. Around: LATE PRESIDEN OF THE UNITED STATES OF AMERICA. Plain edge. (Raymond 2 Bushnell 1303; Garrett 1766). Only 3 or 4 specimens known.

79A	1800	WM	38mm	—	700.	–

As 79.Plain edge. (Raymond 24)

79B	1800	Bronze	38mm	—	800.	190

As 79. Plain edge. About 30 pieces known. (Raymond 24; Crosby sa 346; Stack Collins 85)

79BA	1800	Copper	39mm	—	850.	–

As 79B, but overstruck on Great Britain 1797 Cartwheel twopence coi Only 3 specimens known, the Kessler-Spangenberg piece; Eglit-Stack and one ex-Fuld. Reports of this piece overstruck on a 1797 penny 34mm diameter are inaccurate. Edge partially reeded diagonally; on traces of undertype remain. Rarity 9. (Collins 84)

Baker 79BA fetched $847 in the Coin Galleries July 18, 1995 sale, lot 67, in E with prooflike surfaces.

79C	1800	Fire-gilt bronze	38mm	—	850.	100

As 79. Plain edge.

The diesinker is not known, though it might be John Westwood (1774-1850 working off a 1796 portrait by James Sharpless of England. Struck in England.

79D	1800	Bronzed copper	38mm	—	650.	

As 79. Plain edge. (Stack's 1991 fixed price catalog, lot 142)

WESTWOOD MEDALS

Struck about 1800

Baker	Date	Metal	Size	VF	EF	Proof
80	1799	WM	41mm	—	1000.	—

Bust in civil dress right, WESTWOOD. F. on truncation. Around: GEORGE WASHINGTON ESQR. LATE PRESIDENT OF THE UNITED STATES OF AMERICA. Rv: Within laurel wreath topped by 13 arrows: WITH COURAGE / AND FIDELITY / HE DEFENDED THE / RIGHTS / OF A FREE PEOPLE / DIED DECR. 14, 1799 / AGED / 68 in eight lines. Around: MADE COMMANDER IN CHIEF OF THE AMERICAN FORCES THE 15 JUNE 1775. Plain edge. 4 or 5 specimens known.

80A	1799	Bronze	41mm	—	300.	900.

As 80. Plain edge. (Raymond 25; Garrett 1768; PCAC May 16, 1997 sale, lot 132; PCAC Nov. 15, 1997 sale, lot 254)

80B	1799	Fire-gilt Bronze	41mm	—	900.	1500.

As 80. Plain edge.

Dies by John Westwood in England.

Second reverse

Struck about 1800

Baker	Date	Metal	Size	VF	EF	Proof
81	1799	Bronze	41mm	200.	500.	800.

Obverse as 80. Reverse as 80, but periods after PEOPLE and below 68. The bow of the wreath is different, and the arrows longer. Plain edge. (Raymond 26)

81A	1799	Fire-gilt Bronze	41mm	—	—	400.

As 81. Plain edge.

81B	1799	Tin	40.9mm	1210.	—	—

As 81, but reverse from different die with longer arrows, period between 6 and 8 of 68. Only 4-5 known. (PCAC May 16, 1977 sale, lot 133)

Copper shell

82	ND	Copper	45mm	—	Unique	—

Bust in civil dress right, WESTWOOD on truncation. Around: GEORGE WASHINGTON. A heavy oak wreath surrounds all. Rv: (Struck as a shell, convex). Plain edge. (Wood 454; Norweb coll.)

The head on 82 resembles somewhat that on Baker 79, another supposed Westwood product.

FAME MEDALS
EMANCIPATOR OF AMERICA

Struck about 1801

Baker	Date	Metal	Size	VF	EF	Unc
83	1799	Bronze	44.4mm	9200.	—	—

Bust right, I.W. on truncation. Around: GEORGE WASHINGTON OB: 14 DECR. 1799. AE: 68. Rv: Angel of Fame flies above olive and oak wreath, blowing her trumpet. Within wreath: EMANCIPATOR / OF / AMERICA. Plain edge. Only 2 known. (Appleton 55; in MHS coll.; ex-Garrett; PCAC Dec. 1989 sale; Stack Collins 89)

WISDOM VIRTUE & PATRIOTISM

84	1803	Bronze	39mm	—	1500.	2500.

Bust right similar to that on Baker 79, small H on truncation and tiny acorn and oak leaf below. Around: WASHINGTON / BORN FEBRUARY 11 1732 DIED DECEMBER 21 1799. Rv: Fame flying over land and sea blowing her trumpet, sailing ship in distance, sun on horizon. Around: WISDOM VIRTUE & PATRIOTISM. In exergue: MDCCCIII. Plain edge. (Raymond 27; Stack Collins 90)

Baker	Date	Metal	Size	VF	EF	Unc
84A	1803	WM	39mm	—	2 Known	—

As 84. Plain edge. (Raymond 27)

Both 83 and 84 are of English origin. I.W. = John Westwood. H = unknown, but the die work resembles that on Baker 79, supposedly another Westwood product.

The H could well be John H. Henning (see Baker 55).

ECCLESTON MEDAL

Baker	Date	Metal	Size	EF	AU	Unc
85	1805	Bronze	76mm	600.	900.	1100.

Armored bust right, WEBB. on truncation. Around: GENERAL WASHINGTON / INSCRIBED TO HIS MEMORY BY D: ECCLESTON. LANCASTER MDCCCV. Rv: Indian standing left within central circle, THE LAND WAS OURS. also within circle. Around, in three concentric circles: HE LAID THE FOUNDATION OF AMERICAN LIBERTY IN THE XVIII CENTURY. / INNUMERABLE MILLIONS YET UNBORN WILL VENERATE THE MEMORY -. / OF THE MAN WHO OBTAINED THEIR COUNTRYS FREEDOM. Plain edge. Rarity 6. (Raymond 28; Collins 87)

Baker	Date	Metal	Size	EF	AU	Unc
85A	1805	Fire-gilt Bronze	76mm	—	Unique?	—

As 85. (Norweb coll.)

Baker	Date	Metal	Size	EF	AU	Unc
85B	1805	WM	76mm	—	—	—

As 85. Plain edge. (Appleton 68; Raymond 28). The MHS specimen appears to be Lead.

A superb medal in every respect. Published by Daniel Eccleston of Lancaster, England. Dies cut by Thomas Webb, a British engraver who worked 1804-1827.

This piece seemed to be issued with a twist of subtle satire. The obverse of the medal depicts Washington in a heavy suit of armor - "a singular conceit," notes Baker. The reverse has an Indian standing head downcast, with an arrow in his right hand and leaning on a bow. Then, surrounding the Indian at center are the words THE LAND WAS OURS. The medal appears to be more of a commentary of the expropriation by colonists of Indian lands than a tribute to Washington.

In fact the engraver chose armor to depict Washington as a warrior. Eccleston, an eccentric Quaker, had a lifelong interest in aboriginal rights. In the 1780's he spent three years traveling in North America.

The phrase beginning "Innumerable millions yet unborn" is truly laudatory of the nation's first president and commander-in-chief during the Revolutionary War.

Eccleston issued a British Conder token with his self-portrait.

BETTS MEDALS

DEFENDER OF LIBERTY

Struck 1870's

Baker	Date	Metal	Size	F	VF	Unc
86	1732	Lead	38mm	—	3 Known	—

Undraped bust right. Around: WASHINGTON. BORN FEB. 22. 1732. Rv: U.S.A. within laurel wreath. Around: THE DEFENDER OF LIBERTY. Plain edge. (Norweb, MHS and Smithsonian Institution collections)

A product of C. Wyllys Betts, New Haven, Conn., this is a rudely made piece. It could have been made as late as 1882. The same remarks apply to the following, Baker 87.

HERO OF TRENTON

Struck 1870's

Baker	Date	Metal	Size	F	VF	Unc
87	ND	Lead	48mm	—	2 Known	—

Bust right. Around: GEORGE WASHINGTON. Rv: THE HERO OF TRENTON, PRINCETON, GLOUCESTER, YORKTOWN, & C. Plain edge. (McCoy sale 2348). In Norweb and MHS collections.

UGLY HEAD MEDAL

First reverse
Struck 1863

Baker	Date	Metal	Size	VF	EF	Proof
89	1799	Silver	38mm	—	—	1000.

Facing bust, I.B.G. below. Around: GEORGE WASHINGTON BORN FEBY. 22. 1732. / * DIED DECR. 17. 1799. *. (The 7 in 17 is cut upside down!). Rv: Within olive wreath: A MAN HE / WAS TO ALL / HIS COUNTRY / DEAR. Plain edge. 2 or 3 known.

Baker	Date	Metal	Size	VF	EF	Proof
89A	1799	Copper	38mm	—	330.	475

As 89. Plain edge.

Baker	Date	Metal	Size	VF	EF	Proof
89B	1799	Bronze	38mm	—	—	400

As 89. Plain edge.

Baker	Date	Metal	Size	VF	EF	Proof
89C	1799	WM	38mm	—	—	400

As 89. Plain edge.

Dies were cut by John B. Gardiner, possibly in the 1840's, but they were un used then and medals were not struck until collector Ramsey McCoy arranged thi in 1863. Gardiner is also responsible for HT 79 to 79B, the Henry Clay 1840 cam paign tokens listed in *Hard Times Tokens* by Rulau.

Second reverse
Struck 1863

Baker	Date	Metal	Size	VF	EF	Proo
90	1799	Copper	39mm	—	—	225

Obverse as 89. Rv: Eagle holding olive branch and arrows, surrounde by stars. Plain edge.

Baker	Date	Metal	Size	VF	EF	Proo
90A	1799	WM	39mm	—	—	225

As 90. Plain edge.

MERRIAM MEDALS

Struck 1860's

Baker	Date	Metal	Size	VF	EF	Unc
88	1799	Silver	27mm	—	—	225.

Head right within olive wreath, small M below bow of wreath. Above: WASHINGTON. Rv: Within laurel wreath: DIED / DEC. 14. / 1799. Under bow of wreath: MERRIAM BOSTON. Around: THE HERO OF AMERICAN INDEPENDENCE. *. Plain edge.

Baker	Date	Metal	Size	VF	EF	Unc
88A	1799	Copper	27mm	—	50.00	175.

As 88. Plain edge. Rarity 6.

| 88B | 1799 | Bronze | 27mm | — | 20.00 | 35.00 |

As 88. Plain edge.

| 88C | 1799 | Brass | 27mm | — | 20.00 | 35.00 |

As 88. Plain edge. Rarity 6.

| 88D | 1799 | WM | 27mm | — | 50.00 | 80.00 |

As 88. Plain edge. Rarity 8.

Joseph H. Merriam of Boston used this obverse die muled with a number of store cards and medalets, listed elsewhere in this catalog, beginning about 1859.

One specimen of 88D (ex-F.C.C. Boyd, John Ford) has the name S. A. Bayley incused on edge.

TIME INCREASES HIS FAME

Struck 1860-65

U.S. Mint

Baker	Date	Metal	Size	EF	Unc	Proof
91	ND	Gold	27mm	900.	1100.	—

Head right, GEORGE WASHINGTON above. Rv: Within olive wreath: TIME / INCREASES / HIS / FAME. Plain edge. 10 to 12 specimens known. (Garrett 1772). (These were struck at the U.S. Mint on special order 1860-1900)

| 91A | ND | Silver | 27mm | 85.00 | 110. | — |

As 91. Plain edge. Rarity 5. (Garrett 1773)

| 91B | ND | Copper | 27mm | — | 50.00 | — |

As 91. Plain edge. Rarity 2.

| 91C | ND | Copper | 27mm | — | — | — |

As 91. Plain edge. Double thickness (piefort) flan. (Garrett 1773). Struck 1860-1880.

| 91D | ND | Red Bronze | 27mm | — | 45.00 | 60.00 |

As 91. Plain edge. (Kirtley 1990's sale)

| 91E | ND | Yellow Bronze | 27mm | — | 7.00 | — |

As 91. Plain edge. (Still available from U.S. Mint)

| 91F | ND | Aluminum | 27mm | — | — | Ex. Rare |

As 91. Plain edge.

Obverse die was engraved by William Kneass, U.S. Mint chief engraver 1824-1840. Kneass died in 1840. The reverse die was cut about 1860. Those described as Unc. may in fact include Proofs.

Struck ca. 1950 on

| A91 | 1789 | Yellow Bronze | 33.4mm | — | 17.50 | — |

Bust right, GEORGE WASHINGTON PRESIDENT OF THE UNITED STATES / 1789 around. Rv: Similar to 91 reverse; better work. Philadelphia Mint. (Collins 98)

HE LIVED FOR HIS COUNTRY

First obverse

Struck about 41864

Baker	Date	Metal	Size	VF	EF	Unc
92	ND	Copper	29mm	—	—	150.

Bust left, J. A. BOLEN under truncation. Above: WASHINGTON. Rv: Within olive wreath:......./ HE LIVED, / FOR HIS / COUNTRY / ....Plain edge.

| 92A | ND | Brass | 29mm | — | — | 125. |

As 92. Plain edge.

| 92B | ND | WM | 29mm | — | — | — |

As 92. Plain edge. (Garrett 1774). Just 5 struck; only 2 or 3 known today.

Struck by James Adams Bolen of Springfield, Mass. (1826-1907). Bolen copied the bust by Joseph Wright, according to Baker.

Second obverse

Struck about 1862

Baker	Date	Metal	Size	VF	EF	Unc
93	ND	Copper	29mm	—	—	—

Uniformed bust left, BOLEN under truncation. Around: THE FATHER OF OUR COUNTRY. Rv: Same as 92. Plain edge. Only 2 struck.

| 93A | ND | Nickel | 29mm | — | — | 150. |

As 93. Plain edge. (Fuld coll.)

Struck by James A. Bolen, Springfield, Mass.

The dies for 92 and 93 were sold later to A. R. McCoy of New York, who is reported to have had restrikes made off these dies.

PROVIDENCE LEFT HIM CHILDLESS

Struck 1860

Baker	Date	Metal	Size	VF	EF	Unc
94	1799	Silver	29mm	—	—	75.00

Bust left, KEY under truncation. Around: PATER PATRIAE 1732. Rv: "PROVIDENCE / LEFT HIM / CHILDLESS / THAT THE NATION / MIGHT CALL HIM / FATHER." / 1799. Plain edge.

| 94A | 1799 | Copper | 29mm | — | — | 25.00 |

As 94. Plain edge. Rarity 5. (Garrett 1775)

| 94B | 1799 | Bronze | 29mm | — | — | 25.00 |

As 94. Plain edge.

| 94C | 1799 | Brass | 29mm | — | — | 25.00 |

As 94. Plain edge. Thick flan. (Garrett 1775)

| 94D | 1799 | Brass | 29mm | — | — | 25.00 |

As 94. Plain edge. Thin flan. (Garrett 1775)

| 94E | 1799 | WM | 29mm | — | 45.00 | 65.00 |

As 24. Plain edge. Thick flan. Rarity 5. (Garrett 1775)

| 94F | 1799 | WM | 29mm | — | 45.00 | 65.00 |

As 94. Plain edge. Thin flan. Rarity 5. (Garrett 1775)

Struck by William H. Key of Philadelphia.

DOUBLE HEAD MEDAL

Baker	Date	Metal	Size	VF	EF	Unc
95	1799	Silver	22mm	—	—	225.

Undraped bust left, GEORGE WASHINGTON above, BORN 1732 DIED 1799 below. Rv: Mantled bust left, PATER PATRIAE around. Plain edge. Less than 12 known. (Garrett 1776; Cogan 1878 sale, 2056)

Baker	Date	Metal	Size	VF	EF	Unc
95A	1799	Copper	20.6mm	—	75.00	120.

As 95. Plain edge. Rarity 5.

| 95B | 1799 | Bronze | 22mm | — | — | 40.00 |

As 95. Plain edge.

| 95C | 1799 | Brass | 22mm | — | — | 40.00 |

As 95. Plain edge.

SI QUAERIS MONUMENTUM

Struck 1883

Baker	Date	Metal	Size	VF	EF	Unc
96	ND	Bronze	64mm	—	—	575.

Undraped bust left, C.C.W.F. on truncation, GEORGE WASHINGTON around. Rv: SI QUAERIS / MONUMENTUM / CIRCUMSPICE radiant within circle of linked rings. In each ring are initials of the 13 original states. Plain edge. Less than 12 known. (Garrett 1777; Collins 101)

Obverse die by Charles Cushing Wright was cut much earlier than the date of striking. (See Baker 133 for earlier use)

| 96A | ND | Copper | 64mm | — | 370. | 425. |

As 96. Plain edge.

| 96B | ND | Silver | 64mm | — | Ex. Rare | — |

As 96. Plain edge. (Schuster coll.)

| 96C | ND | WM | 64mm | — | Ex. Rare | — |

As 96. Plain edge. (Schuster coll.)

Si quaeris monumentum circumspice = If you require a monument, look about you! (Quote from Sir Christopher Wren, London). A specimen of 96C in AU fetched $363 in the PCAC Ganter sale, Nov. 1994, lot 196)

FILL BLESSED SUN

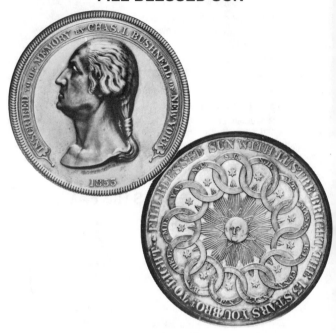

Struck 1853

Baker	Date	Metal	Size	EF	Unc	Proof
E-96	1853	Silver	54mm	—	Unique	—

Nude bust left, C. C. WRIGHT. SC: beneath the truncation. Around: IN-SCRIBED TO HIS MEMORY BY CHAS. I. BUSHNELL OF NEW YORK on a scroll, 1853 below. Rv: Washington's face within radiant sun at center of 13 links in a circle, each bearing the initials of the 13 original states. Around: FILL BLESSED SUN WITH LUSTRE BRIGHT, THE 13 STARS YOU BROT: TO LIGHT. Plain edge. (Ex-Fuld, Brand, Wilson)

Baker	Date	Metal	Size	EF	Unc	Proof
E-96A	1853	WM	54mm	—	—	975

As E-96. Only 3 known. (Stack-Collins 102, ex-Oechsner 1988 sale, lot 1477; Schuster coll.)

The Wright-Bushnell die must be considered one of the finest portrait dies ever cut of George Washington. It is a sensitive adaptation of the Houdon bust. That this medal is virtually unknown is ironic.

Muling

| E-96M | ND | Silver | 55mm | — | Unique | — |

Naked bust left, C. C. W. under truncation, wide border around (an unfinished Wright die). Rv: As reverse of Baker E-96. Plain edge.

| E-96N | ND | WM | 55mm | — | 2 known | — |

As E-96M. (PCAC Nov. 1994 sale, lot 195)

| E-96P | ND | Brass | 55mm | — | Unique | — |

As E-96M.

| E-96Q | ND | Copper | 55mm | — | Unique | — |

As E-96M.

The flan of E-96N is 7.2mm thick. One known specimen realized $715 in the PCAC Nov. 1994 sale, lot 195. The other known piece has a thinner flan.

These E-96M thru 96Q medals may have been struck about 1860 at Bushnell's order.

toning. The obv. connects this with the Bushnell series. Ex Schwartz, June 14, 1954. Earlier probably ex Brand."

Also known in copper and white metal.

WASHINGTON STAR MEDALS

First obverse

Struck ca. 1865

Baker	Date	Metal	Size	EF	Unc	Proof
97	ND	Silver	31mm	—	200.	—

Head right, at upper part of field enclosed by laurel and palm wreath. Rv: WASHINGTON across star-shaped glory of rays, all enclosed by border of arc-shaped lobes - each containing a 5-pointed star. Plain edge. Only 3 or 4 known. (Garrett 1778)

| 97A | ND | Copper | 31mm | 50.00 | 95.00 | — |

As 97. Plain edge. Rarity 6. (Garrett 1778; Frossard 1883 sale, lot 16)

| 97B | ND | WM | 31mm | 50.00 | 70.00 | — |

As 97. Plain edge. Rarity 6. (Garrett 1778)

| 97C | ND | Brass | 31mm | — | 30.00 | — |

As 97. Plain edge. (Schuster coll.)

Second obverse

Struck ca. 1865

| 98 | ND | Silver | 31mm | — | 90.00 | — |

Equestrian figure, full face, in full uniform, hat in right hand. On foreground are cannon balls and initial L; a camp is the distance. Rv: Same as reverse of 97. Reeded edge.

| 98A | ND | Copper | 31mm | — | 30.00 | — |

As 98. Reeded edge.

| 98B | ND | Bronze | 31mm | — | 30.00 | — |

As 98. Reeded edge.

| 98C | ND | WM | 31mm | — | 30.00 | — |

As 98. Reeded edge.

| 98M | ND | Copper | 31mm | — | 30.00 | — |

Muling of obverses of 97 and 98 (thus two heads). Reeded edge. (Fuld)

Smith striking

Both 97 and 98 are products of George Hampden Lovett of New York. Baker 98 has also been reported in brass. Baker 97A is on a thick (5.5mm) planchet; a part-red Unc specimen fetched $72.60 in a May 1997 Kirtley sale.

Baker	Date	Metal	Size	VF	EF	Proof
99	ND	Silver	12mm	—	—	Rare

Undraped bust left. Rv: Star of five points, with diverging rays. Plain edge.

This is a delicately done portraiture on a tiny medalet, by Frederick B. Smith of New York.

| 100M | ND | Silver | 29mm | — | — | 175. |

Obverse as 100. Rv: SI QUAERIS / MONUMENTUM / CIRCUMSPICE within circle of linked chain, each link bearing initials of one of 13 original colonies. Plain edge. Unique. (Dr. Glenn Clark sale, lot 2012, Feb. 17-18, 1984; Dr. I. N. Schuster coll.)

Ex lot 754 of Pinetree's 4.29.1975 Altman-Haffner sale where described by Breen as follows: "...Unpublished. Obv. apparently that of Baker 100, rev. not described anywhere. Proof, obv. deep iridescent toning, rev. light warm iridescent

BUSHNELL SERIES

GEORGE WASHINGTON

LOST TO SIGHT

Struck about 1860

Baker	Date	Metal	Size	VF	EF	Proof
100	ND	Silver	29mm	—	—	—

Head left, GEORGE WASHINGTON around. Rv: THOUGH LOST TO SIGHT TO MEMORY DEAR in five lines, within border of 13 stars. 2 or 3 known. Plain edge.

| 100A | ND | Copper | 29mm | — | — | — |

As 100. Plain edge. 2 or 3 known.

| 100B | ND | Brass | 29mm | — | — | — |

As 100. Plain edge. 2 or 3 known.

| 100C | ND | WM | 29mm | — | — | — |

As 100. Plain edge. 2 or 3 known.

GEORGE THE GREAT

LOST TO SIGHT

Struck about 1860

| 101 | ND | Silver | 29mm | — | — | — |

Head left (same as 100), GEORGE THE GREAT around. Rv: As 100. Plain edge. 2 or 3 known.

Baker	Date	Metal	Size	VF	EF	Proof
101A	ND	Copper	29mm	—	—	—

As 101. Plain edge. 2 or 3 known.

| 101B | ND | Brass | 29mm | — | — | — |

As 101. Plain edge. 2 or 3 known.

| 101C | ND | WM | 29mm | — | — | — |

As 101. Plain edge. 2 or 3 known.

GEORGE WASHINGTON

QUANDO ULLUM

Struck about 1860

| 102 | ND | Silver | 29mm | — | — | — |

Obverse as 100. Rv: Border of 13 stars surrounds: QUANDO / ULLUM / INVENIEMUS / PAREM. Plain edge. 2 or 3 known.

| 102A | ND | Copper | 29mm | — | — | — |

As 102.

| 102B | ND | Brass | 29mm | — | — | — |

As 102.

| 102C | ND | WM | 29mm | — | — | — |

As 102.

GEORGE THE GREAT

QUANDO ULLUM

Struck about 1860

Baker	Date	Metal	Size	VF	EF	Proof
103	ND	Silver	29mm		—	——

Obverse as 100. Rv: As 102. Plain edge.

| 103A | ND | Copper | 29mm | — | — | — |

As 103. Plain edge.

| 103B | ND | Brass | 29mm | — | — | — |

As 103. Plain edge.

| 103C | ND | WM | 29mm | — | — | — |

As 103. Plain edge.

| A103 | ND | Silver | 29mm | — | — | — |

Obverse as Baker 152. Rv: As Baker 103 (QUANDO ULLUM).

| A103A | ND | Copper | 29mm | — | — | — |

As A103.

| A103B | ND | Brass | 29mm | — | — | — |

As A103.

| A103C | ND | WM | 29mm | — | — | 185. |

As A103. (Stack's April 1996 sale, lot 130)

GEORGE WASHINGTON

WHOM ALL DO HONOR

Struck about 1860

Baker	Date	Metal	Size	VF	EF	Proof
104	ND	Silver	27.5mm	—	—	550

Obverse as 100. Rv: Border of 13 stars surrounds 4-line inscription: WHOM ALL DO HONOR MUST BE GREAT. Plain edge 2 or 3 known. (PCAC Nov. 1994 sale, lot 198)

| 104A | ND | Copper | 27.5mm | — | — | — |

As 104. Plain edge.

| 104B | ND | Brass | 27.5mm | — | — | — |

As 104. Plain edge.

| 104C | ND | WM | 27.5mm | — | — | — |

As 104. Plain edge.

| A104 | ND | Silver | 29mm | — | — | — |

Obverse as Baker 152. Rv: As Baker 104 (WHOM ALL DO HONOR). (PCAC Nov. 1994 sale, lot 198)

| A104A | ND | Copper | 29mm | — | — | — |

As A104.

| A104B | ND | Brass | 29mm | — | — | — |

As A104.

| A104C | ND | WM | 29mm | — | — | — |

As A104.

GEORGE THE GREAT

WHOM ALL DO HONOR

Struck about 1860

Baker	Date	Metal	Size	VF	EF	Proof
105	ND	Silver	29mm	—	—	—

Obverse as 100. Rv: As 104. Plain edge. (Also occurs in Copper, Brass and White Metal)

The George Ganter collection, Media, Pa., contained 101 and 104 in silver. Though the Bushnell series was supposedly unique, it is not, in fact.

ROBERT LOVETT SERIES

MARK WELL HIS STEPS

Struck about 1860

Baker	Date	Metal	Size	VF	EF	Proof
106	ND	Silver	27.5mm	—	—	625.

Head right, RL script on truncation. THE GREAT WASHINGTON around. Rv: In eight lines: GREAT WASHINGTON HAS LIVED FOR YOU, MARK WELL HIS STEPS HIS COURSE PURSUE. Plain edge (Steinberg 64 fetched $498; Ganter II 199 realized $616)

| 106A | ND | Copper | 27.5mm | — | — | — |

As 106. Plain edge.

| 106B | ND | Brass | 27.5mm | — | — | — |

As 106. Plain edge.

| 106C | ND | WM | 27.5mm | — | — | — |

As 106. Plain edge.

| A106 | ND | WM | 27.5mm | | — | Unique |

Obverse as obverse of 101. Rv: As reverse of 106. Rarity 10. (PCAC Magriel sale, June 1988, lot 028)

WHILE WE ENJOY THE FRUIT

Struck about 1860

| 107 | ND | Silver | 29mm | — | — | — |

Obverse as 106. Rv: In seven lines: WHILE WE ENJOY THE FRUIT LET US NOT FORGET HIM THAT PLANTED THE TREE. Plain edge.

| 107A | ND | Copper | 29mm | — | — | — |

As 107. Plain edge.

| 107B | ND | Brass | 29mm | — | — | — |

As 107. Plain edge.

| 107C | ND | WM | 29mm | — | — | — |

As 107. Plain edge.

HOW ABJECT EUROPE'S KINGS

Struck about 1860

| 108 | ND | Silver | 29mm | — | — | — |

Obverse as 106. Rv: In seven lines: HOW ABJECT EUROPE'S KINGS APPEAR, BY THE SIDE OF SUCH A MAN. Plain edge. (Also occurs in Copper, Brass and White Metal)

FREEDOM'S FAVORITE SON

Struck about 1860

Baker	Date	Metal	Size	EF	Unc	Proof
109	ND	Silver	28mm	—	—	150.

Obverse as 106. Rv: In six lines: HAIL FAIR FREEDOM'S FAVORITE SON, HAIL IMMORTAL WASHINGTON. Plain edge. Weight 7.63 grams.

| 109A | ND | Copper | 28mm | | 100. | |

As 109.

| 109B | ND | Brass | 28mm | | | |

As 109.

| 109C | ND | WM | 28mm | | | |

As 109.

Supposedly Robert Lovett Jr. of Philadelphia struck only one set of 106-109 for Charles I. Bushnell, but 2 or 3 of some pieces are known. All 106-109 reverses were muled with different Lovett Washington dies.

In one, Washington's head appears above crossed oak and palm branches, with GEORGE WASHINGTON above. On the other, the head is against a plain field. All were mentioned without full description in Baker, and all were supposedly unique.

INDIAN PEACE MEDALS

I - STRUCK MEDALS

"SEASON" MEDALS

THE FARMER

Actually Struck 1798

Baker	Date	Metal	Size	VG	VF	Proof
171	1796	Silver	48mm	—	—	—

Man sowing grain in foreground. House, man plowing, two trees and hills in background. In exergue: U. S. A. On left base of exergue line: KUCHLER. Rv: As 170. Plain edge. (Raymond 8; Prucha 37; Wilson 953; Julian 1P-S3). Rarity 7.

THE SHEPHERD

Actually Struck 1798

Baker	Date	Metal	Size	VG	VF	Proof
170	1796	Silver	48mm	—	—	—

Landscape. In foreground cow with calf, shepherd with two sheep and a lamb. House, tree and hills in background. Two people are in open door of house. In exergue: U. S. A. On right base of exergue line: C. H. KUCHLER. F. Rv: SECOND / PRESIDENCY / OF / GEO: WASHING-TON / MDCCXCVI. within olive and oak wreath. On the bow of the wreath: K. Plain edge. (Raymond 7; Prucha 37; David Hirsch coll.) Rarity 7.

Baker	Date	Metal	Size	VG	VF	Proof
170A	1796	Copper	48.5mm	500.	1840.	—

As 170. Plain edge. (Raymond 7; Prucha 37; Julian 1P-S1; Collins 150). Rarity 7.

	171A	1796	Copper	48.3mm	—	1840.	—

As 171. Plain edge. (Raymond 8; Prucha 37; Wilson 957; Collins 151). Rarity 7. This is the most frequently met Season medal, Baker reported.

THE FAMILY

Actually Struck 1798

Baker	Date	Metal	Size	VG	VF	Proof
172	1796	Silver	48.1mm	—	6000.	—

Within a room, woman spinning at wheel in center foreground, child watching baby in cradle at left. In background, woman weaving at loom and open fireplace at extreme right. In exergue: U. S. A. On right base of exergue line: C. H. K. F. Rv: As 170. Plain edge. Weight 712.4 grains. (Raymond 9; Prucha 37; Julian 1P-S2; B&M Landmark 1989 sale, lot 3349). Rarity 8.

Baker	Date	Metal	Size	VG	VF	Proof
172A	1796	Copper	48.3mm	—	1840.	—

As 172. Plain edge. (Raymond 9; Prucha 37). Rarity 7.

Baker 170 to 172A were authorized Oct. 10, 1796 by Secretary of War James McHenry for presentation to Indians. McHenry asked Rufus King, U.S. minister to Great Britain, to have them prepared in England. The designs were sketched by American artist John Trumbull, then in London, and the dies were cut by Conrad H. Kuchler, a Belgian working for Matthew Boulton, and the medals were struck after much delay by Boulton and Watt in Birmingham. The medals were issued with small loops for suspension.

In all, 500 pieces in silver and 200 in copper were ordered, of all types. In July, 1798 the War Department received 326 silver medals and an unknown number of copper pieces; Prucha says no records exist to show whether all 700 pieces ever reached the United States. Since these pieces arrived when John Adams was president, they were presented to Indian chiefs under Adams' presidency and remainders were used by the Lewis and Clark expedition of 1804-1806 in Thomas Jefferson's term of office.

There are three known proof sets in silver (ANS and British Museum and Royal Bank of Canada collections) and a complete proof set (3 silver, 3 copper) appeared in the Brand estate sale.

One proof set in silver was sold in the Brand II sale (1984) by Bowers & Merena Galleries. The Royal Bank of Canada set was sold by J. Douglas Ferguson to George Fuld in 1966 and eventually reached its present resting place; this set is not in original case.

Superb electrotypes of three silver pieces and two copper pieces of Baker 170-172 were in the Wilson sale as lot 977!

Specimens in VF of 170A, 171A and 172A were offered as a lot of three by Collins for $5,500 in 1991.

Made ca. 1800-1810

Baker	Date	Metal	Size	F	VF	Unc
173	1799	Silver Shell	65mm			12,700.

Bust in Roman mantle right on a pedestal, on which are depicted ship in sail, Cincinnatus plowing and war trophies. Indian warrior and Minerva stand on either side of pedestal. Around: GEN. GEO. WASHINGTON PRESI. OF THE UNIT. STA. In exergue: BORN FEBY. 1732. DIED DECR. 1799. Plain edge. Rarity 9. Only 4 pieces known. (ANS and MHS collections and Easton collection; B&M Brand sale, June 1990, lot 5008; Stack Collins sale, lot 154)

PRIVATE (NEBRASKA) TREATY MEDAL

ROMAN BUST SHELL

Struck about 1890-1900

Baker	Date	Metal	Size	VF	EF	Unc
173M	1789	Copper	63.4mm	300.	500.	—

Washington bust facing, within circle. Around: GEORGE WASHINGTON, THE FATHER OF OUR COUNTRY. / *1789*. Rv: Clasped hands above 1789 and crossed peace pipes are enclosed by wreath within a circle. Around: ******FRIENDSHIP.****** / THE PIPE OF PEACE. Plain edge. (Belden pg. 44 (III), plate 22; Stack Collins 155; PCAC Nov. 16, 1996 sale, lot 148, $528 in EF; Joseph Lepczyk Feb. 25, 1981 Sale, lot 1047, $225 in EF)

Baker	Date	Metal	Size	VG	F	EF
173N	1789	White Metal	63mm	—	600.	—

As 173M. Reeded edge. At least 10 pieces known. Rarity 7. (Stack Collins 157; Kirtley 1994 price list, lot 575)

Baker	Date	Metal	Size	VG	F	EF
173P	1789	Pewter	63mm		Unique?	

As 173M. Plain edge. This piece is cast in pewter, not struck. (Wilson 975)

Baker	Date	Metal	Size	VG	F	EF
173Q	1789	Pewter	79.7mm	300.	500.	—

As 173M, larger size. Only 2 known. Reeded edge. (Stack Collins 158; ANS collection)

It was thought originally that these were struck about 1845, modeled to some extent on the U.S. Mint series of Peace medal. Recent evidence indicates they may have been made privately in Nebraska near the turn of the 19th century. In any event, all are quite rare.

According to Francis Paul Prucha (see Bibliography), an Indian in Pender, Neb. in 1901 owned molds from which at least pewter pieces were made, and he claimed to have made them in large numbers. He offered in 1901 to cast copies in aluminum at $2 each or in silver at $15 a piece.

The Indian stated: "I have sold as many as $800 worth of these medals for use among the Poncas of Oklahoma Territory. I commenced selling them at $15 a piece and sold many of that figure, and later dropped to $10 and never sold them to Indians cheaper. Have sold a few to personal friends among white people for less."

PATER PATRIAE

Certain Latin terms appear on medals pertaining to George Washington, the first "General of the Armies of the United States." Only one other man held this title until the 5-star rank was created in World War II, and that was John J. Pershing, U.S. commander in France in WWI.

Pater Patriae (father of his country) is the apt title frequently appearing. Many other Latin words and phrases appear on items in this catalog; in most cases we have translated these for users.

Baker	Date	Metal	Size	VG	VF	EF
173R	1843	Pewter	90mm	—	250.	—

Crude Washington bust right. Double-bordered circle around bears: THE FATHER OF HIS COUNTRY. / * GEORGE WASHINGTON. **. Rv: (Radiant all-seeing eye) / (crossed tomahawk and peace pipe) / PEACE AND FRIENDSHIP. / (clasped hands, officer's at left and brave's at right) / 1843 / (tiny) B. MEAD. D. S. ST. LOUIS. Plain edge. (Prucha pg. 141)

In 1842 officials of Pierre Chouteau Jr. & Co., a successor to John Jacob Astor's American Fur Company in the Northwest, ordered new peace medals for their Indian trade. Diesinkers in New York provided 92mm pewter medals with the effigy of Astor to right cast from old molds. Then Ramsay Crooks, the A.F.C. president who succeeded Astor, found that diesinker B. Mead in St. Louis could make new medals for Chouteau.

Mead made medals bearing President Van Buren's likeness dated 1842, 92mm, bearing the name PIERRE CHOUTEAU JR. & CO. UPPER MISSOURI OUTFIT and others with Van Buren dated 1844, 90mm, for UNION FUR COMPANY. His third product was the newly-designed Washington portrait piece described here as Baker 173R, which was issued with loop. The reverse imitates the U.S. Mint medals of that period, though none that early had borne Washington's effigy. The medal is scarce; we have traced no recent sales.

IN WAR ENEMIES

Struck about 1865?

Baker	Date	Metal	Size	VG	VF	EF
174	ND	WMOval	16x 21mm	—	—	2 Known

Uniformed Washington bust left, in laurel wreath. IN WAR ENEMIES. Rv: William Penn bust left in olive wreath. IN PEACE FRIENDS. Plain edge. Rarity 8. (HSP and Fuld collections)

174A	ND	SilverOval	16x 21mm	—	—	Unique

As 174, but ENEMIES IN WAR. Plain edge. (Only known specimen is encased in 1865-dated frame)

ANDREW JOHNSON MEDAL

Baker	Date	Metal	Size	F	VF	EF
173V	1865	Silver	62.7mm	5000.	6000.	—

Naked bust of Johnson right. Around: ANDREW JOHNSON PRESIDENT OF THE UNITED STATES. Rv: Toga-clad Indian at left and Columbia with flag at right, shaking hands before a Washington bust on pedestal labeled PEACE in an oval wreath. Symbols of industry and progress at their feet. The field is plain. Tiny script Paquet F. below right end of exergue line. Plain edge. Weight 93.31 grams (1469.4 grains). Specific gravity 10.506. Thickness 4.8mm. (Julian IP-41; Prucha 52; Belden 56; Stack's Jan. 1998 sale, lot 83)

173W	1865	Red Bronze	62.7mm	—	150.	200.

As 173V. Struck in the 19th century at U.S. Mint; last struck 1891-1892.

173X	1865	Silver	76mm	4000.	5000.	—

As 173V in larger size. Only 90 struck and delivered to Indian Affairs Commissioner William P. Dole. (Prucha 52; Julian IP-40)

Baker	Date	Metal	Size	EF	AU	Unc
173Y	1865	Yellow Bronze	76mm	—	—	35.00

As 173V. Plain edge. Reissues from new dies, sold by the Mint at modest cost through the 1970's.

173YA	1865	Silv/Bz	34mm	—	65.00	—

As 173V. Unpublished. (Kirtley Aug. 5, 1997 sale, lot Q 081)

Only 90 of the smaller-sized silver Johnson medals were struck and delivered to the commissioner of Indian Affairs. They were presented to middle-level Indian chiefs. The reverse had been intended for the second series of Lincoln Peace medals, but was used in Andrew Johnson's administration after the Lincoln assassination.

All silver originals are holed, as issued. Silver fineness is .999.

While the same number, 90, was struck of the larger 76mm silver medals for major chiefs, 173V is the rarer today. White metal pieces also exist, Julian says.

Only four public sales have contained Baker 173V in recent years. The 1998 Stack's sale mentioned above; Dreyfuss sale in VF, fetched $5720; Schenkel sale specimen realized $6325; Rich Hartzog 1991 sale, F-VF, fetched $4000.

BUFFALO HISTORICAL SOCIETY

Struck facsimile

Baker	Date	Metal	Size	VF	EF	Unc
174F	1902	Svd/Brass Oval	75x101mm	—	175.	275.

Imitation of a 1792 engraved Indian Peace medal of George Washington, with this inscription in four lines at upper right: FAC-SIMILE / ORIGINAL IN POSSESSION OF / BUFFALO HISTORICAL SOCIETY / PRESENTED BY S. OF R. 1902. Rv: Blank. Plain edge. Looped for suspension. Rarity 6. (Dr. Irving Schuster coll.; Collins 153; PCAC May 16, 1997 sale, lot 167)

S. OF R. = Sons of the Revolution, who donated a Joseph Richardson engraved medal to BHS in 1902.

NUDE BUST

Baker	Date	Metal	Size	F	EF	Unc
174G	ND	Silver	46mm	—	Rare	—

Nude bust left. Ornate fret border at rim. Rv: Blank. Plain edge.

Listed by Bauman L. Belden, page 43, plate 21.

Baker	Date	Metal	Size			
174H	1849	Silver	46mm	—	Rare	—

Obverse as last. Rv: Engraved on reverse in five lines: 1ST PRIZE / PRESENTED BY THE / BROOKLYN INSTITUTE / TO CHARLES B. FISH / FEBY. 22D. 1849 (all in script). Plain edge. Issued with eye for suspension. Bust is separate and soldered to blank flan.

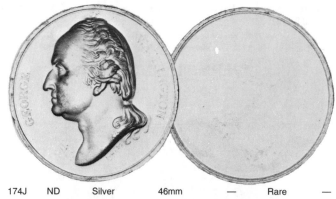

Baker	Date	Metal	Size			
174J	ND	Silver	46mm	—	Rare	—

Nude bust left similar to last, but T. W. Ft. added under truncation. Around: GEORGE WASHINGTON. Rv: Blank. Plain edge.

T. W. Ft. is for Thomas Wyon Fecit (made it). Wyon was an English diesinker and medalist. (See also Baker 75)

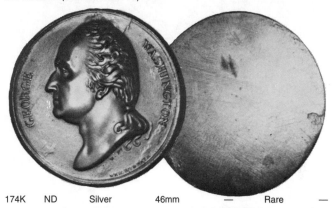

Baker	Date	Metal	Size			
174K	ND	Silver	46mm	—	Rare	—

Obverse as last, but added along lower rim: ..W. WYON .T. (partly illegible). Plain edge.

Baker 174H is known with other reverse inscriptions.

PEACE AND FRIENDSHIP

Struck 1903-1970's

Baker	Date	Metal	Size	VF	EF	Unc
174L	1789	Silver	76mm	—	Very Rare	—

Obverse as Baker A-348, with GEORGE WASHINGTON PRESIDENT OF THE UNITED STATES / 1789. Rv: Crossed tomahawk and peace pipe, PEACE AND FRIENDSHIP around. Struck from modern dies, thought to have been sold first in 1903 by the U.S. Mint.

Baker	Date	Metal	Size	VF	EF	Unc
174LA	1789	Yellow Bronze	76mm	—	—	25.00

As 174L. (PCAC June 1991 sale, lot 1375)

Baker 174L and 174LA were made to complete the early peace medal issues of the presidents. There was no original medal in this design. The U.S. Mint provided 174LA at modest cost to the 1970's, but now sells only 174LB, again at small cost.

The Washington obverse die, based on Duvivier's 1790 Boston siege medal, was produced at the Mint before June 30, 1903, as it appears in the chief engraver's annual report of that date.

Currently struck

Baker	Date	Metal	Size	EF	AU	Unc
174LB	1789-D	Copper	33mm	—	—	6.00

As 174L, struck from new dies with a number of changes. The small mintmark D (for Denver) appears below the bust on obverse.

"VERMEIL MINT" MEDAL

Baker	Date	Metal	Size	EF	AU	Un
174LE	1799	Gold/Bronze*	76mm	—	—	-

* Gold-plated bronze; modernistic work.
Military bust right, WASHINGTON on scroll beneath truncation. Around FIRST PRESIDENT OF THE VNITED STATES / 1732 / 1799. R Clasped officer's and brave's hands, PEACE / . FRIENDSHIP . aroun (Kirtley June 16, 1998 sale, lot B010)

| 174LF | 1799 | Bronze | 76mm | — | — | |

As 174LE. (Kirtley June 1998 sale, lot B011)

Auctioneer Charles Kirtley described these pieces, not connected with the U.S Mint issues, as "1905 Vermeil Mint medal".

II - ENGRAVED MEDALS

The United States Mint did not have the capacity to strike large Indian Peace medals of sizes equal to the British, French and Span ish issues of 75 to 90 millimeter size until about 1800, and in any event was too busy with striking national coinage. Yet the America government wished to issue its own Peace medals to replace the foreign issues.

Beginning in 1789 it turned to skilled silversmiths in Philadelphia and other cities to produce large oval silver hand-engraved medals Issues are known of this type dated 1789, 1792, 1793 and 1795 in the Washington administration. Hundreds must have been issued yet today only about 30 specimens of all types 174M through 174V are known to be genuine, and 80 percent of these are in museum collections.

A few museum pieces themselves are suspected to be later copies, including a 106 by 143mm specimen in the Winterthur Museum in Delaware, made of .939 fine silver with rim and loop of about .860 fine silver (Baker 174MA).

Genuine pieces reside in American Numismatic Society, Buffalo Historical Society, Historical Society of Pennsylvania, Oklahoma Historical Society, Western Reserve Historical Society (Ohio) and Ford Museum (Dearborn, Mich.). Most have long pedigrees. Two private collections in the U.S. hold several specimens each.

Most specimens in private collections today are bogus.

The engraved oval medals of 1795 should be the easiest to find, as government archives record the delivery of at least 114 such pieces, and at least 68 pieces dated 1793 (50 hallmarked JR and 18 with JL) were turned over to Tench Francis, Treasury agent. How ever, the Indian chiefs wore these handsome large medals, frequently "shined" them with sand, and many were buried with their owners or otherwise lost.

For a full discussion of this subject, see George J. Fuld's "Oval Washington Indian Peace Medals" in *The Numismatist* for March 1996, pgs. 278-286.

NOTE: Many forgeries were created in the 1960's in two places -- "The London Shop" in London, England, and the Ohio Valley region and western Ohio. They usually are accompanied by stories of excavation from Indian graves, long-held family heirlooms, etc Your authors have seen many, always with an intriguing tale invented for why they suddenly appear 200 years later.

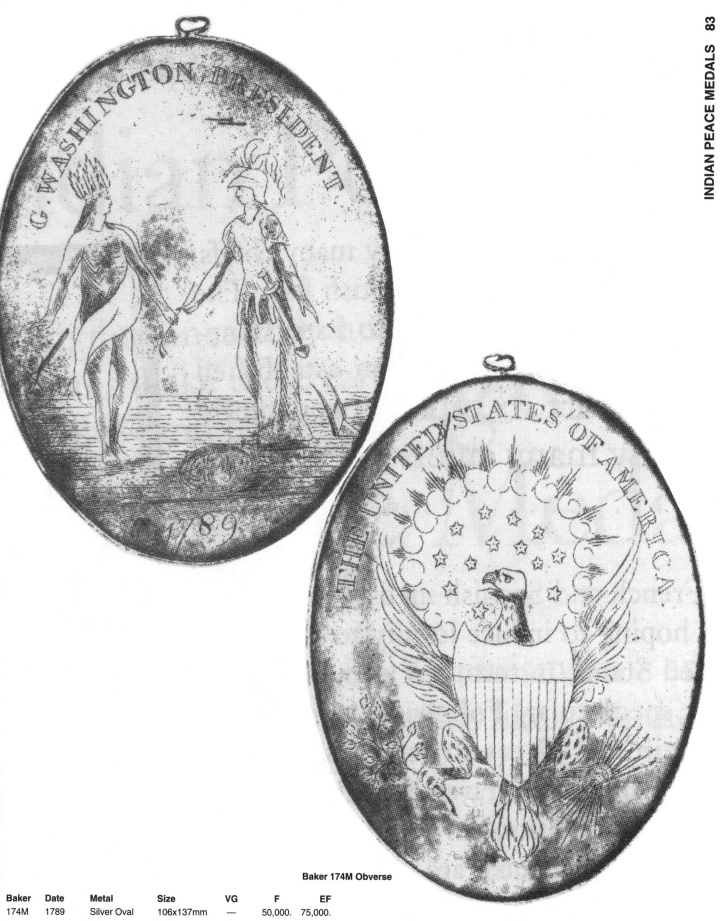

Baker 174M Obverse

Baker	Date	Metal	Size	VG	F	EF
174M	1789	Silver Oval	106x137mm	—	50,000.	75,000.

Indian dropping tomahawk and Minerva-like warrior standing, facing each other, G. WASHINGTON, PRESIDENT. above, 1789 in exergue. Rv: Glory of 13 stars above eagle displayed, U.S. shield on breast. Above: THE UNITED STATES OF AMERICA. Plain edge. (Prucha 22; ANS coll.)

These medals may have been presented to Creek chiefs at the Treaty of New York in 1790.

Above exergue line is an oval marking, large, which appears to be a male face on salver (John the Baptist?), which may be a hallmarking or other signature element.

Baker	Date	Metal	Size	VG	F	EF
174MA	1789	Silver*	106x143mm	—	Unique	—

* .939 fine silver medallion; loop and rim about .860 fine silver.
Similar to 174M, but lettering is different and there is an absence of background detail. This piece, in the Winterthur Museum, may not be contemporary. The oval
face is very different, as is the loop.

About silversmith marks on engraved Peace medals:

There has been no dispute that the "JR" and "IR" hallmarks were used on engraved Indian Peace medals by Joseph Richardson Jr. (1752-1831). Richardson later (1795) became assayer of the U.S. Mint, Philadelphia. What has not been pointed out in the literature is that Richardson used only the "JR" hallmark as his own on medals dated 1793, while he used the "IR" punch of his dead father on those dated 1795. It is not known why.

Joseph Richardson Sr. (1711-84) used the "IR" hallmark. According to Louise C. Belden (pg. 357): He was commissioned 1756 by the Friendly Association for Regaining and Preserving Peace "to make silver ornaments for the Indians." Thus the Richardson silversmith family was making Indian silver ornamentations as early as the French & Indian War for the British, so it was quite natural that the U.S. government should turn to the son to make engraved oval medals.

Other writers have said they did not know who the "JL" hallmark belonged to. Ian M. Quimby (1995) attributed the mark to John I. Leacock of Philadelphia (1748-99), but Leacock used only the "IL" hallmark, not "JL".

Francis P. Prucha nominated three possibles: Loring; "James Lynch of Baltimore" and "J. Lamson, location not known." John Lynch, not James, (1761-1848) used only the J. LYNCH hallmark. John Lamson of Boston was in business only from 1816 on. This leaves Loring.

The "JL" mark appearing on some 1793-dated medals matches exactly one of the marks recorded by Belden for Joseph Loring of Boston (1743-1815). Thus, unless proven wrong, we will stay with our attribution of Baker 174T to Loring.

The human-head-on-salver mark appearing on Baker 174M and 174MA could be merely part of the design, though it does not "fit" into the theme in any way we can imagine. It is large, probably too large to be a hallmark or signature, but that is a possibility earlier writers have overlooked. We can match no recorded mark used by a contemporary silversmith of 1789, although one -- Simeon A. Bayley of New York City, active 1786-99 -- did use a human face design on some of his hallmarked silver wares.

Unfortunately, none of the other oval engraved medals contains hallmarkings, so today we cannot determine their maker(s).

GEORGE WASHINGTON
PRESIDENT.
1792.

Baker	Date	Metal	Size	VG	F	EF
174N	1792	Silver Oval	132x180mm	—	50,000.	75,000.

Indian (5 feathers in headdress) and George Washington standing facing each other, plowing scene in background. In exergue: GEORGE WASHINGTON / PRESIDENT. / 1792. Rv: Eagle similar to 174M, no inscription. Plain edge. (Prucha 25)

A silver replica of 174N, 40.5 by 66.8mm, EF, realized $272.25 in a July 1995 Coin Galleries sale, lot 100! It was made in the mid-20th century.

Baker	Date	Metal	Size	VG	F	EF
174P	1792	Silver Oval	127x171mm	—		50,000.

Similar to 174N, smaller size. Plain edge. (Prucha 23)
Number 174P was presented to Red Jacket, the Seneca chief, in 1792. Other Iroquois chiefs also received 174P.

Baker	Date	Metal	Size	VG	F	EF
174Q	1793	Silver Oval	134x175mm	—	50,000.	75,000.

Similar to 174N, but in exergue: GEORGE WASHINGTON / PRESIDENT 1793. At lower rim of obverse, hallmark JR in relief within rectangular depression is incused. (Prucha 27)

174R   1793   Silver Oval   128x174mm   —   —   —

Similar to 174Q, but hallmark JR is at bottom of reverse. (Prucha 29)

Caution: Fantasy!

Baker	Date	Metal	Size	VG	F	EF
F174	1793	Silver	89.5x124mm	—	—	—

Obverse somewhat resembles Baker 174R, but the engraving is much more careless and there is no evidence of the wear a genuine piece would have to exhibit
(Photo courtesy G. Fuld)

Baker	Date	Metal	Size	VG	F	EF
174S	1793	Silver Oval	105x149mm	—	50,000.	—

Similar to 174Q (hallmark on obverse), but smaller. The Indian has only four feathers in headdress). (Prucha 31).

Baker	Date	Metal	Size	VG	F	EF
174T	1793	Silver Oval	105x144mm	—	50,000.	—

Similar to 174S but in much cruder style. Hallmark reads: JL. (Prucha 32)

The J L engraving on 174T is done less carefully than the J R workmanship and the suspension loops are completely different. One specimen of type 174T was excavated from an Indian grave at Tupelo, Miss. in 1956.

The hallmarks J R and I R are those of Joseph Richardson Jr. of Philadelphia, a silversmith and later (1795) the assayer of the U.S. Mint. Richardson (1752-1831) was in business with Nathaniel Richardson 1777-1790 under the firm name Joseph & Nathaniel Richardson.

In 1796 Richardson executed a silver teapot and waste bowl for George Washington, for which he was paid $44.55, a contemporary receipt reveals.

One variety of Baker 174T with J L hallmark and date 1793, appeared in the Wilson sale as lot 952, measuring 81 by 122mm, with the rim missing. This specimen has not been traced.

The initials J L appearing on an Indian Peace medal (Baker 174T, Prucha 32) of 1793 are one of the hallmarks of silversmith Joseph Loring of Boston, who worked 1760 through 1813. Loring was born in 1743 and died in 1815.

Loring's mark on 174T was J L in relief, in a recessed rectangle.

It is known that Loring engraved a medal in 1792 inscribed "The Gift of / FRANKLIN... of merit to Isaac Harris." Loring may have been an apprentice of Paul Revere II or of Benjamin Burt.

In 1760 and 1767 Loring created silver spoons for Betsey and Nabby Eells, according to Louise Conway Belden.

Baker	Date	Metal	Size	VG	F	EF
174U	1795	Silver Oval	106x149mm	—	—	—

Similar to 174Q, but 1795, and hallmark is I.R in rectangle on reverse. Reverse has 15 stars in the glory (for addition of Vermont, 1791, and Kentucky, 1792, to the Union). Plain edge. (Prucha 33)

| 174V 1792 | | Silver Oval | 81x124mm | — | — | — |

Similar to 174Q but 1792 (with circling tail on 9), and much smaller. Plain edge. (Prucha 34)

Baker	Date	Metal	Size	VG	F	EF
174X	1789	SilverOval	80x105mm	—	—	Unique

Eagle perched on demi-globe at center, THE UNITED STATES OF AMERICA. above, G. WASHINGTON. PRESIDENT. below. Rv: Blank. Plain edge. (Prucha 35)

The only example was excavated in 1929 from a Creek Indian site in Alabama. Now in possession of Alabama State archives.

Baker	Date	Metal	Size	VG	F	EF
174W	1795	Silver Oval	79x109mm	—	—	Ex. Rare

Eagle displayed at center, E PLURIBUS UNUM on scroll above, surrounded by rays. On scroll below: TREATY OF GREENVILLE 3rd August 1795. Rv: Same as obverse. Plain edge. (Prucha 36)

The medal illustrated belonged to The Crane, a Wyandot chief who signed the treaty. It is now in the Pennsylvania Historical Society. The medal probably was not an official government issue. It was issued to the chiefs who signed the Treaty of Greenville some time after 1795.

Excellent forgeries of 174W exist, which are very deceptive!

Baker	Date	Metal	Size	VG	F	EF
174Y	ND	Silver	58mm	—	—	2 Known

Facing military bust with cap at center divides large G - W. Rv: Indian with bow and arrow in right hand and quiver on back is seated at the foot of a curious column, which has 13 hands affixed to its upper portion by the fingertips. Plain edge. (British Museum collection dating back to 1808; another specimen surfaced in Canada in 1975 and is now owned by John J. Ford)

GRADE HEADINGS

Three grade (condition) columns appear in this catalog. Coins and tokens, which circulate, are graded down to VG (Very Good), but medals, which do not circulate, usually are graded no less than VF (Very Fine). Other abbreviations used are F (Fine), EF (Extremely Fine), AU (About Uncirculated), Unc (Uncirculated), and P-L (Prooflike). Proof is spelled out.

ARMY HEADQUARTERS DURING THE REVOLUTION

VALLEY FORGE

First obverse
Struck about 1860

Baker	Date	Metal	Size	VF	EF	Unc
175	1776	Silver	32mm	—	—	125.

Equestrian figure right in uniform, full face, hat in right hand held to the rear; in foreground cannon balls and the letter L. In the distance a camp. Around: GEN. GEORGE WASHINGTON, 1776. (Same obverse as Baker 98). Rv: A farm house. Around: WASHINGTON'S HEADQUARTERS AT VALLEY FORGE. Reeded edge. Rarity 8.

175A	1776	Copper	32mm	—	—	35.00

As 175. Reeded edge. Rarity 7.

175B	1776	Bronze	32mm	—	—	35.00

As 175. Reeded edge. Rarity 7.

175C	1776	Brass	32mm	—	—	40.00

As 175. Reeded edge. Rarity 7.

175D	1776	Gilt	32mm	—	—	40.00

As 175. Reeded edge. Rarity 7.

Baker	Date	Metal	Size	VF	EF	Unc
175E	1776	WM	32mm	—	—	50.00

As 175. Reeded edge. Rarity 7.

Second obverse
Struck about 1860

Baker	Date	Metal	Size	VF	EF	Unc
176	1776	Silver	32mm	—	—	125.

Equestrian figure in uniform, on an eminence, head facing. In the distance is Boston, to the right a camp; to the left a battery of artillery. Around: GEO: WASHINGTON. 1776. (Same obverse as Baker 50). Rv: As Baker 175. Reeded edge. Rarity 8.

176A	1776	Bronze	32mm	—	—	60.00

As 176. Reeded edge. Rarity 8.

176B	1776	WM	32mm	—	—	60.00

As 176. Reeded edge. Rarity 8. (Schuster coll.)

Third obverse
Struck about 1860

177	ND	Copper	32mm	—	—	60.00

Head right, in the upper part of the field, between laurel and palm wreath. (Same obverse as Baker 97). Rv: As reverse of Baker 175. Reeded edge. Rarity 8.

177A	ND	Brass	32mm	—	—	60.00

As 177. Plain edge.

177B	ND	WM	32mm	—	—	60.00

As 177. Plain edge.

177C	ND	Silver	32mm	—	—	200.

As 177. (B&M Sept. 1995 sale; Hirsch coll.)

Numbers 175 through 177 are the work of George Hampden Lovett of New York. The workmanship is not particularly distinguished, in fact the die work seems hasty.

TAPPAN

First obverse
About 1860

Baker	Date	Metal	Size	VF	EF	Unc
178	1776	Silver	32mm	—	—	125.

Obverse as Baker 175. Rv: A farm house. Around: WASHINGTON'S HEADQUARTERS AT TAPPAN. Reeded edge. Rarity 8.

178A	1776	Copper	32mm	—	—	50.00

As 178. Reeded edge. Rarity 7. Also known with plain edge.

178B	1776	Brass	32mm	—	—	50.00

As 178. Reeded edge. Rarity 7.

178C	1776	Gilt/C	32mm	—	—	50.00

As 178. Reeded edge. Rarity 7.

178D	1776	WM	32mm	—	—	50.00

As 178. Reeded edge. Rarity 7.

Third reverse
About 1860

Baker	Date	Metal	Size	VF	EF	Unc
179	ND	Silver	32mm	—	—	150

Obverse as 177 (Head right). Rv: As reverse of 178 (TAPPAN). Reeded edge. Rarity 8.

179A	ND	Copper	32mm	—	—	60.00

As 179. Reeded edge. Rarity 8.

Also known in brass.

ROCKLAND COUNTY

180	1878	Bronze	34.3mm	—	45.00	60.00

Undraped bust right, LOVETT on edge of bust. HISTORICAL & FORESTRY SOCIETY OF ROCKLAND COUNTY / * ORGANIZED FEB. 22 1878. Rv: Farm house in a circle, TAPPAN below design. Around WASHINGTON'S HEADQUARTERS 1780 * ERECTED 1700 *. Plain edge. Rarity 6. (Collins 154)

180A	1878		34.3mm	—	45.00	60.00

As 180. Plain edge. Rarity 6. (Collins 155)

180B	1878	Silver	34.3mm	—	—	175

As 180. Reeded edge. Rarity 8.

NEWBURG

First obverse
About 1860

Baker	Date	Metal	Size	VF	EF	Unc
181	1776	Silver	32mm	—	—	90.00

Obverse as 175 (Equestrian figure). Rv: Farm house, G. H. L. below THE OLD HASBROOK HOUSE NEWBURG, N.Y. Reeded edge. Rarity 8.

181A	1776	Copper	32mm	—	—	60.00

As 181. Reeded edge. Rarity 7.

181B	1776	Brass	32mm	—	—	60.00

As 181. Reeded edge. Rarity 7. (Collins 156)

181C	1776	WM	32mm	—	—	60.00

As 181. Reeded edge. Rarity 7.

Second obverse
About 1860

Baker	Date	Metal	Size	VF	EF	Unc
182	1776	Copper	32mm	—	—	60.00

Obverse as 176 (GEO: WASHINGTON). Rv: As reverse of 181 (NEWBURG). Reeded edge. Rarity 8.

Third obverse
About 1860

Baker	Date	Metal	Size	VF	EF	Unc
183	ND	Silver	32mm	—	—	200.

Obverse as 177 (Head right). Rv: As reverse of 181 (NEWBURG). Reeded edge. Rarity 8. (Hirsch coll.)

| 183A | ND | Copper | 32mm | — | — | 40.00 |

As 183. Reeded edge. Rarity 8.

| 183B | ND | Brass | 32mm | — | — | 40.00 |

As 183. Reeded edge. Rarity 8.

The city's name is Newburgh, indicating George Lovett's haste in cutting these dies.

LOVETT'S SERIES

First Obverse

HARLEM, NO. 1

Baker	Date	Metal	Size	VF	EF	Unc
184	1776	Silver	28mm	—	—	125.

Uniformed bust left, surrounded by border of shields and spears. No buttons on coat. Rv: House in circle, G. H. L. under house. HEADQUARTERS AT HARLEM, N.Y. 1776. / * No. 1 *. Plain edge. Rarity 8.

| 184B | 1776 | Copper | 28mm | — | — | 50.00 |

As 184. Plain edge. Rarity 8.

WHITE PLAINS, NO. 2

Baker	Date	Metal	Size	VF	EF	Unc
185	1776	Silver	28mm	—	—	60.00

Obverse as 184. Rv: House in circle, Around: HEADQUARTERS AT WHITEPLAINS, N.Y. 1776. / * No. 2 *. Plain edge. Rarity 8.

| 185A | 1776 | Copper | 28mm | — | — | 35.00 |

As 185. Plain edge. Rarity 8.

Also known in brass.

CHAD'S FORD, NO. 3

Baker	Date	Metal	Size	VF	EF	Unc
186	1777	Silver	28mm	—	—	60.00

Obverse as 184. Rv: House in circle. Around: HEADQUARTERS NEAR CHAD'S FORD, PA. 1777. / * No. 3 *. Plain edge. Rarity 8.

| 186A | 1777 | Copper | 28mm | — | — | 35.00 |

As 186. Plain edge. Rarity 8.

WHITEMARSH, NO. 4

Baker	Date	Metal	Size	VF	EF	Unc
187	1777	Silver	28mm	—	—	60.00

Obverse as 184. Rv: House in circle. Around: HEADQUARTERS AT WHITEMARSH, PA. 1777. / * No. 4 *. Plain edge. Rarity 8.

| 187A | 1777 | Copper | 28mm | — | — | 35.00 |

As 187. Plain edge. Rarity 8.

VALLEY FORGE, NO. 5

Baker	Date	Metal	Size	VF	EF	Unc
188	1778	Silver	28mm	—	—	60.00

Obverse as 184. Rv: House in circle. Around: HEADQUARTERS AT VALLEY FORGE, PA. 1777 & '78. / * No. 5 *. Plain edge. Rarity 8.

| 188A | 1778 | Copper | 28mm | — | — | 35.00 |

As 188. Plain edge. Rarity 8.

TAPPAN, NO. 6

Baker	Date	Metal	Size	VF	EF	Unc
189	1778	Silver	28mm	—	—	60.00

Obverse as 184. Rv: House in circle. Around: HEADQUARTERS AT TAPPAN, N.Y. 1778. / * No. 6 *. Plain edge. Rarity 8.

| 189A | 1778 | Copper | 28mm | — | — | 35.00 |

As 189. Plain edge. Rarity 8.

MORRISTOWN, NO. 7

Baker	Date	Metal	Size	VF	EF	Unc
190	1780	Silver	28mm	—	—	60.00

Obverse as 184. Rv: House in circle. Around: HEADQUARTERS, MORRISTOWN, N.J. 1779 & 80. / * No. 7 *. Plain edge. Rarity 8.

| 190A | 1780 | Copper | 28mm | — | — | 35.00 |

As 190. Plain edge. Rarity 8.

SUFFERNS, NO. 8

Baker	Date	Metal	Size	VF	EF	Unc
191	1780	Silver	28mm	—	—	60.00

Obverse as 184. Rv: House in circle. Around: HEADQUARTERS NEAR SUFFERNS, N.Y. 1780. / * No. 8 *. Plain edge. Rarity 8.

| 191A | 1780 | Copper | 28mm | — | — | 35.00 |

As 191. Plain edge. Rarity 8.

DOBBS FERRY, NO. 9

Baker	Date	Metal	Size	VF	EF	Unc
192	1781	Silver	28mm	—	—	60.00

Obverse as 184. Rv: House in circle. Around: HEADQUARTERS NEAR DOBBS FERRY, N.Y. 1781. / * No. 9 *. Plain edge. Rarity 8.

| 192A | 1781 | Copper | 28mm | — | — | 35.00 |

As 192. Plain edge. Rarity 8.

NEWBURG, NO. 10

Baker	Date	Metal	Size	VF	EF	Unc
193	1783	Silver	28mm	—	—	60.00

Obverse as 184. Rv: House in circle. Around: HEADQUARTERS AT NEWBURG, N.Y. 1783. / * No. 10 *. Plain edge. Rarity 8.

| 193A | 1783 | Copper | 28mm | — | — | 35.00 |

As 193. Plain edge. Rarity 8.

LOVETT'S SERIES

Second Obverse

Baker	Date	Metal	Size	VF	EF	Unc
194	1776-83	Silver	28mm	—	—	120.

Uniformed bust left, surrounded by border of semicircles and stars. This obverse occurs with all 10 reverses, types Baker 184 through 193. Plain edges. Rarity 9.

Price for 10-piece set: $1000.

194A	1776-83	Copper	28mm	—	—	55.00

As 194. Plain edges. Rarity 5.

Price for set: (Collins 158): $500.

194B	1776-83	Brass	28mm	—	—	750.

Set of 10.

LOVETT'S SERIES

Third Obverse

195	1776-83	Silver	28mm	—	—	—

Uniformed bust left, surrounded by border ornamented with shields and stars. This obverse occurs with all 10 reverses, types Baker 184 through 193. Plain edges. Rarity 9. Price for 10-piece set: $1200.

195A	1776-83	Copper	28mm	—	—	—

As 195. Plain edges. Rarity 8. Price for set: $700.

195B	1776-83	WM	28mm	—	—	—

As 195. Plain edges. Rarity 9. Price for set: $800.

VALLEY FORGE

1890 Reunion

P. O. S. of A.

Baker	Date	Metal	Size	EF	Unc	Proof
H-195	1890	WM	36mm	15.00	25.00	—

Nude bust left on 5-pointed star within shield lettered P. O. S. OF. A. Around: GOD OUR COUNTRY AND OUR ORDER. Rv: Washington's headquarters at Valley Forge, WASHINGTON'S HEADQUARTERS VALLEY FORGE PA. around, REUNION / JUNE 19, / 1890. in exergue Plain edge. (Leon Hendrickson coll.)

H-195A	1890	Bronze	36mm	15.00	25.00	—

As H-195.

112th Anniversary

J-195	1890	Silver	35.13mm	—	85.00	—

Nude bust right within circle. Around: GEN. GEO. WASHINGTON / (13 stars). Rv: The house at Valley Forge. Above: 112TH. ANNIVERSARY OF THE EVACUATION OF VALLEY FORGE / HEADQUARTERS. Below: JUNE 19, / 1890. Plain edge. Rarity 8. (Leon Hendrickson coll.)

J-195A	1890	Copper	35.13mm	—	45.00	—

As J-195. Plain edge. Rarity 5. (Collins 165)

125th Anniversary

Baker	Date	Metal		Size	VF	EFUnc
L-195	1903	White Metal	38mm	—	—	30.00

Military bust in tricornered hat facing, separating 1778 -- VALLEY / FORGE. Above: GEORGE WASHINGTON. Rv: Building. VALLEY FORGE HEADQUARTERS on ribbon below. Around: 125TH ANNIVERSARY / 1778-1903. Beaded border on each side. Plain edge. (Hibler-Kappen 132)

MEDALS WITH HISTORIC FIGURES

I - LAFAYETTE

CERCLE BRITANNIQUE

Original, struck about 1834

Baker	Date	Metal	Size	VF	EF	Unc
196	1834	Bronze	53mm	400.	600.	1000.

Three accolated busts left, small ROGAT. below. Around: TO THE HE-RO'S OF LIBERTY THE FRIENDS OF THE PEOPLE'S INDEPEN-DENCE. Rv: (Wreath) / GEORGE WASHINGTON / BORN THE 22D. FEBY. 1732, AT BRIDGE-CREECK / DIED THE 14TH. DECEMBER 1799, AT MOUNT-VERNON / (wreath) / THADEUS KOSCIUSKO / BORN THE 12TH. FEBY. 1746, AT MERUZOWSZEZYZNA / DIED THE 16TH. OCTR. 1817, AT SOLEURE / (wreath) / LAFAYETTE M. J. P. R. Y. GILBERT DUMOTTIER / BORN THE 6TH. SEPTEMBER 1757, AT CHAVINIAC / DIED THE 20TH. MAY 1834, IN PARIS. / CERCLE BRI-TANNIQUE / RUE NEUVE ST. AUGUSTIN NO. 55 A PARIS. BORREL. Plain edge. Rarity 7. (Raymond 40)

| 196A | 1834 | WM | 53mm | — | — | — |

As 196. Plain edge. Rarity 8. (Raymond 40)

Restrikes

| 196R | 1834 | Copper | 53mm | — | 275. | 325. |

As 196. CUIVRE on edge.

| 196S | 1834 | Bronze | 53mm | — | 150. | 200. |

As 196. BRONZE on edge.

One 196R with edge marking CUIVRE and ship's prow (struck 1841-45) fetched $264 in AU in 1997.

WRIGHT & BALE

Struck 1829-33

Baker	Date	Metal	Size	F	VF	Unc
197	ND	Silver	26mm	—	—	375.

Heads of Washington and Lafayette face each other, within laurel wreath. Below the wreath, W&B. Rv: PAR / NOBILE / FRATRUM within laurel wreath, rose above PAR and rose with two leaves below FRAT-RUM. Plain edge. Rarity 7.

| 197A | ND | Copper | 26mm | — | 35.00 | 50.00 |

As 197. Plain edge. Rarity 6. (Hirsch coll.)

| 197B | ND | S/WM | 26mm | — | — | 40.00 |

As 197. Plain edge. Rarity 6.

| 197C | ND | Nickel | 26mm | — | — | 70.00 |

As 197. Plain edge. Rarity 9.

C. C. WRIGHT

Struck 1824

Baker	Date	Metal	Size	F	VF	Unc
198	1824	Gold	13.6mm	—	—	Unique

Washington head left, GEORGE WASHINGTON around. Rv: Lafayette head right, 1824 below, GENERAL LAFAYETTE around. Plain edge.

| 198A | 1824 | Silver | 13.5mm | 800. | 1000. | 1200. |

As 198. Plain edge. (Raymond 35; Hirsch coll.)

| 198B | 1824 | WM | 13.5mm | — | 300. | 500. |

As 198. Plain edge. (Raymond 35)

COUNTERSTAMPS ON COINS

Struck 1824

Baker	Date	Metal	Size	VG	VF	EF
198C	1824	Copper	29mm	300.	500.	1000.

Dies for each side of Baker 198, struck on U.S. Large cents. 10 pieces known. Dates examined: 1816, 1817, 1818, 1819, 1820, 1822, 1823. (Brunk 41950; Fuld LA. 1824.12)

| 198D | 1824 | Silver | 19mm | 300. | 500. | 1000. |

As 198C, struck over U.S. dimes. 4 pieces known. Dates examined: 1820, 1821, 1822, 1823.

| 198E | 1824 | Silver | 32.5mm | 1000. | 1500. | 3000. |

As 198C, struck over U.S. half dollars. Only 4 or 5 pieces reported. Dates examined: 1810, 1824.

| 198F | 1824 | Silver | 21mm | 500. | 800. | 1600. |

As 198C, struck over Spanish-American 1-real, date worn off. Only 1 reported.

| 198G | 1824 | Silver | 27mm | 500. | 800. | 1600. |

As 198C, struck over Spanish-American 2-reales. Only 1 reported. Dates examined: 1824.

In his book on American and Canadian counterstamps, Dr. Gregory G. Brunk said of Baker 198-198F: "These... were struck from medal dies engraved by Charles Cushing Wright to commemorate the visit of Marquis de Lafayette to the United States in 1824 and 1825. A few strikes of the medal also exist.

"Lafayette traveled extensively across the U.S. and Duffield reports that the countermarked pieces were thrown from carriages in the general's procession to crowds that lined the streets of the towns through which he passed! Since many pieces are found circulated and obviously did not go directly into coin collectors' cabinets after they were minted, this story may actually be true.

"An example of this countermark on a half dollar sold for $650 in the 1950's, an astonishing price in that era of relatively low coin values. This is the only Washington countermark listed by Baker.

"Other Washington countermarks are apparently later fantasies, except the small bust issue (Baker 1053-1053B)."

The authors take into account the seriousness of Dr. Brunk's extensive re-search into countermarked coins in reprinting the explanation here. Proof, of course, is lacking on all these countermarked pieces.

Pricing is for the counterstamp's condition, not for the condition of the host coin!

In the B&M Nov. 1995 Fred-Ward sale, lot 1249, Baker 198C in VF on a VG 1822 Large cent, realized an amazing $1650!

There is also a variety with only the Lafayette bust ctsp on coins. Rare, it is known on U.S. 1823 dime and England 1807 penny.

Struck about 1876

Baker	Date	Metal	Size	F	VF	Unc
199	ND	Silver	9mm	—	—	75.00

Obverse similar to 198, smaller head. Rv: Lafayette head. Plain edge.

Baker	Date	Metal	Size	F	VF	Unc
199F	1776	Silver	9mm	—	—	75.00

Obverse as 199. Rv: 1776 in wreath. Plain edge. (Garrett 1813)

LAYETTE'S 1824-1825 VISIT

Parchment admission ticket to an October 18, 1824 reception for Yves Roch Gilbert du Motier, Marquis de Lafayette. A flying cherub bearing trumpet and wreath flies above wreath-framed oval vignettes of Washington and Lafayette. Shown in actual size 64 by 95 mm, it reads ADMITTANCE TO LA FAYETTE / Ball Room (the latter two words in Old English font) below the cameos. Partially illegible printer's imprint at lower left reads: ...lds & Ashb...

The grandiose admittance pass reveals the heroic nature of Lafayette's events on his second return to the U.S. (the first was in 1784). Congress in 1824 voted him a grant of $200,000 and a large tract of land. Maj. Gen. Lafayette distinguished himself at the Battles of Brandywine, Monmouth and Yorktown. He lived 1757-1834, serving as a member of the legislature 1789-92, 1815 and 1818-24, and commanding the French National Guard 1789-92. and 1830. Joining the French army at 14, he rose to captain in 1776. He was commissioned major general in the Continental army 1777-81. (Ticket shown courtesy Charles E. Kirtley)

NEW YORK MEDAL CLUB

Struck ca. 1860

Baker	Date	Metal	Size	VF	EF	Unc
200	ND	Silver	31mm	—	—	80.00

Washington bust right, in half wreath of palm, LOVETT on truncation of bust, around 13 stars and I. F. W. DES. / N.Y. MEDAL CLUB SERIES NO. 1 / G.H.L. FEC. Rv: Lafayette bust right, GENERAL LAFAYETTE around. Plain Edge.

Baker	Date	Metal	Size			Unc
200A	ND	Bronze	31mm	—	—	55.00

As 200. Plain edge. Rarity 6. (Collins 169; Magriel 418)

| 200B | ND | Copper | 31mm | — | — | 55.00 |

As 200. Plain edge. Rarity 6. (Collins 170)

The Lafayette portrait is from that of Francois Augustin Caunois.

LAFAYETTE DEATH CENTENNIAL

| A200 | 1934 | Bronze | 63mm | — | — | 30.00 |

Mature Lafayette of 1824 standing; busts of Franklin and Washington to left, MDCCLVII LAFAYETTE MDCCCXXXIV. On pedestal, AMERICAS / ADOPTED / SON. In exergue: 19 JF 34 Rv: THE AMERICAN FRIENDS OF LAFAYETTE / MAY XX-MCMXXXIV / (sword, palm, oak and laurel wreath) / CENTENARY OF HIS DEATH. Engraved by John Flanagan. (Greenslet GM-170; Fuld LA. 1934.1)

INTERNATIONAL COLONIAL EXPOSITION

Baker	Date	Metal	Size	EF	Unc	Proof
L-200	1931	Bronze	50mm	—	27.50	—

Jugate nude busts of Washington and Marquis de Lafayette right, WASHINGTON LAFAYETTE around. Incused in lower right field: M DELANNOY. Rv: Cicular plaza surrounded by U.S. pavilion. In exergue: EXPOSITION COLONIALE / INTERNATIONALE / PARIS 1931. Plain edge. Incused on edge is: (Wing) BRONZE.

Designed by Maurice Delannoy and struck at Paris Mint for the International Colonial Exposition in Paris in 1931. The French colonies in this year stretched across North Africa, the Near East, southeast Asia, the Pacific and southern Africa, plus the Caribbean area.

AMERICAN LEGION PARIS VISIT

Baker	Date	Metal	Size	VF	EF	Unc
M200	1927	Bronze	50mm	—	30.00	45.00

Jugate busts of Washington and Lafayette left, their names to either side. Rv: LES / GALERIES / LAFAYETTE / DE PARIS / A / L'AMERI-CAN / LEGION / SEPTEMBER / 1927. (Fuld LA 1927.1)

Gaston Lavrillier, Sc., designed this medal for striking by Paris Art. The American "doughboys" of WWI, who repaid the Yankee debt to the French from 1778-83 with the cry "Lafayette, we are here!" organized a revisit to Paris sponsored by the American Legion ten years after America had entered the war in April, 1917.

Struck 1917

Baker	Date	Metal	Size	VF	EF	Unc
M200B	ND	Bronze	50mm		Scarce	

Obverse similar to Baker M200. Rv: Blank. Supposedly struck 1917 after design by Gaston Lavrillier for Paris Art. (Fuld LA 1917.3)

II - FRANKLIN

JAMES BALE

Struck about 1834-48

Baker	Date	Metal	Size	VF	EF	Unc
201	ND	Silver	20mm	—	—	90.00

Washington bust facing three-quarters left, BALE below bust. Rv: Franklin bust facing three-quarters right, BALE below. Plain edge. (Appleton XXV; Bushnell 1501; Fuld FR.M.NL.18)

201A	ND	Copper	20.8mm	—	—	71.50

As 201. Plain edge. Rarity 7. (Collins 171)

201B	ND	Bronze	20mm	—	50.00	71.50

As 201. Plain edge.

201C	ND	WM	20mm	—	50.00	71.50

As 201. Plain edge.

PAR NOBILE FRATRUM

Struck about 1834-39

Baker	Date	Metal	Size	VF	EF	Unc
202	ND	Silver	26mm	—	115.	175.

Busts of Franklin and Washington three-quarters facing each other. Below, BALE. Rv: As reverse of Baker 197 (PAR NOBILE FRATRUM). Plain edge. (Appleton XXIII; Bushnell 1507; Fuld FR.M.NL.16)

202A	ND	Copper	26mm	—	—	65.00

As 202. Plain edge.

202B	ND	WM	26mm	—	—	50.00

As 202. Plain edge.

FRANKLIN-LAFAYETTE

Struck about 1829-33

Baker	Date	Metal	Size	VF	EF	Unc
203	ND	Copper	26mm	—	—	50.00

Obverse as 202. Rv: Heads of Washington and Lafayette facing each other, within laurel wreath. Below: W&B. (same as obverse of 197). Plain edge. (Appleton XXIV; Fuld FR.M.NL.17). Rare.

Baker	Date	Metal	Size	VF	EF	Unc
203A	ND	Brass	26mm	—	—	50.00

As 203. Plain edge.

203B	ND	WM	26mm	—	—	50.00

As 203. Plain edge.

'WASSINGTON'

Baker	Date	Metal	Size	VF	EF	Unc
H-203	ND	Lead	58mm	—	Ex. Rare	—

Female angel flying toward right, a halo in her left hand and a ribbon from which are suspended two oval medallions in her right. The medal

lions portray Benjamin Franklin and George Washington. Above: FRANKLIN WASSINGTON (sic!). Rv: Blank. Plain edge. (ex-Fuld; ANS coll.)

H-203A	ND	Bronze	75mm	—	—	—

Similar to H-203, before legends added.

JOSEPH MERRIAM

Struck 1860's

204	1732	Copper	31mm	—	55.00	75.00

Washington head right, tiny MERRIAM below truncation. Around: GEORGE WASHINGTON / . BORN FEBRUARY 22, 1732. Rv: Franklin bust left, tiny MERRIAM below truncation. Around: BENJAMIN FRANKLIN / BORN JAN. 17. 1706. Plain edge. Rarity 7.(Appleton XXX; Fuld FR.M.NL.11; Collins 172)

204A	1732	Bronze	31mm	—	40.00	71.50

As 204. Plain edge.

204B	1732	WM	31mm	—	40.00	60.00

As 204. Plain edge. Rarity 7. (Collins 173)

Merriam muled the Washington die with several other dies, including his own store card. Also known in silver.

ERIPUIT COELO FULMEN

First obverse

Baker	Date	Metal	Size	VF	EF	Unc
205	ND	Silver	28mm	—	—	115.

Obverse as Baker 184 (Washington left within border of shields and spears). Rv: Franklin bust left. On scroll below: ERIPUIT COELO FULMEN, SCEPTRUMQUE TYRANNIS. Above: B. FRANKLIN. Plain edge. Very rare.

205A	ND	Copper	28mm	—	40.00	71.50

As 205. Plain edge. Rarity 7. (Collins 174)

205B	ND	Brass	28mm	—	—	71.50

As 205. Plain edge.

ERIPUIT COELO FULMEN

Second obverse

206	ND	Silver	28mm	—	—	115.

Obverse as Baker 194 (Washington left within border of stars and semi-circles). Rv: As reverse of Baker 205 (Franklin). Plain edge. (Fuld FR.M.NL.15). Ex. Rare.

206A	ND	Copper	28mm	—	—	50.00

As 206. Plain edge.

206B	ND	Brass	28mm	—	—	50.00

As 206. Plain edge.

DOCTEUR FRANCKLIN

MEXICO MINT MEDALS

Baker	Date	Metal	Size	VF	EF	Proof
E206	1987	Silver	38mm	—	—	10.00

Seated figures of Benjamin Franklin, George Washington and Alexander Hamilton at writing table, facing. Around: THE CONSTITUTION OF THE U.S.A. 1787-1987 / 200TH ANNIVERSARY. Rv: Old screw press for minting. Above: CASA DE MONEDA DE MEXICO / 1987 / LEY 999. Below: 1 / ONZA / PLATA / PURA / Mo mintmark. Silver fineness: .999 (Collins 21)

| E206A | 1987 | Silver | 65mm | — | — | 75.00 |

As E206 in larger size. Reverse reads: 5 / ONZAS PLATA / PURA. Silver fineness: .999. (Collins 20)

| E206B | 1987 | Silver | 80.2mm | — | — | 150. |

As E206 in larger size. Reverse reads: 12 / ONZAS. Silver fineness: .999. (Collins 19)

This Mexican series of bullion pieces is purely medallic, though struck with the standard reverse of Mexico's current bullion silver series. The pieces are not recognized as bullion coins by either *Standard Catalog of World Coins* or *Unusual World Coins*. Struck at Mexico City Mint to honor the 200th anniversary of the U.S. Constitution.

CIVIL WAR DIE

Struck 1865-70

Baker	Date	Metal	Size	VF	EF	Unc
207	1799	Copper	19mm	—	—	275

Washington bust in civil dress facing three-quarters left, BORN FEB. 22 1732. above, DIED DEC. 14 1799. below. Rv: Franklin bust in fur cap left, BENJAMIN FRANKLIN around. Plain edge. Rarity 8. (H & G 642B Fuld CWT 116/153)

| 207A | 1799 | Brass | 19mm | — | — | 275 |

As 207. Plain edge. Rarity 8.

| 207B | 1799 | GS | 19mm | — | — | 500 |

As 207. Plain edge. Rarity 9.

| 207C | 1799 | WM | 19mm | — | — | 425 |

As 207. Plain edge. Rarity 9.

Though cut by Charles Cushing Wright, this Washington die was never used in his lifetime. This muling is thought to be the work of Key of Philadelphia. No more than four specimens are known of each of 207 to 207C.

Baker	Date	Metal	Size	VF	EF	Unc
A206	ND	Svd/WM	82mm	—	Ex.Rare	—

Military bust left in high relief. General Washington in script incused around bust. Rv: Bust right, Docteur Francklin in script incused around bust. Two concentric circles form rims on each side. Issued with loop ring. (Greenslet GM-19; Fuld photo)

The piece seems to have a French provenance; there are accent marks above each E of General.

Illustration reduced

Baker	Date	Metal	Size	VF	EF	AU
B206	ND	xx	105mm	—	Ex.	Rare

xx 82mm bronzed tin (WM) uniface medal mounted on 105mm green soapstone round; thick.

As obverse of A206 (General Washington) in bronzed WM, minus loop ring, permanently mounted on soapstone base. (Kirtley May 26, 1998 sale, lot AD161)

| C206 | ND | xx | 105mm | Ex. | | Rare |

Companion piece to B206, bronzed WM Docteur Francklin reverse, uniface, mounted on soapstone. (Kirtley lot AD160)

III - MARTHA WASHINGTON

LOVETT MEDALS

Stuck 1860

Baker	Date	Metal	Size	VF	EF	U
208	ND	Silver	20.9mm	—	—	27

Undraped Washington bust right, LOVETT beneath. GEORGE WASHINGTON. Rv: Martha Washington bust left. MARTHA WASHINGTON Plain edge. Rarity 8. (Collins 175)

| 208A | ND | Silver | 20.9mm | — | — | 27 |

As 208. Reeded edge.

| 208B | ND | Copper | 20.6mm | — | — | 35. |

As 208. Plain edge. Rarity 7.

| 208C | ND | Brass | 20.6mm | — | — | 35. |

As 208. Plain edge.

Baker	Date	Metal	Size	VF	EF	Unc
208D	ND	Nickel	20mm	—	—	50.00

As 208. Plain edge.

| 208E | ND | CN | 20mm | — | — | 50.00 |

As 208. Reeded edge.

| 208F | ND | WM | 20mm | — | — | 35.00 |

As 208. Plain edge.

Baker	Date	Metal	Size	VF	EF	Unc
208M	1860	Brass	20mm	—	—	40.00

Obverse as 208. Rv: Date 1860 within olive wreath. Plain ede. Rarity 8.

| 208N | 1860 | Silver | 20mm | — | — | 300. |

As 208M. Plain edge. Rarity 9.

| 208P | 1860 | Copper | 20mm | — | — | 40.00 |

As 208M. Plain edge. Rarity 9.

| 208Q | 1860 | WM | 20mm | — | — | 40.00 |

As 208M. Plain edge. Rarity 8.

Baker 208M thru 208Q occurred when the diesinker took William Idler's small Washington head die and muled it with Edward Cogan's 1860-in-wreath die, without the knowledge of either Idler or Cogan. This information was recorded by Joseph N. T. Levick, according to numismatist Elizabeth W. Steinle, a Cogan specialist. Levick called these pieces "patterns of the diesinker." This muled series also appears in Russ Rulau's *U.S. Merchant Tokens 1845-1860* as numbers Pa 91 thru 98.

Specimens have also been reported in silvered white metal and copper with thick planchet.

Struck about 1860

Baker	Date	Metal	Size	VG	VF	Proof
209	1792	Silver	20mm	45.00	80.00	200.

Obverse as 208, except 1792 added after WASHINGTON. Rv: As reverse of 208, except 1792 added after WASHINGTON. Plain edge. (Garrett 1816)

| 209A | 1792 | Copper | 20mm | — | — | 45.00 |

As 209. Plain edge.

| 209B | 1792 | Nickel | 20mm | — | — | 50.00 |

As 209. Plain edge.

Struck about 1876

| H-209 | 1797 | Silver | 25mm | — | — | 40.00 |

Jugate busts left of Martha Washington in veil and George Washington in civil dress. Around: PRESIDENT -- FIRST LADY * GEORGE MARTHA WASHINGTON * Rv: Eagle displayed, perched atop spade-shaped shield, 1789-97 above, LIBERTY SECURITY below. Plain edge.

| H-209A | 1797 | Gilt/B | 25mm | — | — | 15.00 |

As H-209. Plain edge. (Dr. Schuster coll.)

This is a curious pair of medals. The reverse motif is a conscious imitation of the Washington Colonial "Liberty and Security" halfpenny series. On obverse, neither effigy resembles Martha or George Washington very much; the portrait of Martha Washington is unlike any other the authors have seen.

IV - DANIEL WEBSTER

Undated, struck 1860's

Baker	Date	Metal	Size	VF	EF	Unc
210	ND	WM	28mm	—	—	55.00

Undraped Washington bust left, KEY under bust. PATRIAE PATER. Rv: Roman mantle-draped bust of Webster right, DANIEL WEBSTER. Plain edge

Dated 1732

| 210D | 1732 | WM | 28mm | — | — | 55.00 |

Obverse as Baker 94. Rv: As reverse of 210. Plain edge.

Arched Frame, 1732

| 211 | 1732 | Silver | 28mm | — | — | 140.00 |

Undraped Washington bust left in arched frame, KEY under bust. PATRIAE PATER 1732. Rv: As REVERSE of 210. Plain edge.

| 211A | 1732 | Copper | 28mm | — | — | 55.00 |

As 211. Plain edge.

| 211B. | 1732 | WM | 28mm | — | — | 55.00 |

As 211. Plain edge. Rarity 8.

| 211C | 1732 | Brass | 28mm | — | — | 55.00 |

As 211. Plain edge.

V - HENRY CLAY

Struck about 1860

Baker	Date	Metal	Size	VF	EF	Unc.
212	1799	Silver	28mm	—	—	200.

Obverse as Baker 158 (equestrian figure right). Rv: Clay bust in Roman mantle right , HENRY CLAY. Plain edge.

| 212A | 1799 | Copper | 28mm | — | — | 90.00 |

As 212. Plain edge.

| 212B | 1799 | Brass | 28mm | — | 60.00 | 90.00 |

As 212.. Plain edge.

| 212C | 1799 | WM | 28mm | — | — | 90.00 |

As 212. Plain edge. (Dewitt HC - A(3))(Hirsch coll.)

| 213 | ND | Copper | 28mm | — | — | 150. |

Obverse as Baker 194 (uniformed bust left). Rv: As reverse of Baker 212. Plain edge. 5 struck.

| 213A | ND | Brass | 28mm | — | — | 150. |

As 213. Plain edge. 5 struck.

| 213B | ND | WM | 28mm | — | — | 150. |

As 213. Plain edge.(DeWitt HC-A(4))5 struck.

| 213C | ND | Silver | 28mm | — | — | — |

As 213. (Witham coll.)

VI - EDWARD EVERETT

Struck 1860

Baker	Date	Metal	Size	VF	EF	Unc
214	1794	Copper	31mm	—	25.00	45.00

Obverse as Baker 122 (Bust right, MERRIAM). Rv: Everett bust left, MERRIAM under bust. Around: EDWARD EVERETT BORN APRIL 11, 1794. Plain edge. Rarity 6. (Collins 178)

| 214A | 1794 | Bronze | 31mm | — | — | 45.00 |

As 214. Plain edge.

| 214B | 1794 | WM | 31mm | — | — | 40.00 |

As 214. Plain edge.

Struck 1860's

Baker	Date	Metal	Size	VF	EF	Unc
215	1794	Copper	31mm	—	35.00	45.00

Obverse as Baker 123 (similar to 214, but no MERRIAM). Rv: Similar to reverse of 214, but no Merriam and the bust differs. Plain edge. Rarity 8. (Collins 180)

VII - GEORGE McCLELLAN

Struck 1864

Baker	Date	Metal	Size	VF	EF	Unc
216	ND	Bronze	34mm	—	—	—

Roman-mantled Washington bust right, G.H. LOVETT N.Y. below bust. around: GEORGE WASHINGTON, FIRST PRESIDENT OF THE UD. STATES. Laurel wreath around all. Rv: Uniformed McClellan bust three-quarters right. Around: MAJ. GENERAL McCLELLAN. Plain edge. (De-Witt G. McC. 1864-8E)

| 216F | ND | WM | 34mm | — | — | — |

Obverse as 216. Rv: Blank. Plain edge.

Struck 1864

| 217 | 1864 | Copper | 28mm | — | — | — |

Washington head right, issuing from star-dotted clouds; at each side two American flags; diverging rays above head. Around: THE UNION MUST AND SHALL BE PRESERVED. Rv: Uniformed McClellan bust left, W. H. Key F. below . Around: MAJ. GEN. GEO. B. McCLELLAN. 1864.Plain edge.((DeWitt GMcC 1864-22)

| 217A | | WM | 28mm | — | — | — |

A217. Plain edge (De Witt GMcC 1864-22)

Struck 1864

| 218 | ND | Bras | 28mm | — | — | — |

Obverse as 217. Rv: Uniformed McClellan bust left, L on truncation of bust.

Around: MAJ. GEN GEO. B. McCLELLAN. Plain edge. (DeWitt GMcC 1864-23)

Struck 1864

| 219 | 1864 | Silver | 28mm | — | — | 120. |

Obverse similar to 217, but head rests on clouds. Spear points at right are between E and S and between E and D in PRESERVED. Rv: As reverse of 217. Plain edge.

| 219A | 1864 | Copper | 28mm | — | — | 35.00 |

As 219. Plain edge. (DeWitt GMcC 1864-21)

| 219B | 1864 | Bronze | 28mm | — | — | 35.00 |

As 219. Plain edge.

| 219C | 1864 | WM | 28mm | — | — | 30.00 |

As 219.Plain edge . (DeWitt GMcC 1864-21)

Even the massive Charles McSorley collection, sold by PCAC July 10-11, 1998, contained no examples of Baker 216 thru 219c. However lot 120 in that sale carried a previously unknown piece, WM, 51.9mm, which fetched $154 in AU.

VIIII - EDWIN FORREST

Baker	Date	Metal	Size	VF	EF	Unc	
220	1732	WM	28mm			35.00	45.00

Obverse as Baker 211 (PATRIAE PATER 1732). Rv: Roman-mantled Forrest bust right, KEY on truncation. Around: EDWIN FORREST. Plain edge.

IX KOSCIUSKO and PULASKI

Baker	Date	Metal	Size	VF	EF	UNC.
H-220	1926	Bronze**	55mm	—	25.00	55.00

**Golden-bronzed surface on darker bronze core, giving a handsome tone. Unc. pieces must have full original bronzing.
Civil Washington bust left,POLAND TO THE VNITED STATES OF AMERICA around, - 1776 - JVLY 4 -1926 - below. Rv: Jugate busts left of Kazimierz Pulaski and Tadeusz Kosciusko, with relief hallmark EK monogram and incused signature J. AUMILLER on truncation. Around: POLSKA - STANOM ZJEDNOCZONYM AMERYKI. Plain edge. (Rich Hartzog coll.)

POLISH-AMERICAN NUMISMATIC ASSOCIATION

Chicago, Ill.

Baker	Date	Metal	Size	EF	AU	Unc
HA-220	1976	Silver*	62mm	—	—	65.0

*Sterling (.925 fine) silver, antiqued finish.
Conjoined facing military busts of Pulaski, Washington and Kosciusk facing. Above: (Arc of 13 stars) / WASHINGTON/ KOSCIUSZKO/ PU LASKI. Below: 200 / YEARS OF USA / 1776-1976. Signed Caetani o truncation of Pulaski bust. Rv: Two large bells above sailing ship to righ on choppy waves. Tiny Z. NOWINSKI near right side of waves. Under left bell: LIBERTY BELL / OF USA. Under right bell: SIGISMUND BEL / OF POLAND. Below: POLISH-AMERICAN / NUMISMATIC / ASSOC CHICAGO/ (tiny hallmarks): AIFT in pentagon ? and 925 in oval. Plai edge, with serial number 59 (or another number) incused. (H.J. Levin report)

The strong Polish-American populace of Chicago has always looked to the twin heros of the American Revolution for inspiration. The Polish National Allianc is headquartered there. Spellings Kosciusko and Kosciuszko are both accepted.

Obverse design by Caetani and reverse by Z. Nowinski. The medal is 5.3m thick at its rim. Scarce.

X CHARLES WILLSON PEALE

Stuck ca 1860's

Baker	Date	Metal	Size	VF	EF	A
J-220	1784	Svd/WM	31.9mm	—	—	90

Bust right, tiny LOVETT on truncation of bust, small R.L. below the tru cation. Around: GEORGE WASHINGTON/*SECURITY*. Rv: Pea bust left, CHARLES WILLSON PEALE FOUNDER/1784 around. Pla edge. Very thick (5.6mm) planchet. There are two extreme die brea from 10 o'clock rightward and 4 o'clock leftward which pass (but do touch) each other near Peale's nose and eye. Probably unique. Unp lished. (Irving Schuster coll.)

The muling of the Peale U.S. Mint die (Julian UN-23; Rulau-E Pa 398) an variation of Lovett's Civil War "dog tag" die was probably struck by Robert Lo Jr. of Philadelphia from a cast-off broken U.S. Mint die of 1830, as a mint sport. Schuster acquired the piece from New Netherlands Coin Co. (ex-Virgil Brand tate) on April 30, 1962 for $400, then a very high price even for an unpublish unique Washington muling.

The reverse die of J-220 was engraved by Christian Gobrecht.

Peale (1741-1827) was the most celebrated portrait painter of his day, paint George Washington six times from 1772 to 1795. As a captain of militia, Pe fought at Trenton and Germantown. He founded Peale's Museum in Philadelp in 1784.

He named five of his six sons after painters - Raphael, Rembrandt, Vandy Titian and Rubens Peale. The sixth son, Franklin Peale, became chief coiner at U.S. Mint 1839.

MEDALS WITH PRESIDENTS

EIGHT PRESIDENTS

Struck about 1840

Baker	Date	Metal	Size	VF	EF	Unc
221	ND	WM	47mm	—	140.	175.

Washington bust three-quarters left, in central circular panel, seven smaller circles surrounding. In these are portraits with names of John Adams, Thomas Jefferson, James Madison (MADDISON), James Monroe (MUNROE), John Quincy Adams, Andrew Jackson, Martin Van Buren. GEORGE WASHINGTON. Rv: In 16 lines: FIRST PRESIDENT GEORGE WASHINGTON. SECOND JOHN ADAMS. THIRD THOMAS JEFFERSON. FOURTH JAMES MADISON. FIFTH JAMES MUNROE (sic). SIXTH JOHN QUINCY ADAMS. SEVENTH ANDREW JACKSON. EIGHTH MARTIN VAN BUREN. Near lower edge: W.H. BRIDGENS NEW YORK. Plain edge.

Baker	Date	Metal	Size	VF	EF	Unc
221D	ND	WM	47mm	—	170.	300.

As 221. but no engraver's name. Rarity 6. Plain edge.

Baker	Date	Metal	Size	VF	EF	Unc
221E	ND	Bronze	47mm	—	200.	400.

As 221D. Plain edge. PCAC Nov. 1997 Sale, Lot 263.

Baker	Date	Metal	Size	VF	EF	Unc
221F	ND	Copper	47mm	—	200.	400.

As 221D. Plain edge. (Garrett 1819; PCAC May 1997 Sale, Lot 174).

Struck 1856

Baker	Date	Metal	Size	VF	EF	Unc
221K	1856	Copper	47mm	—	—	—

Obverse as 221D. Rv: Buck leaping over cannon, 1856 between, 32 stars in field, + AND + / BRECKINRIDGE below. Plain edge. Rarity 8 (DeWitt JB 1856-3).

THOMAS JEFFERSON

Struck 1860's

Baker	Date	Metal	Size	VF	EF	Unc
222	ND	WM	25.8mm	45.00	75.00	100.

Obverse as Baker 56 (Washington bust right in Roman mantle, WASHINGTON). Rv: Jefferson bust right, BOLEN under bust, JEFFERSON above. Plain edge. A muling. Rarity 7. (Collins 181).

ANDREW JACKSON

Mint Medal 'P'

Struck 1862-64

Baker	Date	Metal	Size	VF	EF	Proof
223	ND	Gold	18.3mm	—	—	200.

Undraped Washington bust right, tiny P on edge of bust (same obverse as Baker 155). Rv: Head of Jackson left. Plain edge.

Baker	Date	Metal	Size	VF	EF	Proof
223A	ND	Silver	18.3mm	—	30.00	40.00

As 223. Plain edge. Rarity 6. (Julian PR-29; Collins 182).

Baker	Date	Metal	Size	VF	EF	Proof
223B	ND	Bronze	18.3mm	—	—	15.00

As 223. Plain edge. Rarity 4.

Baker	Date	Metal	Size	VF	EF	Proof
223R	ND	Yellow Bronze	18.4mm	—	—	7.00

As 223. Plain edge. Struck 1920-date. Rarity 1.

Baker	Date	Metal	Size	VF	EF	Proof
223S	ND	Lead Irreg	21.8mm	—	100.	—

Obverse as 223, tiny P on truncation. Rv: Blank. Probably unique die impression. (Hartzog coll.)

Baker 223 is a U.S. Mint medal designed by Anthony C. Paquet. There are a number of die varieties, described by Robert W. Julian in his opus on U.S. Mint medals. Number 223R is a current Mint restrike, still available. (See DeWitt AJack-L, page 409).

Mint Medal 'AP'

Struck 1861-64

Baker	Date	Metal	Size	VF	EF	Proof
224	ND	Gold	18.2mm	—	—	Unique

Bust of Washington in civil dress facing right. AP on edge of the bust. Rv: Same as reverse of 223. Plain edge. (Garrett 1820).

Baker	Date	Metal	Size	VF	EF	Proof
224A	ND	Silver	18.2mm	—	40.00	85.00

As 224. Plain edge. Rarity 6. (Julian PR-28).

The obverse is the same as Baker 156, an Anthony C. Paquet engraving using the Gilbert Stuart portrait as a model.

Lovett Model

Struck about 1860

Baker	Date	Metal	Size	VF	EF	Unc
225	ND	Silver	28mm	—	—	—

Equestrian figure of Washington right, hat in his left hand held forward, GEORGE WASHINGTON above. Rv: Equestrian figure of Jackson left, sword in his right hand held forward. Above: GEN'L ANDREW JACKSON. Plain edge, (DeWitt AJack-H (3))

Baker	Date	Metal	Size	VF	EF	Unc
225A	ND	Copper	28mm	—	—	—

As 225. Plain edge. (DeWitt AJack-H (3))

Second obverse

Struck about 1860

Baker	Date	Metal	Size	VF	EF	Proof
226	ND	Silver	28mm	—	—	5 Struck

Uniformed Washington bust left, surrounded by border of semicircles and stars (same obverse as Baker 194). Rv: As reverse of Baker 225. Plain edge. (DeWitt AJack-H (4)).

Baker	Date	Metal	Size	VF	EF	Proof
226A	ND	Copper	28mm	—	—	5 Struck

As 226. Plain edge.

Baker	Date	Metal	Size	VF	EF	Proof
226B	ND	Brass	28mm	—	—	5 Struck

As 226. Plain edge

Baker	Date	Metal	Size	VF	EF	Proof
226C	ND	WM	28mm	—	—	5 Struck

As 226. Plain edge.

Robert Lovett Jr. of Philadelphia struck just five proof sets of numbers 226-226C. All listed as DeWitt AJack-H (4), page 408.

WILLIAM HENRY HARRISON

LOVETT SERIES

First obverse

Struck about 1860

Baker	Date	Metal	Size	VF	EF	Unc
227	1773	Silver	35mm	—	—	—

Washington bust in civil dress facing. Around: UNITY OF GOVERN-MENT IS THE MAIN PILLAR OF INDEPENDENCE. Rv: Uniformed Harrison bust left. Around: MAJ. GEN. W.H. HARRISON. / BORN FEB. 9, 1773. Plain edge. (DeWitt WHH-G (1)).

Baker	Date	Metal	Size	VF	EF	Unc
227A	1773	Copper	35mm	—	—	—

As 227. Plain edge.

| 227B | 1773 | Brass | 35mm | — | — | — |

As 227. Plain edge.

| 227C | 1773 | CN | 35mm | — | — | — |

As 227. Plain edge.

| 227D | 1773 | WM | 35mm | — | — | — |

As 227. Plain edge.

Robert Lovett Jr. muled the Harrison die extensively with other dies he created about 1860.

Second obverse
Struck about 1850

Baker	Date	Metal	Size	VF	EF	Proof
228	ND	Silver	28mm	—	—	—

Obverse as Baker 158 and 225 (Equestrian figure right). Rv: Uniformed Harrison bust left. Around: MAJ. GEN. W.H. HARRISON / ********************* (23 stars). Plain edge. (DeWitt WHH-K (3); Garrett 1821). Only 5 struck.

| 228A | ND | Copper | 28mm | — | — | — |

As 228. Plain edge.

| 228B | ND | Brass | 28mm | — | — | — |

As 228. Plain edge.

Robert Lovett Jr. muled these two dies about 1860. The dies were made by Bale & Smith.

Muling
Struck 1850

Baker	Date	Metal	Size	VF	EF	Proof
229	ND	Silver	28mm	—	—	—

Obverse as Baker 226. Rv: As reverse of Baker 228. Plain edge. (De-Witt WHH-K (4)). 5 struck.

| 229A | ND | Copper | 28mm | — | — | — |

As 229. Plain edge. 5 struck.

| 229B | ND | Brass | 28mm | — | — | — |

As 229. Plain edge. 5 struck.

| 229C | ND | WM | 28mm | — | — | — |

As 229. Plain edge. 5 struck.

Lovett struck five proof sets in each metal of Baker 229 type.

ABRAHAM LINCOLN

F.B. SMITH

Baker	Date	Metal	Size	VF	EF	Unc
230	1865	WM	35mm	—	—	—

Washington and Lincoln busts face each other. Below: THE FATHER / THE SAVIOUR / OF HIS COUNTRY. Rv: Lincoln bust left. Around: ABRAHAM LINCOLN BORN FEB. 12, 1809. ASSASSINATED APR. 14, 1865. Plain edge.

The dies were cut by Frederick B. Smith.

Marr
Struck about 1865

Baker	Date	Metal	Size	VF	EF	Unc
231	ND	WM	31mm	100.	—	—

Washington bust right, MARR on truncation. Around: GEORGE WASH-INGTON THE FATHER OF HIS COUNTRY *. Rv: Lincoln bust right, MARR under the bust. Around: AB. LINCOLN THE PRESERVER OF HIS COUNTRY *. Plain edge. Only 10 struck. Rarity 8. (King 837; David Hirsch coll.).

| 231A | ND | Vulcanite | 31mm | — | — | — |

As 231. Plain edge.

The dies were cut by John Marr of the Milwaukee, Wis. firm of Mossin & Marr, makers of many Civil War tokens. Also, see Melvin & George Fuld's article in *The Numismatist* for Sept., 1955, page 948.

'Ugly Head' Muling
Struck about 1862

Baker	Date	Metal	Size	VF	EF	Unc
232	1799	Copper	38mm	—	—	150

In civil dress, Washington bust facing, I.B.G. beneath the bust. Around: GEORGE WASHINGTON BORN FEBY. 22. 1732. *DIED DECR. 17 1799. *The '7' of 17 is inverted. (Same 'Ugly Head' obverse as Baker 89). Rv: Lincoln bust right, KEY F. beneath. Around: ABRAHAM LIN-COLN. Plain edge.

| 232A | 1799 | WM | 38mm | — | — | 150 |

As 232. Plain edge.

The obverse die was cut much earlier, perhaps about 1840, by John B. Gardiner. Key of Philadelphia muled the obverse with his own reverse long after the 1860 presidential campaign.

BOLEN-MERRIAM

First obverse
Struck late 1860's

Baker	Date	Metal	Size	VF	EF	Unc
233	1809	Copper	27mm	—	—	—

Obverse as Baker 92 (Uniformed Washington bust left, J.A. BOLEN under bust, WASHINGTON above). Rv: Lincoln bust right, MERRIAM under bust. Around: ABRAHAM LINCOLN BORN FEB. 12. 1809. Plain edge. (De Witt AL 1860-45 (G); King 859)

| 233A | 1809 | WM | 27mm | — | — | — |

As 233. Plain edge.

Second obverse
Struck late 1860's

Baker	Date	Metal	Size	VF	EF	Unc
234	1809	Copper	27mm	—	—	—

Obverse as Baker 93 (Uniformed Washington bust left. BOLEN under bust. Around: THE FATHER OF OUR COUNTRY). Rv: As reverse of Baker 233. Plain edge. (DeWitt AL 1860-45 (H); King 860)

| 234A | 1809 | WM | 27mm | — | — | — |

As 234. Plain edge.

James Adams Bolen muled his own dies with those of Joseph H. Merriam to create both Baker 233 and 234.

W.H. KEY

First reverse
Struck 1864

Baker	Date	Metal	Size	VF	EF	Unc
235	1864	Copper	28mm	—	—	—

Obverse as Baker 217 (Washington head issuing from clouds, THE UNION MUST AND SHALL BE PRESERVED). Rv: Lincoln bust left W.H. KEY below bust. Around: ABRAHAM LINCOLN PREST. OF THE U.S. 1864. Plain edge. (DeWitt AL 1864-21; King 90)

| 235A | 1864 | WM | 28mm | — | — | — |

As 234. Plain edge. (DeWitt AL 1864-21; King 90)

Second reverse
Struck 1864

Baker	Date	Metal	Size	VF	EF	Unc
236	1864	Silver	28mm	—	—	—

Obverse as 234. Rv: Smaller Lincoln bust left, W.H. KEY below bust; 3 stars around. Legend: ABRAHAM LINCOLN PRESIDENT OF THE U.S 1864. Plain edge. (DeWitt AL 1864-27; King 94)

Baker	Date	Metal	Size	VF	EF	Unc
236A	1864	Copper	28mm	—	—	—

As 236. Plain edge.

| 236B | 1864 | Bronze | 28mm | — | — | — |

As 236. Plain edge.

| 236C | 1864 | Brass | 28mm | — | — | — |

As 236. Plain edge.

| 236D | 1864 | WM | 28mm | — | — | — |

As 236. Plain edge.

Key, Second obverse
First reverse

Baker	Date	Metal	Size	VF	EF	Unc
237	1864	Silver	28mm	—	—	—

Obverse as Baker 219 (Washington head resting on clouds dotted with stars, THE UNION MUST AND SHALL BE PRESERVED). Rv: As reverse of 235. Plain edge. (DeWitt AL 1864-19; King 89)

| 237A | 1864 | Copper | 28mm | — | — | — |

As 237. Plain edge. (Holland 319; Zabriskie 104)

| 237B | 1864 | Brass | 28mm | — | — | — |

As 237. Plain edge. (King 89A; Holland 319)

Baker	Date	Metal	Size	VF	EF	Unc
237C	1864	CN	28mm	—	—	—

As 237. Plain edge. (King 89)

Baker	Date	Metal	Size	VF	EF	Unc
237D	1864	WM	28mm	—	—	—

As 237. Plain edge. (King 89)

Baker	Date	Metal	Size	VF	EF	Unc
237E	1864	Lead	28mm	—	—	—

As 237. Plain edge. (DeWitt AL 1864-19; King 89)

Key, Second obverse
Second reverse

Baker	Date	Metal	Size	VF	EF	Unc
238	1864	Silver	28mm	—	—	—

Obverse as 237. Rv: As reverse of 236. Plain edge. (DeWitt AL 1864-26; King 93)

Baker	Date	Metal	Size	VF	EF	Unc
238A	1864	Copper	28mm	—	—	—

As 238. Plain edge. (King 93; Zabriskie 91)

Baker	Date	Metal	Size	VF	EF	Unc
238B	1864	Brass	28mm	—	—	—

As 238. Plain edge. (King 93)

Baker	Date	Metal	Size	VF	EF	Unc
238C	1864	WM	28mm	50.00	70.00	100.

As 238. Plain edge. Rarity 6. (King 93; Zabriskie 92; Hirsch coll.)

Baker	Date	Metal	Size	VF	EF	Unc
238D	1864	Gilt/WM	28mm	—	Ex. Rare	—

As 238. Plain edge. (Holland sale, lot 2626)

Key, Crude Obverse

Baker	Date	Metal	Size	VF	EF	Unc
239	1864	Copper	25mm	—	—	—

Obverse similar to Baker 235, but much more crude. Rv: Lincoln bust right, ABRAHAM LINCOLN 1864 around. Plain edge. (DeWitt AL 1864-31; King 97; Holland 251)

Baker	Date	Metal	Size	VF	EF	Unc
239A	1864	Brass	25mm	—	—	—

As 239. Plain edge. (King 97; Holland 252)

Baker	Date	Metal	Size	VF	EF	Unc
239B	1864	WM	25mm	—	—	—

As 239. Plain edge. (King 97)

William H. Key did not sign the die for Baker 239. Most of these pieces are found badly struck and without rim, undoubtedly due to an attempt to match the larger reverse made for Baker 235 to this smaller reverse. The Lincoln die of this combination is found muled with store cards of Charles K. Warner and James E. Wolff.

'REVERSE' MEDAL

Baker	Date	Metal	Size	VF	EF	Unc
240	ND	Silver	28mm	—	—	400.

Nude Washington bust right, GEORGE at left, WASHINGTON at right. Above: - FIRST IN WAR, FIRST IN PEACE - / AND FIRST IN. Below: THE HEARTS / OF HIS COUNTRYMEN. Rv: Lincoln head left, REVERSE above, ******LINCOLN****** around and below. Plain edge. (King 856)

Baker	Date	Metal	Size	VF	EF	Unc
240A	ND	Copper	28mm	—	—	250.

As 240. Plain edge. (King 856; Garrett 1822)

Baker	Date	Metal	Size	VF	EF	Unc
240B	ND	Bronze	28mm	—	—	250.

As 240. Plain edge. (King 856)

Baker	Date	Metal	Size	VF	EF	Unc
240C	ND	WM	28mm	—	—	250.

As 240. Plain edge. Rarity 7. (King 856; Garrett 1822; Cogan sale Sept. 16-20, 1878, lot 2079; PCAC Magriel 1988 sale, lot 052A)

It has been thought by many people that the "REVERSE" inscription above Lincoln was satirical and was meant to imply that while Washington was father of his country and first in the hearts of his countrymen (as the obverse inscription notes), Lincoln was the reverse of this. In other words, he wasn't any of these. However, Q. David Bowers tends to believe that the "REVERSE" inscription was merely a mistake in communications. It is entirely possible that the person who designed the medal was not the person who engraved it. A sketch could have been made showing Lincoln with stars surrounding and the inscription LINCOLN below. To indicate to the diecutter that this was intended for the reverse of the medal - and it would have been logical to have indicated this, for a head or portrait normally would appear on the obverse - the word REVERSE was put on the sketch. The diecutter mistakenly thought this word was part of the inscription!

The true reason for this ludicrous inscription may never be learned.

Struck 1883

Baker	Date	Metal	Size	VF	EF	Unc
A240	ND	Copper	28mm	—	Rare	—

Obverse as Baker 240 obverse. Rv: As Baker 296 obverse (Washington bust right). (PCAC 1988 Paul Magriel sale, lot 052)

WRIGHT-KEY
Struck about 1870

Baker	Date	Metal	Size	VF	EF	Unc
241	1864	Silver	19mm	—	—	250.

Obverse as Baker 76 (Washington bust three-quarters left, BORN FEB 22 1732. DIED DEC. 14 1799.) Rv: Draped Lincoln bust right, K under bust. Around: ABRAHAM LINCOLN 1864. Plain edge. (DeWitt AL 1864-74C; King 116; Fuld CWT 116/129)

Charles Cushing Wright cut the obverse die, which was muled by Key with his own reverse die to form a Civil War token.

PAQUET
First reverse

Baker	Date	Metal	Size	VF	EF	Unc
242	ND	Silver	18mm	—	—	60.00

Obverse as 241. Rv: Undraped Lincoln bust right, Paquet on truncation. Plain edge. Rarity 8. (Garrett 1823; B&M Witham 2168)

Baker	Date	Metal	Size	VF	EF	Unc
242A	ND	Copper	18mm	—	—	15.00

As 242. Plain edge.

Second reverse

Baker	Date	Metal	Size	VF	EF	Unc
243	ND	WM	18mm	—	—	20.00

Obverse as 241. Rv: Lincoln head left. Plain edge.

This is not a Civil War token.

PATER PATRIAE

244	1864	Copper	19mm	—	—	100.

Roman-mantled Washington bust left, PATER PATRIAE. (Same obverse as Baker 95). Rv: Lincoln head left, 1864 below, 13 stars around. Plain edge. (DeWitt AL 1864-61; King 220; Fuld CWT 113/127)

U.S. MINT SERIES BY PAQUET

Lincoln Head, 1864-1866

Baker	Date	Metal	Size	EF	Unc	Proof
245	ND	Gold	18mm	400.	—	825.

Undraped Washington bust right, small P on truncation of bust. (Same obverse as Baker 155). Rv: Lincoln head right. Plain edge. Only 169 struck, Rarity 7. (King 112; Julian PR-30; Collins 187)

Baker	Date	Metal	Size	EF	Unc	Proof
245A	ND	Silver	18mm	—	35.00	50.00

As 245. Plain edge. 5677 struck. Rarity 6.

Baker	Date	Metal	Size	EF	Unc	Proof
245B	ND	Bronze	18mm	—	—	—

As 245. Plain edge.

Baker	Date	Metal	Size	EF	Unc	Proof
245E	ND	White Metal	18mm	50.00	75.00	—

As 245. Plain edge. Probably struck outside the Mint after 1868. (Collins 191)

Baker	Date	Metal	Size	EF	Unc	Proof
245R	ND	Yellow Bronze	18mm	—	—	4.00

As 245. Plain edge. (A current Mint restrike, still available).

Die varieties of this medallic design exist.

Draped Lincoln bust

Baker	Date	Metal	Size	EF	Unc	Proof
245T	ND	Bronze	18mm	—	—	—

Obverse as 245. Rv: Draped Lincoln bust right, P on truncation.

Undraped Lincoln bust

Baker	Date	Metal	Size	EF	Unc	Proof
245X	ND	Bronze	18mm	—	—	—

Obverse as 245. Rv: Undraped Lincoln bust right, Paquet on truncation of the bust. Plain edge.

U.S. MINT SERIES BY BARBER

Struck 1868-1890's

Baker	Date	Metal	Size	VF	EF	Unc
246	ND	Silver	18mm	—	38.00	45.00

Obverse as 245. Rv: Lincoln head right, small B incused on truncation. Plain edge. Rarity 7.

| 246A | ND | Bronze | 18mm | 10.00 | 15.00 | 22.50 |

As 246. Plain edge. Rarity 4.

BRAMHALL MEDAL

Struck 1860

Baker	Date	Metal	Size	VF	EF	Unc
247	1809	Silver	19mm	—	—	95.00

Washington bust left. Around: REPRESENTED BY WM. LEGGETT BRAMHALL. Rv; Beardless Lincoln bust right within circle of beads. Around: *ABRAHAM LINCOLN. * / NATUS. FEB. 12, 1809. Plain edge. (DeWitt AL 1860-73(A); King 629). Rarity 8.

| 247A | 1809 | Copper | 19mm | — | — | 40.00 |

As 247. Plain edge. Rarity 7

| 247B | 1809 | CN | 19mm | — | — | 40.00 |

As 247. Plain edge. Rarity 7. Only 15 struck.

| 247C | 1809 | WM | 19mm | — | — | 40.00 |

As 247. Plain edge. Rarity 7

Bramhall commissioned George Hampden Lovett of New York to cut these dies, and the pieces were struck by the Scovill Mfg. Co. in Waterbury, Connecticut. Bramhall may have produced the first political medals of the 1860 campaign to bear Lincoln's portrait; a bit earlier he had caused the Waterbury firm to strike the NOT ONE CENT FOR SLAVERY tokens (De-Witt AL 1860-59), probably the first pieces of the 1860 political season.

BROWN'S STATUE

Struck 1864

Baker	Date	Metal	Size	VF	EF	Unc
248	1864	Copper	19mm	—	—	40.00

Brown's equestrian statue of Washington, left, FIRST IN WAR, FIRST IN PEACE around, 1863 below. Rv: Bearded Lincoln bust left within circle of 13 stars. 1864 below. Plain edge. (DeWitt AL 1864-54; Fuld CWT 127/177; King 207; Holland 286). Rarity 9.

| 248A | 1864 | Nickel | 19mm | 50.00 | 85.00 | 150. |

As 248. Plain edge. Rarity 5. Magnetic! (Holland 287; Hirsch coll.)

| 248B | 1864 | CN | 19mm | — | — | 300. |

As 248. Plain edge. Rarity 9.

| 248C | 1864 | GS | 19mm | — | — | 250. |

As 248. Plain edge. Rarity 7.

| 248D | 1864 | Lead | 19mm | — | — | 100. |

As 248. Plain edge. Rarity 9. (King 207)

Struck 1864

| 248G | 1864 | Copper | 19mm | — | — | 50.00 |

Long-necked bearded Lincoln bust left, 18 ABM. LINCOLN 64 / PRESIDENT. Around. Rv: As obverse of Baker 248 (Brown's equestrian statue left). Plain edge. (DeWitt AL 1864-53; King 206; Fuld dies 1161 and 1144)

Baker	Date	Metal	Size	VF	EF	Unc
248H	1864	Nickel	19mm	—	—	200.

As 248G. Plain edge. Magnetic! (DeWitt AL 1864-53)

Brown's equestrian statue of Washington is in Union Square, New York City. Designed by sculptor Henry K. Brown, it was erected July 4, 1856 in the southeast corner of the square. It stands near the spot where the citizens of New York met General Washington on the Bowery Road when he was entering the city to take possession upon its evacuation by the British, Nov. 25, 1783 (Evacuation Day, lon celebrated in New York).

Interestingly, the first statue erected in New York City after that of King Georg III in 1770 was the Washington statue by Brown. The gilt statue of George III wa pulled down by a mob on July 10, 1776 from its pedestal in the Bowling Green, an the lead from which it was made was melted in Connecticut and made into 42,00 bullets.

ULYSSES SIMPSON GRANT

KEY SERIES

First obverse

Struck 1868

Baker	Date	Metal	Size	VF	EF	Un
249	ND	Silver	28mm	—	—	50.0

Obverse as Baker 217 and 235 (small Washington head right on sta studded clouds; spear points of flags at right point to second E and be yond D of PRESERVED). Rv: Military Grant bust left, W.H.K. belo bust. Around: LIEUT. GEN. U.S. GRANT. Plain edge. (DeWitt US 1868-25) Rarity 8.

| 249A | ND | Brass | 28mm | — | — | 20.0 |

As 249. Plain edge. Rarity 8.

| 249B | ND | WM | 28mm | — | 8.50 | 15.0 |

As 249. Plain edge. Rarity 6.

The dies were cut by William H. Key of Philadelphia.

Second obverse

Struck 1868

| 250 | ND | Silver | 28mm | — | — | 50.0 |

Obverse similar to 249, but spear points between E and S and at D PRESERVED. Rv: As reverse of 249. Plain edge. (DeWitt USG 186 26). Rarity 8.

Baker	Date	Metal	Size	VF	EF	Un
250A	ND	Copper	28mm	—	—	13.5

As 250. Plain edge. Rarity 7.

| 250B | ND | Bronze | 28mm | — | — | 13.5 |

As 250. Plain edge. Rarity 7.

| 250C | ND | GS | 28mm | — | — | 25.0 |

As 250. Plain edge. Rarity 8.

| 250D | ND | WM | 28mm | — | — | 15.5 |

As 250. Plain edge. Rarity 8.

G.H. LOVETT

| 251 | ND | Copper | 28mm | — | — | 70.0 |

Undraped Washington bust right, LOVETT on truncation. G. H. L. belo bust. Around: GEORGE WASHINGTON (same obverse as Baker 136 Rv: Uniformed Grant bust right, GENERAL U.S. GRANT around. Pla edge. Rarity 7.

| 251A | ND | WM | 28mm | — | — | 70.0 |

As 251. Plain edge. Rarity 7.

U.S. MINT SERIES

Struck 1876's

Baker	Date	Metal	Size	EF	Unc	Pro
252	ND	Silver	19mm	30.00	—	45.0

Undraped Washington bust right, P on truncation (same obverse a Baker 155). Rv: Grant head right. Plain edge. Rarity 6.

| 252A | ND | Gold | 19mm | — | — | 12 |

As 252. Plain edge. Rarity 8.

| 252B | ND | Bronze | 18.2mm | — | 22.50 | |

As 252. Plain edge. Rarity 4.

| 252C | ND | Yellow Bronze | 19mm | — | 4.00 | |

As 252. Plain edge. Rarity 1. (Current restrike still offered by the U.S Mint)

SOLEY MEDAL

Struck 1876

253	ND	Silver	18mm	—	—	12.50

Undraped Washington bust right. Rv: Grant head right. Plain edge. Rarity 7.

253A	ND	Copper	18mm	—	—	4.00

As 253. Plain edge. Rarity 5.

253B	ND	Bronze	18mm	—	—	4.00

As 253. Plain edge. Rarity 5.

Published by George B. Soley of Philadelphia in 1876.

F. C. KEY

Struck 1868

Baker	Date	Metal	Size	VF	EF	Unc
254	1799	Copper	19mm	—	—	275.

Washington bust in civil dress three-quarters left. Around: BORN FEB. 22 1732. DIED DEC. 14 1799. (same obverse as Baker 76). Rv: Uniformed Grant bust left, KEY F. below bust. Plain edge. (Fuld CWT 116/144). Rarity 8.

254A	1799	Brass	19mm	—	—	300.

As 254. Plain edge. Rarity 9.

254B	1799	WM	19mm	—	—	325.

As 254. Plain edge. Rarity 9.

PATER PATRIAE

Struck 1868

255	1868	Copper	21mm	—	—	100.

Washington bust in Roman mantle left, PATER PATRIAE around. (same obverse as Baker 95 and 244). Rv: Uniformed Grant bust right, 1868 below, GENERAL U.S. GRANT around. Plain edge. Only 10 struck. Rarity 7.

255A	1868	Brass	21mm	—	—	100.

As 255. Plain edge. Rarity 7.

Struck about 1878

Baker	Date	Metal	Size	VF	EF	Unc
256	1877	Copper	20mm	—	—	30.00

Obverse as 255. Rv: Uniformed Grant bust right. On a scroll beneath: PRES 1869 to '77. Around: GENERAL U.S. GRANT. The bust is the same as on Baker 255. Plain edge. Rarity 6.

256A	1877	Brass	20mm	—	—	30.00

As 256. Plain edge. Rarity 6.

RUTHERFORD B. HAYES

Mint Medal 'P'

Struck 1877

Baker	Date	Metal	Size	VF	EF	Unc
256X	ND	Bronze	19mm	—	—	200.

Obverse as Baker 155 and 223 (undraped bust right, tiny P on truncation of bust. Rv: Rutherford B. Hayes head left (a reduction of George T. Morgan's head). Plain edge. Unique. Not listed in Robert W. Julian's *Medals of the United States Mint*.

Baker 256X, previously unpublished, appeared as lot 271 in the Presidential Coin & Antique Co. sale of May 14, 1983. Obverse die by Anthony C. Paquet, reverse by George T. Morgan. The specimen reposed for a long time in the personal collection of Mint engraver Charles Barber.

RESIDENCE AND TOMB

SMITH'S MOUNT VERNON

First obverse

Struck about 1858

Baker	Date	Metal	Size	VF	EF	Proof
110	ND	WM	64mm	—	150.	—

Bust in Roman mantle left, F.B. SMITH F. N.Y. beneath. GEORGE WASHINGTON around. Rv: View of Mount Vernon. In exergue: RESI-DENCE OF WASHINGTON / MOUNT VERNON, VIRGINIA / (tiny) F.B. SMITH F. N.Y. Plain edge.

Second obverse

Struck about 1860

111	ND	WM	64mm	—	—	19.

Undraped bust left, F.B. SMITH & HARTMANN N.Y. beneath GEORGE WASHINGTON around. Rv: As 110. Plain edge.

Third obverse

Struck about 1865

Baker	Date	Metal	Size	VF	EF	Proof
112	ND	WM	64mm	—	180.	225.

Obverse resembles 110 (Roman mantle), but F.B. SMITH & HORST N.Y. beneath, Rv: As 110. Rarity 6. Plain edge.

Frederick B. Smith (born 1811) was a pupil of Charles Cushing Wright and had few peers as an engraver and modeler. He had a succession of partners - James Bale 1835-1848; Herman Hartmann 1848-1865; Horst 1865-on.

There is known a muling of the Residence reverse (Baker 110) with the Tomb reverse (Baker 119) in White Metal, sold in the 1981 Garrett sale, lot 1779 (see Baker 119A).

WRIGHT'S TOMB ENTRANCE

Struck about 1854

Baker	Date	Metal	Size	VF	EF	Proof
118	ND	Silver	67mm	—	—	Unique

Undraped bust left, C.C.W.F. on truncation. GEORGE WASHINGTON around. Rv: As 117. Plain edge. (Garrett 1782)

118A	ND	Bronze	67mm	—	—	Unique

As 118. Plain edge. (Garrett 1782)

118B	ND	WM	67mm	—	—	Unique

As 118. Plain edge. (Garrett 1782)

Charles Cushing Wright cut the obverse die - the same as Baker 96 - used here by Smith & Hartmann. This obverse die was first used on Baker 133.

Only one set of 118 to 118B was struck.

SMITH'S TOMB ENTRANCE

Struck about 1858

Baker	Date	Metal	Size	VF	EF	Proof
117	ND	Silver	67mm	—	—	600.

Obverse as Baker 111 (F. B. SMITH & HARTMANN). Rv: Entrance to the tomb in a half wreath of oak and olive, small S&H below bow. Around: TOMB OF WASHINGTON / MOUNT VERNON, VIRGINIA. Plain edge.

| 117A | ND | Bronze | 67mm | — | 275. | 325. |

As 117. Plain edge.

| 117B | ND | WM | 67mm | — | — | 285. |

As 117. Plain edge.

Dies were cut by Frederick B. Smith. Struck by Smith & Hartmann, New York.

GRADE HEADINGS

Three grade (condition) columns appear in this catalog. Coins and tokens, which circulate, are graded down to VG (Very Good), but medals, which do not circulate, usually are graded no less than VF (Very Fine). Other abbreviations used are F (Fine), EF (Extremely Fine), AU (About Uncirculated), Unc (Uncirculated), and P-L (Prooflike). Proof is spelled out.

SMITH'S TOMB

First obverse

Struck about 1858

Baker	Date	Metal	Size	VF	EF	Proof
119	ND	WM	65mm	—	100.	200.

Obverse as 110. Rv: Full view of tomb, with obelisk at each entrance and people in front. In exergue: TOMB OF WASHINGTON, / MOUNT VERNON, VIRGINIA / (tiny) F.B. SMITH F.N.Y. Plain edge.

| 119A | ND | WM | 65mm | — | Rare | — |

Obverse as reverse of 110 (Residence). Reverse as reverse of 119 (Tomb). Plain edge. (Garrett 1779)

| 119B | 1876 | WM | 65mm | — | 325. | — |

Obverse as 119 reverse. Rv: Reverse of Baker 423. (Stack's April 1996 sale, lot 111, ex-Magriel)

Dies cut by Frederick B. Smith of New York. Struck by Smith & Horst.

Second obverse

| | | Struck about 1860 | | | | |

Baker	Date	Metal	Size	VF	EF	Proof
120	ND	WM	67mm	—	—	160.

Obverse as 111. Rv: As 119. Plain edge.

Dies by Frederick B. Smith. Struck by Smith & Hartmann.

Third obverse

Struck about 1865

Baker	Date	Metal	Size	VF	EF	Proof
121	ND	WM	65mm	—	125.	160.

Obverse as 112. Rv: As 119. Plain edge.

Dies by Frederick B. Smith. Struck by Smith & Horst.

LOVETT'S MOUNT VERNON

PRESIDENTIAL RESIDENCES

Struck about 1861

Baker	Date	Metal	Size	VF	EF	Unc
113	ND	Silver	35mm	—	—	200.

Bust in Roman mantle right, G. H. LOVETT N.Y. beneath. Around: GEORGE WASHINGTON, FIRST PRESIDENT OF THE UD. STATES. All surrounded by border of roses and leaves. Rv: View of Mount Vernon. G.H.L. N.Y. beneath. Around: WASHINGTON'S RESIDENCE / AT MOUNT VERNON. Plain edge. (Garrett 1780). Less than 12 specimens known.

113A	ND	Copper	35mm	—	30.00	50.00

As 113. Plain edge. Rarity 4. (Collins 110)

113B	ND	Bronze	35mm	—	30:00	50.00

As 113. Plain edge. Rarity 4.

113C	ND	WM	35mm	—	30.00	50.00

As 113. Plain edge. Rarity 4.

113G	ND	WM	35mm	—	—	100.

Obverse similar to 113, but wreath of laurel around head. Rv: Blank. Plain edge. Rarity 7.

Baker 113 is one of a set of 16 medals showing all the presidents and their residences from Washington to Abraham Lincoln (1861-1865), cut by George Hampden Lovett of New York.

THE HOME

First obverse

Struck 1860

Baker	Date	Metal	Size	VF	EF	Proof
114	1776	Silver	32mm	—	—	150.

Obverse as Baker 98. Rv: View of the house, G.H.L. beneath. Around: THE HOME OF WASHINGTON / MOUNT VERNON. Reeded edge. R9.

114A	1776	Copper	32mm	—	—	30.00

As 114. Reeded edge.

114B	1776	Bronze	32mm	—	—	30.00

As 114. Reeded edge.

114C	1776	Brass	32mm	—	—	40.00

As 114. Reeded edge.

114D	1776	WM	32mm	—	—	25.0

As 114. Reeded edge.

114G	ND	Copper	32mm	—	Rare	60.0

Obverse as reverse of 114. Rv: THE WOMEN OF AMERICA (etc.) - No 7 of Aug. B. Sage's historical tokens. (Garrett 1781)

Second obverse

Struck 1860

Baker	Date	Metal	Size	VF	EF	Proo
115	1776	WM	32mm	—		35.00

Obverse as Baker 50. Rv: As 114. Reeded edge.

115A	1776	Copper	32mm	—		40.00

As 115. Reeded edge.

Third obverse

Struck 1860

Baker	Date	Metal	Size	VF	EF	Proo
116	ND	Silver	32mm	—	—	125

Obverse as Baker 97. Rv: As 114. Reeded edge.

116A	ND	Copper	32mm	—	—	35.00

As 116. Reeded edge.

116B	ND	WM	32mm	—	—	35.00

As 116. Reeded edge.

116C	ND	Brass	32mm	—	—	35.00

As 116. Reeded edge.

George Hampden Lovett produced 114 to 116 for sale to the public, muling many of his dies to create extra varieties.

MERRIAM'S TOMB

Original medal

Struck 1860's

Baker	Dates	Metal	Size	VF	EF	Unc
122	1799	Silver	31mm	—	300.	475.

Undraped bust right, MERRIAM beneath. Around: GEORGE WASHINGTON, BORN FEBRUARY 22. 1732. Rv: Tomb. Around: DIED DECEMBER 14, 1799 RESURGIMUS. Plain edge. Rarity 8. (PCAC Nov. 1996 sale, lot 142)

122A	1799	Copper	31mm	—	30.00	65.00

As 122. Plain edge. Rarity 5. (Collins 116)

122B	1799	Bronze	31mm	—	—	65.00

As 122. Plain edge. Rarity 5.

122C	1799	WM	31mm	—	30.00	65.00

As 122. Plain edge. Rarity 5.

122M	1732	WM	31mm	—	—	125.

Obverse as 122. Rv: As obverse of 123. Double head muling. Plain edge. Rarity 8. (Fuld coll.)

"Dog Tags"

122T	1861	WM	31mm	—	150.	—

Obverse as 122. Rv: Blank, except that small WAR OF / 1861 has been incused in lower center field. Plain edge. (Garrett 1783)

Another example

Merriam adapted his 122 obverse die to prepare Civil War dog tags for soldiers in this manner. The first piece shown, in the Garrett sale of 1981, was later personalized for one F. Arbuckle of Company D, 10th Regiment of Massachusetts Volunteers, whose home was in Chicopee, Mass. (Misspelled Chickopee on the tag).

122U	1732	WM	31mm	—	120.	

Obverse as 122. Rv: Blank. Plain edge. Rarity 8.

122V	1732	Copper	31mm	—	100.	

As 122U. Plain edge. Rarity 8.

Copy medal
Struck 1860's

Baker	Date	Metal	Size	VF	EF	Proof
123	1799	WM	31mm	—	—	50.00

Undraped bust right, no MERRIAM. GEORGE WASHINGTON BORN FEBRUARY 22. 1732. around. Rv: Tomb. Around: DIED DECEMBER 14. 1799. RESURGIMUS. Plain edge.

Baker 123 is a copy of the Merriam striking, but not nearly as well executed.

NOTE: Regarding Baker 122T (Civil War dog tags): The PCAC June 1988 Magriel sale offered one inscribed J. W. WALLACE / CO. C / HAWKINS / 9th N.Y.V. / ZOUAVES. / NEW YORK. The Coin Galleries Dec. 5, 1995 sale, lot 84 was inscribed: FRED MIL * EN.

LOVETT'S TOMB

First obverse
Struck 1860

Baker	Date	Metal	Size	VF	EF	Proof
124	ND	Copper	27.8mm	—	—	425.

Bust in Roman mantle right, GEORGE WASHINGTON around. Rv: Tomb in beaded circle. Around: WASHINGTONS TOMB, MT. VERNON, VA. and 13 stars. Plain edge. Less than 12 known.

124M	1799	Copper	27.5mm	—	—	250.

Obverse as reverse of 124 (tomb). Rv: As reverse of Baker 143. Plain edge. Rare.

Second obverse
Struck 1860

125	ND	Copper	27.8mm	—	—	115.

Undraped bust left. Rv: As 124. Plain edge. Less than 12 known.

125A	ND	Silver	27.8mm	—	—	300.

As 125. Plain edge.

Third obverse
Struck 1860

Baker	Date	Metal	Size	VF	EF	Proof
126	ND	Copper	29mm	—	—	75.00

Statue by Houdon, WASHINGTON STATUE RICHMOND, VIRGINIA around. Rv: As 124. Plain edge. Less than 12 known. (Garrett 1784)

126A	ND	Silver	29mm	—	—	150.

As 126. Plain edge.

Fourth obverse
Struck 1860

127	ND	Copper	29mm	—	—	125.

Brown's equestrian statue, WASHINGTON STATUE above, N.Y. in exergue. Rv: As 124. Plain edge. Less than 12 known. (Garrett 1784)

127A	ND	Silver	29mm	—	—	200.

As 127. Plain edge.

Small flan

Baker	Date	Metal	Size	VF	EF	Proof
128	ND	Gold	19mm	—	2 Known	800.

Bust in Roman mantle left. Rv: Washington's tomb within lobed circle, 13 stars outside. Tiny letter L below. Plain edge.

128A	ND	WM	19mm	—	245.	—

As 128. Plain edge. (Garett 1785) Rarity 7.

128B	ND	Copper	19mm	—	—	150.

As 128. Plain edge. (Parsons 1914 sale). Only 3 known.

Numbers 124 through 128 are products of George Hampden Lovett of New York City.

PATER PATRIAE

Certain Latin terms appear on medals pertaining to George Washington, the first "General of the Armies of the United States." Only one other man held this title until the 5-star rank was created in World War II, and that was John J. Pershing, U.S. commander in France in WWI.

Pater Patriae (father of his country) is the apt title frequently appearing. Many other Latin words and phrases appear on items in this catalog; in most cases we have translated these for users.

CRUTCHETT PLATES

WOODEN WALL DECORATIONS

Illustration reduced

Baker	Date	Metal	Size	VF	EF	Unc
R-128	1859	**	**	125.	200.	250.

Obverse: Central disc printed on paper. Glass cover. George Washington mantled bust right in circle of 13 stars at center, against view of Mount Vernon, seated Liberty, scroll, tomb, shield, etc. Above: DESIGNED BY H. BILLINGS ENGRAVED BY THE AMERICAN BANK NOTE CO. Below: ENTERED ACCORDING TO ACT OF CONGRESS IN THE YEAR 1859 BY H. BARNES IN THE CLERK'S OFFICE OF THE DISTRICT COURT OF THE DISTRICT OF MASSACHUSETTES. Rv: Metallic central disc. View of Mt. Vernon. In exergue: MOUNT VERNON / IN 1796. / J. CRUTCHETT, MT. VERNON FACTORY. Plain edge. Issued with top loop for hanging. (Collins 122).

** Engraved print mounted on brass disc of 54.05mm diameter, itself mounted on a wooden frame.

Illustration reduced

Baker	Date	Metal	Size	VF	EF	Unc
S-128	1859	Wood/Brass	-mm	—	175.	250.

Obverse as S-128. Rv: On metal shell: Two men stand before entrance to Washington's tomb at Mt. Vernon. In exergue: TOMB OF WASHINGTON / J. CRUTCH-ETT, MT. VERNON FACTORY. Plain edge. Issued with top loop for hanging.

Shell alone, uniface, $150 in EF.

T128
S128

Electrotype Crutchett Medal

Baker	Date	Metal	Size	VF	EF	Unc
T128	ND	Copper *	84.9mm	Ex. Rare		

* Copper electrotype, two shells joined at edge.

Nude bust right, A. DEMAREST, / SC. N.Y. under truncation. Thick border of bound fasces-like ornaments. Around effigy: GEORGE WASHINGTON / J. CRUTCH-ETT, MT. VERNON FACTORY. Rv: As reverse of Baker R-128 medallion shell (View of Mount Vernon). (H. J. Levine report)

Illustrated above is obverse of T128 (Washington bust) and central uniface shell from Baker S128 (tomb entrance).

Abraham Demarest engraved the die for T128, made by J. Crutchett. The "Crutchett plates" were wall hanging decorations made starting 1859 from wood which, in part, was grown on the Mount Vernon estate. In the PCAC Magriel sale of 1988, lot 395, a uniface obverse shell of T128 fetched $121, a price which was quite right for a decade ago, in our opinion.

T128 today (complete electrotype, both shells joined) should be worth about $500.

Chapter 14

FUNERAL MEDALS

George Washington died Dec. 14, 1799. Two massive funeral processions were held in Boston, the first on Feb. 11, 1800, a Masonic event attended by 1,600 brethren. The second was a civic procession, on Feb. 22, 1800. At both these events special funeral medals had been made to be worn, Baker 165 at the Masonic event and Baker 166 at the civic event.

The funeral medals, while a small group, are among the most popular and eagerly sought mementos of Washington's life. Unless stated, all funeral medals were struck early in 1800.

VICTOR SINE CLADE

Baker	Date	Metal	Size	VF	EF	Unc
164	1799	WM	58mm	—	Ex. Rare	—

Uniformed bust left, within wreath of olive leaves. GEORGE WASHINGTON. around. Rv: Minerva with U.S. shield and a boy leaning against the funeral urn, weep against an altar labeled VICTOR / SINE / CLADE in oval medallion. Implements of peace and war are scattered around. Above: HE IS IN GLORY, THE WORLD IN TEARS. In exergue: BORN FEB. 11. 1732 / OB. DEC. 14. 1799 / AET. 68. Plain edge. Only 2 or 3 known in decent condition.

The dies for 164 were cut by Nicholas Pearce, after designs by Dudley A. Tyng, U.S. collector of Customs at Newburyport, Mass.

| 164A | 1799 | Lead | 58mm | — | — | — |

Cast lead imitations of the Victor Sine Clade medal are fairly numerous. Wayte Raymond (in *The Early Medals of Washington*) reported that the Victor Sine Clade medal was a die trial.

SKULL AND CROSSBONES

Baker	Date	Metal	Size	VF	EF	Unc
165	1799	Gold	29mm	—	Ex. Rare	—

Uniformed bust left, HE IS IN GLORY, THE WORLD IN TEARS. around Rv: Skull and crossbones at lower center. Above, in four concentric arcs of text: B. FEB. 11. 1732. GEN. AM. ARMIES. 1775. / RE. 1783, PRES. U.S. AM. '89. R. '96. / GEN. ARM. U.S. AM. '98. / OB. D. 15. '99. Plain edge. (Raymond 21). 2 known: Norweb & Garrett.

There are two different obverse dies used on 165, differing in the spacing of their letters, and a single reverse type. The differences are minor.

The dies for 165 were executed by Jacob Perkins of Newburyport, Mass., after the designs of Dudley A. Tyng.

Baker	Date	Metal	Size	VF	EF	Unc
165A	1799	Silver	29mm	—	6600.	—

As 165. Plain edge. Rarity 8. (Raymond 21; Stack Collins 146)

| 165B | 1799 | Copper | 29mm | Unique | — | — |

As 165. Plain edge. (Fuld)

| 165C | 1799 | WM | 29mm | 2200. | — | — |

As 165. Plain edge. Rarity 9. (Raymond 21; Crosby 326; David Hirsch coll.)

FUNERAL URN MEDALS

Small bust, 29mm

Baker	Date	Metal	Size	VF	EF	Unc
166	1799	Gold	29mm	—	3500.	4500.

Same as 165 (uniformed bust left, within laurel wreath). Rv: Funeral urn at center inscribed GW in script. Around, in two concentric lines: B.F. 11. 1732. G. A. ARM. '75. R. '83. P. U.S.A. '89 / R. '96. G. ARM. U.S. '98. OB. D. 14. 1799. Plain edge. Rarity 7. 18 to 20 pieces known. (Raymond 22; Garrett 1803)

Baker	Date	Metal	Size	VF	EF	Unc
166A	1799	Silver	29.3mm	1715.	1950.	2200.

As 166. Plain edge. Rarity 6. 25 to 40 pieces reported. (Raymond 22; Clark sale 2027; Collins 149; Moffatt March 1998 sale, lot 7, estimated $600 in VG-F; PCAC July 1998 sale, lot 193, fetched $1705 in VF)

| 166B | 1799 | Copper | 29mm | — | — | — |

As 166. Plain edge. (Crosby 322)

| 166C | 1799 | White metal | 29mm | 150. | 350. | 500. |

As 166. Plain edge. Rarity 6. 35 to 70 pieces reported. (Raymond 22; Moffatt March 1998 sale, lot 8, estimated $300 in F-VF)

There are at least three different reverse dies used, one with a period after the 'S' atop the urn, and there are four different obverse dies. None of the die differences is very important. George Fuld reports there are about six different die combinations in known collections, so additional combinations may await discovery.

Dies for 166-166C were cut by Jacob Perkins of Newburyport, Mass. (1766-1849), one of America's most important early engravers. Perkins also cut dies for some of the 1787-88 Massachusetts copper coinage and a very rare private pattern dollar. The designs for the funeral medals were submitted to Perkins by Dudley A. Tyng, U.S. collector of customs at Newburyport.

All these and other funeral medals were issued holed for suspension.

Large bust, 30.1mm

Baker	Date	Metal	Size	F	VF	EF
167	1799	White metal	30.1mm	1600.	—	—

Similar to 166, but larger bust within wreath. Rv: Funeral urn, the base inscribed G W in serif capitals. The inscription around is similar to 166. Plain edge. Rarity 9. 3 pieces known. (Crosby 319; Stack Collins 152 ex-Fuld, Picker, B&R Sieck July 1981 lot 2650, PCAC Dec. 1986 lot 169, W. T. McTiernan, PCAC June 1991 lot 157; $1550 in VG)

Indian Princess

Oval Badge

Baker	Date	Metal	Size	VG	F	EF
168	1799	WM	Oval 27x36mm	3700.	—	—

Bust left within oval wreath, 1732 below bust. Around: GEN. WASHINGTON. BORN. VIRGINIA. F. 11. Rv: Funeral urn with base inscribed G.W. At left: America personified by a female Indian with feather headdress stands, weeping. A weeping willow tree shades the urn. 1799 below. Around: G. A. ARM. 75. R. 83. P. U. A. 87. R. 96. G. AR. U.S. 98. Plain edge. Only 2 pieces known. Rarity 9. (Raymond 23; Holland 883 to Appleton, MHS; other specimen Stack-Collins 153, ex-Gould, Fuld, Picker, PCAC Patterson Dec. 1986, lot 170, W. T. McTiernan, now in David Hirsch coll.)

Uniface Oval Badge

Baker	Date	Metal	Size	VF	EF	Unc
169	1799	Gold	Oval 25x31mm	17,600.	—	—

Bust left within olive wreath, G. W. below bust. Around: HE IN GLORY, THE WORLD IN TEARS. OB. D. 14. '99 AET. '68. Rv: Blank. Plain edge. About 8 pieces are known. (Raymond 23; Appleton 63)

An unmounted, slightly impaired piece sold in PCAC 48 of June, 1990, lot 302, while an earlier PCAC Great Eastern sale with a Baker 169 mounted in a locket realized $17,600.

Baker	Date	Metal	Size	VF	EF	Unc
169A	1799	Bronze	Oval, 25 by 31mm	—	2 Known	—

As 169. Plain edge. Only known specimens are in the MHS and Fuld collections. The bronze pieces are solid, not shells.

Baker	Date	Metal	Size	VF	EF	Unc
169X	ND	Copper	29mm	—	Unique	—

Hub of the funeral bust of 169, within oval depression, struck on a U.S. Large cent of indeterminate date. (Fuld)

SPECIAL RARITY SCALE FOR THE FUNERAL MEDALS IN CHAPTER 14

OBV.	REV.	TYPE	METAL	VARIETY	No. Pcs. Known
1	A1	Skull crossbones	Silver		15-25
			WM		4-6
			Copper		1
2	A2	Skull crossbones	Gold		2
			Silver		1 Rep.
1	B	Urn	Gold	2 periods	10-12
			Silver		25-40
			WM		35-70
			Copper		2-3
2	C1	Urn	Gold	1 period	1
			Silver		25-40
			WM		35-70
3	B	Urn	Gold	2 periods	1 rep.
			Silver		25-40
			WM		35-70
3	C2	Urn	Silver	1 period	25-40
			WM		35-70
4	C2	Urn	Silver	1 period	25-40
			WM		35-70
4	D	Urn	Silver	No periods	25-40
			WM		35-70
5	E	Urn (pattern)	WM	GW on base	2-3
6	F	Urn (pattern)	WM	GW on base	2-3

OBV. REV. TYPE	METAL VARIETY	No.Pcs.Known
Baker 168 oval w/Indian princess	WM	
Baker 169 oval, uniface, rev. incuse	Gold	8
	Copper	2
Baker 164 Large Victor Sine Clade	WM	6-10
	(Many copies are known)	

DIES EXPLAINED

Baker 165, Skull & Crossbones. Obverse 1. Double berry under right side of 'W' of WORLD. Also berry under center of 'H' of THE, This is the commonly met obverse of the Skull & Crossbones type.

Baker 165, Skull & Crossbones. Reverse A1. Standard legend. Notable features are: First 7 of 1775 over center of R in AM. '89. R.'96. Also, right side of N of AM.'98 under left side of leg of R in AM.'89.R.'96. This die is remarkably similar to the die A2 that follows.

(1/A1). The combination is known in silver (15-20), white metal (406) and copper (unique), ex-Fuld.

Obverse 2. Two berries at 12 o'clock, one between 'E' of THE and 'W' of WORLD, and one under left side of W. Small period after TEARS.

Reverse A2. Remarkably similar to A1, but some spacing changes on right. The first 7 of 1775 is well to the right of center of the R in AM.'89.R.'96. Right side of M of AM.'98 under left leg of R.

(2/A2). This combination is very rare. The gold Garrett piece, lot 1802, is of this combination.

Obverse 1. E of HE higher than H. 1st berry under space between IS. Upper left serif of Y slants upward. Die Break: Rim thru left serif of 'T' thru wreath towards eye center of denticle just touching tips of inner & outer leaves and crossing center of middle leaf.

Obverse 2. HE touch at base. E slightly lower than H, most noticeable at tops of letters. 1st berry under right side of upright of E. Comma after Y is too high. Upper left serif of H of THE overlaps right top of T. N of 2nd IN is upside down, and slightly higher than I.

Obverse 3. Very similar to #2. HE touch at base and are even with each other in height. 1st berry just past upright of E. Comma after Y in correct lower position. H and E of THE lean to the right. The lower left serif of E overlaps the lower right serif of H. Crossbar of H slants upward. Serif of crossbar of E is double cut. N of 2nd IN is upside down and even with I.

Obverse 4. Lower left upright of H of HE is double cut. E higher than H. 1st berry under lower right edge of E. Crossbar of H of THE is unfinished. Lower left serif of E overlaps lower right serif of H as in #2. In 'TEARS', T lower than E, and close to it. E lower than A which is too large, and distant from it.

Obverse 5. Obverse of GW-on-base patterns, and only worn specimens observed. Apparently similar central bead, and wreath, but no obvious berries showing. Single large leaf to right of I of IN. Another long leaf below center of O of GLORY.

Obverse 6. Other obverse of GW-on-base pattern; only one specimen observed. Also no apparent berries. Double leaf below left side of I of IN, long leaf below R of GLORY, rather than under the O.

Reverse B. **Periods after U and S left of the top of urn in 2nd circular line**. Tops of both 8's of 1st line are open and double cut. Last 9 of 1st line is merged with the base. Lower leg of 4 in 2nd line is over a period. Die break develops from rim over 'B' from top third of F thru period, bases of II, tail of 7, lower part of 3, and thru center of 2. Lower loops of 3's are partly squared off.

Reverse C1. **Period after U, no period after S, left of the top of urn in 2nd circular line**. 1st period just touches base of F. II touch at bottom and all but touch at top. Bottom of last 9 of 1st line points to lower portion of 8 and almost touches it. Bottom loops of 3's are round. Top of 1 of 1799 in 2nd line is slightly below left top of 7.

Reverse C2. **Period after U, no period after S, left of the top of urn in the 2nd circular line**. 1st period is evenly spaced between B and F. II is properly separated, the 2nd being slightly recut, noticeable mostly at the left base and right top. Bottom of last 9 of 1st line points just below 8 and is well separated from it. Bottom loops of 3's are squared off. Top of 1 of 1799 in 2nd line is very slightly above the left top of 7. (This does not show up in photo due to shadow).

Reverse D. **No period after U or S, left of the top of urn in the 2nd circular line**. 2 of 1732 is recut in the proper position after having first been cut too high. The last 8 in the 1st line is recut, and a thin engravers scratch protrudes from the bottom of it in a slanting position. The last 9 in the 1st line is merged with the base. 1st R in 2nd line is merged with the period. The lower serif of S is recut. The lower loops of the 3's are squared off.

Reverse E. GW on base type. Lettering apparently identical to Reverses B, C and D, but urn shorter and top is below S of U.S. - has "two periods" as on type B, but no script GW on urn, but block letters GW on base. Only available specimen is worn but mostly legible.

Reverse F. GW on base type. Similar to E, but top of urn bisects the U and there is no period after U, one after S. The GW on base is smaller than on type E. The letter on right is quite far from base. Only a single specimen seen, ANA sale 1981 by Bowers & Ruddy, lot 2650.

It is certainly a mystery why no well preserved specimens of 5E or 6F have been noted. Why, if patterns, are all so worn and even holed? Sometime an observant collector will discover a well preserved specimen of these types.

Die Combinations Seen

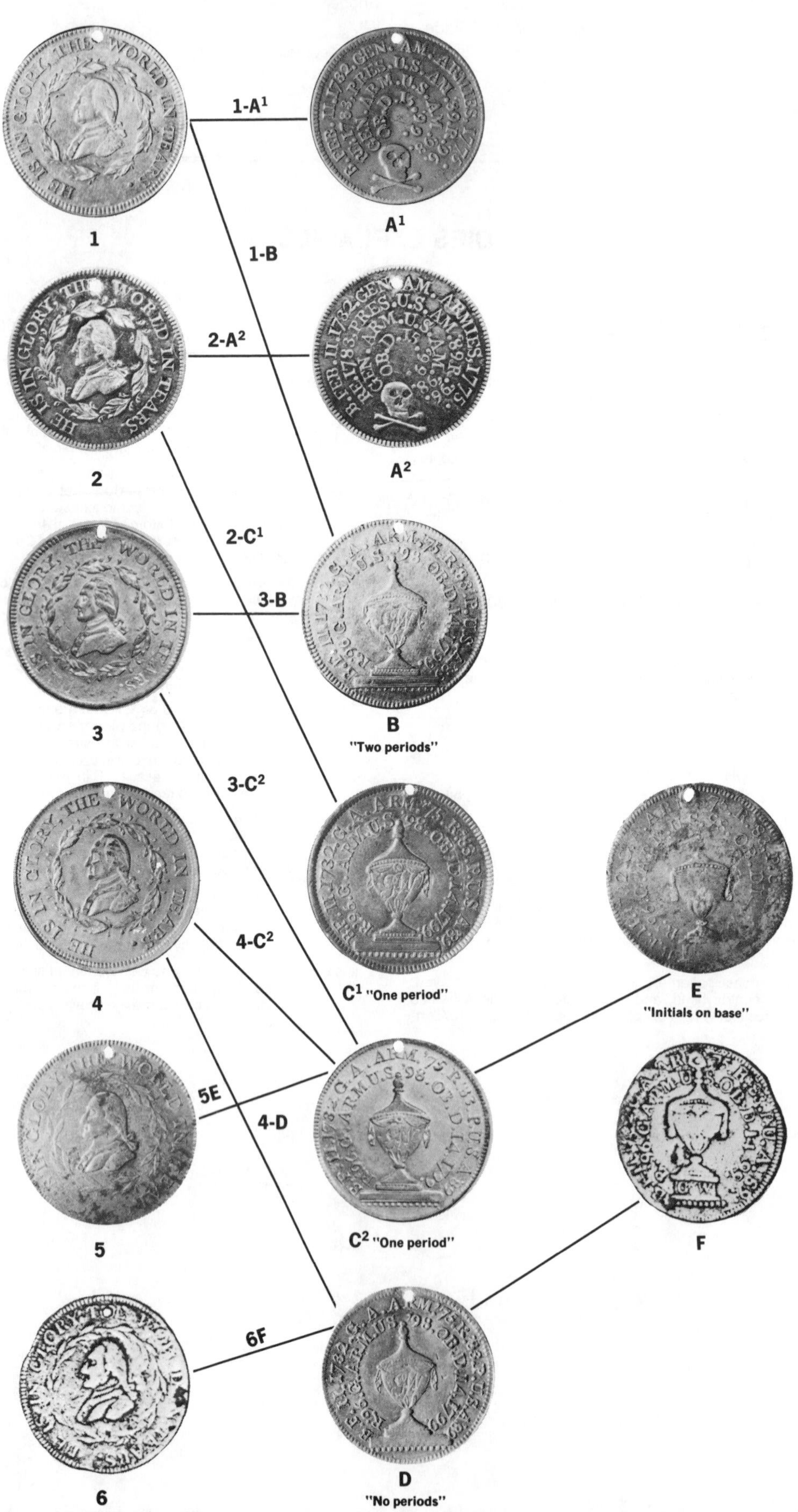

1

A[1]

B
"Two periods"

2

2-A[2]

A[2]

1-A[1]

1-B

3

2-C[1]

3-B

C[1] "One period"

E
"Initials on base"

3-C[2]

4

4-C[2]

4-D

5E

5

C[2] "One period"

F

6F

6

D
"No periods"

Chapter 15

BIRTH AND DEATH

STUART PORTRAIT

Baker	Date	Metal	Size	F	VF	Unc
129	1799	WM	44.3mm	200.	275.	800.

Bust in civil dress left. GENL. GEORGE WASHINGTON around. Rv: BORN / FEB 22D. 1732. / DIED DECR. 14 / 1799 within oak wreath. Plain edge. (Raymond 31; Magriel 393; PCAC Nov. 1997 sale, lot 258)

Little is known of this medal's origins. The portrait is after Gilbert Stuart, and the striking is early 19th century, probably in England.

B129	1799	WM	48mm	—	2 Known	—

Facing bust in crude style, PRESIDENT OF THE U.S. GEN GEORGE WASHINGTON around. Rv: Eagle displayed at center, glory of 13 stars around its head, BORN FEBY 22D 1732 above, DIED DECR 14. 1799 below. Around all, a wreath encompasses the rim. Plain edge.

It is believed this medal, unknown to Baker, is very early 19th century. Nothing is known of its background.

SERIES NUMISMATICA

Bacon, 1819

Baker	Date	Metal	Size	VF	EF	Unc
130	1819	Bronze	41.3mm	—	160.	300.

Head right, tiny BACON SCULP. below truncation. Around: GEORGIUS WASHINGTON. Rv: NATUS / VIRGINIAE IN / AMERICA FOEDERATA / AN. M.DCC.XXXII. / OBIIT / AN. M.DCC.XCIX. / (ornament) / SERIES NUMISMATICA / UNIVERSALIS VIRORUM ILLUSTRIUM / (ornament) / M.DCCC.XIX. / DURAND EDIDIT. Plain edge. (Raymond 32; Garrett 1786)

130A	1819	WM	41.3mm	—	—	Rare

As 130. Plain edge.

130B	1819	Silver	41.3mm	—	—	Unique

As 130. Plain edge. (Fuld)

Struck 1842-45

Baker	Date	Metal	Size	VF	EF	Unc
130E	1819	Bronze	41.3mm	—	—	200.

As 130, but Paris Mint restrike. Edge markings: (Prow of ship) and CUIVRE. (PCAC Nov. 16, 1996 sale, fetched $176 in Unc)

Vivier, Error

Struck ca. 1830

Baker	Date	Metal	Size	VF	EF	Unc
131	1819	Bronze	41.3mm	—	250.	350.

Head left, tiny VIVIER F. below truncation. Around: GEORGIUS WAS-INGTON (sic!). Rv: Similar to 130, from recut dies with larger letters. Plain edge. Rarity 7. (Raymond 33; Collins 124)

131A	1819	Bronze	41.3mm	—	300.	—

As 131, but the plain edge is incused: MONACHII. Rarity 9. (PCAC May 16, 1997 sale, lot 145, where this rarity realized only $121 in AU)

Monachii = Munich, Germany, apparently

Vivier, Correct

Struck about 1830

Baker	Date	Metal	Size	VF	EF	Unc
132	1819	Bronze	41mm	90.00	135.	200.

Similar to 131, from new die, WASHINGTON spelled correctly. Rv: As 131. Plain edge. (Raymond 34; Garrett 1787)

132A	ND	Bronze	41mm	—	—	250.

Obverse as 132. Rv: Blank. (Roelofs coll.)

A muling of Baker 132 obverse with another obverse of the Series Numismatica is in the Norweb collection.

Series Numismatica is a lengthy series of medals depicting famous men struck at the Paris Mint between 1819 and 1830, all published by Amedee Durand. Only those depicting Washington are included here.

Baker 130 is by John R. A. Bacon (1762-1819) of England. The portrait is purely fictitious, bearing no resemblance to George Washington. It was intended for French distribution.

Baker 131 and 132 are by Mathias Nicole Marie Vivier (1788-1859) of France. Both have realistic portraits.

BIRTH AND DEATH 118

BORN IN VIRGINIA

Wright obverse

S&H obverse

Baker	Date	Metal	Size	VF	EF	Proof
134	1799	Silver	67mm	—	—	80●

Similar to 133, but F. B. SMITH & HARTMANN N.Y. on truncation of th●
bust. Obverse letters smaller. Plain edge. Only 2 struck. (Garrett 178●

Baker	Date	Metal	Size	VF	EF	Proof
134A	1799	Bronze	67mm	—	—	67●

As 134. Plain edge. Only 3 struck. (Garrett 1789)

Baker	Date	Metal	Size	VF	EF	Proof
134B	1799	WM	67mm	—	—	67●

As 134. Plain edge. Only 3 struck. (Garrett 1789)

Baker 133 was designed by Charles Cushing Wright, who died in 1854. Bak●
134 was cut by Frederick B. Smith and Herman Hartmann. Two complete 3-med●
sets in proof of Baker 133 and 134 were sold in the Bowers & Ruddy sale of th●
John Work Garrett collection in 1980. These medals are considered among th●
most beautiful Washington pieces ever struck, but they are little known since s●
few were struck.

FIDELI CERTA MERCES

Baker	Date	Metal	Size	VF	EF	Pro●
135	1860	Silver	53mm	—	Unique	-

Undraped bust right, small LOVETT / PHILA. Beneath the truncation ●
the neck. Around: GEORGIUS WASHINGTON PRAES. PRIM. RE●
CONF. AMER. MDCCLXXXIX. Rv: Minerva seated on altar left, MD●
CCLX in exergue, surrounded by legend FIDELI CERTA MERCES an●
palm branches — all at center. Around: NATUS FEB. XXII. MDCCXX●
OBIIT DEC. XIV. MDCCXCIX. Plain edge. (McCoy sale, lot 2322).

Baker	Date	Metal	Size	VF	EF	Pro●
135A	1860	Bronze	53mm	—	80.00	11

As 135. Plain edge. (Garrett 1790)

Baker	Date	Metal	Size	VF	EF	Pro●
135B	1860	Brass	53mm	—	—	12

As 135. Plain edge. (Fuld)

Baker	Date	Metal	Size	VF	EF	Proof
133	1799	Silver	67mm	—	—	900.

Undraped bust left, C. C. W. F on truncation of bust. GEORGE WASH-
INGTON around. Rv: Within oak wreath: BORN / IN VIRGINIA / FEB.
22, 1732 / DIED / IN VIRGINIA / DEC. 14. 1799. Plain edge. Only 2
struck. (Garrett 1788)

Baker	Date	Metal	Size	VF	EF	Proof
133A	1799	Bronze	67mm	—	—	475.

As 133. Plain edge. Only 3 struck. (Garrett 1788)

Baker	Date	Metal	Size	VF	EF	Proof
133B	1799	WM	67mm	—	—	475.

As 133. Plain edge. Only 3 struck. (Garrett 1788)

Baker	Date	Metal	Size	VF	EF	Proof
135C	1860	WM	53mm	60.00	150.	175.

As 135. Plain edge. Rarity 6.

| 135D | 1860 | Lead | 53mm | — | Ex. Rare | — |

As 135. Plain edge. (Schuster coll.) A die trial.

Dies were cut by Robert Lovett Jr. of Philadelphia.

Baker 135A (bronze) is 7mm thick and much more scarce than 135C (white metal), though it brings lesser prices at auction.

BIRTH, DEATH

By Robert Lovett Jr.

Struck 1859

Baker	Date	Metal	Size	VF	EF	Proof
136	1799	Silver	30.9mm	—	—	275.

Undraped bust right, LOVETT on truncation. Around: GEORGE WASHINGTON. Rv: Within olive wreath: BORN FEB 22 / 1732 / DIED DEC: 14 / - 1799 - in four lines, the first and last curved. Reeded edge. (Garrett 1791; PCAC Nov. 16, 1996 sale, lot 146)

| 136A | 1799 | Bronze | 30mm | — | — | 60.00 |

As 136. Reeded edge. Rarity 6.

| 136B | 1799 | Bronze | 30mm | — | — | 40.00 |

As 136. Plain edge.

| 136C | 1799 | Copper | 31.2mm | — | 35.00 | 50.00 |

As 136. Reeded edge. Rarity 5. (Garrett 1791)

| 136D | 1799 | Copper | 30mm | — | — | 100. |

As 136C, but on thick planchet. Reeded edge. Rarity 9.

| 136E | 1799 | WM | 30mm | — | — | 50.00 |

As 136. Reeded edge. Rarity 5.

| 136F | 1799 | WM | 30mm | — | — | 50.00 |

As 136. Plain edge. Rarity 5.

| 136G | ND | Copper | 30mm | — | — | V. Rare |

Obverse as 136. Rv: Blank. (Fuld coll.)

All Baker 136 varieties were prepared by Robert Lovett Jr., Philadelphia.

Both dies were stolen on Dec. 14, 1859, according to coin dealer Edward Cogan of Philadelphia. The obverse die with the Washington portrait had been used on Cogan's own 1859 store cards.

A specimen of 136D in Copper, plain edge, was offered at $40 in Collins'1991 list.

By George H. Lovett

First obverse
Struck 1860's

Baker	Date	Metal	Size	VF	EF	Unc
137	1799	Silver	27mm	—	—	275.

Undraped bust right. Rv: Within olive wreath in three lines: WASHINGTON. / BORN, 1732. / DIED, 1799. Plain edge.

| 137A | 1799 | Copper | 27mm | — | — | 35.00 |

As 137. Plain edge.

| 137B | 1799 | Bronze | 27mm | — | — | 35.00 |

As 137. Plain edge.

Baker	Date	Metal	Size	VF	EF	Proof
137C	1799	Brass	27mm	—	—	40.00

As 137. Plain edge.

| 137D | 1799 | WM | 27mm | — | — | 35.00 |

As 137. Plain edge.

| 137G | ND | WM | 27mm | — | — | 70.00 |

Obverse as 137. Rv: Blank. Plain edge. Die trial.

| 137H | 1799 | WM | 27mm | — | — | 70.00 |

Obverse as reverse of 137. Rv: Blank. Plain edge. Die trial.

| 137M | ND | Copper | 27mm | — | — | 60.00 |

Obverse as 137. Rv: As obverse of 139. Plain edge. (Stewart Witham coll.)

Second obverse
Struck 1860's

Baker	Date	Metal	Size	VF	EF	Proof
138	1799	Copper	29mm	—	—	150.

Uniformed bust left, surrounded by border of semicircles and stars. Rv: As 137. Plain edge. Rarity 8. (Garrett 1791; Hirsch coll.)

| 138A | 1799 | Brass | 29mm | — | — | 200. |

As 138. Plain edge. (Garrett 1791). First surfaced in 1980 in the Garrett collection sales by Bowers & Ruddy Galleries. Rarity 9.

Third obverse
Struck 1860's

| 139 | 1799 | Copper | 29mm | — | — | 100. |

Uniformed bust left, surrounded by border of shields and stars. Rv: As 137. Plain edge. Rarity 9. (Garrett 1791)

| 139A | 1799 | Brass | 29mm | — | — | 100. |

As 139. Plain edge. (Garrett 1791)

Baker 137, 138 and 139 are by George Hampden Lovett of New York. The obverse for 137 was created expressly for this series, but the obverse dies of 138 and 139 were borrowed from G. H. Lovett's own "Headquarters" series of medals (Baker 184 to 195).

SHIELD & STAR

First obverse
Struck 1860's

Baker	Date	Metal	Size	VF	EF	Proof
140	1799	Silver	29mm	—	—	250.

Obverse as 137 (undraped bust right). Rv: A wreath of palm branches is joined at base by a U.S. shield. and a star is in the opening at top. Within the wreath: WASHINGTON / BORN, 1732 / DIED, 1799. Plain edge.

| 140A | 1799 | Copper | 29mm | — | — | 75.00 |

As 140. Plain edge. (Garrett 1792)

| 140B | 1799 | Brass | 29mm | — | — | 75.00 |

As 140. Plain edge. (Garrett 1792)

Second obverse
Struck 1860's

| 141 | 1799 | Copper | 29mm | — | — | 90.00 |

Obverse as 138 (uniformed bust left, semicircles and stars in border). Rv: As reverse of 140. Plain edge. (Garrett 1792)

| 141A | 1799 | Brass | 29mm | — | — | 75.00 |

As 141. Plain edge. (Garrett 1792)

Third obverse
Struck 1860's

| 142 | 1799 | Silver | 29mm | — | — | 250. |

Obverse as 139 (uniformed bust left, shields and stars in border). Rv: As reverse of 140. Plain edge.

| 142A | 1799 | Copper | 29mm | — | — | 100. |

As 142. Plain edge. Rarity 7. (Garrett 1792)

| 142B | 1799 | Brass | 29mm | — | — | 75.00 |

As 142. Plain edge. (Garrett 1792)

The dies for Baker 140, 141 and 142 were executed by George Hampden Lovett of New York.

U.S. SHIELD

First obverse

Struck 1860's

Baker	Date	Metal	Size	VF	EF	Proof
143	1799	Silver	29mm	—	—	350.

Bust in Roman mantle right, GEORGE WASHINGTON around. (Same obverse as Baker 124). Rv: U.S. shield within crossed laurel branches, BORN 1732 above, DIED 1799 below. Plain edge.

| 143A | 1799 | Copper | 29mm | — | — | 335. |

As 143. Plain edge. Less than 12 known. Rarity 7. (Garrett 1793)

| 143B | 1799 | Brass | 29mm | — | — | 85.00 |

As 143. Plain edge.

Second obverse

Struck 1860's

| 144 | 1799 | Silver | 27.8mm | — | — | 350. |

Undraped bust left. (Same obverse as Baker 125). Rv: As 143. Plain edge.

| 144A | 1799 | Copper | 27.8mm | — | — | 335. |

As 144. Plain edge. Less than 12 known. (Garrett 1793)

Third obverse

Struck 1860's

| 145 | 1799 | Copper | 27.8mm | — | — | 175. |

Statue by Houdon, WASHINGTON STATUE RICHMOND, VIRGINIA around. (Same obverse as Baker 126.) Rv: As 143. Plain edge. Less than 12 known. (Garrett 1793)

| 145A | 1799 | Brass | 29mm | — | — | 85.00 |

As 145. Plain edge.

Fourth obverse

Struck 1860's

| 146 | 1799 | Copper | 27.8mm | — | — | 230. |

Brown's equestrian statue. WASHINGTON STATUE N.Y. around. (Same obverse as Baker 127.) Rv: As 143. Plain edge. Less than 12 known. (Garrett 1793; PCAC July 1993 sale, lot 189)

Baker 146 has fetched $215 to $280 at auction in Unc. in the past decade.

LIBERTY CAP

First obverse

Struck 1860's

Baker	Date	Metal	Size	VF	EF	Proof
147	1799	Silver	27.8mm	—	—	275.

Bust in Roman mantle right, GEORGE WASHINGTON around. (Same obverse as Baker 124 and 143). Rv: Radiant Phrygian (Liberty) cap above: WASHINGTON / NATUS 1732 / OBIT 1799 - all surrounded by border of alternating stylized eagles and six-pointed stars. Plain edge.

| 147A | 1799 | Copper | 27.8mm | — | — | 138 |

As 147. Plain edge. (Garrett 1794)

Second obverse

Struck 1860's

| 148 | 1799 | Copper | 29mm | — | — | 175 |

Undraped bust left. Rv: As reverse of Baker 147. Plain edge. (Garrett 1794)

Third obverse

Struck 1860's

Baker	Date	Metal	Size	VF	EF	Proof
149	1799	Silver	29mm	—	—	275

Statue by Houdon, WASHINGTON STATUE RICHMOND, VIRGINIA around. (Same obverse as Baker 126 and 145). Rv: As reverse of Baker 147. Plain edge.

| 149A | 1799 | Copper | 27.8mm | — | — | 215 |

As 149. Plain edge. Rarity 6. (Garrett 1794)

Fourth obverse

Struck 1860's

| 150 | 1799 | Silver | 29mm | — | — | 30 |

Brown's equestrian statue, WASHINGTON STATUE N.Y. around. (Same obverse as Baker 127 and 146). Rv: As reverse of Baker 147. Plain edge.

| 150A | 1799 | Copper | 29mm | — | — | 30 |

As 150. Plain edge. Rarity 6. (Garrett 1794)

Baker 147 through 150 are more products of the prolific New York City engraver, George Hampden Lovett.

BUSHNELL MEDAL SERIES

First obverse

Struck 1860

Baker	Date	Metal	Size	VF	EF	Proof
151	1799	Silver	29mm	—	—	30

Head left, within laurel wreath, no legend. (Same head as Baker 100) Rv: Within laurel wreath in four lines: BORN / FEB. 22. 1732 / DIED DEC. 14. 1799. All enclosed within border of 13 stars. Plain edge.

| 151A | 1799 | Copper | 29mm | — | — | 20 |

As 151. Plain edge.

| 151B | 1799 | Brass | 29mm | — | — | 20 |

As 151. Plain edge.

| 151C | 1799 | WM | 29mm | — | — | 20 |

As 151. Plain edge.

Second obverse
Struck 1860

Baker	Date	Metal	Size	VF	EF	Proof
152	1799	Silver	29mm	—	—	300.

Head left, within three—quarter wreath of laurel, WASHINGTON around. (Same head as Baker 100). Rv: As reverse of Baker 151. Plain edge.

152A	1799	Copper	29mm	—	—	200.

As 152. Plain edge.

152B	1799	Brass	29mm	—	—	200.

As 152. Plain edge.

152C	1799	WM	29mm	—	—	200.

As 152. Plain edge.

Third obverse
Struck 1860

153	1799	Silver	29mm	—	—	300.

Head left, GEORGE WASHINGTON around. (Exactly the same obverse as Baker 100). Rv: As reverse of Baker 151. Plain edge.

153A	1799	Copper	29mm	—	—	200.

As 153. Plain edge.

153B	1799	Brass	29mm	—	—	200.

As 153. Plain edge.

153C	1799	WM	29mm	—	—	200.

As 153. Plain edge.

Fourth obverse
Struck 1860

Baker	Date	Metal	Size	VF	EF	Proof
154	1799	Silver	29mm	—	—	300.

Head left, GEORGE THE GREAT around. (Same obverse as Baker 101). Rv: As reverse of Baker 151. Plain edge.

154A	1799	Copper	29mm	—	—	200

As 154. Plain edge.

154B	1799	Brass	29mm	—	—	225.

As 154. Plain edge. (PCAC Ganter II sale, Nov. 1994, lot 215).

154C	1799	WM	29mm	—	—	200.

As 154. Plain edge.

Dies for numbers 151 through 154 were executed before his death (in 1854) by Charles Cushing Wright for collector Charles I. Bushnell. Supposedly only one impression in each metal was made - just as the similar set, Baker 100 through 109. It is not recorded who did the 1860 striking for Bushnell.

Several duplicates of some of the 151-154 varieties have been reported, so the description "unique" for the entire set should be Rarity 9.

All were struck in Proof only!

FEB. 22 BIRTHDAY

Baker	Date	Metal	Size	VF	EF	Unc
A154	ND	WM	29mm	—	—	25.00

Nude bust right with 35 stars forming border from 1 to 11 o'clock. Rv: (Ornament) / WASHINGTON'S / (ornament) / FEB. 22 (ornament) / BIRTHDAY / (two arcs). Plain edge. Issued holed. (Roelofs coll.)

PAQUET'S MINT SERIES

Struck circa 1862

Undraped bust obverse

Baker	Date	Metal	Size	EF	Unc	Proof
155	1799	Gold	18mm	—	—	615.

Undraped bust right, small P on truncation of bust. Rv: Within olive wreath: BORN / 1732 / DIED / 1799. Plain edge. Only 10 struck.

155A	1799	Silver	18mm	60.00	—	100.

As 155. Plain edge. Rarity 5. (Garrett 1795)

Baker	Date	Metal	Size	EF	Unc	Proof
155B	1799	Bronze	18mm	10.00	—	20.00

As 155. Plain edge.

Civil dress obverse

Baker	Date	Metal	Size	EF	Unc	Proof
156	1799	Gold	18.3mm	—	350.	—

Bust in civil dress right, small AP on truncation of bust. Rv: Similar to 155, but the letters are smaller. Plain edge. Only 2 known. (Garrett 1796)

156A	1799	Silver	18mm	—	60.00	100.

As 156. Plain edge. (Garrett 1795)

156B	1799	Copper	18mm	10.00	15.00	25.00

As 156. Plain edge. (Garrett 1795)

156C	1799	Bronze	18mm	—	185.	225.

As 156. Plain edge. Rarity 5.

There are numerous die varieties of Baker 155, discussed by Max Schwartz in a *Numismatic Review* article in 1945.

Anthony C. Paquet of the U.S. Mint staff engraved the dies for both 155 and 156. He modeled the head on 155 after Houdon and that on 156 after Gilbert Stuart. Baker 155, struck at the U.S. Mint at Philadelphia, is considered a very beautiful medalet.

BIRTH DAY

Baker	Date	Metal	Size	VF	EF	Unc
B-156	ND	Silver	31mm	—	—	300.

Nude bust right in central circle, 13 stars above, GEO. WASHINGTON below. Rv: WASHINGTON'S BIRTH DAY / FEBY. / 22. / . / *** amid scrolls. Plain edge. (ANS collection)

A bronze version is worth $35 in Unc.

BIRTH, DEATH BY KEY

Issued 1869

Baker	Date	Metal	Size	VF	EF	Proof
157	1799	Silver	9.7mm	—	—	200.

Uniformed bust right, 13 stars around. Rv: NATUS 1732 / Washington's signature on a tablet / OBIIT 1799. Plain edge. Weight .59 gram.

157A	1799	Fire-gilt silver	9.7mm	—	—	250.

As 157.

157B	1799	Gold	9.7mm	—	—	1000.

As 157. Fineness about .417 (10 Karat). (Schuster coll.)

Only a few impressions of these tiny medals were made when the dies broke. The obverse is a reduction of W. H. Key's Norwalk Memorial medal of 1869, Baker 369 in this catalog.

These perfect medalets are a fantastic diecutting achievement seldom duplicated since.

BIRTH, DEATH BY BALE & SMITH

Struck 1860

Baker	Date	Metal	Size	EF	Unc	Proof
158	1799	Silver	29mm	—	—	300.

Equestrian figure of Washington right, hat in his left hand held forward, GEORGE WASHINGTON above, exergue line below. Rv: Within circle of alternating Liberty caps and stars: BORN, / FEB. 22D. 1732. / PRESIDENT / 1789 TO 1796 / DIED, / 1799. Plain edge. (Garrett 1797; Cogan Sept. 1876 sale, lot 385)

158A	1799	Copper	29mm	—	—	95.00

As 158. Plain edge.

158B	1799	Brass	29mm	—	—	75.00

As 158. Plain edge.

158C	1799	WM	29mm	—	—	50.00

As 158. Plain edge.

158M	ND	Copper	29mm	—	—	100.

Obverse as 158 (equestrian figure). Rv: As obverse of 159 (uniformed bust left, surrounded by semicircles and stars). Plain edge

158N	ND	Silver	27.5mm	—	—	425.

As 158M. Possibly unique.

Struck 1860's

159	1799	Silver	29mm	75.00	—	300.

Uniformed bust left, surrounded by border of semicircles and stars. (Same obverse as Baker 138 and 194). Rv: As reverse of Baker 158. Plain edge.

159A	1799	Copper	29mm	—	60.00	80.00

As 159. Plain edge.

159B	1799	Brass	29mm	—	—	75.00

As 159. Plain edge.

159C	1799	WM	29mm	—	—	60.00

As 159. Plain edge.

The obverse figure on Baker 158 greatly resembles that of Washington used on the store cards of Atwood's Railroad Hotel and Bale & Smith Engravers, both of New York City, cut in the 1830's by Bale & Smith. Baker 159 apparently is a muling by George Hampden Lovett of New York City of one of his own dies with the B&S reverse, while 158M is a muling of the Lovett obverse with the B&S obverse. Both W. S. Baker and George Fuld attribute 158 to Bale & Smith without hesitation, but struck later.

Baker 158N also known in brass and WM.

EQUESTRIAN MEDAL

by F. Koch

Baker	Date	Metal	Size	EF	Unc	Proo
B-159	1799	WM	64mm	—	300.	—

Facing bust (after Stuart portrait) above crossed oak sprays, tiny F KOCH. N.Y. below. Around: GEORGE WASHINGTON FIRST PRESI DENT OF THE UNITED STATES OF AMERICA. Rv: Equestrian mili tary effigy of Washington left, GENERAL GEORGE WASHINGTON BORN FEBRUARY 22, 1732 DIED DECEMBER 14. 1799 * around. Plain edge. Rarity 7. (Dr. Schuster coll.) Only 50 struck.

B-159A	1799	WM	64mm	—	145.	—

As B-159, but restrike in WM off original dies made about 1963. Re strikes by Paul Franklin.

B-159B	1799	Silver	64mm	—	—	250

As B-159, but in silver. 101 pieces restruck ca. 1963. Each edge num bered! (PCAC May 16, 1997 sale, lot 153; Schuster coll. without edge number)

About half of Baker B159B were remelted. These were .999 fine.

OBVERSE AND REVERSE

The term Obverse refers to the "heads" or "face" side of a piece. Where there is a human head or bust, this is easy to determine, but where there is no head, the side with the "principal device" is the Obverse. The opposite side is the Reverse. In some cases determining Obverse and Reverse must be arbitrary, especially where a head is on each side.

Each piece also has a third side, the Edge, which is described as Reeded, Plain, Lettered, etc. The term Rim is not the edge, but the periphery of one face or another.

BIRTH CENTENNIAL 1832

PHILADELPHIA CIVIC PROCESSION MEDALS

Original struck 1832

Baker	Date	Metal	Size	VF	EF	Unc
160	1832	Silver	32.4mm	—	750.	900.

Undraped bust right in oval cameo carried by eagle in flight three-quarters left. Rays emanate from eagle's head, and below is a ribbon reading: PATRIAE PATER. Rv: In 11 lines: STRUCK/ & DISTRIBUTED IN / CIVIC PROCESSION / FEBRY.22ND.1832 / THE CENTENNIAL / ANNIVERSARY OF THE / BIRTH DAY OF / WASHINGTON / BY THE GOLD & SILVER / ARTIFICERS OF / PHILAD. Plain edge. Original medals issued with eye and ring for suspension. (Raymond 38; Cogan Sept. 1878 sale, lot 2053; Garrett 1798). Less than 10 known. Rarity 8. (Collins 147)

Original struck 1832

160A	1832	WM	32.4mm	—	150.	350.

As 160. Plain edge. (Raymond 38; Garrett 1799). Less than 100 specimens known. An EF-AU specimen realized $247.50 in May, 1997 (PCAC sale).

Perfect restrikes 1858

Baker	Date	Metal	Size	VF	EF	Pf-Like
160B	1832	Copper	32.4mm	—	175.	275.

As 160, restruck later from still-perfect dies. (Garrett 1800; PCAC Nov. 1994 sale, lot 220; Magriel 45)

Later restrikes
Reverse die cracked

160C	1832	Silver	32.4mm	—	—	385.

As 160, but restruck up until about 1885 from cracked reverse die. The restrikes exist in proof, one of which fetched $418 in July, 1998.

160D	1832	Copper	32.4mm	—	90.00	130.

As 160B. Plain edge. (Garrett 1801)

160E	1832	Bronze	32mm	—	—	130.

As 160B. Plain edge. (Raymond 38)

160F	1832	WM	32mm	45.00	90.00	130.

As 160B. Plain edge. (Garrett 1801)

160H	1832	Cop/Lead	32mm	85.00	—	—

As 160C, struck from die with one serious die crack, running through ANNIVERSARY. Plain edge. (Hartzog report)

It is reported that an original specimen of 160 in gold was presented to General Lafayette. The silver originals were presented to the officials of the parade held Feb. 22, 1832 in Philadelphia. The dies were also made in Philadelphia, but the engraver's name has been lost. The tin (white metal) impressions were distributed during the large and remarkable procession.

The copper restrikes, 160B, were prepared in 1858 before the reverse die had cracked. Later restrikes are easily distinguished by the broken reverse dies.

TINSMITHS' MEDAL

Original made 1832

Baker	Date	Metal	Size	VF	EF	Unc
161	1832	WM	42mm	—	Ex. Rare	—

Undraped bust left, GEO. WASHINGTON. FEB 22 1832 around. Rv: Intaglio of obverse. Plain edge.

The tinsmiths of Philadelphia made Baker 161 for the same 1832 civic procession celebrated by 160. It was struck as a shell after the die had been cut into the face of a hammer.

CORDWAINERS' MEDAL

Struck 1832

162	1832	WM	38mm	—	3 Known	—

Uniformed bust right, small CONRADT, 170 N. FOURTH S. beneath truncation. Rv: In six lines: THE FATHER OF HIS COUNTRY FEBRUARY 22D. 1832. At the base: PHILA. Plain edge. (Known specimens in collections Massachusetts Historical Society; Norweb, ex-England; and Parsons sale.)

Godfrey Conradt, engraver, appears in Philadelphia directories at 170 No. 4th St. in 1831-1832. He prepared Baker 162 for wear in the civic procession by the cordwainers. Conradt was still in business in 1848.

THOMAS MEDAL

163	(1832)	WM	36mm	—	Unique	—

Bust right, small THOMAS N-Y. below, WASHINGTON BORN FEBY. 22ND 1732 around. Rv: In six lines: CENTENNIAL / FIRST IN WAR, / FIRST IN PEACE, / FIRST IN THE HEARTS / OF HIS COUNTRYMEN / CELEBRATION. Plain edge. (Appleton 76). Only known specimen in MHS collection.

The mysterious "THOMAS N-Y" signature in 1832 appears to belong to the same medalist who cut the dies for the 1827 sunday school medal of St. Thomas Church, New York; personal medal for Robert Raikes, and a religious medal depicting Moses striking the rock. (Ref: Leonard Forrer, Biographical Dictionary of Medallists, VIII, 235)

CENTENNIAL ANNIVERSARY

Baker	Date	Metal	Size	VF	EF	Unc
163F	1832	WM	40.5mm	2300.	—	—

Cast copy of the C.C.A.U.S. medal (Baker 57 obverse, military bust left, G. WASHINGTON C.C.A.U.S. around). Rv: CENTENNIAL / *** / ANNI-VERSARY, / 22d . FEBRUARY / 1832. Plain edge. Cast in white metal. This piece was in the J. J. Mickley collection, lot 2385, then appeared as Bushnell sale lot 1365, then was in Gilpin sale (1883) lot 600; Chapman May 1885 sale, lot 660; Elder 1926 sale, lot 1562; then Hull, Brand, Fuld, Picker. It realized $2365 in VF-minus as lot 157 in PCAC May, 1997 sale, lot 157.

PATER PATRIAE

Certain Latin terms appear on medals pertaining to George Washington, the first "General of the Armies of the United States." Only one other man held this title until the 5-star rank was created in World War II, and that was John J. Pershing, U.S. commander in France in WWI.

Pater Patriae (father of his country) is the apt title frequently appearing. Many other Latin words and phrases appear on items in this catalog; in most cases we have translated these for users.

GRADE HEADINGS

Three grade (condition) columns appear in this catalog. Coins and tokens, which circulate, are graded down to VG (Very Good), but medals, which do not circulate, usually are graded no less than VF (Very Fine). Other abbreviations used are F (Fine), EF (Extremely Fine), AU (About Uncirculated), Unc (Uncirculated), and P-L (Prooflike). Proof is spelled out.

PATRIOTIC INSCRIPTIONS

Letter to Hamilton

Struck 1864

Baker	Date	Metal	Size	VF	EF	Proof
257	ND	Silver	59mm	—	—	1750.

Uniformed bust left, J. A. BOLEN curved beneath bust. GEORGE WASHINGTON around. Rv: In 12 lines, the last curved: I HOPE. THAT / LIBERAL ALLOWANCES / WILL BE MADE, FOR THE / POLITICAL OPINIONS OF / EACH OTHER. WITHOUT THESE / I DO NOT SEE HOW THE REINS / OF GOVERNMENT ARE TO BE / MANAGED, OR HOW / THE UNION OF THE STATES / CAN BE MUCH LONGER / PRESERVED. / WASHINGTON'S LETTER, TO HAMILTON. Plain edge. (Bolen 12; Garrett 1824). Only 5 struck.

257A	ND	Bronze	59mm	—	—	600.

As 257. Plain edge. Only 10 struck. (Garrett 1824)

257B	ND	WM	59mm	—	400.	500.

As 257. Plain edge. Only 14 struck. (Bolen 12; Collins 198)

James Adams Bolen of Springfield, Mass. made these beautiful medals in 1864. The head is modeled after the profile portrait of Washington etched by Joseph Wright in New York in 1790, and is faithful in that respect, though not really an artistic success on Bolen's part. The reverse quotes from Washington's well-known letter to Alexander Hamilton.

Some clandestine restrikes may have been made from Bolen's original dies. They are indistinguishable.

An apparent cast copy in pewter of Baker 257, 59mm, weight 1093.7 grains, is in the Schuster coll.

Extremes of Party Spirit

Struck 1862

Baker	Date	Metal	Size	VF	EF	Proof
258	ND	Silver	28mm	—	—	400.

Civil bust of Washington left, J. A. BOLEN below. GEORGE WASHINGTON around. Rv: Within oak wreath: AVOID / THE / EXTREMES / OF PARTY / SPIRIT. Plain edge. (DeWitt U-1862-1; Bolen 6; Garrett 1825; Johnson 6). Only 6 struck.

258A	ND	Oroide	29mm	—	230.	300.

As 258. Plain edge. Only 75 struck. (Garrett 1825)

258B	ND	Brass	29mm	—	—	100.

As 258. Plain edge. Rarity 9.

258C	ND	WM	29mm	—	—	75.00

As 258. Plain edge. Rarity 6.

Bolen struck this piece to satisfy the anti-war sentiment felt in some parts of the North. These people preferred a political settlement to hostilities. The "oroide" resembles copper but has a small gold content, according to Bolen's writings.

Struck for the Philadelphia Union League.

Both of T. Harrison Garrett's specimens were obtained in 1878 in proof from the Edward Cogan sale of September 16-20, lots 1604 and 2045. These were sold along with all the other Garrett Washington holdings of Johns Hopkins University in 1981.

The Main Prop

Struck 1880's

Baker	Date	Metal	Size	VF	EF	Unc
259	ND	Silver	25mm	—	—	500.

Washington bust in Roman mantle right, BOLEN under the bust. WASHINGTON above. Rv: In 7 lines: GEORGE WASHINGTON. / THE UNION, / IS THE / MAIN PROP / OF OUR / LIBERTY / 1ST PRESIDENT. U.S. Plain edge. (Bolen 25; Garrett 1826; Clark sale 2048). Only 2 struck.

259A	ND	Copper	25mm	—	90.00	165.

As 259. Plain edge. Only 16 struck.

259B	ND	Brass	25mm	—	—	Unique

As 259. Plain edge. Only 1 struck.

259C	ND	WM	25mm	—	95.00	200.

As 259. Plain edge. Only 3 struck originally, but now Rarity 7. (Garrett 1826)

Struck by James Adams Bolen of Springfield, Mass. Restrikes exist. A bronze specimen, Collins 202, was offered at $137.50 in AU.

May Our Country

First obverse

Struck 1860's

Baker	Date	Metal	Size	VF	EF	Unc
260	1786	Silver	28mm	—	—	50.00

Head left, within circle. GEO. WASHINGTON, THE DEFENDER OF HIS COUNTRY. Rv: Within central circle: "MAY / OUR COUNTRY / NEVER WANT / PROPS, / TO SUPPORT / THE / GLORIOUS FABRIC" / G.W. 1786. Outside the circle are continuous ornaments, alternating shields and stars. Plain edge. Rarity 8.

260A	1786	Copper	28mm	—	—	30.00

As 260. Plain edge. Rarity 7. (Garrett 1827)

260B	1786	Bronze	28mm	—	—	30.00

As 260. Plain edge. Rarity 7.

260C	1786	Brass	28mm	—	—	30.00

As 260. Plain edge. Rarity 7.

Baker 260 and its companions, Baker 261 through 263, were struck by George Hampden Lovett of New York City.

Second Obverse

Struck 1860's

Baker	Date	Metal	Size	VF	EF	Unc
261	ND	Copper	28mm	—	—	35.00

Obverse same as Baker 137 (undraped bust right). Rv: As reverse of 260. Plain edge. Rarity 8. (Garrett 1827)

261A	ND	Brass	28mm	—	—	Unique

AS 261. Plain edge. (Garrett 1827)

261F	ND	Brass	28mm	—	—	60.00

Obverse as 261. Rv: As obverse of Baker 260. Plain edge. A muling. Rarity 8. (Garrett 1828)

Third Obverse

Struck 1860's

262	ND	Copper	28mm	—	—	—

Obverse as Baker 194 (uniformed bust left, surrounded by circle of semicircles and stars). Rv: As reverse of 260. Plain edge. (Garrett 1827)

262A	ND	Brass	28mm	—	—	Unique

As 262. Plain edge. (Garrett 1827; B&M Patterson March 1985 sale, lot 1742)

Fourth obverse

Struck 1860's

Baker	Date	Metal	Size	VF	EF	Unc
263	ND	Copper	28mm	—	—	35.00

Uniformed bust left, surrounded by border of shields and stars. Rv: As reverse of 260. Plain edge. Rarity 8.

263A	ND	Brass	28mm	—	—	Unique

As 263. Plain edge. (B&M March 1985 sale, lot 1742)

263F	ND	Copper	28mm	—	—	Rare

Obverse as 263. Rv: As obverse of 260. Plain edge. (Garrett 1828)

Unity of Government

Struck 1861-62

Baker	Date	Metal	Size	VF	EF	Unc
264	1776	Silver	35mm	—	150.	290

Bust in civil dress, facing slightly right. Around: UNITY OF GOVERNMENT IS THE MAIN PILLAR OF INDEPENDENCE. Rv: LIBERTY AND INDEPENDENCE / HE IS / A FREEMAN / WHOM THE TRUTH / MAKES FREE. / *JULY 4 1776*. Plain edge. (DeWitt C 1861-4; Hibler-Kappen 114; Garrett 1829)

264A	1776	Copper	35mm	—	—	200.

As 264. Plain edge. (PCAC May 1997, lot 96)

264B	1776	Bronze	35mm	—	—	—

As 264. Plain edge.

264C	1776	Brass	35mm	—	—	—

As 264. Plain edge.

264D	1776	Nickel	35mm	—	—	—

As 264. Plain edge. Magnetic! Rarity 8.

264E	1776	WM	35mm	—	75.00	—

As 264. Plain edge. Rarity 7.

264F	ND	Silver	35mm	—	—	—

Obverse as 264. Rv: Blank. Plain edge. (Clark sale 2049)

264G	ND	Copper	35mm	—	—	—

As 264F. Plain edge.

The obverse die is the same as Baker 227, but 264 is the original combination of dies. All cut by Robert Lovett Jr. of Philadelphia. Baker 264F also is known in brass and WM.

Baker	Date	Metal	Size	EF	AU	Unc
A264	1773	WM	35mm	—	225.	—

Obverse as 264. Rv: William H. Harrison military bust left. Around: MAJ. GEN. W. H. HARRISON. / BORN FEB: 9. 1773. Unpublished. (Kirtley March 25, 1997 sale, lot AB 47; realized $198 in AU)

The reverse is that of the 1840 Harrison political campaign medal, DeWitt WHH-G. Lovett apparently obtained the old die and made this illogical muling as a "mint sport." Rare.

SUCCESS TOKENS
LARGE SIZE

Struck 1793?

Baker	Date	Metal	Size	F	VF	EF
265	ND	Brass	26mm	160.	325.	600.

Uniformed bust of Washington right, GEORGE WASHINGTON around. The nose is long and sharp. Rv: An eye (or a boss) surrounded by diverging rays at center, encircled by 15 6-petaled rosettes resembling stars, and around all the legend: *SUCCESS TO THE UNITED STATES. Reeded edge. (DeWitt GW 1792-1; Snowden 93; Garrett 1736-1739-1740; WA. 1792. 5.2.B) Rarity 6.

Nearly all specimens of 265 show a strong die break under the I of WASHINGTON, extending past the nose, through the end of the NG of WASHINGTON. It crosses the flan from the 11 o'clock to 3 o'clock positions.

265A	ND	Brass	26mm	500.	1000.	—

As 265. Plain edge. Rarity 8. (Garrett 1737; WA. 1792. 5.2a.Br)

Baker	Date	Metal	Size	VF	EF	Proof
265B	ND	Brass	26mm	—	600.	2000.

As 265, but apparently struck from the dies before the obverse die break began. Reeded edge. (Garrett 1739-1740; WA 1792. 5.2.Br)

| 265C | (17)76 | Brass | 26mm | — | — | — |

As 265, but large ornate numerals 76 incused into reverse flan adjoining the eye or boss at center. This type was illustrated by DeWitt under his GW 1792-1 listing, but not referred to in the text. Reeded edge.

| 265D | ND | Brass | 26mm | — | — | — |

As 265B. Plain edge. (WA. 1792. 5.2a.Br)

Restrike, about 1860

266	ND	Brass	26mm	250.	500.	—

Obverse similar to 265, but the die has been recut. The nose of Washington is more curved and other features are executed differently. This type has been referred to by Fuld and in the Garrett sale as 'Baker 265A.' Reeded edge. Rarity 7. (DeWitt GW 1792-2; WA. 1792. 5.1Br)

| 266A | ND | S/Brass | 26mm | — | — | — |

As 266. Reeded edge.

| 266B | ND | Brass | 26mm | — | — | — |

As 266. Plain edge. (WA. 1792. 5.1a.Br)

| 266C | ND | Copper | 26mm | — | — | — |

As 266. Reeded edge. (WA. 1792. 5.1b.Cu)

| 266D | ND | Silver | 26mm | — | Unique | — |

As 266. Scalloped edge (WA. 1792. 5.1c.Ag)

SMALL SIZE

Struck 1793?

Baker	Date	Metal	Size	F	VF	EF
267	ND	Brass	20mm	220.	400.	800.

Similar to 265 (minus die break), but in reduced size. Reeded edge. (DeWitt GW 1792-3; Snowden 94; Garrett 1741-1742). Rarity 6.

| 267A | ND | Brass | 20mm | 320. | 500. | 850. |

As 267. Plain edge. Rarity 4.

| 267B | ND | S/Brass | 20mm | — | 2000. | — |

As 267. (DeWitt GW-1792-3)

The peculiarly reeded edge on 267 has been referred to as a scalloped edge or an engrailed edge. A merely Good specimen of 267 fetched $66.55 in a 1995 auction.

| 267R | ND | Copper | 20mm | — | — | — |

As 267. Plain edge. This is a restrike. (DeWitt GW 1792-4)

| 267S | ND | WM | 20mm | — | — | 600. |

As 267. Plain edge. This may be a restrike.

Baker, DeWitt and other authorities assign the Success tokens to George Washington's second inauguration on March 4, 1793. Their thin fabric, however, is unlike any other coin, token or medal of this period, and more nearly resembles the mid-19th century spielmarken (game counters) produced in Germany. As did Q. David Bowers in the description for lots 1736 to 1742 in the March 25-26, 1981 sale of the John Work Garrett collection of Johns Hopkins University, we wonder whether these pieces did not in fact first appear on the numismatic scene in the 19th century, perhaps in the 1820's.

See Russ Rulau and George Fuld's 1972 opus, *American Game Counters*, where they are labeled as counters.

The Success tokens were listed as Colonials by Crosby and other sources, and still are in the "Red Book" (A Guide Book of United States Coins) by R. S. Yeoman. In his July 1998 PCAC sale (lot 196), H. J. Levine asserts there are no provable restrikes in this series.

PRO PATRIA

First obverse, 1859

Baker	Date	Metal	Size	VF	EF	Unc
268	ND	Silver	31mm	—	100.	—

Bust in Roman mantle right, GEORGE WASHINGTON around. Rv: Within open-end olive wreath: PRO / PATRIA. Small LOVETT PHILA near bottom rim. Reeded edge. Rarity 7. (Garrett 1830)

| 268AA | ND | Silver | 31mm | — | 100. | — |

As 268. Plain edge. Rarity 7? (Hirsch coll).

| 268A | ND | Copper | 31mm | — | — | 45.00 |

As 268. Reeded edge.

| 268B | ND | Copper | 31mm | — | — | 35.00 |

As 268. Plain edge. Rarity 5. (Bullowa-Lessin sale, lot 85; Collins 206)

| 268C | ND | Bronze | 31mm | — | — | — |

As 268. Plain edge.

| 268D | ND | WM | 31mm | — | — | — |

As 268. Reeded edge.

| 268E | ND | WM | 31mm | — | 30.00 | 40.00 |

As 268. Plain edge. Rarity 5. (Bullowa-Lessin sale, lot 84; Collins 207)

To the order of coin dealer Edward Cogan, Robert Lovett Jr. muled the obverse die of Baker 136 with the PRO PATRIA die. According to Cogan, the obverse die was stolen on Dec. 14, 1859 (see Baker 136).

Baker	Date	Metal	Size	VF	EF	Unc
268M	ND	Copper	31mm	—	—	70.00

Obverse as 268. Rv: Blank. Plain edge. (Hartzog coll.)

Second obverse

Baker	Date	Metal	Size	VF	EF	Unc
269	ND	Copper	32mm	—	—	85.00

Undraped bust right. LOVETT on truncation and R.L. beneath bust. Around: GEORGE WASHINGTON / *SECURITY*. Rv: As reverse of 268. Plain edge. Rarity 6. (Collins 208)

Third obverse

Baker	Date	Metal	Size	VF	EF	Unc
270	1776	Silver	32mm	—	—	—

Obverse as Baker 50 (uniformed equestrian figure on an eminence, the American army before Boston in background, GEO: WASHINGTON, 1776) Rv: As reverse of 268. Plain edge. Rarity 7.

270A	1776	Copper	32mm			

As 270. Reeded edge. Plain edge. Rarity 7. (Schuster coll).

Numbers 268 through 270 were struck by Robert Lovett Jr. in Philadelphia

HONOR IS THE REWARD OF LOYALTY

Baker	Date	Metal	Size	VF	EF	Unc
A270	ND	WM	31.5mm	—	22.50	—

Liberty seated left, small wreath in each hand. Eagle at right knee, shield behind, sword and branch crossed below exergue line. Small fancy RL between Liberty and shield. Above: HONOR IS THE REWARD OF LOYALTY. Rv: As reverse of Baker 268 (PRO PATRIA). Plain edge. (Roelofs coll.)

Designed and struck by Robert Lovett Jr. This is muling of two Lovett dies, Baker 268 alone pertaining to Washington.

EJUSQUE LIBERTATE

Struck 1860

Baker	Date	Metal	Size	VF	EF	Unc
271	ND	Silver	21mm	—	—	70.00

Draped bust left, ornamental border around. Rv: In four lines: PRO PATRIA / EJUSQUE / LIBERTATE. Small G.H.L. below. Plain edge. Rarity 7.

271A	ND	Bronze	21mm	—	—	55.00

As 271. Plain edge. Rarity 5.

271B	ND	Brass	21mm	—	—	55.00

As 271. Plain edge. Rarity 5. (Collins 209)

271C	ND	Copper	21mm	—	—	55.00

As 271. Plain edge. Rarity 6. (Collins 210)

LIBERTY AND INDEPENDENCE

Struck early 1860's

Baker	Date	Metal	Size	VF	EF	Unc
272	ND	Silver	33mm	—	—	175.

Washington bust in civil dress three-quarters left. Around: THE FATHER OF OUR COUNTRY. Rv: Liberty seated, holding a cup to an eagle standing on a rock; at her side the U.S. shield, the pole and Liberty cap in her left hand; a vessel in the distance. Around: LIBERTY AND INDEPENDENCE. Plain edge. Rarity 9.

272A	ND	Copper	33mm	—	—	80.00

As 272. Plain edge. Rarity 7.

272B	ND	Bronze	33mm	—	—	80.00

As 272. Plain edge. Rarity 7.

Baker	Date	Metal	Size	VF	EF	Unc
272C	ND	WM	33mm	—	70.00	90.0

As 272. Plain edge. Rarity 7. Issued holed. (Collins 211)

Baker 272 was probably made by Davis in Birmingham, England. The bust modeled after the Gilbert Stuart portrait, but not too successfully, W.S. Baker note in 1885.

UNITED WE STAND

Baker	Date	Metal	Size	VF	EF	Un
273	ND	WM	35mm			90.0

Obverse as 272. Rv: Two clasped hands within diverging rays. UNITED WE STAND DIVIDED WE FALL around, all within an olive wreath tie by a bow. Plain edge. Rarity 8.

Davis of Birmingham is apparently responsible for Baker 273.

VIRTUE LIBERTY & INDEPENDENCE

Struck 1860's

Baker	Date	Metal	Size	VF	EF	Un
274	1732	Silver	28mm	—	—	100

Undraped Washington bust left, KEY under the bust. Around: PATRIA PATER 1732 (same obverse as Baker 94). Rv: VIRTUE / LIBERTY / & / INDEPENDENCE. in four lines. Plain edge. Rarity 8. (Garrett 1831)

274A	1732	Copper	28mm	—	30.00	50.0

As 274. Plain edge. Rarity 4. (Collins 213)

274B	1732	Bronze	28mm	—	—	—

As 274. Plain edge. Rarity 4.

274C	1732	Brass	28mm	—	—	Uniqu

As 274. Plain edge. (Garrett 1831)

274D	1732	WM	28mm	—	30.00	50.0

As 274. Plain edge. Rarity 4.

All struck from the designs of F.C. Key of Philadelphia.

Liberty Cap

Baker	Date	Metal	Size	VF	EF	Un
275	ND	Silver	29mm	—	—	200

Obverse as 262. Rv: Liberty cap, radiant, at center. Around: UNITED STATES OF AMERICA / *LIBERTY*. Plain edge. Rarity 8. (Garret 1832)

275A	ND	copper	29mm	—	—	75.00

As 275. Plain edge.

275B	ND	Brass	29mm	—	—	75.00

As 275. Plain edge.

Baker	Date	Metal	Size	VF	EF	Unc
275C	ND	WM	29mm	—	—	75.00

As 275. Plain edge.

Baker 275 is the work of George Hampden Lovett of New York. No recent sales records.

SAGE'S LIBERTY TREE

Struck about 1860

Baker	Date	Metal	Size	VF	EF	Unc
276	1776	Silver	32mm	—	—	80.00

Equestrian figure in uniform, full face, hat in right hand held to the rear. In foreground, cannon balls and letter L. In distance, a camp. Around: GEN. GEORGE WASHINGTON, 1776. (obverse same as Baker 98). Rv: Pine tree at center, LIBERTY TREE above. Below: No. 10 AUG. B. SAGE'S HISTORICAL TOKENS. Plain edge. Rarity 8.

Baker	Date	Metal	Size	VF	EF	Unc
276A	1776	WM	32mm	—	—	50.00

As 276. Plain edge. Rarity 8.

Baker	Date	Metal	Size	VF	EF	Unc
276B	1776	Brass	32mm	—	—	50.00

As 276. Reeded edge. (Schuster coll.)

George Hampden Lovett created these medals for coin dealer Augustus B. Sage of New York, part of Sage's historical series of medals. The Washington pieces are not nearly as common as others in Sage's series.

Struck about 1860

Baker	Date	Metal	Size	VF	EF	Unc
P-276	ND	Brass	32mm	—	—	60.00

Obverse as Baker 276. Rv: House at center, G.H.L. below. THE OLD HASBROOK HOUSE above, NEWBURG, N.Y. below. Reeded edge. (Rich Hartzog coll.)

Struck by George Hampden Lovett for coin dealer Augustus B. Sage, both of New York City.

CINCINNATUS OF AMERICA

First Reverse

Struck 1861

Baker	Date	Metal	Size	VF	EF	Unc
277	1799	Silver	31.3mm	—	—	135.

Military bust left. Around: GEORGE WASHINGTON, THE CINCINNATUS OF AMERICA / B. 1732 D. 1799. Rv: Within a circle of 35 stars: THE / UNION / MUST & SHALL / BE / PRESERVED in five lines. Reeded edge. Rarity 8.

Baker	Date	Metal	Size	VF	EF	Unc
277A	1799	Copper	31.3mm	—	—	85.00

As 277. Reeded edge. Rarity 7. (Collins 213)

Second reverse

Struck 1861

Baker	Date	Metal	Size	VF	EF	Unc
278	1799	Copper	31.3mm	—	—	140.

Obverse as 277. Rv: Radiant eye at center. Around: THE UNION MUST AND SHALL BE PRESERVED. Reeded edge. Rarity 8.

This reverse was re-used on Civil War tokens.

Third reverse

Struck 1861

Baker	Date	Metal	Size	VF	EF	Unc
278F	1799	WM	32mm	—	—	400.

Obverse as 277. Rv: Sheaf of wheat at center, within circular wreath. No inscription on reverse. Reeded edge. Rarity 9. (Garrett 4041)

The military portrait of Washington as the "Cincinnatus of America" on numbers 277 and 278 is one of George Hampden Lovett's best artistic effigies of our first president. The portrait is unique among all the Washington medals. It is modeled on the du Simitiere profile.

Lovett prepared this obverse die to respond to the tide of patriotism sweeping the country as the nation plunged toward civil war, and the old motto "The Union must and shall be preserved" was resurrected.

Cincinnatus (Lucius Quinctius Cincinnatus) was a 5th century B.C. Roman farmer, soldier and statesman. The Roman Senate made him dictator in 458 B.C. to rescue a Roman army faced with annihilation by the Aequi. He defeated the Aequi in 16 days and resigned the dictatorial powers to return to his farming. Again, in 439 B.C., he was made dictator and suppressed an incipient plebeian insurrection and killed the traitor Spurius Melius. Again he resigned the dictatorship. A partly legendary figure. Cincinnatus has long served as the role model for the citizen-soldier, and the comparison to farmer, soldier and statesman George Washington is particularly apt.

Cincinnatus also gave his name to the Society of the Cincinnati, founded by American and foreign officers of the Continental Army, in May 1783, a hereditary organization with memberships limited to direct or collateral descendants of officers who served at least three years honorably in the Revolutionary War (1775-1783).

The obverse die of Baker 277 was muled with the beautiful 1861 store cards of coin dealer John K. Curtis of New York (Miller NY 171 through 174).

MINT ALLEGIANCE MEDAL

Originals, struck 1861

Baker	Date	Metal	Size	VF	EF	Unc
279	1861	Silver	30mm	—	250.	400.

Undraped Washington bust right, Paquet below bust. Around: "THE CONSTITUTION IS SACREDLY OBLIGATORY ON ALL" Rv: Within olive wreath: U.S. MINT / - / OATH OF ALLEGIANCE / TAKEN BY THE / OFFICERS AND WORKMEN / SEPT. 2. 1861 / - / JAS. POLLOCK, DIR. Plain edge. Rarity 7. Only 259 struck. (Garrett 1833; Julian CM-2; Collins 215)

Baker	Date	Metal	Size	VF	EF	Unc
279A	1861	Copper	30mm	—	—	—

As 279. Plain edge. Rarity 5.

Baker	Date	Metal	Size	VF	EF	Unc
279B	1861	Bronze	30mm	—	30.00	45.00

As 279. Plain edge. Rarity 5.

Baker	Date	Metal	Size	VF	EF	Unc
279C	1861	Aluminum	30mm	—	—	—

As 279. Plain edge. Rarity 9.

Baker	Date	Metal	Size	VF	EF	Unc
279B	1861	Yellow Bronze	30mm	—	—	5.00

As 279. Plain edge. Restrikes, still available from the U.S. Mint.

Baker 279 was struck after all Mint employees had taken an oath of allegiance to the Union after the outbreak of the Civil War. Baker 279 and 279B are known on thick planchets, rarity not determined.

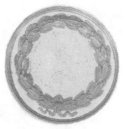

Wreath reverse

Baker	Date	Metal	Size	VF	EF	Unc
279T	ND	Silver	30mm	—	175.	215.

Obverse as 279. Rv: Blank field inside olive wreath tied by a bow. Plain edge. Rarity 8.

| 279U | ND | Bronze | 30mm | 70.00 | 90.00 | 110. |

As 279T. Plain edge. Rarity 8.

OUR COUNTRY AND OUR FLAG

Struck Ca. 1870

Baker	Date	Metal	Size	VF	EF	Unc
280	ND	Bronze	22mm	—	37.50	60.00

Roman-mantled Washington bust right. Around: GEO: WASHINGTON *FATHER OF HIS COUNTRY* Rv: Military trophy of stack of arms, drums, flags, cannon, etc: a wreath over the grouping. Around: OUR COUNTRY AND OUR FLAG NOW & FOREVER. Reeded edge. Rarity 6. Issued with looped ring attached.

| 280A | ND | Brass | 22mm | — | 37.50 | 60 |

As 280. Reeded edge. Rarity 6. (Collins 221)

Military Trophy, 1864

| 281 | 1864 | WM | 19mm | — | — | 1, |

Civilian bust three-quarters left. Around: BORN FEB. 22 1732. DI DEC. 14 1799. (same obverse as Baker 76). Rv: Military trophy, v 1864 below the grouping. Plain edge. (Fuld CWT 116/349). Rarity 9

A DECISIVE WAR

Struck 1861

Baker	Date	Metal	Size	VF	EF	U
282	1861	WM	23.5mm	—	—	5

Full length Washington figure facing a chart in his right hand, swor the left. Around: THE FOUNDER OF OUR UNION. 1776. Rv: A / DE SIVE / WAR ONLY / CAN RESTORE / PEACE AND / PROSPERIT 1861. Issued with loop. Plain edge. Rarity 9. (Garrett 1835; PCAC M 1997 sale, lot 182)

The logic of the reverse inscription is convoluted; it may have satisfied the j goistic attitude of the North of that day, however.

Struck 1861

| 282F | 1861 | WM | 26mm | — | — | 1 |

Obverse as reverse 282 (7-line inscription). Rv: VICTORY TO UNIC DOWN WITH TREASON AND REBELLION, 1861. Plain edge. (DeV C 1861-12; Holland sale, lot 2271)

FAMILY ARMS, GENEALOGY

Cave Castle, the ancient seat of the Washingtons in England. Drawn circa 1910, from an older sketch.

Residence of the Washington family at Bridges Creek, Westmoreland County, Virginia in 1732.

George Washington's coat of arms. The field is silver (or white). Across upper third are three 5-pointed stars in red, aligned horizontally. Below are two horizontal red bars the width of the shield. The cresting (top ornament) is a knight's helmet, closed, to left, wearing a crown on which is perched a bird, wings upraised, facing left. Scroll below, bearing motto: Exitus Acta Probat.

The combined arms of the branches of the Washington family. Here a seated griffin is atop the crowned knight's helmet top, and the scroll motto is: Virtus Sola Nobilitas. George Washington's paternal line arms are in the upper left and lower right elevenths into which the shield is divided (4, 4 and 3 top to bottom), the position of honor.

A brief account of George Washington's family history follows, introducing his coat of arms, genealogy and background in England. Cave Castle in England is the oldest traceable seat of the paternal line (bearing the surname).

King Henry VIII (reigned 1509-1547) took a liking to the family, most likely after 1533 because they supported his divorce from Catherine of Aragon and marriage to Anne Boleyn that year. It is said the paternal lineage had distinction before that.

Henry VIII gave lands to the family, and family members held various offices in England. Laurence and Robert Washington built Sulgrave Manor House in Northamptonshire in the 16th century, and George Washington's direct paternal line of descent claims Northamptonshire as site of origin as a result. In 1914 the "Anglo-American Peace Centenary Committee" purchased Sulgrave Manor and has maintained it ever since as a Washington memorial.

The fortunes of the family declined during the English civil wars (1642-48) and especially after the Battle of Marston Moor, July 2, 1644. England's northern and west central counties had stood with King Charles I (1625-49), but the north belonged to Cromwell's forces after defeating the cavalier army under Prince Rupert. During the Commonwealth of Oliver Cromwell (1649-60), John Washington, George's great-grandfather, emigrated to Virginia in 1657. A Royalist, he felt America offered him better chances than Cromwell's "Roundheads."

John Washington settled at Bridges Creek in Westmoreland County and, after Charles II came to the throne in 1660, became a member of Virginia's House of Burgesses. Little is known of the Washington family in Virginia until John's grandson Augustine Washington, a man of energy who died in 1743. Augustine at one time was part owner of an iron mine and smelter near Fredericksburg, and managed lands at Hunting Creek (now Mount Vernon) on the Potomac, and on the Rappahannock. Augustine Washington married twice, to Jane Butler, who bore him four children (including sons Lawrence and Augustine), and after her death to Mary Ball, who bore him six children (George being the first).

George Washington was born in the small house at Bridges Creek, near Fredericksburg, on Feb. 22, 1732. The house, on the Rappahannock River, had four rooms. At age 11, George's father died and he went to live with Lawrence Washington in the newly-built Mount Vernon on the large Hunting Creek estate in Fairfax County.

Lawrence Washington, George's eldest half-brother (1718-52), became a captain in the British army and joined Col. Wentworth and Admiral Vernon in the disastrous attack on Cartagena, in which 20,000 British soldiers and sailors perished in 1741. He fell ill, and spent the rest of his life fighting ill health. He married Anne Fairfax in July, 1743, naming his manor after the gallant Admiral Vernon, who had been the hero of the attack on Portobello. In 1751 Lawrence and George visited Barbados in an attempt to refresh Lawrence's battle against consumption, returning in May 1752. Lawrence died in July. George Washington inherited Mount Vernon, its miles of Potomac waterfront, its slaves and outbuildings, and other property valued at $200,000.

In January, 1759 George Washington, just shy of 27 years of age and a colonel in the Virginia militia (he was commissioned major 1753, lieutenant colonel 1754, brevet colonel under Gen. Braddock in 1755 and full colonel in charge of all Virginia militia in Aug. 1755) married Martha Dandridge Custis, an extremely wealthy widow with surviving children. Stories that George delayed marriage because of infatuation with the married Sally Fairfax may or may not be true. In any event, fate was to leave him childless, as his wife (born May, 1732) never again conceived.

George and Martha Washington did raise two children, George Washington Parke and Eleanor Parke Custis, children of one of Martha's sons who had died, from 1789 on. George died Dec. 14, 1799, aged 67.

An entry in the bible of Mary Ball Washington, George's mother, records her first son's birth and baptism: "George Washington son of Augustine & Mary his Wife was Born ye 11th Day of February 1732 about 10 in the Morning & was Baptized the 3:th of April following. Mr. Beverley Whiting & Capt. Christopher Brooks godfathers and Mrs. Mildred Gregory godmother." Both dates are given in the Old Style calendar then in use; he was born Feb. 22 and baptized April 14 in the current calendar.

The ancestors of Mary Ball Washington, George's mother, were also said to be prominent. She is believed to have been a lineal descendant of John Ball, the medieval champion of the rights of man, who was executed at Coventry in 1381 for participating in Wat Tyler's rebellion. Colonel William Ball, a native of Kent, migrated from England with his family about 1650, settling in Lancaster County, Va. Col. Ball died in 1659, leaving two sons, William and Joseph, and a daughter, Hannah. William in turn left eight sons and one daughter, Mary, who was born 1706. Mary's uncle Joseph was commissioned colonel by Governor Spottswoode of Virginia. Mary Ball married Augustine Washington in 1730. She died in August, 1789, living to see her son become president of the United States.

Of George Washington's descendants, some things are known. John Augustine Washington, great-great-grandnephew of George, was born May 3, 1821 in Blakely, Jefferson County, Va. He graduated from University of Virginia in 1840. At the beginning of the Civil War he was commissioned lieutenant colonel and became aide-de-camp to Gen. Robert E. Lee. He was killed at the skirmish of Rich Mountain, Va., Sept. 13, 1861.

Lewis William Washington was born in Georgetown, D.C. about 1825. He became a planter in Jefferson County, Va. During John Brown's raid on Harper's Ferry Arsenal in 1859, Lewis was captured by Brown and held as a hostage. During the Civil War his property was confiscated, but later returned. He formed a valuable collection of George Washington relics, including the sword presented by Frederick the Great. He died at Harper's Ferry, then in West Virginia, Oct. 1, 1871.

John Marshall Washington, connection to George not established, was born in Virginia in Oct. 1797; graduated U.S. Military Academy, West Point, 1814. Promoted 1st Lieutenant of artillery 1820; fought in Seminole War in Florida 1836-39. He won distinction during Mexican War at Battle of Buena Vista while a major. He was breveted Lieutenant Col. after Buena Vista. With his regiment, 3rd Artillery, he was aboard the vessel *San Francisco* when it was lost off Delaware Dec. 24, 1853. J. M. Washington, many other officers, and 180 soldiers drowned.

-•-•-•-•-•-•-

George Washington's eldest nephew was Colonel William Augustin Washington, who received from his uncle while he was still living, probably during his second presidential term, George's brass surveyor's plotting scale and a leather case containing a set of three drawing instruments. An affidavit rendered in 1922 attesting to the genuineness of these items permits us to follow the male line, father to son, of the successive owners of these items:

Col. William A. Washington's son, Col. George Corbin Washington, was the next owner, and he died in 1854, willing them to his son, Colonel Louis William Washington. G. C. Washington attended Harvard, and his son Princeton.

Louis Washington's son, Major James Barroll Washington, was given the items in 1859 when he entered the U.S. Military Academy, West Point. In 1883 the items were presented to J. B.

Washington's son, William Lanier Washington, on his entry into Western University of Pennsylvania. William Lanier Washington still owned them when the affidavits were executed, one in 1921 and another in 1922.

It may be of interest that Bowers & Merena Galleries auctioned the surveyor's scale for $1166 and the instrument case for $880, on March 26, 1985, as part of their giant Patterson-Boyd-Brand sale.

The Slavery Issue

George Washington inherited a number of slaves along with his half-brother Lawrence's Mount Vernon estates. The institution of slavery apparently disturbed him during his extremely busy life, but not until his presidency ended in1797 could he dwell upon the subject. He died in December, 1799.

On his deathbed he promised feedom to his Negro slaves, then numbering more than 100, as soon as his wife died. Martha Washington freed all the Mount Vernon slaves in late 1800 by executing documents of manumission, well before her death. It was one of the earliest acts of such large-scale compassion in U.S. history.

Beginning in 1997, a very few "politically correct" Americans began castigating Washington as a slaveholder, but the movement seemed to collapse of its own weight. A few years earlier, such "PC" re-examination of history -- applying late 20th century standards of conduct -- effectively diminished the 500th anniversary celebrations of Columbus's discovery of America in 1992 by castigating the explorer as a butcher of Indians.

Swords in Washington's Time

The so-called "hunting sword" was a typical civilian arm from about 1750 on, and many such weapons were carried by officers of the Continental Army and the militia units. These swords were useful as symbols of rank, though of little use in actual combat. Senior American officers such as Generals Washington, Montgomery, Von Steuben and Dearborn carried them. The blades were typically about 26.5 inches (32 inches overall with the hilt) and slightly curved. The grips were made of such materials as bone, ivory, wood, stag horn, brass and the best of silver. The blades were generally incused with the mark of their maker; a typical surviving example marked: **1759 / (Running wolf)**. The wolf was the mark of the swordsmiths at Solingen, Germany.

An infantry officer's saber (28.25 inch blade, 35 inches overall) has survived in a number of examples. Each blade is engraved with: **G (Panoply of arms and eagle's head) W**. The grips are of walnut and the guard of brass. These are thought to be post-Revolutionary and honoring George Washington.

Decorative swords bearing a nude Houdon bust of Washington left in oval medallion with a 5-pointed star above and letter W below -- all part of the gilded brass hilt -- were made in France about 1801 to honor the general, and these found favor with American officers as the swords conformed to Army regulations promulgated in 1801 for artillery officers.

The most famous silver-mounted sword of American manufacture, however, is the hunting sword worn by General Washington himself during most of the Revolutionary War. John Bailey of Fishkill, New York, who was both silversmith and cutler, made this weapon, using a 30-inch single-edged blade (36 inches overall). The sword's original leather scabbard with silver mountings exists, and one of these mountings is engraved: **J Bailey Fish Kill** in script lettering.

Washington's personal sword reposes today in the Smithsonian Institution in Washington, D.C. Exactly when it was made is not certain, but Charles Willson Peale's portrait of Washington at Valley Forge in 1778 shows it clearly, in detail.

John Bailey is an interesting man. This silversmith worked in New York City 1754-75 and in Fishkill, N.Y. 1775-80, returning to New York City 1780. New York was under British occupation 1776-83.

Cavalry officers during the Revolution used the cavalry saber (blades from 32.75 to 36 inches, 38.75 to 42.5 inches overall). Famous cavalry leaders such as "Light Horse Harry" Lee and George Washington's distant kinsman Col. William Washington used them.

SIGNATURE

Baker	Date	Metal	Size	VF	EF	Unc
283	ND	Bronze	47mm	—	—	60.00

Undraped Washington bust right. Rv: A tablet bears a facsimile of the signature of George Washington. Plain edge. Rarity 8.

FAMILY ARMS

First obverse

Baker	Date	Metal	Size	VF	EF	Unc
284	ND	Silver	28mm	—	—	100

Roman-mantled bust right, GEORGE WASHINGTON around (same obverse as Baker 124). Rv: Crested shield of arms within roped circle at center, FAMILY ARMS above, of GEORGE WASHINGTON below. The motto on the scroll under the shield is: EXITUS ACTA PROBAT. Plain edge. (Clark sale, lot 2053)

Baker	Date	Metal	Size	VF	EF	Unc
284A	ND	Copper	28mm	—	65.00	80.00

As 284. Plain edge. Rarity 5. (Collins 222)

Second obverse

Baker	Date	Metal	Size	VF	EF	Unc
285	ND	Copper	28mm	—	—	250

Undraped Washington bust left (same obverse as Baker 125). Rv: A reverse of 284. Plain edge. Rarity 8.

Jack Collins claimed 284-285 were struck circa 1810; certainly incorrect. George Hampden Lovett was the maker; struck 1850-60.

Family Coat of Arms

Baker	Date	Metal	Size	EF	Unc	Proof
R-456	1883	WM	42mm	—	50.00	—

Crested shield of arms. In three concentric circles around the shield: WASHINGTON'S FAMILY COAT OF ARMS FROM WHICH THE AMERICAN FLAG WAS DESIGNED / (13 equally spaced 5-pointed stars) / HE WAS MOST NOBLY CROWNED BY REFUSING TO BE CROWNED. Rv: Headquarters building, tiny A. DEMAREST, SC. N.Y below ground line. Above: 1783 -- CENTENNIAL -- 1883 / CELEBRATION AT NEWBURGH, N.Y. / OCTOBER 18TH. Below: WASHINGTON'S HEADQUARTERS / PROCLAMATION OF PEACE DISBANDMENT OF THE ARMY. Plain edge. (Leon Hendrickson coll.)

Baker	Date	Metal	Size	EF	Unc	Proof
R-456A	1883	Bronze	42mm	—	50.00	—

As R-456. Plain edge. (Hibler-Kappen 134)

Dies cut by Abraham Demarest, New York City.

FAMILY ARMS / EVACUATION

Struck 1883

Baker	Date	Metal	Size	VF	EF	Unc
A285	ND	WM	32mm	25.00	30.00	50.00

Crested, mantled shield of arms. Around, in two concentric circles: (13 5-pointed stars) / ORIGIN OF THE STARS & STRIPES / . THE WASHINGTON FAMILY COAT OF ARMS. Rv: Van Arsdale climbing flagpole to fly American flag. Above: EVACUATION OF / NEW YORK / BY THE BRITISH / NOV. 25' 1783. Below: DAVID VAN ARSDALE, / UNFURLING THE AMERICAN FLAG AT THE BATTERY. Plain edge. Issued holed for suspension by red ribbon. (Reigh L. Roelofs coll.)

This unpublished medal is not signed, and is likely very scarce.

BOOKPLATE MEDALS

First obverse

Struck about 1877

Baker	Date	Metal	Size	VF	EF	Unc
286	1799	Silver	33mm	—	—	200.

Civilian bust three-quarters left, KEY on truncation of bust. Rv: Washington's ornate bookplate, and beneath it a facsimile of the signature. In small letters along lower rim: HARZFELD'S SERIES. Plain edge.

286A	1799	Copper	33mm	—	—	75.00

As 286. Plain edge. Rarity 6. (Collins 223)

286B	1799	Bronze	33mm	—	—	60.00

As 286. Plain edge. Rarity 6.

286C	1799	Brass	33mm	—	—	60.00

As 286. Plain edge. Rarity 6.

286D	1799	WM	33mm	—	—	70.00

As 286. Plain edge. Rarity 6. (Collins 226)

Second obverse

Struck about 1877

Baker	Date	Metal	Size	VF	EF	Unc
287	1799	Silver	33mm	—	—	125.

Obverse similar to 286, but legend GEORGE WASHINGTON has been added around the bust. Rv: As 286. Plain edge. Rarity 8. (Garrett 1836 in PROOF, where it was mistakenly identified as Baker 286)

287A	1799	Bronze	33mm	—	—	42.50

As 287. Plain edge. Rarity 6.

287B	1799	WM	33mm	—	—	42.50

As 287. Plain edge. Rarity 6. (Collins 227)

287F	1799	Bronze	33mm	—	—	42.50

As 287, but HARZFELD'S SERIES has been removed from the die. Plain edge. Rarity 6.

Sigmund K. Harzfeld, the publisher of Baker 286 and 287, was a collector of coins and a German who emigrated to Philadelphia in 1876. While there he commissioned William H. Key, then assistant engraver at the U.S. Mint, to prepare the Bookplate series. Harzfeld returned to Germany in 1881, dying at Wiesbaden, Dec. 13, 1883.

Harzfeld is also the publisher of Baker 302, a Masonic medal using the obverse of Baker 286.

Bookplate/Centennial Mule

Baker	Date	Metal	Size	VF	EF	Proof
A286	1832	WM	33mm	—	—	230.

Muling of cracked die reverse of Baker 160 with reverse of Baker 286. Rarity 9. (PCAC May 1997 sale, lot 156)

NOTE: See Baker R-456 in Chapter 26 for another coat of arms medal.

SULGRAVE MANOR

ANCESTRAL HOME IN ENGLAND

Issued 1921

Baker	Date	Metal	Size	F	VF	AU
A-287	1914	Lead	44mm	275.	325.	—

Manor house with trees in background. SULGRAVE MANOR HOUSE NORTHAMPTONSHIRE around. In exergue: BUILT IN THE 16TH CENTURY BY / LAURENCE & ROBERT / WASHINGTON. Rv: ACQUIRED / BY THE / ANGLO-AMERICAN / PEACE CENTENARY / COMMITTEE / AS A PERMANENT MEMORIAL / OF THE CENTURY OF / PEACE / BETWEEN GREAT BRITAIN / AND THE UNITED STATES / 1814-1914. Only 16 pieces struck. (Joseph Lepczyk Feb. 25, 1981 sale, lot 1049; $150-plus estimate in F-VF; Laurence Brown N/L)

A letter accompanying the Lepczyk sale specimen certifies this medal is one of 16 struck from lead of the roof of Sulgrave Manor, presumably when it was being remodeled for the committee owners. George Washington's ancestors can be traced to Northamptonshire, England in the 1500's.

The medals were engraved by A. E. Gale.

George Washington was the eldest son of Augustine Washington (died 1743) and Augustine's second wife, Mary Ball (1708-89). Augustine was a member of the colonial aristocracy in Westmoreland County, where George was born Feb. 22, 1732. George's older half-brother Lawrence Washington, who had built Mount Vernon in Fairfax County in 1743, had George live with him when their father died. Mount Vernon was named after Admiral Edward Vernon, Commander at Cartagena in 1741 under whom Lawrence served in the British Army.

Lawrence Washington (1718-52) and his brother Augustine formed the Ohio Company in 1747 to speculate in western lands, and in 1749 the Privy Council of Virginia granted them 200,000 acres of land between the Monongahela and Great

Kanawha Rivers, bringing them into conflict with the French. George Washington inherited Mount Vernon on Lawrence's death in 1752.

This medal celebrates the 100 years of peace begun with the Treaty of Ghent (Belgium) on Dec. 24, 1814 (though the War of 1812's most overwhelming American victory took place in the Battle of New Orleans Jan. 8, 1815 because the contending forces had not learned that peace had been declared).

SULGRAVE CERAMIC PLATE

Illustration reduced

Made ca. 1810-30?

Baker	Date	Metal	Size	VF	EF	New
B-287	ND	Glazed Porcelain**	—	1500.	—	

** 254mm diameter plate for hanging. The multicolored plate shows four vignettes and two tablets in its design.
Upper center: View of Sulgrave Manor in Northamptonshire; on tablet below: Sulgrave Manor / Old English home / of the Washingtons. At left: Coat of arms of the Washington family in line sketch, labeled: The Washington Arms / at Sulgrave Manor. At right: Depiction of 1790 Jacques Manly medal obverse of type Baker 61. At bottom: View of Sulgrave Church; on tablet below: Sulgrave Church / From an / old print. (David Hirsch coll.)

Washington expert David H. Hirsch, Simi Valley, Calif., purchased this plate in 1991 in an Internet auction, sight unseen. Its depiction of a Manly medal to show what Washington looked like may well indicate that it is a very early 19th century product. The Houdon and Stuart depictions would soon be far better known than the obscure Manly piece, known only to few people outside curators, artists, etc.

The 10 inch (254mm) ceramic plate was examined by a California expert on antique plates, who declared that it was made of porcelain and the "crazing" (small cracks in the glaze) was genuine. The expert stated that crazing does not begin to occur until at least 50 to 75 years have passed, and that the well-advanced crazing indicated the plate was much older than that. He would not hazard a guess as to its age of manufacture.

Owner David H. Hirsch and your authors concur in the 1810-1830 era. The primary colors used in the scenes are green, brown, tan, red and a buff-gold shade, with black used in the outermost and innermost of the circular borders.

MARY ANN WASHINGTON

Baker	Date	Metal	Size	VF	EF	AU
C-287	1914	Gold	37mm	—	600.	—

Entire medal is hand engraved! Virginia arms, VIRGINIA above, SIC SEMPER TYRANNIS below, within ornate shield-shaped cartouche. Around: Mary Ann Washington / 1864. November 17. 1914. Rv: Mantled, supported arms of the Keyser family, scroll motto below: FATTI MASCHII PAROLE FEMINE. Around: Henry Irvine Keyser / 1864. November 17. 1914. Plain edge. Unsigned. Unique. Gross weight 28.1 grams (.905 troy ounce). (Kirtley Jan. 9, 1996 sale, lot A009; fetched $495 in EF, test mark on edge)

Issued on the occasion of the 50th wedding anniversary of these two members of the prominent Washington and Keyser families, the hand engraving of the complex Keyser arms and handsome Virginia Commonwealth arms would probably be impossible today -- and difficult enough in the world of 1914, when most true craftsmen had given way to machine engraving.

The medal, unfortunately not signed by its artist, contains 434.4 grains of 22 karat (.9167 fine) gold, or a pure gold content of .8296 troy ounce.

We have not traced Miss Washington's branch of the family, or the obviously important Keyser family. A Keyser descendant, retired Navy Capt. (chaplain) Charles Lovett Keyser Jr. (born 1930), was appointed 1986 rector of Washington and Montross parishes of Virginia and, in 1990, bishop for the Armed Forces Episcopal Church, New York, Va.

WILLIAM WASHINGTON

BATTLE OF COWPENS

Originals struck 1790

Baker	Date	Metal	Size	VF	EF	Unc
D287	1781	Silver	46mm	—	—	—

Captain William Washington, mounted, charging left, Victory with wreath and palms flying left above. Around: GULIELMO WASHINGTON LEGIONIS EQUIT. PRAEFECTO. In exergue: COMITIA AMERICANA. Signature DUV above exergue line, at right. Rv: Circular laurel wreath within which is: QUOD / PARVA MILITUM MANU / STRENUE PROSE CUTUS DEDIT / IN PUGNA AD COWPENS / XVII JAN. MDCCLXXXI. Plain edge. (Snowden 10; Stahl 70; Appleton 1874; Loubat 9; Betts 594)

Obverse legend translates: "To William Washington, cavalry regiment commander, American Committee" (Congress). Alan Stahl (1995) chose to translate Washington's rank as lieutenant, and other authors refer to him as colonel. At the time of the Battle of Cowpens in South Carolina his rank was captain. He was later promoted to lieutenant colonel.

Reverse legend translates (freely): "Since he pursued the enemy diligently with a small band of soldiers, he gave a signal example of native courage at the Battle of Cowpens, Jan. 17, 1781."

Restrike, before 1842

| D287A | 1781 | Red bronze | 46mm | — | — | — |

As D287. Plain edge. (Betts 594; Stahl 71-72)

Restrike, 1860-1879

| D287B | 1781 | Copper | 46mm | — | — | — |

As D287. Plain edge, marked: (Bee) CUIVRE. (Springfield 4177; Kessler-Spangenberger 1654; Stahl 73)

Restrike after 1880

| D287C | 1781 | Silver | 46mm | — | 800. | — |

As D287. Plain edge, marked: (Cornucopia) ARGENT. (Stahl 75)

| D287D | 1781 | Bronze | 46mm | — | 250. | — |

As D287. Plain edge, marked: (Cornucopia) BRONZE. (Stahl 76)

The Continental Congress authorized the silver medal as part of its 11-design Comitia Americana series. Designed by Pierre Simon Benjamin Duvivier, it was first struck 1790 in Paris. The Paris Mint executed Baker D287 to 287D, while the Philadelphia Mint struck Baker D287F and 287G.

Restrike 1863-on

D287F   1781   Dark bronze   45mm   —   300.   350.

    As D287, reissue from Philadelphia Mint dies first used 1863. Plain edge. (Stahl 77; Julian MI-8; Stack's 1991 fixed price list, lot 21)

Restrike 20th century

D287G   1781   Yellow bronze   45mm   —   —   17.00

    As 287F, still being sold by U.S. Mint at modest cost. Plain edge. (Stahl 78)

Lt. Col. William Washington was a distant relation of George Washington.

At Cowpens, Brig. Gen. Daniel Morgan's 1050 Americans severely defeated Lt. Col. Banastre Tarleton's famed British Legion of 1100 veterans. The Americans had 12 killed and 60 wounded. The British suffered 100 killed, 230 wounded (all captured), and 600 more captured unwounded.

Captains William Washington and James McCall led a small cavalry force which harassed Tarleton's flank and rear, leading to decimation of the British dragoons and Highlander infantry. Washington and Tarleton engaged in a personal saber-and-pistol combat at the end; Washington's horse was wounded and Tarleton rode from the field, 930 of his 1100 men lost.

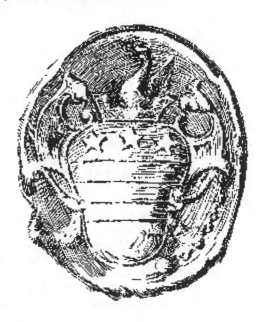

Washington's seal, used to impress his mark upon envelopes or documents, is taken from a letter to Bouquet written in 1758. The seal design is a variation of his coat of arms, drawn about 1910 by artist H. A. Ross (signature H A R in script).

Chapter 19

MASONIC MEDALS

Non Nobis Solum Sed Toto Mundo Nati

Masonic medals have a special place in any cabinet of Washingtonia. The connection of George Washington with the Masonic fraternity commenced early in his life, his initiation as a member of the Fredericksburgh Lodge in Virginia taking place on Nov. 4, 1752, nearly four months before reaching the age of 21. The lodge was one of the earliest under regular warrant in this country. It is stated that the Bible on which Washington was obligated, and the old record book are still in existence.

After attaining his majority, he passed Fellow Craft, March 3, 1753, and was raised Master Mason on Aug. 4, 1753.

During the Revolutionary War he held no official position in the order, though he often attended meetings of various lodges, some of which were held in the army, but always as a private brother. In 1788 he was chosen Master of Alexandria Lodge, No. 22. A few years after his death the lodge changed its name to Alexandria Washington Lodge, No. 22.

At a meeting held Jan. 13, 1780, the Grand Lodge of Pennsylvania elected Washington as General Grand Master of the United States. This action did not meet with favor from other grand lodges, and the office was never established. But the Pennsylvania action created the impression there was such an office, and that Washington held it, and the error was propagated by the legend on Baker 288 - G. W. G. G. M. (George Washington, General Grand Master) - a medal struck in 1797.

Medals and tokens reflecting Masonic themes may be found elsewhere in this volume than this chapter, as the book is arranged by subjects which often conflict. Readers may consult the detailed index for guidance to other Masonic pieces.

GENERAL GRAND MASTER

Struck 1797

Baker	Date	Metal	Size	VG	F	EF
288	1797	Silver	34mm	—	—	60,000.

Uniformed Washington bust left, G. WASHINGTON PRESIDENT . around, 1797 below. Rv: Two pillars topped by globes; All-seeing eye, G, square and compasses, open book, three burning candles, level, plumb and gavel, trowel - all within central circle. Around: AMOR. HONOR. ET. JUSTITIA. Below: - G.W.G.G.M.-. Engrailed edge. (Marvin 264; Rulau-E Med 12; Garrett 1837). Only 1 or 2 specimens known.

288A	1797	Silver	34mm	—	—	—

As 288. Plain edge. Baker noted that the piece in the Bushnell sale, lot 1301, had a plain edge. The location of this piece today is not known.

288B	1797	Brass	34mm	—	15,000.	Ex. Rare

As 288. Engrailed edge. (Marvin 264; Rulau-E Med 11)

The pedigree is Stickney, Wilson 856, Brand, Fuld, Picker, Craige, Spink; PCAC June 1990, lot 321; PCAC June 1994, lot 189; Alan Weinberg coll.)

288C	1797	Brass	34mm	—	—	2000.

Obverse as 288. Rv: Blank. Plain edge. (Rulau-E Med 13). Only 4 to 6 specimens known.

288D	1797	S/Brass	34mm	—	—	2000.

As 288C. Plain edge. (Garrett 1838)

288E	1797	S/Brass	34mm	—	5000.	—

As 288, overstruck on silver-washed brass counterfeit Mexico 8-Reales, thin flan. Plain edge. (Alan Weinberg coll., ex-Fuld, 1996 ANA sale)

The Washington effigy on Baker 288 is copied from the portrait drawn from life in the winter of 1778-79 at Philadelphia by Pierre Eugene du Simitiere, a cultured Swiss gentleman who settled there in 1766. The du Simitiere original (possibly only a sketch) is no longer in existence but is preserved in engravings from it published in Madrid (1781), at Paris, and at London (1783).

It is not known for certain who made the 1797 Masonic medals, but most authorities agree it was probably Peter Getz of Lancaster, Pa., himself a Mason, who executed the Washington half dollars in 1792. Compare the portrait on Baker 288 with those of the Getz half dollars (Baker 23 to 25) and the similarity will be noticed.

The uniface pieces (Baker 288C) were snuff box tops.

NON NOBIS SOLUM

First obverse

289	1859	Bronze	50mm	—	—	225

Head right within circular frame, G.H.L. under head and GEORGE WASHINGTON around. Outside circle at top is an eagle with long ribbon in its beak, U.S. shield and trophies of war at the bottom. On the ribbon: TALEM FERENT NULLUM SECLA FUTURA VIRUM. Rv: Mosaic pavement on which rests two pillars, globes atop them, and in field are many Masonic symbols. Around: NON NOBIS SOLUM SED TOTO MUNDO NATI. At bottom: MDCCCLIX. Plain edge. (Marvin 266; Clark sale, lot 2055) Rarity 7.

289A	1859	Bronze	51mm	—	—	200

Similar to 289, but it has serrated rims on both sides. (Clark sale, lot 2057)

289B	1859	Bronze	51mm	—	—	200

As 289A, but struck on thick planchet. Rarity 7. (Ex-George Fuld coll. Clark sale, lot 2058; Kirtley March 1997 sale, lot AB48)

289C	1859	Gilt/B	50mm	—	—	240

As 289 (non-serrated rims). Plain edge. Unique? (Clark sale, lot 2059)

Undraped Washington bust left, A C M under truncation. Around: UNIT-ED STATES OF AMERICA / GEORGE WASHINGTON. within circle. Outside circle: Olive and oak wreath underneath, eagle and flag, radiant, at top, E PLURIBUS -- UNUM separated by eagle. Rv: As reverse of 289. Plain edge. (Marvin 705; Garrett 1840). Rarity 9.

The only traceable specimen was purchased by T. Harrison Garrett in W. Elliot Woodward's 69th sale, lot 792, and was sold by Bowers & Ruddy Galleries with the other Garrett Washington holdings on March 25, 1981.

The initials A.C.M. are those of diesinker Alexander C. Morin of Philadelphia, who collaborated with George Hampden Lovett on this medal. The Morin obverse was also used on the Crystal Palace medal of 1853, Baker 361.

Third obverse

Baker	Date	Metal	Size	VF	EF	Unc
291	1859	WM	53mm	—	Unique	

Undraped Washington bust left in a sunken field, surrounded by a broad raised border. Small C. C. W. under the bust. Rv: As reverse of 289. Plain edge. (Bushnell 1400)

Baker 291's obverse die was cut by Charles Cushing Wright, probably the best engraver of medals this nation produced in the 19th century.

MAGNA EST VERITAS

Struck 1875

292	1876	Silver	50mm	—	—	300.

Undraped bust left, R.L. on truncation and R. LAUBENHEIMER below bust. Around: FIRST IN WAR, FIRST IN PEACE, AND FIRST IN THE HEARTS OF HIS COUNTRYMEN. / BORN FEB. 22. 1732 -- DIED DEC. 14. 1799. in two curving lines. Laurel wreath around all, radiant star at top and square-and-compass below. Along bottom rim: PATENTED JUNE 8. 1875. Rv: Scene of Washington's father and youthful George with hatchet near chopped-down cherry tree. GW monogram within wreath in sky above. Above: MAGNA EST VERITAS ET PRAEVALEBIT. Below: I CAN NOT TELL A LIE. / 1876. Plain edge. Rarity 8. (Marvin 267)

292A	1876	Copper	50mm	—	—	90.00

As 292. Plain edge. (Clark sale, lot 2063)

292B	1876	Bronze	50mm	—	—	90.00

As 292. Plain edge. (Garrett 1841)

292C	1876	Brass	50mm	—	—	90.00

As 292. Plain edge. (Garrett 1841)

292D	1876	WM	50mm	—	—	90.00

As 292. Plain edge. Rarity 5.

292E	1876	Wood	62mm	—	—	175.

As 292. Plain edge. (Schuster coll.)

292F	1876	Lead	51mm	—	Unique	—

Die trial of 292, without collar. (ex-Leidman 1986, lot 4131; NASCA 1981 Kessler-Spangenberger, lot 1911)

Rudolph Laubenheimer, a German by birth who settled in New York about 1855, enshrined the story of George Washington and the cherry tree (true or utrue) in metal in connection with the International Exposition in Philadelphia in 1876.

1876 CENTENNIAL

289D	1859	WM	51mm	80.00	—	250.

As 289A. Plain edge. Rarity 8. (Marvin 266; Clark sale, lot 2060; Hirsch coll.)

289E	1859	Gilt/WM	51mm	—	—	300.

As 289. Plain edge. (Schuster coll.)

289F	1859	Brass	51mm	—	—	125.

As 289. Plain edge. (Schuster coll.)

289G	ND	Silver	50mm	—	—	250.

Obverse as 289. Rv: Blank, except multiple-lined circle appears. Plain edge. Rarity 9. (Clark sale, lot 2061)

289H	ND	WM	50mm	—	—	125.

As 289E. Plain edge. Rarity 8.

Struck 1859

Baker	Date	Metal	Size	VF	EF	Proof
289S	ND	Silver	51mm	—	Unique	—

Obverse as 289A. Rv: Allegory of three toga-draped females working with a hand-screw coining press. Under the exergue line, at left: G.H. LOVETT. Plain edge. (Garrett 1839)

Second obverse

Baker	Date	Metal	Size	VF	EF	Proof
290	1859	Bronze	50mm	—	—	200.

Baker	Date	Metal	Size	VF	EF	Unc
293	1876	Silver	32mm	—	—	200.

Draped bust left, WASHINGTON and crossed palm branches below. Around: ****** . ****** / 1776 100TH YEAR OF OUR 1876 / NATIONAL INDEPENDENCE. Rv: Mosaic, pillars and symbols scene similar to the reverse of Baker 289, in reduced size, all within a circular wreath of oak. Plain edge. (Marvin 268; Clark sale, lots 2067 and 2068) Only 6 struck.

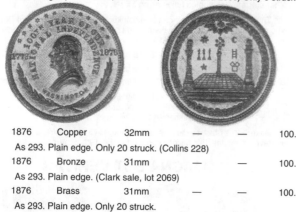

Baker	Date	Metal	Size	VF	EF	Unc
293A	1876	Copper	32mm	—	—	100.

As 293. Plain edge. Only 20 struck. (Collins 228)

293B	1876	Bronze	31mm	—	—	100.

As 293. Plain edge. (Clark sale, lot 2069)

293C	1876	Brass	31mm	—	—	100.

As 293. Plain edge. Only 20 struck.

The obverse die broke when the limited mintages recorded had been struck, according to Holland's list of centennial medals in *American Journal of Numismatics* for Oct., 1878.

BOSTON MASONIC TEMPLE

Struck about 1862

Baker	Date	Metal	Size	VF	EF	Unc
294	1732	Silver	31mm	—	—	225.

Obverse as Baker 122 (undraped bust right, MERRIAM under bust; GEORGE WASHINGTON. BORN FEBRUARY 22. 1732. around). Rv: View of the temple. On the curb: W. N. WEEDEN. MASONIC TEMPLE above, BOSTON below. Plain edge. (Marvin 269)

294A	1732	Bronze	31mm	—	—	90.00

As 294. Plain edge. Under 30 struck. Rarity 8. (Clark sale, lot 2073)

294B	1732	WM	31mm	—	—	90.00

As 294. Plain edge. (Clark sale, lot 2074)

William T. R. Marvin reported that less than 30 pieces of 294 -- in all metals -- had been struck. The Boston Masonic Temple was destroyed by fire on April 5, 1864. (See Russ Rulau's *U.S. Trade Tokens 1866-1889* for tie-in numismatic items of the destruction of this temple.)

NEW BOSTON TEMPLE

Struck 1867

Baker	Date	Metal	Size	VF	EF	Unc
295	1867	Bronze	31mm	—	—	75.00

Obverse as 294. Rv: NEW MASONIC TEMPLE / (radiant seeing eye) / DEDICATED / JUNE 24. A. L. 5867 / CHAS. C. DAME / (square and compass) / GRAND MASTER. Plain edge. Rarity 8.

There is an interesting muling of the reverse of Baker 294 (the old temple) with the reverse of 295 (text about the new temple), in white metal, recorded as a commemorative token in Rulau's 1866-1889 store card reference as number Ma-Bo 60. Such mulings were made about 1871 or later by Merriam's successors.

FREDERICKSBURGH LODGE

Lovett issues

Error reverse

Baker	Date	Metal	Size	VF	EF	Unc
296	1752	Silver	28mm	—	—	22

Bust right, LOVETT on truncation and G.H.L. beneath bust. Around GEORGE WASHINGTON. Rv: Square, compass and G within cent circle. Around: INITD. IN FREDERICKSBURGH LODGE, MD. / NOV. 1752. Plain edge. (Marvin 270; Clark sale, lot 2075; PCAC sale 58, 24, in July, 1995)

296A	1752	Copper	28mm	—	—	10

As 296. Plain edge. Rarity 8. (Clark sale, lot 2076)

296B	1752	Brass	28mm	—	—	10

As 296. Plain edge.

There were only 10 medals struck in all metals when the error 'MD.' was di covered, instead of 'VA.'. The reverse die was then destroyed by George Hampde Lovett. Possibly more than 10 were struck.

A copy of 296B exists with a partially corrected state name attempting to co rect MD to VA. This may have been done by the engraver, but we doubt it. (PCA Dec. 1993 sale, lot 83, ex-Fuld, Brand, Hall)

Correct reverse

Baker	Date	Metal	Size	VF	EF	Unc
297	1752	Silver	28mm	—	—	15

Obverse as 296. Rv: Square, compass and G with central circle Around: INITD. IN FREDERICKSBURGH LODGE NO. 4 VIRGINIA NOV. 4. 5752. Plain edge. (Marvin 271). Only 10 struck.

297A	1752	Copper	28mm	—	—	85.0

As 297. Plain edge. Only 25 struck.

297B	1752	Brass	28mm	—	—	85.0

As 297. Plain edge. Only 25 struck.

George Hampden Lovett seemed to have bad luck with the Fredericksburg Lodge medals. First the wrong state on 296, and then the dies broke on 297 afte the small mintages recorded by William T.R. Marvin.

WASHINGTON LODGE NO. 59

Baker	Date	Metal	Size	VF	EF	Unc
M-297	1893	Bronze	35mm	—	35.00	50.00

Civil bust facing three-quarters left, 1793 1893 around. Rv: CENTENNI AL ANNIVERSARY / OF THE / CONSTITUTION / OF / WASHINGTON LODGE / NO. 59. F. & A.M. / PHILADELPHIA / PA. / JUNE 24. 1893 Plain edge. (Marvin 1128; Bullowa-Lessin sale, lot 15)

M-297A	1893	WM	35mm	—	30.00	45.00

As M-297. (Schuster coll.)

M-297E	1893	Lead	Irreg 46mm	—	Unique	?

Lead die splasher (struck without collar) of obverse of M-297. Rv: Blank. (Kirt-ley Feb. 10, 1998 sale, lot W056)

WASHINGTON LODGE

Roxbury, Mass.

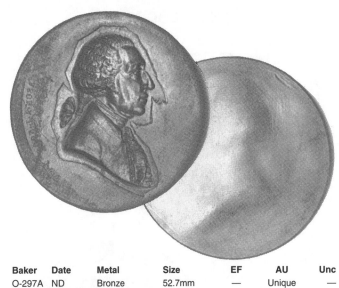

Baker	Date	Metal	Size	EF	Unc	Proof
N-297	1896	Bronze	39mm	—	—	60.00

Washington head left, within circle. Around: WASHINGTON LODGE OF A.F. & A.M. / .1796. CENTENARY .1896. Rv: Compass and square on open book lettered HOLY BIBLE, radiant G above, all within circle. Around: FAITH: HOPE: CHARITY +. Plain edge. Issued with mounted loop. (Marvin 1176; Bullowa-Lessin sale, lot 14)

Pristine originals still have attached their suspension pin, a scroll, compass and square arrangement of metal, with the scroll reading: ROXBURY, MASS. (see illustration above).

GRAND LODGE OF PENNSYLVANIA

Baker	Date	Metal	Size	EF	AU	Unc
O-297A	ND	Bronze	52.7mm	—	Unique	—

Hub punch impression of obverse of O-297. Portions of legend (illegible) appear at left. Rv: Blank, bulged. Plain edge. (Irving Schuster coll. in bright Unc)

Illustration reduced

Struck 1967

Baker	Date	Metal	Size	EF	AU	Unc
O-297F	ND	Bronze	76mm	—	—	35.00

Washington at prayer right, tiny DELUE S.C. on right ground. Above: WASHINGTON AT PRAYER. In exergue: FREEDOMS FOUNDATION / (sprays) / VALLEY FORGE. Rv: Variation of reverse of O-297 from new dies; the Apollo head less leonine. (Kirtley May 26, 1998 sale, lot C12)

Dies cut by Donald DeLue. Struck by Medallic Art Co., New York

Struck 1902

Baker	Date	Metal	Size	EF	Unc	Proof
O-297	5902	Bronze	52mm	65.00	90.00	—

Civil bust left. Around: SESQUI-CENTENNIAL. OF. WASHINGTON'S. INITIATION. AS. A. FREEMASON. A.L. 5902. Under the bust: E.A. NOV. 4.5752. / F.C. MAR.8.5753 / M.M.AUG.4.5653. Rv: Radiant leonine Apollo head facing at center, GRAND LODGE OF PENNSYLVANIA around, VIRTUTE SILENTIO AMORE below. Plain edge. Rarity 6. (Leon Hendrickson coll.; Collins 231)

Though unsigned, this medal may be the work of August C. Frank Co. of Philadelphia.

Baker	Date	Metal	Size	EF	AU	Unc
O-297G	1976	Bronze	76mm	—	—	35.00

Obv: As O-297F. Rv: JOHN L. McCAIN AMERICAN 1976 BICENTENNIAL around inner circle inscribed: R.W. GRAND MASTER OF MASONS IN PENNSYLVANIA around triangle center with radiant Apollo face.

PHILO LODGE 444

Struck 1902

Baker	Date	Metal	Size	VF	EF	Unc
PA-297	1902	Bronze	51.4mm	—	50.00	70.00

Nude bust left, tiny FRANK under truncation. Around: SESQUI-CEN-TENNIAL OF THE INITIATION OF WASHINGTON INTO FREEMA-SONRY / .NOV. 4.A.L. 5752. Rv: Jugate busts left of Tennis and Kinsey. Above: PHILO LODGE, NO. 444, F.&A.M. PHILADELPHIA. Below: EDGAR A. TENNIS R.W. GRAND MASTER. JOHN L. KINSEY WOR-SHIPFUL MASTER / NOVEMBER 29. A.D. 1902. Plain edge. (Dr. Schuster coll.)

Struck by the August C. Frank Co., Philadelphia. This bust punch is also used on Baker 945 thirty years later.

HOLY BIBLE MEDALS

Photo enlarged

Baker	Date	Metal	Size	VF	EF	Unc
299	ND	Silver	18mm	25.00	—	75.00

Undraped Washington bust right. Rv: Open Bible, on which are the com-pass, square and G. Plain edge. (Marvin 272; Clark sale, lot 2084)

299A	ND	Copper	18mm	—	—	25.00

As 299. Plain edge.

299B	ND	Brass	18mm	—	—	25.00

As 299. Plain edge. (Clark sale, lots 2084-2085)

299C	ND	Nickel	18mm	—	—	25.00

As 299. Plain edge. Magnetic.

299D	ND	WM	18mm	—	—	25.00

As 299. Plain edge.

These medals were published by George B. Soley of Philadelphia using a re-duction of Duvivier's head on Washington Before Boston medal. This and numbers 300 and 301 resemble the U.S. Mint medals of the period. A number of specimens of 299, including some in prooflike Unc., have been holed for suspension.

PAQUET HEAD

Baker	Date	Metal	Size	VF	EF	Proof
300	ND	Silver	18mm	—	—	75.00

Undraped bust facing right. (The head is larger and quite different than that on 299). Rv: As reverse of 299. Plain edge. (Marvin 273; Garrett 1842)

300A	ND	Copper	18mm	—	—	25.00

As 300. Plain edge. (Clark sale, lot 2086)

300B	ND	Bronze	18mm	—	—	25.00

As 300. Plain edge.

300C	ND	Brass	18mm	—	—	25.00

As 300. Plain edge. (Clark sale, lot 2086)

300D	ND	Gilt/Bz	18mm	—	—	25.00

As 300. Plain edge.

300E	ND	WM	18mm	—	—	25.00

As 300. Plain edge.

The Washington effigy was modeled by Anthony C. Paquet.

		Paquet bust right				
Baker	Date	Metal	Size	VF	EF	Unc
301	ND	Silver	18mm	—	—	75.00

Bust in civil dress right, AP on truncation of the bust. Rv: As reverse of 299. Plain edge. (Marvin 274; Garrett 1842)

301A	ND	Copper	18mm	—	—	25.00

As 301. Plain edge. Rarity 5. (Clark sale, lot 2087)

301B	ND	Brass	18mm	—	—	25.00

As 301. Plain edge. Rarity 5.

301C	ND	Gilt/B	18mm	—	—	25.00

As 301. Plain edge. Rarity 5.

301D	ND	Nickel	18mm	—	—	25.00

As 301. Plain edge. Magnetic. Rarity 7.

301E	ND	WM	18mm	—	—	25.00

As 301. Plain edge. Rarity 5.

Military bust

301J	ND	Gilt/Brass	16mm	—	—	85.00

Military bust right, K on truncation of bust. Rv: All-seeing eye above open Bible on which Masonic emblem is superimposed. Plain edge. (Clark coll., lot 2088; Collins 234)

Baker 301J was unpublished until the Dr. Glenn M. Clark collection was sold by Herbert I. Melnick Inc. on Feb. 17-18, 1984, though this piece had appeared as lot 2254 in the Hall collection sale.

FORTITUDE, PRUDENCE

Baker	Date	Metal	Size	VF	EF	Proof
302	1799	Silver	33mm	—	—	200.00

Obverse as Baker 286 (civil bust three-quarters left, KEY on truncation, with 1732-1799 below). Rv: Square, compasses and rule within an open wreath of acacia and olive. Above, a radiant 6-pointed star on which the G is incused. Above: FORTITUDE, PRUDENCE, JUSTICE. Along low-er rim: HARZFELD'S SERIES. Plain edge. (Marvin 275; Garrett 1843; Clark sale, lot of 2089)

302A	1799	Bronze	33mm	—	—	50.00

As 302. Plain edge.

302B	1799	Brass	33mm	—	—	50.00

As 302. Plain edge.

302C	1799	WM	33mm	—	—	50.00

As 302. Plain edge.

Sigmund K. Harzfeld commissioned William H. Key to strike this medal series for him, probably about 1877.

Second Obverse

Baker	Date	Metal	Size	VF	EF	Unc
303	1799	Silver	33mm	—	—	250.

Obverse as Baker 287 (obverse die similar to 302 but with GEORGE WASHINGTONadded around bust). Rv: As reverse of 302. Plain edge. (Clark sale, lot 2094)

303A	1799	Bronze	33mm	—	—	50.00

As 303. Plain edge. Rarity 6. (Collins 235)

303B	1799	Brass	33mm	—	—	40.00

As 303. Plain edge.

303C	1799	WM	33mm	—	—	70.00

As 303. Plain edge. Rarity 6. (Collins 236)

Sigmund K. Harzfeld and William H. Key collaborated on Baker 303. See Baker 302 and 286 and 287.

SOLOMON'S LODGE

Struck Ca. 1870's

Baker	Date	Metal	Size	VF	EF	Unc
304	1782	Silver	33mm	—	—	250.

Draped bust left within square-and-compass. Legend: "BRO. GEO. WASHINGTON COMMANDER-IN-CHIEF" / VISITED THE LODGE / DEC. 27. 1782. Rv: Within central circle: SOLOMON'S-LODGE, NO. 1. PO'KEEPSIE / N.Y. / FOUNDED / APRIL 18, 1771. / (scroll in triangular form, on which is: JAS. LIVINGSTON. ESQ. FIRST MASTER) / WOOD'S SERIES "C" NO. 2 I.F.W. DES. G.H.L. FEC. Around the outside of the circle: * KING SOLOMON SENT AND FETCHED * A WIDOW'S SON * FILLED WITH WISDOM AND UNDERSTANDING. Plain edge. (Marvin 307: Clark sale, lot 2096). Only 15 struck.

304A	1782	Copper	34mm	—	40.00	75.00

As 304. Plain edge. Only 50 struck. Rarity 7. (Clark sale, lots 2097-2098)

304B	1782	Bronze	33mm	—	—	75.00

As 304. Plain edge. Rarity 6.

304C	1782	Brass	33mm	—	—	75.00

As 304. Plain edge. Rarity 6.

304D	1782	WM	33mm	—	—	40.00

As 304. Plain edge. Rarity 5. (Collins 239)

The commemorative "visit" medal for the Poughkeepsie, N.Y. Lodge No. 1 was the work of engraver George Hampden Lovett and medal publisher Isaac F. Wood. Struck circa the 1870's.

KEYSTONE

Baker	Date	Metal	Size	VF	EF	Unc
305	ND	Gold	10mm	—	—	150.

Undraped Washington bust right. Rv: Keystone at center, on which are square and compasses enclosing a radiant all-seeing eye. Trowel to left, gavel to right, slipper at bottom, Reeded edge. (Marvin 326). Rarity 8.

305A	ND	Silver	10mm	—	—	75.00

As 305. Reeded edge. Rarity 6. (Clark sale, lot 2102)

305B	ND	Copper	10mm	—	—	10.00

As 305. Reeded edge. Rarity 6. (Clark sale, 2102)

305C	ND	Brass	10mm	—	—	10.00

As 305. Reeded edge. Rarity 6. (Garrett 1844)

305D	ND	WM	10mm	—	—	10.00

As 305. Reeded edge. Rarity 6.

305F	ND	Gold	10mm	—	—	100.

Obverse as 305. Rv: Blank. Reeded edge. Rarity 8.

305G	ND	Silver	10mm	—	—	25.00

As 305F. Reeded edge. Rarity 6. (Clark sale, lot 2103)

305H	ND	Copper	10mm	—	—	10.00

As 305F. Reeded edge. Rarity 6. (Clark sale, lot 2103)

305J	ND	Brass	10mm	—	—	10.00

As 305F. Reeded edge. Rarity 6. (Clark sale, lot 2103)

305K	ND	WM	10mm	—	—	10.00

As 305F. Reeded edge. Rarity 6.

MOUNT VERNON CHAPTER

Baker	Date	Metal	Size	VF	EF	Proof
306	1799	Silver	31mm	—	—	250.

Undraped bust right, I.F.W. - G.H.L. under bust. Around: "TRUE, AND WISE, AND MERCIFUL AND JUST." / 1732-99. Rv: Washington's tomb at Mount Vernon within central circle. Around: MOUNT VERNON CHAPTER NO. 228 R:A:M: / MNT. VERNON. N.Y. Plain edge. (Marvin 704; Clark sale, lots 2104-2105). Only 15 struck. (King 494)

306A	1799	Bronze	31mm	—	—	50.00

As 306. Plain edge. Rarity 7. (Clark sale, lot 2106; E. King 494B; Collins 240)

306B	1799	Aluminum	31mm	—	—	35.00

As 306. Plain edge. Rarity 4. (King 494A)

Baker	Date	Metal	Size	VF	EF	Proof
306C	1799	WM	31mm	—	—	30.00

As 306. Plain edge. Rarity 4. (Garrett 1844; Clark sale, lot 2107; Virgil Brand sale, lot 1212; Collins 241)

Dies were cut by George Hampden Lovett, commissioned for the task by publisher Isaac F. Wood, both of New York City.

Chicago collector Virgil M. Brand, a natural hoarder, put away 45 pieces of Baker 306C in white metal in proof condition and these were sold off in 1984 in the Brand sale catalog by Bowers & Merena Galleries, Wolfeboro, N.H. The hoard is now mostly dissipated.

Sale of the Brand hoard of Proof 306B medals dropped their Rarity from 8 to 4.

MASONIC BOARD OF RELIEF

Baker	Date	Metal	Size	VF	EF	Unc
A306	1891	WM	38.5mm	—	—	30.00

All-seeing eye and rays above Capitol. Around: MASONIC BOARD OF RELIEF / WASHINGTON D.C. Rv: Washington national monument. Around: 6TH ANNUAL MEETING GEN'L MASONIC RELIEF ASSOC'N / UNITED STATES AND CANADA / SEP. 23-25, 1891. (Roelofs coll.)

PLUMB, LEVEL AND SQUARE

First obverse

Baker	Date	Metal	Size	VF	EF	Proof
307	ND	Silver	28mm	—	—	Rare

Draped bust left within olive wreath. Around (below): WASHINGTON THE FATHER OF OUR COUNTRY. Rv: Radiant all-seeing eye above plumb, level and square. Plain edge (Marvin 706; Garrett 1845). Only 3 or 4 struck.

307A	ND	Copper	28mm	—	—	50.00

As 307. Plain edge. Rarity 8. (Clark sale, lot 2108; Collins 242)

307B	ND	Bronze	28mm	—	—	50.00

As 307. Plain edge. Rarity 8. (Clark sale, lot 2109)

307C	ND	Brass	28mm	—	—	50.00

As 307. Plain edge. Rarity 8. (Collins 243)

Second obverse

Baker	Date	Metal	Size	VF	EF	Proof
308	ND	Copper	28mm	—	—	50.00

Undraped bust right, LOVETT on truncation and G.H.L. under bust. GEORGE WASHINGTON around (same obverse as Baker 296). Rv: As reverse of 307. Plain edge. Rarity 8. (Clark sale, lots 2110-2112)

308A	ND	WM	28mm	—	—	50.00

As 308. Plain edge. Rarity 8. (Collins 244)

Third obverse
Struck 1875

Baker	Date	Metal	Size	VF	EF	Proof
309	1875	Copper	28mm	—	—	50.00

Undraped bust right, LOVETT on truncation, monogram GW beneath the bust. Around: 1775 -- 100 YEARS -- 1875 / I. F. W. DES. G.H.L. FEC. Plain edge. Rarity 8. (Clark sale, lots 2113-2114; Collins 245)

Baker 307 through 309 are the work of George Hampden Lovett, and 309 was published by Isaac F. Wood. The undated 307 and 308 types were probably struck about 1875.

The obverse die on 309 was intended for a larger flan. See Baker 436.

LAKE CITY LODGE

Struck 1875

Baker	Date	Metal	Size	VF	EF	Proof
310	1875	Copper	28mm	—	—	—

Obverse as 309. Rv: Within a beaded circle: LAKE / CITY, / FLA. / G.H.L. Outside circle: LAKE CITY LODGE NO. 27 +. Plain edge. Rarity 7. (Clark sale, lot 2115)

310A	1875	WM	28mm	—	—	—

As 310. Plain edge. Rarity 7.

PITTSBURGH BIRTHDAY MEDAL

Baker	Date	Metal	Size	EF	AU	Unc
A-310	1896	WM	32mm	27.50	35.00	—

Houdon bust right in circle. On wide dentilated border: WASHINGTONS BIRTHDAY CELEBRATION / * PITTSBURGH. PA. FEBY. 22. 1896. * Rv: Open-shield cartouche encloses compass, square and G. Around JR. -- O. -- U. -- A. M. Plain edge. (Kirtley March 31, 1998 sale, lot Q89 fetched $27.50 in holed EF)

JR. O. U. A. M. = Junior Order United American Mechanics. The compass-square-G attests its Masonic character.

SANTA BARBARA FAMILY

Santa Barbara, Calif.

Baker	Date	Metal	Size	EF	AU	Unc
C-310	1976	Bronze	35mm	—	6.00	11.00

Washington standing next to pedestal, G on medallion at upper left. Border: (nine Masonic symbols) /. GEORGE WASHINGTON - THE MASON. Rv: Pen, inkwell and unscrolled text. Around: SANTA BARBARA COUNTY MASONIC FAMILY /. 1776 - BICENTENNIAL - 1976. Plain edge.

PLEASANTVILLE NO. 886

Member's medal

Baker	Date	Metal	Size	EF	AU	Unc
E-310	1928	Bronze	29mm	—	—	15.00

Washington standing in room, right hand on Bible, tiny D. & C. c 1928 above shoulders. At lower left: GEN. / GEORGE / WASHINGTON / AS A / MASON. Wide border made up of many surnames in tiny letters. Rv: Wide bar for engraving a name, BRO. at its left end, superimposed over radiant compass-square-G and F & A M. Around: (incused) PLEAS-ANTVILLE (small rectangle) No. 886 / RAISED AS M. M. Plain edge. (Kirtley March 1998 sale, lot Q91; realized $13.20 in Unc)

Bro. = Brother. M.M. = Master Mason. Struck by Dieges & Clust of Boston. The diesinker's task on this medalet was made very difficult by the need to place so many surnames in a manner both readable under magnification and yet appearing to the casual viewer as a "pebbled" border.

CHICAGO 50TH ANNIVERSARY

Baker	Date	Metal	Size	EF	AU	Unc
G-310	1908	Bronze	57.2mm	—	50.00	

Civil bust facing 3/4 left. Around: WASHINGTON. CHAPTER. NO. 45. R. A. M. / * CHICAGO, ILL. *. Rv: Within wreath: COMMEMORATING / THE / 50th ANNIVERSARY / CHARTERED / OCTOBER 1st / 1858. Date 1908 on bow of wreath. Unpublished. Thick (6.2mm) flan. (Kirtley March 31, 1998 sale, lot Q83; realized a mere $17.23 although scarce; Irving Schuster coll.)

PAST MASTER'S JEWEL

NOTE: In this series, Baker 311 through 314, all pieces are supposedly unique. In this Bushnell series, only one specimen of each type in each metal was supposedly struck. Two specimens of 312 surfaced in the 1984 Clark sale by Herbert I. Melnick.

Baker	Date	Metal	Size	VF	EF	Unc
311	ND	Silver	28mm		Unique	

Washington head left within laurel wreath. Rv: Compasses, the points extended and supported by a curved gauge, blazing sun in center; surrounded by a plain band. Plain edge.

311A	ND	Copper	28mm	—	Unique	—

As 311. Plain edge.

311B	ND	Brass	28mm	—	Unique	—

As 311. Plain edge.

311C	ND	WM	28mm	—	Unique	—

As 311. Plain edge.

Second obverse

312	ND	Silver	28mm	—	2 known	

Head left, in a three-quarter wreath of laurel, WASHINGTON above (same obverse as Baker 152). Rv: As reverse of 311. Plain edge.

312A	ND	Copper	28mm	—	Unique	—

As 312. Plain edge.

312B	ND	Brass	28mm	—	Unique	—

As 312. Plain edge. (Clark sale, lot 2116)

312C	ND	WM	28mm	—	Unique	—

As 312. Plain edge. (Clark sale, lot 2117)

Third obverse

313	ND	Silver	28mm	—	Unique	—

Head left, GEORGE WASHINGTON around (same obverse as Baker 153). Rv: As reverse of 311. Plain edge.

Also struck in Copper, Brass and White Metal

Fourth obverse

314	ND	Silver	28mm	—	Unique	—

Head left, GEORGE THE GREAT around (same obverse as Baker 154). Rv: As reverse of 311. Plain edge.

Also struck in Copper, Brass and White Metal.

Charles Cushing Wright designed the dies, and a single set was struck off of numbers 311 through 314 for numismatist Charles I. Bushnell, who will be remembered for also having struck for his personal collection a number of Hard Times tokens of unusual design.

MASONRY IN BOTH AMERICAS

Struck 1970's

Baker	Date	Metal	Size	EF	AU	Unc
B-314	ND	Silver	40mm	—	—	47.50

Facing busts of (from left) George Washington, Benito Juarez and Jose Marti. Above is radiant all-seeing eye in triangle, with LIBERTAD IGUALDAD FRATERNIDAD around. Masonic emblems prove a border around all. Rv: Three South American liberators, (from top) Jose de San Martin, Simon Bolivar and Bernardo O'Higgins, radiant square and compass and G to their right, legend above: A LA MASONERIA DEL CONTINENTE AMERICANO, Masonic emblems provide a border around all. Weight 27.5 grams. (Grove M68a; Kirtley Feb. 10, 1998 sale, lot W062)

B-314A	ND	Gold	40mm	—	—	400.

As B-314. (Grove M68)

These medals were initiated by Cuernavaca, Mexico, Lodge 23, F. & A.M., and struck in Mexico City to the order of the numismatic House of Baron in the 1970's.

SUPREME COUNCIL

C-314	1975	Bronze	46mm	—	—	30.00

Washington standing, facing, his right hand on a Bible atop a pedestal, 175TH / YEAR at left, OCTOBER / 1975 at right, G-in-circle above. Around: WASHINGTON - SOLDIER - STATESMAN - FREEMASON / THE SUPREME COUNCIL, 33: S.J. U.S.A. Rv: Liberty Bell. (Kirtley Feb. 10, 1998 sale, lot W060)

TAMPA CONSISTORY

D-314	1952	CN	32mm	—	17.50	22.50

Washington stands facing, his right hand on a Bible on a pedestal, 1752 at left, 1952 at right. Around: GEORGE WASHINGTON / * BI-CENTENNIAL *. Rv: Double-headed eagle displayed, motto on scroll below. SPES MEA IN DEO EST. Around: TAMPA CONSISTORY No. 1, A. & A. S. R. / * VALLEY OF TAMPA *. (Kirtley March 31, 1998 sale, lot Q8)

This handsome medalet, unsigned, celebrates the 200th anniversary of Washington's taking the oath of Masonry, an event barely noted in numismatic annals. The double eagle is seldom used as a motif in medallic Americana.

ISAAC WOOD ISSUES

Struck 1870's

298	1799	Bronze	51mm	—	—	100.

Uniformed bust facing three-quarters left, framed at bottom by compass, square and GW monogram, and by scroll (on which: SUO - SE - ROBORE - FIRMAT). Above, an all-seeing eye casts rays downward across entire field of metal. Legend along bottom rim: HE WAS A BROTHER OF THE MYSTIC TIE. Rv: Seal of the Fredericksburgh Lodge at upper cener, Masonic emblems and dates Washington attained various degrees of Masonry are scattered. At bottom: I. F. WOOD, DES. G.H. LOVETT, FEC. Plain edge. Rarity 7.

298A	1799	WM	51mm	—	—	100.

As 298. Plain edge. Rarity 7.

298B	1799	Gilt/WM	51mm	—	—	200.

As 298. Plain edge. Rarity 9. (Clark sale, lot 2083)

MASONIC MARK PENNIES

The largest collection of Masonic mark pennies ever assembled occupied 53 pages in the Bowers & Merena Russell Patterson sale catalog of March 25-26, 1985, where the Virgil M. Brand collection was sold at public auction. The multi-thousand item sale contained a large number of unique or extremely rare off-metal strikes. The lots were offered in large groupings in most cases (that is, up to 100 different pieces in a single lot), so the high prices realized may have been in fact exaggeratedly low. Some pieces had never before (or since) been offered.

Your author Russ Rulau cataloged this section in late 1984 for Q. David Bowers. The timing of the sale, unfortunately, precluded its pricing outcome and newly-reported specimens to be reflected in the 1985 edition of the present Washington reference; Chapter 19 had already been typeset.

Now, with the advantage of 13 years' hindsight, all the Brand prices can be evaluated more methodically and additional illustrations included for many George Washington-connected lodge pennies.

All Masonic chapter pennies were issued in small quantities and frequently restruck based on demand, often from new dies. Many lodge pennies therefore are available with minor die variations. Specialist Rich Hartzog notes that he possesses 6 to 8 different die varieties from the same Rockford, Ill. chapter!

WASHINGTON CHAPTER 150

Washington, Pa.

Struck after 1910

Baker	Date	Metal	Size	VF	EF	Unc
P297	1828	Bronze	33mm	—	30.00	50.00

Undraped bust right. Around, in concentric lines: WASHINGTON ROYAL ARCH CHAPTER NO. 150 / CONSTITUTED FEB. 4TH 1828 / WASHINGTON, PA. Rv: Keystone against plain field, ONE PENNY in arc below. Plain edge. (King 234B)

P297A	1828	Silver	33mm	—	75.00	135.

As P-297. Plain edge. (King 234; B&M Brand sale, March 25-26, 1985, lot 1152)

P-297M	ND	Bronze	33mm	—	—	20.00

Muling of two reverse dies of type P-297. Plain edge.

Specimens of P-297 and P-297A from the Max Schwartz collection appeared as lots 1415-1416 in the Rich Hartzog sale of Sept. 4, 1984.

Issued ca. 1900

P297R	1828	Copper	32mm	—	10.00	25.00

ONE / PENNY in central circle, surrounded by two concentric circles lettered: WASHINGTON ROYAL ARCH CHAPTER NO. 150 WASHINGTON, PA. / CONSTITUTED FEB. 4TH 1828. Rv: Keystone letters H.T.W.S.S.T.K.S. in a circle. Plain edge. (King 5615)

Issued 1903

P-297S	1903	Copper	32mm	—	12.50	25.00

Obverse similar to P-297R, from different die. Rv: Keystone at center, 75TH ANNIVERSARY CELEBRATION above, NOV. 19", 1903 below. Plain edge. (King 5615a)

Types P-297M, 297R and 297S do not show a portrait of George Washington but cannot be disassociated from the other Chapter Pennies of this lodge.

Washington Chapter No. 150 is said to be the first chapter constituted as such by the Grand Chapter of Pennsylvania, though there are a few chapters with lower numbers. The other chapters apparently retained the old numbers under warrants of the Grand Lodge (the Harmony Chapter in Philadelphia was founded in 1794, preceding organization of the Grand Chapter, and the Jerusalem Chapter in Philadelphia was instituted in 1758, for example).

WASHINGTON CHAPTER 43

Chicago, III.

Struck after 1900

Q-297	1858	Copper*	32.2mm	—	15.00	30.00

Draped bust left, WASHINGTON CHAPTER NO. 43, R.A.M. / . CHICAGO . around. Rv: Keystone, CHARTERED OCT. 1ST, A.D. 1858 around, * ONE PENNY * in exergue. Plain edge. (King 235 and 235A; Collins 233)
* Both copper and oxidized copper specimens have been issued.

Q-297A	1858	Aluminum	32.5mm	—	15.00	30.00

As Q-297. Plain edge. (King 235B)

Q-297B	1858	Bronze	32.5mm	—	15.00	35.00

As Q-297. Plain edge. (King 235C)

Q-297C	—	Brass**	32.5mm	—	—	35.00

As Q-297. Plain edge. (King 235E)
** Antiqued brass.

Q-297D	1858	Silver	32.5mm	—	—	200.

As Q297. (Brand 1985 sale, lot 1032).

NOTE: E. A. King lists a die variety in bronze as 235D, but gives no description and we have not examined the piece.

WASHINGTON CHAPTER 2

Washington, D.C.

Struck after 1900

R-297	ND	Bronze	32.5mm	—	40.00	60.00

Civil bust facing three-quarters right, WASHINGTON CHAPTER NO. 2 R.A.M. / "A DAY'S WAGES" above, WASHINGTON, D.C. below. Rv: Keystone separates chisel (left) and mallet (right) ONE above, PENNY below. Plain edge. (King 239A, 239D)

R-297A	ND	Aluminum	32.5mm	—	50.00	70.00

As R-297. Plain edge. (King 239)

R-297B	ND	Silver	32.5mm	—	100.	150.

As R-297. Plain edge. (King 239B)

R-297C	ND	Brass	32.5mm	—	—	60.00

As R-297. Plain edge. (King 239C)

R-297D	ND	Gold	32.5mm	—	—	400.

As R-297. Plain edge. Unique. (King 239E)

There are three different die varieties of Type R-297, mostly distinguishable on reverse in the chisel and mallet. The aluminum piece is type 1, the silver and brass type 2 and the gold type 3. Bronze pieces are known in types 1 and 3. The differences are minor.

Struck since 1930?

R-297N	ND	Bronze	32mm	—	60.00	70.00

Small facing civil bust. Around: WASHINGTON CHAPTER NO. 2 R.A.M. / "A DAY'S WAGES" / WASHINGTON, D.C. Rv: Keystone between chisel and mallet, ONE PENNY above. (Kirtley March 1998 sale, lot Q94; realized $66 in choice AU)

Struck in 1920's

R-297G	ND	Copper	31mm	—	10.00	20.00

Obverse similar to R-297, from different, smaller die. Rv: Large keystone separates three crossed tools at left and chalice cup at right. Plain edge. (King 239F)

R-297H	ND	Bronze	31mm	—	10.00	20.00

As R-297G. Plain edge. (King 239J)

R-297J	ND	Silver	31mm	—	50.00	100.

As R-297G. Plain edge. (King 239G)

R-297K	ND	Aluminum	31mm	—	10.00	20.00

As R-297G. Plain edge. (King 239H)

R-297L	ND	Brass	31mm	—	10.00	20.00

As R-297G. Plain edge. (King 239I)

The legend "A day's wages" reflects one of the early symbols of Masonry, a denarius (penny) representing a day's wage for an able-bodied man. All legends and devices on Mark Pennies are steeped in symbolism.

WASHINGTON CHAPTER 2

Platteville, Wis.

Struck after 1900

S-297	1823	Copper	32.5mm	—	12.50	20.00

Undraped bust right, WASHINGTON CHAPTER NO. 2, R.A.M. - PLATEVILLE, WIS. around. Rv: Keystone at center, CHARTERED JUNE 5, 1823 around, * ONE PENNY * in exergue. Plain edge. (King 233)

S-297A	1823	Bronze	32.5mm	—	12.50	20.00

As S-297. Plain edge. (King 233A)

S-297F	1850	Copper	32.5mm	—	25.00	40.00

Obverse similar to S-297, from different dies. Rv: Keystone separates chisel (left) and mallet (right). CHARTERED AUG. 8TH. A.D. 1850 around, * ONE PENNY * in exergue. Plain edge. (King 233B; Wright 311)

S-297G	1850	Bronze	32.5mm	—	25.00	40.00

As S-297F. Plain edge. (King 233C)

Note the difference in charter dates in types S-297 and S-297F.

WASHINGTON CHAPTER 25

Akron, Ohio

Struck late 1880's

T-297	ND	Copper	29mm	—	200.	—

Undraped bust right in circle of 13 stars, WASHINGTON CHAPTER NO. 25. R.A.M. / AKRON, IND. around. Initials G.H.L. under bust. Rv: Keystone on triangle (Delta), ONE PENNY above, crossed chisel and mallet below. Plain edge. Rarity 9, (King 4984b); Brand 1985 sale, lot 1142)

T-297A	ND	Silver	29mm	—	200.	—

As T-297. Plain edge. Rarity 9. (King 4984C)

George Hampden Lovett executed the dies for Baker T-297 but erroneously placed 'IND.' instead of 'OHIO' on them. Samples sent to the chapter were returned and the order was refused and the dies destroyed. Years later, in 1927, a descendant of Lovett sent the samples to the chapter; probably they are the only extant specimens.

Struck 1890's

T-297C	ND	Copper	32mm	—	10.00	22.50

Obverse and reverse similar to T-297, in larger size, with 'OHIO' replacing 'IND.' on obverse. Plain edge. (King 4984a)

T-297E	ND	Copper	—mm	—	—	—

Shekel type Mark Penny. No description available. (King 4984)

Struck after 1900

T-297H	1841	Copper	35mm	—	8.50	20.00

Civil bust left, WASHINGTON CHAPTER NO. 25, R.A.M. around, AKRON, OHIO in exergue. Rv: Keystone within beaded circle, CHARTERED OCTOBER 25TH 1841 around, ONE PENNY in exergue. Plain edge. (King 237)

T-297J	1841	Bronze	35mm	—	8.50	20.00

As T-297H. Plain edge. (King 237D)

T-297K	1841	Aluminum	35mm	—	8.00	14.00

As T-297H. Plain edge. (King 237B)

T-297L	1841	Brass	35mm	—	10.00	16.50

As T-297H.

T-297M	1841	Silver	35mm	—	60.00	125.

As T-297H. Plain edge. (King 237A)

T-297N	1841	GS	35mm	—	—	85.00

As T-297H. Plain edge. (King 237E)

T-297P	1841	Gold	35mm	—	—	400.

As T-297H. Plain edge. (King 237F)

WASHINGTON CHAPTER 4

Muscatine, Iowa

Struck late 1880's

U-297	ND	Copper	29mm	—	25.00	35.00

Undraped bust right, G.H.L. under bust, WASHINGTON CHAPTER R. A. M. 4 / MUSCATINE, IOWA. around, .*.*.*. below. Rv: Large star at center, ONE above, PENNY below. Around rim, beaded circle encloses 16 stars. Plain edge. (King 2226E)

U-297A	ND	Silver	29mm	—	60.00	100.

As U-297. Plain edge. (King 2226F)

Both above struck by George Hampden Lovett of New York City. They are quite rare.

There are two different types of Washington Chapter 4 Mark Pennies listed by E. A. King, none described, and we have not examined so they cannot be cataloged here. They are copper, 33mm; copper and three off-metals, 31mm with wreath reverse, listed as King 2222 and 2226a through 2226d, respectively. Presumably none bears a Washington effigy.

Struck 1890's

U-297F	1852	Copper	31mm	—	—	25.00

In central circle: CHARTERED / SEPT. / 17, 1852. Around: WASHINGTON CHAPTER NO. 4 R.A.M. IOWA. Rv: Keystone separates chisel (left) and mallet (right), ONE PENNY above. Plain edge. (King 2223Y; Wright 312)

U-297G	1852	Bronze	31mm	—	—	25.00

As U-297F. Plain edge. (King 2226)

U-297H	1852	Brass	31mm	—	—	25.00

As U-297F. Plain edge. (King 2225; Wright 312)

U-297J	1852	Silver	31mm	—	—	200.

As U-297F. Plain edge. (King 2224; Wright 312)

U-297K	1852	Aluminum	31mm	—	—	10.00

As U-297F. Plain edge. (King 2224A; Wright 312)

Dr. Wright reports that U-297F thru 297K were struck in Minneapolis.

WALLA WALLA CHAPTER 1

Walla Walla, Wash.

V-297	1884	Copper	35mm	—	20.00	35.00

Civil bust facing three-quarters left, CHARTERED above, 1884 below, all within beaded circle. Around: WALLA WALLA CHAPTER NO. 1. R.A.M. / WALLA WALLA, WASH. Rv: Scene of a man at left beneath a tree facing four nude Indians, grain field in background and mountain range beyond that, over which sun rises. Below scene is radiant crossed crow, shovel and pickaxe, Triple Tau at left and Delta right. Above: "THEY RECEIVED EVERY MAN A PENNY". Plain edge. (King 238)

V-297A	1884	Bronze	35mm	—	20.00	35.00

As V-297. Plain edge. (King 238A)

The distinctive reverse die was also used on the Chapter Pennies of Ousatonic Chapter 33 in New Milford, Conn. (King 158 etc.), which have a standing Indian on obverse.

WASHINGTON CHAPTER 9

Richmond, Va.

W-297	1887	Silver	32mm	—	Rare	—

No description available. (King 6767)

Number W-297 probably resembles W-297C.

W-297C	1887	Copper	33mm	—	8.00	15.00

ONE / PENNY within central circle. Around, in two concentric circles: * RETURN TO WASHINGTON CHAPTER NO 9 R.A.M. RICHMOND, VA. / ...CHARTERED...OCT. 6, 1887. Rv: Keystone separates chisel (left) and mallet (right). Plain edge. (King 460)

W-297D	1887	Bronze	33mm	—	8.00	15.00

As W-297C. Plain edge. (King 460A)

GEORGE WASHINGTON CHAPTER 176

Chambersburg, Md.

X-297	?	Copper	?	—	10.00	15.00

No description available. (King 5638)

X-297A	?	Bronze	?	—	10.00	15.00

As X-297. (King 5639)

X-297B	?	Tin	?	—	Rare	—

As X-297. (King 5640)

WASHINGTON CHAPTER 15

Flint, Mich.

Struck 1890's

Y-297	1857	Copper	31mm	—	—	15.00

Rectangular tablet at center, FLINT above, MICH. below, each with sunburst. Around: WASHINGTON CHAPTER NO. 15, R.A.M., small star in exergue. Rv: Keystone separates chisel (left) and mallet (right). Around: CHARTERED JANUARY 14TH. 1857 / * ONE PENNY *. Plain edge. (King 28; Wright 149)

Y-297A	1857	Bronze	31mm	—	—	15.00

As Y-297. Plain edge. Thinner planchet. (King 28A)

Y-297C	1857	Copper	31mm	—	—	15.00

Similar to Y-297, from different die. No further description. (King 28b)

Y-297E	1857	Copper	31mm	—	—	Scarce

As Y-297, except that 'LODGE' is inscribed in error instead of 'CHAPTER' on obverse. Plain edge. (King 28c)

WASHINGTON CHAPTER 18

Portland, Ore.

Z-297	1881	Copper	34.5mm	—	80.00	—

WASHINGTON CHAPTER NO. 18 R.A.M. / ...... / ONE / PENNY / -. JUNE .- / 13 / ..1881.. / PORTLAND OR: Rv: Keystone in plain field. Plain edge. (King 5461; Wright 313; Brand 1985 sale, lot 1150)

WASHINGTON CHAPTER 2

Houston, Texas

ZA-297	ND	Copper	31mm	—	60.00	70.00

Small facing civil bust. Around: WASHINGTON CHAPTER NO. 2 / R.A.M. / HOUSTON, TEXAS. Rv: Keystone superimposed on crossed spade, crowbar, pickax and spray. ONE PENNY below. (Kirtley March 31, 1998 sale, lot Q93; fetched $66 in AU)

Chapter 20

STATUES, MONUMENTS, MEMORIALS

Among the statues of George Washington reproduced on medals, two are of particular significance:

The full length statue of the Father of His Country at Richmond, Virginia, is the only statue modeled from life (1796), by Jean Antoine Houdon. This statue was placed in position on May 14, 1796, 3 1/2 years before Washington's death.

The first equestrian statue erected to Washington's memory is that of Henry K. Brown in New York City, discussed in detail under Baker 248, which was dedicated July 4, 1856, on the 80th anniversary of the Declaration of Independence. The Brown statue became well-known in the world of numismatics through its strong usage on Civil War tokens, medalets and medallions.

The Houdon statue should not be confused with the Houdon portrait of Washington, which was completed by the same artist in October, 1785, and first used in medallic art on the Washington Before Boston medal, and which has come to be recognized as THE best medallic representation of the man.

Among monuments represented on medals, the Baltimore Monument, the shaft of which is surmounted by a full length statue of Washington, is the work of Andre Causici of Italy, completed in 1829.

The National Monument at Washington, an obelisk better known as the Washington Monument, had its cornerstone laid July 4, 1848. It was so long in completion that it was still unfinished when Baker was working on his *Medallic Portraits of Washington* manuscript in late 1883, and it became the object of satirizing on a medal series (Baker 321-322, in 1876).

The Washington Monument was dedicated in 1884. It is 555 feet high, is 16,000 square feet at its foundation, and weighs 36,912 tons.

Also in this chapter are covered other types of memorials, such as Baker 325 and 326, struck to commemorate the inauguration of the Cabinet of Washington Medals in the United States Mint at Philadelphia (now in the Smithsonian Institution). These were prepared by assistant Mint engraver Anthony C. Paquet in 1859 and 1860, and restrikes in yellow bronze could still be purchased from the U.S. Mint in recent years at modest cost.

HOUDON STATUE, RICHMOND

Struck ca. 1860

Baker	Date	Metal	Size	VF	EF	Proof
315	ND	Copper	27.8mm	—	—	250.

Roman-mantled Washington bust right, GEORGE WASHINGTON around (same obverse as Baker 124). Rv: Facing view of the Houdon statue. Around: WASHINGTON STATUE RICHMOND, VIRGINIA. Plain edge. Rarity 7. (Garrett 1846)

315A	ND	Silver	29mm	—	—	400.

As 315. Plain edge. (Witham coll.)

316	ND	Copper	29mm	—	—	250.

Undraped Washington bust left (same obverse as Baker 125). Rv: As reverse of 315. Plain edge. Rarity 7. (Garrett 1846)

Baker 315 and 316 are the work of George Hampden Lovett.

BROWN'S STATUE, NEW YORK

Struck 1861

Baker	Date	Metal	Size	VF	EF	Unc
317	1861	Silver	51mm	—	—	225.

Head right, G.H.L. under truncation, GEORGE WAHINGTON around, all within central circle. Outside circle, at top, is an eagle with a long ribbon in its beak, on which is: TALEM FERENT NULLUM SECLA FUTURA VIRUM. At bottom is the U.S. shield amid trophies of war. There are 45 stars intermingled with the long ribbon. (Same obverse as Baker 289). Rv: Brown's equestrian statue left, WASHINGTON STATUE UNION SQUARE, N.Y. around, MDCCCLXI/GHL in exergue. Plain edge. Rarity 8. (Garrett 1847)

317A	1861	Bronze	51mm	—	50.00	70.

As 317. Plain edge. Rarity 7. (Garrett 1847)

317B	1861	WM	51mm	—	125	160.

As 317. Plain edge. Rarity 7.

Small size, I

Baker	Date	Metal	Size	VF	EF	Proof
318	ND	Copper	28mm	—	70.00	100.

Obverse as Baker 315 (Roman-mantled bust right). Rv: Brown's equestrian statue left, enclosed by a railing, with a lamp at each side. Plain edge. Rarity 7. (Garrett 1848)

318A	ND	Silver	28mm	—	—	150.

As 318. (Witham coll.)

Small size, II

Baker	Date	Metal	Size	VF	EF	Proof
319	ND	Copper	28mm	—	75.00	100.

Obverse as Baker 316 (undraped bust left). Rv: As reverse of 318. Plain edge. Rarity 7. (Garrett 1848; Hirsch Coll.)

319A	ND	Silver	28mm	—	—	250.

As 319. Plain edge. (Witham coll.)

319F	ND	Copper	28mm	—	—	185.

Obverse as reverse of 318 (Brown's equestrian statue). Rv: As reverse of 316 (Houdon statue in Richmond). Plain edge. Rarity 4.

319G	ND	Silver	28mm	—	—	360.

As 319F.

PATER PATRIAE

Certain Latin terms appear on medals pertaining to George Washington, the first "General of the Armies of the United States." Only one other man held this title until the 5-star rank was created in World War II, and that was John J. Pershing, U.S. commander in France in WWI.

Pater Patriae (father of his country) is the apt title frequently appearing. Many other Latin words and phrases appear on items in this catalog; in most cases we have translated these for users.

WASHINGTON STATUE IN WALL STREET

NEW YORK STOCK EXCHANGE

AMERICAN NUMISMATIC SOCIETY

Baker	Date	Metal	Size	VF	EF	Unc
S-319	1883	Bronze	58mm	—	165.	185.

Standing statue of Washington, radiant, divides 1783 - 1883, 13 stars around rim. Rv: Three round seals across center. Above: TO COMMEMORATE / THE / CENTENNIAL ANNIVERSARY / OF THE EVACUATION OF NEW YORK / BY THE / BRITISH. Below: AND THE ERECTION / BY THE / CHAMBER OF COMMERCE / OF THE STATE OF NEW YORK OF THE / WASHINGTON STATUE / IN / WALL STREET. Plain edge. Convex Planchet. Only 332 struck. Rarity 4. (Collins 250)

Baker	Date	Metal	Size	VF	EF	Unc
S-319A	1883	Silver	58mm	—	—	400.

As S-319. Plain edge. (Ex-Fuld)

Published by the American Numismatic Society, this medal was designed by Charles Osborne of the ANS and engraved by Lea Ahlborn. It was struck at the Royal Swedish Mint, Stockholm.

Baker	Date	Metal	Size	VF	EF	Unc
T-319	1922	Bronze	70mm	—	70.00	100

Three men converse in foreground, a tree, two buildings and a stage coach in background. The scene, from 1792, shows the Tontine Coffee House in left background, the original stock exchange in New York City. Date 1792 in exergue. Rv: Rear view of the Washington statue in Wall Street facing toward the then-new (in 1922) stock exchange building. A left above: THE / NEW YORK / STOCK / EXCHANGE / 1922. Plain edge, with MACO markings. (Kirtley June 16, 1998 sale, lot B015)

This medal, struck by Medallic Art Co., New York, is little known and very scarce. Its scenes on each side reveal the growth of the New York Stock Exchange, the world's largest, from its inception in 1792 over 130 years. The NYSE was known as the Merchants Exchange in its earlier years.

For an interesting histopry of the Tontine Coffee House, see *The Standard Catalog of U.S. Tokens 1700-1900* by Russ Rulau, 2nd edition, 1997, Hard Times to kens segment.

Washington National Monument Society original donor's membership certificate. The cornerstone was laid 1848.

WASHINGTON MONUMENT
COMMENCEMENT

Baker	Date	Metal	Size	VF	EF	Unc
320	1848	WM	40mm	100.	165.	210.

Undraped Washington bust right. Around: THE FATHER OF HIS COUNTRY BORN FEB. 22, 1732. Rv: Imaginative depiction of the proposed monument at Washington, D.C. Around: NATIONAL MONUMENT. Below: JULY 4 1848. Plain edge. Rarity 7. (Garrett 1848; Bullowa-Lessin sale, lot 75; Collins 251)

Baker	Date	Metal	Size	VF	EF	Unc
320A	1848	Silver	40mm	—	2-3 Known	—

As 320. Plain edge.

Baker	Date	Metal	Size	VF	EF	Unc
320B	1848	Copper	37mm	—	150.	Rare

Shell of B-320 obverse, possibly a die trial. Ex Fuld, Presidential 62 11/97, lot 1114.

This medal shows the monument proposed by Robert Mills and is quite rare.The specimen in the Garrett sale catalog is holed at the top and- presumably for that reason - was lumped together with proof copper specimens of Baker 318 and 319 in a single lot, 1848. This relegation of such a significant piece is difficult to understand. All WM pieces seen are holed.

The designer of this medal is not known.

WOOD'S SERIES
Struck 1875

Baker	Date	Metal	Size	VF	EF	Proof
321	1876	Silver	39mm	—	—	385.

Undraped bust right, LOVETT on truncation. Around: 1775 - 100 YEARS - 1875 / I.F.W. DES G.H.L. FEC. All with central circle. Around, outside circle: FIRST IN WAR AND IN PEACE / * LAST IN SECURING *. Rv: Unfinished monument divides vertical WASHINGTON - D.C. Around: (PRESIDENCY OF U.S. GRANT) / WOOD'S SERIES "C" NO. 3. All in circle. Outside: A MONUMENT . / * CORNER STONE LAID 1848. COMPLETED 1876(?) *. Plain edge. Only 30 struck. Rarity 8. (Garrett 1849)

Baker	Date	Metal	Size	VF	EF	Proof
321A	1876	Bronze	39mm	—	45.00	60.00

As 321. Plain edge. Rarity 5. (Garrett 1850). The catalogers of the Garrett sale say this piece is actually copper with a bronzed surface.

Baker	Date	Metal	Size	VF	EF	Proof
321B	1876	WM	39mm	—	55.00	70.00

As 321. Plain edge. Rarity 5. (Collins 253)

Second reverse

Baker	Date	Metal	Size	VF	EF	Unc
322	1876	Silver	39mm	—	—	300

Obverse as 321. Rv: Similar to reverse of 321, but question mark in outer legend now precedes 1876 instead of following it. Plain edge. Rarity 8.

Baker	Date	Metal	Size	VF	EF	Unc
322A	1876	Bronze	39mm	—	—	45.00

As 322. Plain edge. Rarity 5.

Baker	Date	Metal	Size	VF	EF	Proof
322B	1876	Brass	39mm	—	—	45.00

As 322. Plain edge. Rarity 5.

Baker	Date	Metal	Size	VF	EF	Proof
322C	1876	WM	39mm	—	—	45.00

As 322. Plain edge. Rarity 5.

Designed and published by Isaac F. Wood and engraved by George Hampden Lovett, Baker 321 and 322 are satires on the unfinished Washington Monument "First in war and in peace, Last in securing a monument." These medals were struck in 1875, but Wood and Lovett had to wait nine more years, until 1884, before the obelisk was completed.

The American Journal of Numismatics for 1875, page 10, notes: "The issue in silver is strictly limited to 30." Isaac Wood is quoted as saying: "Any surplus over and above the cost of the medal that may accrue from its sale (an experience I have never yet realized), will be cheerfully devoted to the monument fund. Mayhap there will be enough to buy one brick. The idea of this medal was derived from a paragraph going the rounds of the papers last winter and credited New Orleans Picayune that 'Washington was first in war, first in peace, and last in getting a monument'."

The medals were distributed on July 3, 1875, the centenary of Washington's assumption of command of the Continental army before Boston. Wood originally intended the medals to be distributed for Washington's birthday, Feb. 22, but they were not ready in time.

DEDICATION

Baker	Date	Metal	Size	EF	Unc	Proof
M-322	1885	WM	31mm	20.00	30.00	—

Nude laureate bust left, 13 stars around head. Around: BORN FEBRUARY 22ND 1732/ - DIED DECEMBER 14th 1799. -Rv: Washington monument above crossed flags, sunrise in background, three rows of stars above. Below: CORNERSTONE LAID JULY 4, 1848 - DEDICATED FEB'Y 21, 1885. Plain edge.

Baker	Date	Metal	Size	EF	AU	UNC
N-322	1885	Silv/WM	45mm	70.00	90.00	—

Obverse as Baker E-452 (undraped bust left, GEORGE WASHINGTON around, the Chatham Artillery piece). Rv: Obelisk at center, WASHINGTON MONUMENT / COR. STONE LAID DEDICATED / JULY 4. 1848 FEB. 21. 1885 / 555 FT. HIGH / 81200 TONS around. In exergue: WASHINGTON D.C. Plain edge. Thick flan. (Kirtley March 31, 1998 Sale, lot Q97; realized $90.20 in AU.)

Interestingly, neither this medal nor the 1891 Chatham Artillery piece are signed, yet the unusual Houdon bust treatment is presented in high relief.

Baker	Date	Metal	Size	EF	AU	Unc
O-322	1885	Svd/WM	45mm	70.00	90.00	—

Bust right within thick open-top laurel wreath. GEORGE WASHINGTON around. Rv: As reverse of N-322. Unpublished. (Kirtley March 31, 1998 sale, lot Q98; fetched $78.10 in AU)

Baker	Date	Metal	Size	EF	AU	Unc
S-322	1885	Svd/WM	32mm	—	35.00	45.00

Nude periwigged bust right, GEORGE WASHINGTON around. Rv: Similar to reverse of P-322, in smaller size. Unpublished. (Kirtley March 31, 1998 sale, lot Q99; realized $30.25 in AU)

Baker	Date	Metal	Size	EF	AU	Unc
P-322	1885	WM	36mm	—	85.00	—

Houdon bust right in sunken circle, tiny underscored-T mongram (?) at lower left. Dentilated rim and wide pebbled border are matte surfaced. Rv: Obelisk separates: DEDICATED - - FEB. 21. 1885. Around: WASHINGTON NATIONAL MONUMENT. Unpublished. (Kirtley May 1997 sale, lot AD139; fetched $79.20 in AU)

SOUVENIR MEDALET

Baker	Date	Metal	Size	VF	EF	Unc
Q-322	ND	Svd/WM	18mm	27.50	—	—

Obelisk, WASHINGTON MT. above. Rv: SOUVENIR / OF / WASHINGTON, D.C. Crude work. (Kirtley May 1997 sale, lot AD140)

Souvenir, probably 19th century, but not necessarily connected with the 1885 dedication.

HIGH RELIEF MEDAL

Baker	Date	Metal	Size	EF	AU	Unc
R-322	1885	WM	45mm	75.00	85.00	—

High relief bust right, GEORGE WASHINGTON around. Rv: Obelisk. Around: WASHINGTON MONUMENT / COR. STONE LAID DEDICATED / July 4. 1848 Feb. 21.1885/

555 FT. HIGH / 81200 TONS / WASHINGTON, D.C. Unsigned. (H&K 145; Kirtley May 1997 sale, lot AD141; fetched $78.10 in AU)

BALTIMORE MONUMENT

Struck 1860's

Baker	Date	Metal	Size	VF	EF	Unc
323	1799	Silver	21mm	—	—	110.

Undraped bust left. Around: GEORGE WASHINGTON BORN 1732 DIED 1799 (same obverse as Baker 95). Rv: Elevation of Washington Monument at Baltimore, Md., legend around: MONUMENT AT BALTIMORE, all within olive wreath. Plain edge. Rarity 8. (Clark sale, lot 2118)

323A	1799	Copper	21mm	—	—	50.00

As 323. Plain edge. Rarity 4.

323B	1799	Bronze	21mm	—	—	20.00

As 323. Plain edge. Rarity 4.

323C	1799	Brass	21mm	—	27.50	40.00

As 323. Plain edge. Rarity 6.

323D	1799	Nickel	21mm	—	—	80.00

As 323. Plain edge. Magnetic. Rarity 7.

323E	1799	Svd/WM	21mm	—	—	40.00

As 323. Plain edge. Rarity 5.

George Hampden Lovett cut the dies for Baker 323.

BATTLE MONUMENT, BALTIMORE

Struck 1860's

Baker	Date	Metal	Size	VF	EF	Unc
324	1814	Silver	31.7mm	—	—	85.00

Roman-mantled bust right, GEORGE WASHINGTON around (same obverse as Baker 268). Rv: Elevation of the Battle Monument at Baltimore; on the enclosing wall: LOVETT PHILA. Around: NORTH POINT AND FORT McHENRY. SEPT. 12' & 13' 1814. Reeded edge. Rarity 7.

324A	1814	Copper	31mm	—	—	45.00

As 324. Reeded edge. Rarity 5.

324AA	1814	Copper	31mm	—	—	60.00

As 324. Plain edge. Rarity 8.

324B	1814	Bronze	31mm	—	—	45.00

As 324. Reeded edge. Rarity 5.

324C	1814	WM	31mm	—	—	55.00

As 324. Reeded edge. Rarity 5.

324D	1814	WM	31mm	—	—	60.00

As 324. Plain edge. Rarity 8.

The 1814 battle referred to on the medal is the same in which Francis Scott Key wrote The Star Spangled Banner. The monument, by the Italian Andre Causici, was completed in 1829. Robert Lovett Jr. of Philadelphia designed this medal, one of the more beautiful renderings in this chapter.

WASHINGTON MONUMENT AT PHILADELPHIA

SOUVENIR

Baker	Date	Metal	Size	VF	EF	Unc
T-324	1897	Brass	26mm	—	6.00	9.00

Undraped bust right, 1732 at left, 1799 at right. Rv: Monument divides two lines of text: WASHINGTON - MONUMENT/PHILA. - 1897. Plain edge. Rarity 2. Issued holed for suspension.

Baker	Date	Metal	Size	VF	EF	Unc
T-324	1897	Silver	26mm	—	—	22.50

As T-324. Plain edge. (Leon Hendrickson coll.)

Morgan Series

First Obverse
Designer "M"

Baker	Date	Metal	Size	EF	AU	Unc
U-324	1897	Bronze	35mm	—	60.00	80.00

Houdon bust right, small M on truncation. Around: GEORGE WASH-INGTON / 1789. Rv: Monument, WASHINGTON MONUMENT around 1897 in exergue. Unpublished. (Kirtley May 6, 1997 sale, lot AD136 fetched $90.20 in Unc)

Baker	Date	Metal	Size	EF	AU	Unc
U-324A	1897	WM	35mm	—	90.00	110

As U-324, prooflike fields. (Kirtley AD135, $104.50 realized in AU)

Second Obverse

Baker	Date	Metal	Size	EF	AU	Unc
U-324C	1897	Bronze	35mm	—	—	95.00

Civil bust three-quarters left, 1793 1893 around. Rv: Same as U-324 reverse. (Kirtley AD137, $90.20 in Unc)

Third Obverse

Baker	Date	Metal	Size	EF	AU	Unc
U-324E	1897	Bronze	35mm	—	—	14

Military bust right, Washington family coat of arms at left, G. WASHING-TON at right, scroll below. On scroll: EXITUS ACTA PROBAT. Rv: Same as U-324 reverse. Unpublished. (Kirtley AD 138; $138.60 in Unc)

Prices are still volatile in the "M" series. In Kirtley's March 31, 1998 sale, another Unc U-324 fetched $60.50, while another AU U-324A made $53.90.

M = George T. Morgan.

SOCIETY OF THE CINCINNATI

Baker	Date	Metal	Size	VF	EF	Unc
S-324	1897	Silver	76mm	—	—	450.

Detailed, intricate monument with equestrian George Washington uniformed at top. AUG. C. FRANK. PHILA. and PETER L. KRIDER CO. PHILA. under the statue. in four lines underneath: IN. COMMEMORA-TION.OF.THE.UNVEILING.OF.THE/ WASHINGTON.MONUMENT / AT.PHILADELPHIA. / MAY 15th, 1897. Rv: Seal of the society at center. Around: .SOCIETAS. CINCINNATORUM.INSTITUTA./.A.D. MDC-CLXXXIII. Plain edge. (Hume 4)

Baker	Date	Metal	Size	VF	EF	Unc
S-324A	1897	WM	76mm	—	175.	200.

As S-324. Plain edge. Rarity 6. (Rich Hartzog Sept. 4, 1984 sale, lot 2607; Collins 263)

Designed by Peter L. Krider and struck by the August C. Frank Co., both of Philadelphia. The medal is almost 10mm thick!

Prof. Rudolph Siemerling of Berlin, Germany accepted the commission of the Pennsylvania Cincinnati in 1877 to create a monument to Washington, and it was unveiled in Fairmount Park on May 15, 1897 by Pres. William McKinley. Also present were Vice President Garret Hobart, French Ambassador Jules Patenotre, the governors of Pennsylvania, Delaware and New Jersey, the mayors of Philadelphia and New York, the Secretaries of Treasury, War, Agriculture and Interior, Postmaster-General, Attorney-General, senior Army and Navy officers, the entire Pennsylvania General Assembly and many other dignitaries. The Cincinnati had begun collecting funds for this enterprise in 1810.

The presiding officer at the ceremonies was Major William Wayne, great-grandson of General 'Mad Anthony' Wayne of Revolutionary War fame. The silver-medal was presented to official guests and dignitaries at the unveiling ceremonies and banquet that evening.

HEART-SHAPED PENDANT

Baker	Date	Metal	Size	VF	EF	Unc
U-324J	ND	xx	38x44mm	—	22.50	—

xx Brass pendant, border and statue in brass against pinkish enamel field. Rv: Blank. No legends. Resembles Revolutionary War "purple heart" decoration. (Kirtley May 1997 sale, lot AD 145; brought $18.70 in EF)

WASHINGTON MONUMENT, ALLEGHENY PARK

Baker	Date	Metal	Size	VF	EF	Unc
M-324	1891	Silver	37mm	—	—	45.00

Facing civil bust within central circle, * GEORGE WASHINGTON FIRST PRESIDENT OF THE UNITED STATES around. Rv: Equestrian statue at center, WASHINGTON MONUMENT ALLEGHENY PARK, PA. / DEDICATED FEB. 23. 1891 around in concentric arcs. Plain edge. (ANS collection)

Baker	Date	Metal	Size	VF	EF	Unc
N-324	1891	Bronze	38mm	—	—	115.

Houdon bust right in depressed circle. On raised border: GENERAL GEORGE WASHINGTON *. Rv: Monument. Around: WASHINGTON MONUMENT ALLEGHENY PARK, PA. / DEDICATED FEB. 23. 1891. Unpublished. (Kirtley May 1997 sale, lot AD142; realized $108.90 in Unc)

JR. ORDER UNITED AMERICAN MECHANICS

Baker	Date	Metal	Size	VF	EF	Unc
P324	1891	WM	38mm	—	—	40.00

As obverse of Baker B324. Rv: Small arm and hammer within compass and square, bordered by outline shield. Around: ERECTED BY THE JR. ORDER UNITED AMERICAN MECHANICS (small star). Plain edge. (Hibler-Kappen 763 variety; PCAC Dec. 1995 sale, lot 1482; Reigh Roelofs coll.)

PAQUET BUST

Baker	Date	Metal	Size	VF	EF	Unc
PA324	1891	Bronze	38mm	—	—	50.00

Bust right by Paquet (as B279) in sunken circle. On raised border around: GENERAL GEORGE WASHINGTON / (small star). Rv: As reverse of M324. Plain edge. (Hibler-Kappen 763)

TRENTON BATTLE MONUMENT

B-324	1893	Brass	38mm	—	—	15.00

Undraped bust left, tiny BECHTEL TRENTON under truncation. Around: To COMMEMORATE THE BATTLE OF TRENTON, N.J. / .DECEMBER 26. 1776. Rv: Columnar monument with standing figure on top. Around: TRENTON BATTLE MONUMENT/ .CORNER STONE LAID DEC.28 1892 DEDICATED OCT.19.1893. Plain edge. Issued holed for suspension from tricolored ribbon, on which is printed: "ALL OUR HOPES / WERE BLASTED / BY THAT UNHAPPY / AFFAIR AT TRENTON" / LORD GERMAIN / BRITISH SEC OF STATE. The ribbon is mounted with a metallic hanger labeled SOUVENIR. (Leon Hendrickson coll.)

B-324 A	1893	Aluminum	38mm	—	—	15.00

As U-324. Plain edge.

These medals have been renumbered from U-324 and U-324A.

Baker	Date	Metal	Size	EF	AU	Unc
C-324	1893	Bronze	38mm	—	—	135.

Periwigged bust right, GENERAL WASHINGTON / 1776 around. Rv: Battle monument, partly surrounded by a medium-width raised scroll border. On scroll: TRENTON BATTLE MONUMENT OCT. 10. 1893. (Kirtley AD 132)

C-324A	1893	WM	38mm	—	80.00	90.00

As C-324. (Kirtley AD 131)

C-324B	1893	Bronze	**	—	75.00	—

** As C-324, attached to brass pin bar and red-white-blue ribbon. (Kirtley AD 133)

This beautiful C-324 series, unsigned, is unpublished. The first two appeared in Charles E. Kirtley's 42nd and 144th mail bid auctions. Kirtley numbers given above are for sale 144, May 6, 1997, with these prices realized: C-324 Unc, $121; C-324A lustrous BU, $66; C-324B, AU, $72.60.

D-324	1893	WM	38mm	—	—	175.

Houdon bust right in sunken circle. On wide raised border: GENERAL GEORGE WASHINGTON. Rv: Monument. Around, in two concentric circles within dentilated rim: TRENTONS REVOLUTIONARY BATTLE MONUMENT * / DEDICATED OCT. 19. 1893. Unsigned. Unpublished. (Kirtley AD 134)

In prooflike BU, D-324 realized $169.40 in the Kirtley May, 1997 sale.

TRENTON MONUMENT WITH SEALS

Baker	Date	Metal	Size	VF	EF	Unc
E324	1926	Svd/Copper	38mm	—	20.00	—

Monument between medallions containing seals of Trenton 1792 and New Jersey. Around: BATTLE MONUMENT / 1776-77 / TRENTON. Rv: Washington crossing the Delaware. Around: NEW JERSEY SESQUI-CENTENNIAL CELEBRATION / *1776-1926*. Plain edge. (H.J. Levine report)

FAIRMOUNT PARK MONUMENT

Baker	Date	Metal	Size	VF	EF	Unc
Q-324	1897	WM	32mm	—	35.00	50.00

Obverse as Baker 1831 thru 1833. Rv: Monument. Around: WASHINGTON MONUMENT FAIRMOUNT PARK PHILADA, PA. Below: DEDICATED / *MAY 15. 1897*. (Witham coll.)

Baker 1831 (1899), 1832 (1901) and 1833 (1902) use the obverse die of Baker Q-324 of 1897. The excellent obverse die is unsigned.

Q-324A	1897	Bronze	32mm	—	50.00	75.00

As Q-324. (Kirtley March 31, 1998 sale, lot Q106)

SOLDIERS MONUMENT

Bridgeport, Conn.

V-324	1888	Gilt/B	35mm	—	25.00	35.00

Nude bust right within circle of stars. Around: SOUVENIR, GRAND CELEBRATION AT / BRIDGEPORT, CONN. July 4, 1888. Rv: Monument with SOLDIERS MONUMENT SEA SIDE PARK around. Around all: BRIDGEPORT 1836-1888 / WE LIVE TO ADVANCE, NOT TO RECEDE. Plain edge. (Dr. Schuster coll.)

CAPITOL CORNERSTONE

Washington, D.C.

Released 1973?

Baker	Date	Metal	Size	EF	AU	Unc
X-324	1971	Bronze	63mm	—	—	40.00

Standing figure of Washington left in full Masonry regalia, applying mortar to a suspended cornerstone. Spread eagle above, medallions of U.S. Capitol at left and U.S. Senate shield at right. At lower right: CORNERSTONE / OF CAPITOL / .LAID./ SEPTEMBER 18TH / .1793./ Rv: Excellent rendering of Capitol rotunda's exterior. Signature incused at lower left: RALPH J. MENCONI / C 1971. Incused at lower right: AUTHORIZED / .BY./ THE UNITED/ STATES CAPITOL / HISTORICAL / SOCIETY. Four semicircular lines around rotunda, the outer of stars and inner three a lengthy inscription beginning WE THE PEOPLE. In exergue: A PLACE OF / RESOUNDING / DEEDS. (Kirtley Feb. 10, 1998 sale, lot W061)

Overall, this is a fine post-WWII medallic memento of George Washington. Intended for issuance in 1973, the 180th anniversary of the U.S. Capitol's Cornerstone laying. The figure of mason Washington is depicted much younger than his 61 years in 1793. Struck by Medallic Art Co.

Baker	Date	Metal	Size	VF	EF	Unc
Y-324	1893	Bronze	35mm	—	—	50.00

Houdon bust right, within sunken circle. Around: GEN. GEO. WASHINGTON / (arc of 13 stars). Rv: Capitol, WASHINGTON, D.C. on scroll at top. Around: CENTENNIAL OF LAYING / OF CORNER STONE / OF U.S. CAPITOL/SEP. 18. 1893. Unpublished. (Schuster coll.; Kirtley March 31, 1998 sale, lot Q3, fetched $46.70 in Unc)

MEMORIAL PORTAL AT BROOKLYN BRIDGE

Baker	Date	Metal	Size	VF	EF	Unc
Z-324	1928	Bronze	51.7mm	—	35.00	55.00

Small Washington bust within plaque surrounded by laurel sprays, at top. Multiline inscription about Washington's message to the troops at Long Island below. Rv: View of Memorial Portal to Brooklyn Bridge, MEMORIAL / PORTAL TO / BROOKLYN/ BRIDGE above, 1928 below. Lengthy legend around periphery and in arc below. Tiny signature LA VELLE at lower right of portal. Tiny J.G. GRAHAM, PRES. near bottom of medal. Unpublished. (Kirtley May 6, 1997 sale, lot AD 143; realized $50.60 in AU)

Dies cut by John LaVelle. Struck by Medallic Art Co., New York.

MINT CABINET MEMORIAL

Originals struck 1859

Baker	Date	Metal	Size	EF	Unc	Proof
325	1859	Gold	21mm	—	400.	—

Washington bust in civil dress, head facing right, AP on truncation. Around:

PATER PATRIAE. Rv: In 6 lines: A / MEMORIAL / OF THE / WASHINGTON / CABINET / MAY 1859, all within olive wreath. Plain edge. Rarity 8. (Garrett 1851)

325A	1859	Silver	21mm	—	75.00	—

As 325. Plain edge. Rarity 6. (Clark sale, lot 2119). Mintage: 510

| 325B | 1859 | Copper | 21mm | — | 27.50 | |

As 325. Plain edge. Rarity 5.

| 325C | 1859 | Bronze | 21mm | — | 27.50 | |

As 323. Plain edge. Thick (3.5mm)flan. Rarity 5.

| 325D | 1859 | Yellow Bronze | 21mm | — | 9.00 | |

As 323. Plain edge. Restrike, still available from the U.S. Mint.

The dies were cut by Anthony C. Pauquet and the medals struck at the Philadelphia Mint.

MINT CABINET MEDAL

Originals struck 1860

Baker	Date	Metal	Size	EF	Unc	Proof
326	1860	Silver	60mm	250.	—	600.

Undraped bust right in a sunken field srrounded by a raised border, Paquet. F. under bust. Around: GEORGE WASHINGTON * BORN FEB. 22 1732. * DIED DEC. 14 1799. * in the border. Rv: View of the upright case containing (the original arrangement) of Washington medals at the U.S. Mint, surmounted by a bust of Washington in civil dress, facing right, in a sunken field surrounded by a raised border. Around: WASHINGTON CABINET OF MEDALS, U.S. MINT.*INAUGURATED FEB. 22,1860. * in the border. Plain edge. Only 112 struck. Rarity 8. (Garrett 1853; Collins 268)

| 326A | 1860 | Bronze | 60mm | — | 75.00 | — |

As 326. Plain edge. Rarity 5. (Garrett 1854)

| 326B | 1860 | Yellow Bronze | 60mm | — | 15.00 | — |

As 326. Plain edge. Restrike, still available from the U.S. Mint; circa 1980.

Designed by Anthony C. Paquet and struck by the Philadelphia Mint.

Chapter 21

SOCIETY, ASSAY, AWARD MEDALS

WASHINGTON BENEVOLENT SOCIETY

New York

Struck 1808

Baker	Date	Metal	Size	EF	AU	Proof
327	1808	Silver	43mm	1500	2000	2500

Undraped bust right on a pedestal inscribed DEFENDER / OF HIS / COUNTRY, small letter R at the base. Goddess of Liberty with staff and Phrygian cap in her right hand, stands, about to place a laurel wreath on the bust with her left hand. Around: WASHINGTON BENEVOLENT SOCIETY. In exergue: 1808. Rv: Good Samaritan at left advances to succor a man on the floor. Small R in lower right corner. Above: BENEVOLENCE. In exergue: NEW-YORK. Plain edge. Rarity 6. (Raymond 30; Garrett 1855; Julian RF-23; Stack's 1991 sale, lot 157).

Both dies are the work of John Reich of Philadelphia. The U.S. Mint workmanship is superb.

The Washington Benevolent Societies were originally in 1808 charitable in purpose but starting about 1812 they became essentially Federalist Party organs, quietly opposed to the war with Great Britain, and eventually passed out of existence by about 1820.

WASHINGTON TEMPERANCE SOCIETY

Struck 1840's

Baker	Date	Metal	Size	VF	EF	Unc
328	ND	Copper	42mm	—	85.00	125.

Undraped bust right, LOVETT NY beneath bust. Around: WASHINGTON TEMPERANCE SOCIETY. Rv: Within oak wreath, clasped hands at top opening: (in 7 lines) WE AGREE TO ABSTAIN FROM ALL INTOXICATING LIQUORS EXCEPT FOR MEDICAL PURPOSES AND RELIGIOUS ORDINANCES. Around: TEMPERANCE DECLARATION / TEMPERANCE IS THE FOUNTAIN OF HEALTH. Plain edge. Rarity 5.

Baker	Date	Metal	Size	VF	EF	Unc
328A	ND	Bronze	42mm	—	85.00	125.

AS 328. Plain edge. Rarity 5.

Baker	Date	Metal	Size	VF	EF	Unc
328C	ND	Brass	42mm	—	85.00	125.

As 328. Plain edge. Rarity 5. (Bullowa-Lessin sale, lot 74).

Baker	Date	Metal	Size	VF	EF	Unc
328D	ND	WM	41.7mm	—	100.	—

As 328. Plain edge. Rarity 7. (Schuster coll.)

Dies engraved by Robert Lovett Sr. of New York City, father of the three talented brothers Robert Lovett Jr., George Hampden Lovett and John D. Lovett.

The Washington Temperance Society was an outgrowth of the Washington Society of Baltimore, organized in 1840 on a basis of total abstinence.

HOUSE OF TEMPERANCE

Struck 1840's

Baker	Date	Metal	Size	VF	EF	Unc
329	ND	Bronze	42mm	—	80.00	110

Obverse as 328. Rv: Scene of a home's interior with couple and child at round table, the husband (left) reading and wife fussing over her daughter. The scene is intended to show a family which uses no alcoholic beverages. In exergue: HOUSE OF / TEMPERANCE. Plain edges. Rarity 5. (Garrett 1856)

Baker	Date	Metal	Size	VF	EF	Unc
329A	ND	Brass	42mm	—	85.00	

As 329. Plain edge. Rarity 5.

Baker	Date	Metal	Size	VF	EF	Unc
329B	ND	WM	42mm	—	100.	125

As 329. Plain edge. Rarity 5. (Hirsch coll.)

A companion issue to 328, it was also designed by Robert Lovett Sr.

WASHINGTON TEMPERANCE BENEVOLENT SOCIETY

UNITED WE STAND

Baker	Date	Metal	Size	VF	EF	Unc
330	ND	WM	21mm	35.00	50.00	70.00

Head right. Around: WASHINGTON TEMPERANCE BENEVOLENT SOC. * . Rv: Two hands clasped at center, in the midst of a four-line legend: UNITED WE STAND DIVIDED WE FALL. Plain edge. Rarity 8. (Hirsch coll.)

Baker	Date	Metal	Size	VF	EF	Unc
330A	ND	Brass	21mm	35.00	50.00	70.00

As 330. Plain edge. Rarity 8.

TEMPERANCE FOUNTAIN

Baker	Date	Metal	Size	VF	EF	Unc
331	ND	WM	21mm	20.00	35.00	55.00

Obverse as 330. Rv: Flowing fountain at center; two birds stand on the edge drinking and two others are descending through the air. Ornament of scrollwork at bottom. Plain edge. Rarity 7.

It is not known who rendered the Houdon head on Baker 330 and 331. The medals may have been produced in the late 1840's.

TYRANT ALCOHOL

Roses and Leaves

Baker	Date	Metal	Size	VF	EF	Unc
332	ND	Silver	21mm	150.	200.	275

Head right within olive wreath, BALE below crossing of branches WASHINGTON TEMPERANCE BENEVOLENT SOCIETY. Around Rv: WE SERVE / THE TYRANT / ALCOHOL / NO LONGER, roses and leaves between the lines and a rose at either side. Reeded edge. Rarity 8. (PCAC May 1997, lot 187)

Baker	Date	Metal	Size	VF	EF	Unc
332A	ND	Copper	21mm	90.00	135.	170.

As 332. Reeded edge. Rarity 6.

| 332C | ND | Gold/S | 25mm | — | Unique | — |

As 332, but encased in a gold frame for use as a membership badge. (Fuld collection)

| 332D | ND | Silver | 21mm | — | Unique | — |

As 332. Plain edge.

Rosettes and periods

Baker	Date	Metal	Size	VF	EF	Unc
333	ND	Silver	21mm	150.	200.	275.

Obverse as 332, but bow added at base of wreath and BALE now beneath head. Rv: As reverse of 332, but rosettes are between lines of text, and a period is at either side. Reeded edge? Rarity 8. (Clark sale, lot 2120)

KING ALCOHOL

Struck 1840's

Baker	Date	Metal	Size	VF	EF	Unc
334	ND	Gilt/Brz	24mm	11.00	20.00	40.00

Washington head left, WASHINGTON UNITED STATES OF AMERICA around. Rv: In seven lines: TO THE CAUSE OF TEMPERANCE TEN DOLLARS TO KING ALCOHOL NOT ONE CENT. Reeded edge. Rarity 4.

This is the most commonly available Washington-head temperance piece. It must have been distributed in good quantities, much as political tokens of its day were. It is, in fact, a political - a temperance political. Its engraver or publisher are not known.

Specimens occur with gilt surfaces.

Some authorities believe 334 was struck in 1870's, long after temperance movements flourished.

HONOR TEMPERANCE

Baker	Date	Metal	Size	VF	EF	Unc
335	1844	Silver	18mm	300.	350.	400.

Undraped bust in a circle, at center of a 7-pointed star, SCHMIDT F. below the bust. Around: HONOR TEMPERANCE. Rv: IN HOC SIGNO VINCES in a circle, on a 7-pointed star. On six of the star's points: FOUNDED 22 FEB. 1844. Plain edge. (Wood 768; PCAC Nov. 1996 sale, lot 155). Only 6 specimens known. Rarity 8.

Solomon Schmidt was an obscure New Orleans diesinker who later engraved some Confederate notes.

ORDER UNITED AMERICAN MECHANICS

Struck 1860-1870

Baker	Date	Metal	Size	VF	EF	Unc
336	1789	Silver	25mm	—	90.00	125.

Roman-mantled bust right, R L on truncation. Around: GEN. GEORGE WASHINGTON. FIRST PRES. U.S. 1789. Rv: O.U. - A.M. divided by compasses and square enclosing arm and hammer. Around: HONESTY INDUSTRY AND SOBRIETY. Plain edge. Rarity 8.

| 336A | 1789 | Copper | 25mm | 55.00 | 70.00 | 90.00 |

As 336. Plain edge. Rarity 6.

Baker	Date	Metal	Size	VF	EF	Unc
336B	1789	Brass	25mm	—	70.00	90.00

As 336. Plain edge. Rarity 6.

| 336C | 1789 | Gilt/B | 25mm | — | 70.00 | 90.00 |

As 336. Plain edge. Rarity 6.

Robert Lovett Jr. of Philadelphia executed these dies.

MOBILE JOCKEY CLUB

While retaining their original Baker numbers, 337 and 337A, these have now been placed under Mobile, Alabama in Chapter 35, 19th Century Store Cards.

WASHINGTON MARKET CHOWDER CLUB

Baker	Date	Metal	Size	VG	F	EF
338	1818	Gold	24mm	—	—	30,000.

Small head right within olive wreath, MEMBERS above, BADGE below. Rv: WASHINGTON / MARKET / CHOWDER / CLUB / 1818. Plain edge. Unique (Levick 2529; Rulau-E NY 931; Raymond 41). In Ford coll.

| 338A | 1818 | Silver | 24mm | — | 2,000. | 3,000. |

As 338. Plain edge. 4 specimens known. (Rulau-E NY 930; Raymond 41; Norweb)

| 338B | 1818 | Copper | 24mm | — | — | — |

As 338. Plain edge. (Witham coll.)

| 338C | 1818 | Bronze | 24mm | — | — | — |

As 338. Plain edge. (Witham coll.)

| 338D | 1818 | WM | 24mm | — | — | — |

As 338. Plain edge. (Witham coll.)

The gold specimen realized $25,000 in the Bowers & Ruddy Galleries sale of the Garrett collection. It is not known who struck these pieces.

The club may have been a fraternal group, or a marching or singing organization. Nothing is known about it. Washington Market was a large 19th century open-air marketplace in New York City, erected 1771 on Dey Street at the river. It became known as Washington Market in 1812.

LANCASTER COUNTY A. & M. SOCIETY

Struck 1859-60

Baker	Date	Metal	Size	VF	EF	Proof
339	1858	Silver	45mm	—	100.	150.

Undraped bust right, KEY F. under bust, THE FARMER OF MOUNT VERNON below. Around all: LANCASTER CO AGRICULTURAL & MECHANICAL SOCIETY / .1858. Rv: Broken column, cogwheel, wheat sheaf, plow and farming implements, a stalk of corn at either side, all along lower rim. At top: AWARDED TO. Plain edge. Rarity 7. (Garrett 1859; Clark sale, lot 2121; Julian AM-27)

The piece in the Garrett sale was uninscribed. The piece in the Clark sale is engraved: KENDRICK & FLINN / FOR / SANDFORDS / CHALLENGE / HEATER / 1860.

339A	1858	Copper	45mm	—	90.00	115.

As 339. Plain edge. Rarity 5.

339B	1858	Bronze	45mm	—	97.00	125.

As 339. Plain edge. Rarity 5. (Garrett 1859)

The piece in the Garrett sale, a bronze proof, is engraved: HIRSH & BRO. / FOR SILK / UMBRELLAS / 1859.

339C	1858	WM	45mm	—	100.	

As 339. Plain edge. Rarity 7.

Struck ca. 1880

339D	1858	**	45.4mm	—	—	150.

** Black fiber.

As 339. Struck about 1880 from original dies. (PCAC 1988 Magriel sale, lot 062)

Dies by William H. Key. Mintages: Baker 339 - 85 pcs. Baker 339A - 130 pcs.

B'NAI B'RITH

Struck 1990

Baker	Date	Metal	Size	EF	AU	Unc
A339	ND	Bronze	63mm	—	—	40.00

Large stylized menorah dominates left side, view of synagogue at right center. Below: B'NAI B'RITH / AMERICAN / FREEDOM / SERIES. Along right border: IN THE TRADITION OF RELIGIOUS LIBERTY. Tiny A. GLICKMAN Sc along lower left rim. Rv: Civil bust right, tiny R. ADELMAN on truncation. At right:
... TO BIGOTRY / NO SANCTION. / TO PERSECUTION / NO ASSISTANCE / G Washington (signature) / LETTER TO THE / TOURO SYNAGOGUE / AUGUST 1790. Plain edge. (H. J. Levine report)

Obverse designed by A. Glickman and reverse by R. Adelman. Struck in Israel.

B'nai B'rith (Hebrew for "children of the Covenant") is a Jewish service organization founded in New York City 1843. Among its agencies is the Anti-Defamation League. International headquarters building in Washington, D.C., dedicated 1957, houses the B'nai B'rinth Klutznick museum. The organization claims 500,000 members worldwide.

UNION AGRICULTURAL SOCIETY

Originally struck 1858

Baker	Date	Metal	Size	VF	EF	Unc
340	1858	Silver	28mm	—	—	—

Undraped bust left in a sunken field surrounded by a raised border. Around: THE PATTERN OF PATRIOTISM, INDUSTRY AND PROGRESS. Rv: In an olive and oak wreath: UNION AGRICULTURAL SOC: OF RIDGEWAY & SHELBY. Around: ORGANIZED JULY 17th. 1858. Plain edge. Rarity 8.

340A	1858	WM	28mm	—	—	—

As 340. Plain edge. Rarity 8.

The obverse die appears to be the work of Charles Cushing Wright.

MECHANICS LITERARY ASSOCIATION

Rochester, N.Y.

Struck circa 1850

Baker	Date	Metal	Size	VF	EF	Unc
341	ND	Copper	42mm	—	—	—

Obverse as Baker 328 (undraped bust right, LOVETT NY beneath bust, WASHINGTON TEMPERANCE SOCIETY around). Rv: Franklin bust left, LOVETT NY under bust. Around: MECHANICS LITERARY ASSOCIATION / ROCHESTER. Plain edge. Rarity 7.

341A	ND	Bronze	42mm	—	—	—

As 341. Plain edge. Rarity 7.

341B	ND	WM	42mm	—	150.	250.

As 341. Plain edge. Rarity 8 or 9. (Garrett 1860; Hirsch coll.)

Robert Lovett Sr. of New York created this illogical muling.

NEW HAVEN NUMISMATIC SOCIETY

Struck 1880's

Baker	Date	Metal	Size	VF	EF	Unc
617	1862	WM	44mm	—	—	350.

Uniformed bust left in a circle surrounded by eight others, picturing the obverses and reverses of the Connecticut cent, Franklin Press cent, Auctori Plebis and Granby token. Around: WASHINGTON PRESIDENT 1791. Rv: Within oak wreath: FOUNDED NOV. 25TH. 1862. Around: NEW HAVEN NUMISMATIC SOCIETY. Plain edge. Rarity 8. (Magriel sale 090)

Made by C. Wyllys Betts of New Haven, Conn. The medal exhibits his preoccupation with Colonial coinages. This piece is very rare and seldom appears in numismatic circles. Made by low relief, hand made dies. Only 6 pieces seen in 40 years.

I. A. P. N.

(International Association of Professional Numismatists)

Baker	Date	Metal	Size	VF	EF	Unc
A-617	1973	Silver	32mm	—	—	45.00

Nude bust left,. IAPN 22ND ASSEMBLY. above, SEPTEMBER 15-19,1973. WASHINGTON, D.C. below. Rv: Blank, with tiny (monogram) / FINE SILVER incused at bottom. Plain edge. (ANS collection)

The bust, also used on the AINA medal which follows, is of fine Workmanship.

The IAPN assembly was held in both New York and Washington in 1973, with the American Numismatic Society and Smithsonian Institution co-hosting the gathering. Enroute by bus between the two cities, the guests stopped at the Evergreen House of Johns Hopkins University in Baltimore to view the John Work Garrett numismatic collection then on public display there. (The Garrett collection has since been auctioned off, 1980-81)

The medals were intended as award medals for significant achievements and honored George Washington on the occasion of the first-ever IAPN assembly on U.S. soil. Xavier Calico of Barcelona, Spain was the IAPN president that year. Your author Russ Rulau was among the large number of American delegates attending all the functions, covering the event for Coin World and World Coins. The medals are quite scarce.

The IAPN assembly was conducted alongside the much larger International Numismatic Congress.

WASHINGTON NUMISMATIC SOCIETY

Baker	Date	Metal	Size	EF	AU	Unc
AA617	1952	Silver	32mm	—	35.00	—

Obverse as Baker EA-678 in reduced size. Rv: WASHINGTON NUMIS-MATIC SOCIETY / 1927 / PRESIDENT / GEO. H. RUSSELL / E. WARD RUSSELL / PRESIDENT / 1952 / (tiny) THE ROBBINS CO. STERLINT (sic!) (illegible), MASS. / - SILVER ANNIVERSARY -.

Struck by the Robbins Company, Attleboro, Mass. in .925 fine (sterling) silver.

A.I.N.A.

(American Israel Numismatic Association)

Baker	Date	Metal	Size	VF	EF	Unc
B-617	1976	Silver	37mm	—	—	30.00

Nude bust left (same bust as on A-617) above script signature G Washington, * TO BIGOTRY NO SANCTION above, TO PERSECUTION NO ASSISTANCE below. Rv: AINA seal divides 1776 - 1976, AMERICAN REVOLUTION / (arc of 6 stars) above, (arc of 7 stars) / BICENTENNIAL below. Plain edge. (ANS coll.)

GRADE HEADINGS

Three grade (condition) columns appear in this catalog. Coins and tokens, which circulate, are graded down to VG (Very Good), but medals, which do not circulate, usually are graded no less than VF (Very Fine). Other abbreviations used are F (Fine), EF (Extremely Fine), AU (About Uncirculated), Unc (Uncirculated), and P-L (Proof-like). Proof is spelled out.

OBVERSE AND REVERSE

The term Obverse refers to the "heads" or "face" side of a piece. Where there is a human head or bust, this is easy to determine, but where there is no head, the side with the "principal device" is the Obverse. The opposite side is the Reverse. In some cases determining Obverse and Reverse must be arbitrary, especially where a head is on each side.

Each piece also has a third side, the Edge, which is described as Reeded, Plain, Lettered, etc. The term Rim is not the edge, but the periphery of one face or another.

MORRIS MORGENSTERN FOUNDATION

Baker	Date	Metal	Size	VF	EF	Unc
C-617	1956	Bronze	31mm	—	—	8.00

Nude bust left (as bust on A-617) between oak branches, TO BIGOTRY NO SANCTION above, GEORGE / WASHINGTON below: Rv: PRE-SENTED / BY / THE MORRIS MORGENSTERN / FOUNDATION / IN / "SALUTE TO YOUTH" / FEB. 22, 1956. Plain edge. Issued with loop for suspension from ribbon. (ANS collection)

AMERICAN NUMISMATIC ASSOCIATION

Baker	Date	Metal	Size	VF	EF	Unc
E-617	1926	Cast Copper	49.5mm	—	—	—

Washington head right, "THE CONSTITUTION IS SACREDLY OBLIG-ATORY ON ALL", within circle. Around: AMERICAN. NUMISMATIC . ASSOCIATION. Rv: Eagle with folded wings perched left, building in background. Around: METROPOLITAN COIN CONVENTION / 1926. (Stuart Mosher coll., 1947)

Baker	Date	Metal	Size	VF	EF	Unc
K-617	1971	Bronze	37mm	—	—	22.50

Military bust right. Around: 80th ANNIVERSARY CONVENTION 1971 / * WASHINGTON, D.C. *. Rv: Washington Monument before ANA seal, flag and Capitol building. Around: OUR NATION'S CAPITAL / AMERICAN / NUMISMATIC ASSOCIATION. Looped for suspension from ribbon.

P.O.S. OF A.

(Patriotic Order Sons of America)

Reading, Pa.

Baker	Date	Metal	Size	VF	EF	Unc
R-341	1888	WM	35mm	—	20.00	25.00

Obverse as T-341 in larger size. Rv: 12TH ANNUAL CONVENTION / NATIONAL CAMP / P.O.S. OF A. / READING, PA. / JUNE 19. TO 21. 1888. Plain edge. (Rich Hartzog coll.)

Lebanon, Pa.

Baker	Date	Metal	Size	EF	Unc	Proof
S-341	1890	WM	35mm	36.50	50.00	—

Small undraped bust right. DEDICATED TO GOD OUR COUNTRY / AND OUR ORDER above, MAY 26, 1890. /. below. Rv: Building, P.O.S. OF A. HALL above, LEBANON PA. in exergue. Plain edge. Rarity 6. (Leon Hendrickson coll.)

T-341	1900	WM	32mm	—	40.00	60.00

Small head on star within shield lettered P.O.S. OF A. and, around all, GOD OUR COUNTRY AND OUR ORDER. Rv: STATE CAMP. OF PENNA. / P.O.S. OF A. / LEBANON / PA. / AUG. 27-31, 1900. Plain edge. Rarity 7. (Dr. Schuster coll.)

T-341A	1900	Bronze	32mm	—	55.00	70.00

As T-341. Plain edge. Rarity 7. (Hartzog coll.)

T-341M	1900	WM	32mm	—	25.00	35.00

Obverse as Baker 1831 (naked bust right within thick border). Rv: As reverse of Baker T-341. Plain edge.

T-341N	1900	Bronze	32mm	—	35.00	—

As T-341M.

T-341P	ND	Gilt/Brass	19mm	—	—	12.50

Bust left on 5-pointed star within shield, P.O.S. OF A. above. Rv: Lord's prayer. Plain edge. A souvenir issue.

Struck about 1900

Baker	Date	Metal	Size	EF	Unc	Proof
U-341	ND	Gilt/B	13.5mm	—	30.00	—

Obverse as T-341 in reduced size. Rv: Schoolhouse, THE LITTLE RED SCHOOL HOUSE around, crossed U.S. flags in exergue. Plain edge. (Dr. Schuster coll.)

U-341B	ND	Gilt/Bs	**	—	—	17.50

** Cross-shaped, 31mm.
Baker U-341 in brass encased in a Maltese-cross-shaped frame. Each arm of the cross contains a branch with blooms. Rv: Cross is blank. Plain edge. Issued with loop.

Philadelphia, Pa.

V341	1907	Gilt/Bs	19mm	—	8.00	—

P.O.S. of A. central device from T-341 and U-341 separates 19 -- 07. P.O.S. OF A. above, PHILADELPHIA below. Rv: 60TH ANNIVERSARY / JUBILEE / AUG. 26-30 / 1907 / PHILADELPHIA. Plain edge.

The Patriotic Order Sons of America was founded in 1847.

PATER PATRIAE

Certain Latin terms appear on medals pertaining to George Washington, the first "General of the Armies of the United States." Only one other man held this title until the 5-star rank was created in World War II, and that was John J. Pershing, U.S. commander in France in WWI.

Pater Patriae (father of his country) is the apt title frequently appearing. Many other Latin words and phrases appear on items in this catalog; in most cases we have translated these for users.

GENERIC CAMP MEDAL

Baker	Date	Metal	Size	VF	EF	Unc
X-341	ND	CN	36mm	—	—	12.50

Facing civil bust at center of P.O.S. of A. shield, all above wreath. Rv: MEMBER / OF/ CAMP / NO. The balance of the reverse is blank for engraving. Plain edge.

Membership medalet for the Patriotic Order Sons of America for use at encampments.

Baker	Date	Metal	Size	VF	EF	Proof
342	ND	Silver	39mm	—	85.00	200.

Large Washington head left, F. N. MITCHELL. F. on truncation. Rv: Shield-shaped blank space at center. On a scroll around: PRESENTED BY THE METROPOLITAN MECHANICS INSTITUTE. Plain edge. Rarity 8 (Garrett 1861; Julian AM-44; Magriel sale 064)

The specimen in the Garrett sale of 1981, a proof, was engraved: GEORGE GEMUNDER / N YORK / VIOLINS. The Magriel 1988 sale specimen was engraved: MATTEAWAN MACHINE CO., MATTEAWAN N.Y. STEAM ENGINE.

Baker	Date	Metal	Size	VF	EF	Proof
342A	ND	Copper	38mm	—	—	35.00

As 342. Plain edge. Rarity 6.

342B	ND	Bronze	38mm	—	—	35.00

As 342. Plain edge. Rarity 6.

342C	ND	Brass	38mm	—	—	35.00

As 342. Plain edge. Rarity 6.

342F	ND	Silver	38mm	—	—	110.

Obverse as 342. Rv: Blank. Plain edge. Rarity 8.

Engraved by F.N. Mitchell, the medals were struck at the U.S. Mint in Philadelphia.

WASHINGTON CAMP

Baker	Date	Metal	Size	VF	EF	Unc
Y-341	1919	Copper *	**	—	40.00	55.00

* Copper, with blue enamel within keystone, and white enamel around Washington-in-star.
** Shield-shaped medal, 40 by 40mm, looped for suspension from ribbon. Overall height with ribbon is 71mm.
Seal of the P.O.S. of A. as on Baker T-341, within keystone, all within ornate shield-shaped flan. Rv: PRESENTED / BY / WASHINGTON CAMP / NO. 11 P.O.S. OF A. / TO THE / MEMBERS WHO SERVED / IN THE WORLD WAR / 1917 - 1919 / (tiny) MADE BY "L.F. GRAMMES & SONS ALLENTOWN, PA."

World War I technically ended with the armistice of Nov. 11, 1918, but American soldiers fighting in northern European Russia were not brought home until June, 1919, and this was considered an extension of the general war. Those Americans in combat in eastern Siberia until 1920 were regular enlisted forces on a special Allied mission to save Vladivostok from Red control. Thus the 1917-1919 date on this badge is correct. The badge is quite scarce.

LADIES LOYAL LEAGUE

Baker	Date	Metal	Size	VF	EF	Unc
Z-341	ND	—	**	—	—	25.00

** Maltese cross-shaped flan, 23x23mm.
Washington bust right within circle of 13 stars. On each arm of the Maltese cross are: LADIES / LOYAL / LEAGUE / (winged U.S. shield). Rv: Blank. Looped for suspension.

METROPOLITAN MECHANICS INSTITUTE

Struck 1850-57

AMERICAN INSTITUTE

Struck 1876

Baker	Date	Metal	Size	VF	EF	Unc
343	1876	Bronze	32mm	—	200.	300.

Undraped bust right, LOVETT on truncation. Around: AMERICAN INSTITUTE / * CENTENNIAL MEDAL, 1876. *. Rv: Olive and oak wreath with AWARDED TO at top opening encloses blank field. Plain edge. Rarity 7.

343A	1876	WM	32mm	—	200.	300.

As 343. Plain edge. Rarity 9.

343B	1876	Gold	34mm	—	—	2400.

As 343. 22K (.9167 fine) gold. Only known specimen engraved to B.B. Tilt & Son 1876. (PCAC May 1997, lot 192)

Struck by Robert Lovett Jr. of Philadelphia.

WASHINGTON COLLEGE VIRGINIA

Struck 1868-76

344	ND	Bronze	33mm	—	—	300.

Undraped bust left. LONGACRE under the bust. Around: WASHINGTON COLLEGE VIRGINIA. Rv: Oak and olive wreath enclose blank field. Around: ROBINSON PRIZE MEDAL. Plain edge. Rarity 8. (Julian SC-62)

This medal was designed by James B. Longacre, chief engraver of the United States Mint from Sept. 16, 1844 to his death on Jan. 1, 1869. It is the only medallic head of Washington Longacre executed. Longacre is best known as the engraver of the 'National Portrait Gallery' series in 1834 and as designer of the Indian Head cent in 1859.

The bust was also used on the obverse of Baker 345.

Mint records indicate 12 medals in fine gold of type Baker 344 were struck 1868-1871. Their present location is not known.

WASHINGTON UNIVERSITY

Baltimore, Md.

Baker	Date	Metal	Size	VF	EF	AU
A344	1851	Gold	34.6mm	—	—	5000.

Entire medal (portrait, border, text) is hand engraved! Skillfully hand-made by a goldsmith who left no signature on his creation.

Civil bust facing 3/4 right. Around: PATER PATRIAE SCIENTIAEGUE LIRERALIS (sic!). The AE in 2nd and 3rd words is ligate. Rv: PALMAM QUI MERUIT FERAT. / Presented / TO / Levi S. Burridge, M.D. / BY / Washington University / of / Baltimore / March / 1851. (All block lettering and date are open. All upper-lower case lettering is in script.) Wide ornate border on each side, and same design on outside of hanger. Plain edge. Issued with loop, to which the gold hanger has been skillfully attached. Unique. Unpublished. (Alan V. Weinberg coll., ex-David Kleiner, Rex Stark)

The Latin legend on obverse contains two apparent errors made by the goldsmith. The words SCIENTIAEGUE LIRERALIS were probably intended to be these words: SCIENTIAEQUE LIBERALIS.

The medal weighs 12.1 grams and its specific gravity is 11.308, indicating a gold fineness of 14-karat (.585 fine), using copper as an alloy. The 14K gold was, before the Civil War and still today, the preferred gold alloy of smiths, jewelers and other artisans. Discovering which smith made this piece may be difficult, as Baltimore had a number of skilled precious metal craftsmen in this era, and it may have been made elsewhere.

Washington University of Baltimore has not existed for a very long time. In 1857 it was transformed into an Episcopal hospital called The Church House and Hospital, and this in turn became part of Helix in 1993.

Dr. Levi Burridge does not appear in Baltimore directories of the period around 1851; apparently he practiced elsewhere. We may assume that medicine was a major academic discipline of Washington University of Baltimore, which might well be completely forgotten were it not for a medallic memento such as Baker A344.

WASHINGTON AND LEE UNIVERSITY

Struck 1882-95

Baker	Date	Metal	Size	VF	EF	Unc
345	ND	Bronze	33mm	—	—	50.00

Undraped Washington bust left. Rv: As reverse of 344. Plain edge. Rarity 8. (Julian SC-64)

James B. Longacre designed the bust used on this obverse. The U.S. Mint also struck this medal in fine gold, 46 pieces.

NEW YORK AMERICAN

Baker	Date	Metal	Size	VF	EF	Unc
Q-345	1920	Silver	34mm	—	37.50	—

Facing civil bust at right, AMERICA FIRST above, FEB. 22/ 1920 at right. At left: WASHINGTON / ESSAY / PRIZE / AWARDED BY THE / NEW YORK / AMERICAN / TO. Rv: Blank, but tiny DIEGES & CLUST / STERLING incused at bottom. Plain edge. Issued with eye for suspension.

Struck by Dieges & Clust, Boston, in .925 fine silver. These medals were engraved when awarded. The Rich Hartzog specimen is engraved: PAUL / WINKOPP.

Baker	Date	Metal	Size	VF	EF	U
R-345	ND	Bronze	38mm	—	7.50	

Facing busts of Washington and Woodrow Wilson, NEW YORK AMERICAN and the paper's logo above, ESSAY CONTEST below. Rv: PRESENTED BY / NEW YORK AMERICAN / AS AN AWARD OF MERIT FOR AN ESSAY ON / WOODROW WILSON'S / LIFE OF / GEORGE WASHINGTON / (tiny) W&H CO NEWARK N.J. Plain, irregular edge.

PITTSBURGH PRESS

Baker	Date	Metal	Size	VF	EF	U
R-345M	1927	Brass	Irreg 32mm	—	7.50	

Civil bust right against pebbled field, GEORGE WASHINGTON around. Rv: PRESENTED BY / THE / PITTSBURGH PRESS / WASHINGTON / ESSAY CONTEST / 1927 / (tiny) WHITEHEAD & HOAG. Plain edge. Slotted eye for suspension. (Hartzog coll.)

SOCIETY OF THE CINCINNATI

THE DIAMOND EAGLE

Baker	Date	Metal	Size	EF	AU	U
S-345	1783	**	**	—	500,000. #	

** The eagle itself measures approx. 26x35mm. Overall height including white-bordered light blue ribbon and ornate hanger and clasp is about 107mm. Eagle, hanger and clasp (bottom to top) are of gold, studded throughout with diamonds. Each eye of the eagle is a ruby, wreath encircling eagle's head studded with tiny emeralds. On eagle's breast is the seal of the society, three senators presenting a sword to farmer Cincinnatus (Washington), all four in 18th century garb, with motto around OMNIA: RELINQUIT: SERVARE: REMPUBLICAM *. The seal is white enamel, but red, blue, green and brown are used for the figures, sky, ground and partial building at right.

Estimated for insurance valuation. It is doubtful the unique Diamond Eagle of the Cincinnati will ever be sold.

The Society of the Cincinnati was organized at Fishkill, N.Y. on May 10, 1783 by Continental Army officers who fought in the Revolution (1775-1783), before the Treaty of Paris ended the war and the British evacuated New York. The organizers were led by Gen. Henry Knox and included Gen. Washington, Gen. Friedrich Wilhelm von Steuben, Alexander Hamilton, Gen. Nathanael Greene. The French officers Marquis de Lafayette, Gen. Rochambeau, Adm. Comte de Grasse; Polish Col. Tadeusz Kosciusko; Russian Baron Gustavus Heinrich von Wetter-Rosendahl (he renamed himself Major John Rose) were among some 5500 officers of the American and French forces eligible, and of these 2150 officers did join.

George Washington was elected President General 1783, serving until his death 1799. The first presiding officer was Von Steuben and the society's originator has always been considered Gen. Knox. The motto Omnia relinquit servare rempublicam means "He gave up everything to serve the republic."

The Fishkill assembly authorized Major Pierre Charles L'Enfant (who later laid out the plan for the city of Washington, D.C.) to have the eagle badge made. The French engineering officer had the court jewelers of Louis XVI in France prepare the Diamond Eagle and it was presented to Gen. Washington in 1784. The Eagle has remained with the society ever since, being worn for ceremonial functions by each President General of the Cincinnati.

Major Edgar Erskine Hume, numismatist and society historian, writing in 1933, stated "the dies are believed to have been brought back to the U.S. (by L'Enfant); it is not known whether any gold or silver strikes of the badge were made" in this country.

William Russell Raiford in Feb. 1996, then and now Vice President General of the society, informed your authors of the state of affairs of the original Eagle, which reposes at Anderson House, the society museum, at 2118 Massachusetts Ave. N.W., Washington, D.C. The museum has been open to the public since 1940. Anderson House was the gift of Larz Anderson III (1866-1937) and his wife, Isabel Weld Perkins; Anderson was a descendant of Richard Clough Anderson, an aide de camp to Gen. Lafayette. The item depicted as Baker S-345 in the 1985 edition of this text has been determined to be a later replica badge made in New Hampshire and appears herein as Baker S-345T.

The original purpose of the society, besides cameraderie between the French and Continental officers (light blue in the ribbon is for France, white for America), was to aid members and their families when in need. Since Congress was unwilling to tax, military pensions were unknown until 1832, when surviving Revolutionary War veterans were pensioned off and military pensions have since become institutionalized.

The Society of the Cincinnati is an hereditary organization with today about 3500 members. Eligibility is by primogeniture in the male line of direct descent from original members (the eldest son in each family, or the eldest in a collateral branch where there is no male heir); original members must have served a minimum period (usually three years) as a commissioned officer in the regular (line) American army (not militia forces) or the French forces of Gen. Rochambeau and Adm. de Grasse. Today there are 14 society chapters, one in each of the 13 original colonies, and one in France with 250 members. (The French chapter was inactive 1792-1925 as most members were guillotined or exiled in the Reign of Terror.) Today the society also accepts direct male descendants of officers killed in action or who died of other causes in the Revolution.

Perhaps without justification, the Society of the Cincinnati has been called by its detractors "America's only order of nobility." A far more worthy title would be "America's first veterans organization." George Washington has always been its patron saint.

NOTE: The Diamond Eagle is shown in full color on this catalog's cover!

Replica, 1865-1880

Baker	Date	Metal	Size	VF	EF	Unc
S-345R	1783	Gold / Enamel	—	—	—	2,000.

Similar to last, but prepared from new dies in 18-karat gold. Weight 480 grains. (Springfield 4100)

The replica badge was made for members of the Society by Bailey, Banks & Biddle Co. of Philadelphia.

George Washington was elected the first president of the Society of the Cincinnati (for whom the city of Cincinnati was named), and, while he is not portrayed on the badge, the figure of 'Cincinnatus' wears 18th century garb, not pre-Christian Roman garb as would be more correct and thus the figure more probably represents a modern-day Cincinnatus, as George Washington has been called.

(For full treatment of the badge and other medals of the Cincinnati, see the articles by Major Edgar E. Hume in The Numismatist for Dec. 1933, March 1934 and April 1934 entitled "George Washington's Eagle of the Society of the Cincinnati" and "The Medals of the Society of the Cincinnati")

Under this heading we are listing only those Cincinnati medals portraying Washington or his monument, but there are others alluding to the first president.

GRADE HEADINGS

Three grade (condition) columns appear in this catalog. Coins and tokens, which circulate, are graded down to VG (Very Good), but medals, which do not circulate, usually are graded no less than VF (Very Fine). Other abbreviations used are F (Fine), EF (Extremely Fine), AU (About Uncirculated), Unc (Uncirculated), and P-L (Prooflike). Proof is spelled out.

OBVERSE AND REVERSE

The term Obverse refers to the "heads" or "face" side of a piece. Where there is a human head or bust, this is easy to determine, but where there is no head, the side with the "principal device" is the Obverse. The opposite side is the Reverse. In some cases determining Obverse and Reverse must be arbitrary, especially where a head is on each side.

Each piece also has a third side, the Edge, which is described as Reeded, Plain, Lettered, etc. The term Rim is not the edge, but the periphery of one face or

NEW HAMPSHIRE REPLICA

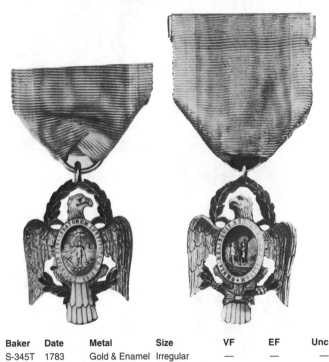

Baker	Date	Metal	Size	VF	EF	Unc
S-345T	1783	Gold & Enamel	Irregular	—	—	—

* Eagle-shaped badge of gold with enameling in green, white and blue, and a ruby as each eye of the eagle. The obverse seal is similar to that on S-345, as is the reverse seal, to wit: Flying Fame crowns standing Cincinnatus with a wreath. Motto around: SOCIETAS: CINCINNA-TORUM: INSTITUTA; AD 1783: (Previously numbered Baker S-345; extremely rare, no public sales traced; ANS coll.)

The American Numismatic Society records reveal the New Hampshire provenance. The state has had a Cincinnati chapter since the 18th century.

OTHER CINCINNATI EAGLE BADGES

(all in collection of American Numismatic Society)

France

Early Silver

American

Since 1902

New York State

Ca. 1860

Unknown origin

WASHINGTON AND LEE UNIVERSITY

Created 1891

Baker	Date	Metal	Size	VF	EF	Unc
T-345	ND	Gold	51mm	—	Ex. Rare	—

Jugate undraped busts right of George Washington and Robert E. Lee in high relief, BARBER under bust. Around: WASHINGTON AND LEE UNIVERSITY / (ornaments). Rv: CINCINNATI ORATORS MEDAL in semicircular curve, within thick wreath of oak. The words are engraved in block letters. Remainder of space is for recipient's information engraved in this fashion: AWARDED / FITZGERALD / FLOURNOY / JUNE 1921. Plain edge. (Hume 3; Julian SC-66 var.)

Baker	Date	Metal	Size	VF	EF	Unc
T-345A	ND	Copper	51mm	—	Rare	—

As T-345.

The Cincinnati Oration was instituted at (then) Washington College in 1838 by President Ruffner. Robert E. Lee accepted the presidency of the college after the Civil War and, after his death, it was renamed Washington and Lee University. In 1891 the university authorized a gold medal for award to the deliverer of that year's Cincinnati Oration if it measures up to sufficient "scholarship, thought and power of expression." The oration is not delivered each year and deliverers do not necessarily receive a medal. For example the first medal awarded after authorization in 1891 was in 1912, to T. McP. Glasgow, and thus the medals are extremely rare. There were no awards 1922-1933.

For other medals of Washington and Lee University and its predecessor Washington College, both by James B. Longacre, see Baker numbers 344 and 345, the Robinson Prize Medals.

WASHINGTON MONUMENT

PENNYSLVANIA CINCINNATI

For medals struck in 1897 for the unveiling of the Washington Monument in Fairmount Park by the Society of the Cincinnati of Pennsylvania, see Baker S-324 and S-324A in the chapter on Statues, Monuments and Memorials.

1914 GENERAL SOCIETY MEETING
AT BALTIMORE

Struck 1914

Baker	Date	Metal	Size	VF	EF	Unc
U-345	1783	Bronze	50mm	—	—	100.

Three senators present sword to Cincinnatus as his wife looks on from in front of a log cabin, OMNIA - RELINQUIT - REMPUBLICAM around, crossed branches in exergue. Rv: Flying Fame places a wreath on standing Cincinnatus, rising sun. ships and houses in background, emblem and 1783 below. Around: SOCIETAS - CINCINNATORUM - INSTITUTA. Plain edge, stamped WHITEHEAD & HOAG. (Hume 8)

A copy of the medal was given to each general officer, delegate and alternate at the triennial meeting of the General Society of the Cincinnati at Baltimore in 1914. The design was made by Major Pierre C. L'Enfant in 1783 for a medal, but this was never struck at the time. This replica was to provide a copy of the original L'Enfant design. (L'Enfant later laid out the plans for the city of Washington, D.C.).

Struck by the Whitehead & Hoag Co., Newark, N.J. There were perhaps 125 medals distributed. A few specimens were presented to museums, etc.

L'ENFANT MEDAL DESIGN
by Victor D. Brenner

Struck about 1900

Baker	Date	Metal	Size	VF	EF	Unc
V-345	1783	Bronze	44mm	—	Rare	—

Design similar to that on the preceding, Baltimore 1914 medal. This is another replica of the L'Enfant Cincinnati medal design. On reverse, at bottom, is: AN. D. MDCCLXXXIII. reading inverted. The execution is totally different than the Whitehead-Hoag version. Plain edge. (Hume 18)

| V-345A | 1783 | WM | 44mm | — | Rare | — |

As last. Plain edge. (Hume 18)

Brenner, designer in 1909 of the Lincoln cent, made these trial pieces in limited number to show off his own skill and to perpetuate the medallic design of L'Enfant, which had never eventuated into a medal. Specimens in both metals are in the ANS collection.

1929 MEETING IN BOSTON

Struck 1929

Baker	Date	Metal	Size	VF	EF	Un
X-345	ND	Gilt/BZ	65mm	—	—	70.0

Civil bust after Stuart facing three-quarters left, the bust extending to th lower rim. There is no inscription or signature. Rv: Blank. Plain edge (Hume 15)

This medallion was presented to attendees at the Boston conclave and wa struck by the Robbins Co., Attleboro, Mass., from a stock die which was als for other purposes, e.g. the Rhode Island 1932 Washington Bicentennial meda However, it was issued in this unadorned form at the Cincinnati gathering in Bos ton, presented mounted on a background of black velvet and enclosed in a woode frame of black and gold measuring 4 1/2 by 5 1/2 inches.

This piece was available new as late as 1950.

1923 MEETING IN WILMINGTON

Baker	Date	Metal	Size	VF	EF	Unc
W-345	1923	Bronze	69mm	—	—	70.00

Half-length bust in civil dress left. Around: FIRST. PRESIDENT. GEN-ERAL. OF. THE. SOCIETY. OF. THE. CINCINNATI. INSTITUTED. 1783 / WASHINGTON. Rv: Within laurel wreath in 10 lines: IN / COM-MEMORATION / OF THE / TRIENNIAL MEETING / OF THE / GENER-AL SOCIETY / OF THE / CINCINNATI / WILMINGTON DELAWARE / MAY 10. 1923. Plain edge. (Hume 10)

Designed by George T. Morgan and struck at the U.S. Mint. Copies were pre-sented to each officer, delegate and alternate at the Wilmington conclave.

YORKTOWN SESQUICENTENNIAL 1931

The medal issued by the Virginia Society of the Cincinnati in 1931 to commem orate the Battle of Yorktown is listed as Baker E-454 in the chapter on Centennia of Revolutionary Events to keep it with other Yorktown memorabilia.

GENERAL SOCIETY PLAQUE OF 1932

Baker	Date	Metal	Size	VF	EF	Unc
Y-345	1932	Bronze	Rect 50x68mm	—	—	135.

Civil bust facing three-quarters left, seals of the U.S. and the French Republic in circular medallions above. 1732-1932 / OMNIA (shield) RELINQUIT / SERVARE REMPUBLICAM below. Rv: Independence Hall. Below: COMMEMORATING THE TRIENNIAL / MEETING OF THE GENERAL SOCIETY / OF THE CINCINNATI PHILADELPHIA, PA / MAY 5 1932 AND THE BICENTENNIAL / OF THE BIRTH OF GEORGE WASHINGTON / FIRST PRESIDENT GENERAL / (eagle badge amid scroll motto of the Society). Plain edge. (Hume 17; Hansen 70)

Struck by Bailey, Banks & Biddle Co. of Philadelphia.

U.S. MILITARY ACADEMY

Struck 1865-66

Baker	Date	Metal	Size	VF	EF	Unc
346	ND	Bronze	27.6mm	—	175.	250.

Undraped bust left. PAQUET F under bust. Around: UNITED STATES MILITARY ACADEMY. Rv: Octagonal tablet at center, ACADEMIC above, MERIT below, all within circular oak wreath. Plain edge. Only 15 struck. Rarity 8. (Garrett 1862: PCAC Nov. 1997 sale, lot 374)

Designed by Anthony C. Paquet and struck at the U.S. Mint, Philadelphia, for West Point. There has been some doubt these were actually issued, because engraved specimens have not been known. The medals are rare.

An 1867 report noted Sylvester S. Crosby exhibited one medal engraved: Presented to Cadet Palfrey 1866. The 1990 Middendorf sale had an uninscribed piece in choice Unc. which realized $242.

U.S. Mint records indicate Baker 346 was struck in 10 gold, 10 silver and 15 bronzed copper specimens.

GRAND ARMY OF THE REPUBLIC

Baker	Date	Metal	Size	VF	EF	Unc
S-346	1866	Bronze	32mm		15.00	25.00

Draped female with table and laurel crown stands in front of Washington statue, DEPARTMENT OF THE POTOMAC G.A.R. around WASHINGTON / D.C. in exergue. Rv: G.A.R. seal at center, within olive wreath open at top. Plain edge. Issued with loop (Bullowa - Lessin sale, lot 36)

ANNUAL ASAY MEDALS

1876

Baker	Date	Metal	Size	VF	EF	Proof
347	1876	Bronze	33mm	—	—	350.

Undraped bust right, BARBER beneath bust. Rv: Oak wreath encloses : 1776. (radiant) / ANNUAL / ASSAY / 1876, all within central circle. Around: YEAR ONE HUNDRED / * OF AMERICAN INDEPENDENCE * . Plain edge. Rarity 8.

347A	1876	Silver	33mm	—	—	—

As 347. Plain edge. Rarity 9; at least 3 known.

347B	1876	Aluminum	33mm	—	—	—

As 347. Plain edge. Rarity 9.

1677

Baker	Date	Metal	Size	VF	EF	Proof
A347	1877	Copper	33mm	—	—	1250.

Obverse as 347. Rv: Within wreath: ANNUAL / ASSAY / 1877. Heavy milling marks above left top of wreath. Weight 302.3 grains. Ex. rare. (JK-AC-17; Fred-Ward 1995 Sale, lot 1032)

Baker A347 may have been struck in the 1892-97 period, for unknown reasons. The 1877 medal presented to commissioners depicts Archimedes in an archway on obverse (JK-AC-16).

1878

348	1878	Bronze	33mm	—	—	310.

Obverse as 347. Rv: Within olive wreath: ANNUAL / ASSAY / 1878. Plain edge. Rarity 8.

The Assay Medal was issued by the U.S. Mint at the time of the Annual Assay, and was only presented to members of the Assay Commission, the director of the Mint and heads of the Treasury department. The design was changed every year.

The first medals were struck 1860, the last in 1977. Unlike 1860-1976 medals, the 1977 pieces were sold to the public after Pres. Carter abolished the commision, and are common.

1936

Baker	Date	Metal	Size	EF	Unc	
B-348	1936	Yellow Bronze	76mm	—	1100.	—

Obverse is the regular presidential medal device of the U.S. Mint. Rv.
Roosevelt bust right, PRESIDENT.OF.THE.UNITED STATES above,
FRANKLIN / DELANO / ROOSEVELT at left. Edge is inscribed incuse
with date and annual assay character of the piece. Rarity 7. (Leon Hendrickson coll.; VK-AC-80a)

This assay medal was prepared by muling two obverse medal dies already i
Mint possession, and inscribing the edge. Very rare, and little known.

1932

Baker	Date	Metal	Size	EF	AU	Unc
A-348	1932	Yellow Bronze	51mm	—	800.	1300.

Medallion portrait of Washington right separates 1732 -- 1932 at lower
part, with tree-lined distant view of Mount Vernon, MOUNT VERNON
across top. Rv: Building of first U.S. Mint in Philadelphia within central
circle. Around: MINT . OF . THE . UNITED . STATES / * ANNUAL AS-
SAY 1932 *. Only 25 medals were struck. Two were offered in a Bowers
& Ruddy Galleries sale in the 1970's. (JK-AC-76a).

Designed by Laura Gardin Fraser. The commission met Feb. 10, 1932. The
specimen in the Rogers M. Fred sale (1995) weighed 981.4 grains.

1942

Photo reduced

Baker	Date	Metal	Size	VF	EF	Proo
E-348	1942	Yellow Bronze	58mm	—	—	2350

Franklin Roosevelt bust right in circular depression. Around: ANNUAI
ASSAY COMMISSION / ** 1942 **. Rv: Houdon Washington head righ
in circular depression. Around: 150TH ANNIVERSARY UNITED
STATES MINT / .1792.1942. Weight 1326.0 grains. Only 18 pieces
struck for the commission, which met Feb. 10, 1942. (JK-AC-87; Rogers
Fred sale, Nov. 13-14, 1995, lot 1135)

1946

Baker	Date	Metal	Size	VF	EF	Proof
F-348	1946	Yellow Bronze	51mm	—	—	1550.

Military bust of Washington left, 1732 / 1799 below. Rv: Tree-lined view of Mount Vernon. Below: UNITED STATES / ASSAY COMMISSION 1946 / 154TH ANNUAL SESSION / AT PHILADELPHIA / MINT. Weight 1007.2 grains. (JK-AC-91; Rogers Fred 1995 sale, lot 1139)

The obverse was designed by Laura Gardin Fraser and the reverse by John R. Sinnock. Struck at the U.S. Mint. Rare.

1974

Baker	Date	Metal	Size	EF	AU	Unc
C-348	1974	Pewter	57mm	—	—	950.

Obverse is a copy of the Washington Before Boston medal, Baker 47, with three words added at lower right: ASSAY / COMMISSION / 1974. Rv: Eagle of the Great Seal before clouds and sunrays, PEACE above, top of globe with 5-line inscription on it below. Border of stars encircles the rim. Plain edge. Rarity 6. Only 38 pieces struck. (Charles Colver coll.; JK-AC-118)

| C-348-A | 1974 | Bronze | 57mm | — | — | 30.00 |

As C-348. Restrike in bronze, sold only at the San Francisco Mint but not by mail. About 2,000 pieces struck. These are NOT genuine Assay medals; merely official restrikes!

Only medals struck in pewter (91% tin, 8% Copper, 1% antimony in this case) were presented to the 1974 Assay commissioners.

In 1977 President Jimmy Carter abolished the Assay Commission which had been in existence since 1792, as a body with public members. Its functions continue within the Treasury department. The last Assay medals struck thus were dated 1977, and they were oval and depicted Martha Washington. Since there was no commission in 1977, the pewter medals were sold for a short time to the public at $25 each and are sought primarily as numismatic curiosities.

The Assay, or Trial of the Pyx, tradition is being kept alive to an extent by a private group, Old Timer Assay Commissioners Society (OTACS), whose members are former Commissioners appointed by various presidents. Since OTACS is not a hereditary organization, it will eventually die out.

1976

Baker	Date	Metal	Size	EF	AU	Unc
D-348	1976	Pewter	Rect76x60mm	—	—	1200.

Facing bust of William E. Simon, Treasury secretary, above ANNUAL ASSAY COMMISSION. At left: WILLIAM E. SIMON / SECRETARY OF THE / TREASURY. At right three lines of text. Rv: Washington crossing the Delaware. Around: INDEPENDENCE . BICENTENNIAL / 1776 - 1976 / WASHINGTON CROSSING THE DELAWARE. (Julian A-120; PCAC June 1994 sale, lot 308)

1939

It has been reported that the 1939 Assay medal carries a Washington effigy. This report is inaccurate; Henry Morgenthau is depicted thereon.

DAVIS OF BIRMINGHAM MEDALS

VIA AD HONOREM

Struck 1840-1850

Baker	Date	Metal	Size	VF	EF	Unc
349	1799	WM	50mm	—	100.	130.

Undraped bust right in an oval frame at the base, around which: GEORGE WASHINTON BORN 1732 DIED 1799. Beneath: DAVIS BIRM. Eagle displayed at top, with ribbon in its beak on which is E PLURIBUS UNUM; 12 stars at each side. Between eagle and bust, in four lines: FIRST IN WAR FIRST IN PEACE AND FIRST IN THE HEARTS OF HIS COUNTRYMEN. Rv: Interior of a room, in which a young man is seated at a table reading, book cases and globes at each side, and at right on a pedestal stands Fame. On a shelf a Minerva head and two antique lamps. DAVIS BIRM at base of design. In exergue: VIA AD HONOREM. Plain edge. Rarity 7.

SCIENTIA MORES EMOLLIT

Baker	Date	Metal	Size	VF	EF	Unc
350	1799	WM	50mm	—	100.	130.

Obverse as 349. Rv: Interior of a room, in which a woman is seated at a table writing, a globe on the table and book cases at either side. To the left, a harp. DAVIS BIRM at base of design. In exergue: SCIENTIA MORES EMOLLIT. Plain edge. Rarity 7.

REWARD OF SUPERIOR MERIT

351	1799	WM	50mm	—	100.	140.

In the early 19th century, Davis of Birmingham, England prepared numbers 349, 350 and 351. Baker thought the reverse of 351 was of more recent vintage than the other pieces. Little is known of them.

REWARD OF MERIT

Struck 1840-50

353	ND	WM	33mm	160.	—	300.

Obverse as Baker 272 (bust three-quarters left, THE FATHER OF OUR COUNTRY). Rv: Within olive wreath: REWARD / OF / MERIT. Plain edge. Rarity 8. (Hirsch Coll.)

Made by Davis of Birmingham, England.

REMEMBER THY CREATOR

(Muling by Davis)

Struck 1840-50

Baker	Date	Metal	Size	F	VF	EF
A353	ND	WM	33mm	—	—	300.

Gentleman seated in chair left, right arm reaching out to small child in dress holding book, standing at his knee. Cornucopia, branches and pillars behind, sunrays at upper left, small DAVIS. BIRM at rim above exergue line. In exergue: REMEMBER NOW / THY CREATOR / ECCL. C. 12. V. 1. Rv: As reverse of Baker 353 (REWARD / OF / MERIT in wreath). Plain edge. Issued holed for suspension. (Roelofs coll.)

KEY'S REWARD OF MERIT

Struck 1850-60

Baker	Date	Metal	Size	VF	EF	Unc
354	1799	Brass	38mm	—	—	50.00

Uniformed bust right. KEY F under bust. On a scroll below: BORN FEB. 27, 1732 DIED DEC. 14, 1799 in two lines. GEORGE WASHINGTON above. Rv: Within oak and laurel wreath: REWARD OF MERIT on a scroll. Plain edge. Rarity 7.

Dies cut by William H. Key of Philadelphia.

INDUSTRY PRODUCES WEALTH

Struck 1860

Baker	Date	Metal	Size	VF	EF	Unc
352	1799	Silver	31mm	—	—	250.

Obverse as Baker 277 (uniformed bust left, THE CINCINNATUS OF AMERICA). Rv: Palm wreath encloses blank field. Around: INDUSTRY PRODUCES WEALTH. Reeded edge. Rarity 8.

352A	1799	Copper	31mm	—	—	160.

As 352. Reeded edge. Rarity 7.

352B	1799	Brass	31mm	—	—	150.

As 352. Reeded edge. Rarity 7.

352C	1799	WM	31mm	—	—	150.

As 352. Reeded edge. Rarity 7.

The dies were cut by George Hampden Lovett of New York City.

MEMBERSHIP BADGE

Baker	Date	Metal	Size	VF	EF	Unc
B-356	ND	—	XX	—	—	—

XX Eagle-shaped, 31x33mm.

Naked bust left in small oval on 13-point star, on breast of eagle badge. Rv: Blank 13-point star on eagle's breast. Issued with loop for suspension from ribbon. (ANS collection)

HALL OF FAME FOR GREAT AMERICANS

New York, N.Y.

AWARDED TO

by Robert Lovett Sr.

355	1789	WM	50mm	—	Unique	—

Undraped bust right. Around: GEORGE WASHINGTON, FIRST PRESIDENT OF THE U.S.A. MDCCLXXXIX. Rv: Olive and oak wreath, connected at top by: AWARDED TO, encloses blank field. Plain edge. (Edwards 2704; Parsons 1914 sale)

by Robert Lovett Jr.

Baker	Date	Metal	Size	VF	EF	Unc
356	ND	Copper	39mm	—	—	100.

Undraped bust right, LOVETT NY under bust. Around: WASHINGTON TEMPERANCE SOCIETY. Rv: Oak and palm wreath connected at top by: AWARDED TO, encloses blank field. Plain edge. Rarity 7.

356A	ND	Bronze	39mm	—	—	100.

As 356. Plain edge. Rarity 7.

356B	ND	WM	39mm	—	—	100.

As 356. Plain edge. Rarity 7.

Dies cut by Robert Lovett St., of New York, probably in the 1840's.

Baker 356 in AU fetched $166 recently; perhaps an aberration.

DAUGHTERS OF THE AMERICAN REVOLUTION

Baker	Date	Metal	Size	VF	EF	Unc
A-356	ND	Yellow Bronze	32mm	—	—	15.00

Nude bust left, GOOD CITIZENSHIP AWARD around, laurel branches below. Rv: Radiant torch, across which is blank panel for inscribing name. Around: PRESENTED TO / * DAUGHTERS OF THE AMERICAN REVOLUTION *. Plain edge. Issued with loop. (Rich Hartzog coll.)

Baker	Date	Metal	Size	EF	AU	Unc
E356	1900	Silver	68.6mm	450.	500.	650.

Facing half-length bust 3/4 left, modeled after Gilbert Stuart. Tiny A. Scharff at lower right rim. Around (at right side only): GEORGE WASHINGTON / BORN 1732 / DIED 1799. Rv: Facade of Hall of Fame building, tablet below. On tablet is incused: NEW.YORK.VNIVERSITY.CHARTERED.MDCCCXXXI/VNIVERSITY. HEIGHTS.PVRCHASED.MDCCCXXI / UNIVERSITY.COLLEGE.REMOVED.MDCCCXCIV / THIS. HALL.OF.FAME.WAS.COMPLETED. MCM / IN.HONOR.OF.GREAT.AMERICANS. In two concentric arcs above: HALL OF FAME FOR GREAT AMERICANS / ERECTED IN THE CITY OF NEW YORK IN 1900. Plain edge, on which are two hallmarks: (J. C in relief in rect. depression) (Male head right in relief in 6-petaled depression). Unpublished. (Brand II 1984, lot 1157; Irving L. Schuster coll.; Virgil Brand's inventory no. 97,505; PCAC May 26, 1997, lot 206)

Baker	Date	Metal	Size	EF	AU	Unc
E356A	1900	Red Bronze	68.6mm	—	—	250.

As E356. Plain edge; no edge-markings. (Schuster coll.)

Baker	Date	Metal	Size	EF	AU	Unc
E356B	1900	Yellow Bronze	68.6mm	—	—	250.

As E356. Plain edge; no edge-marks. (Schuster coll.)

The Dr. Irving Schuster collection, to be sold at public auction beginning in 1999, contains three specimens of the silver version, E356, each edge-marked.

The silver medal is of paramount interest. The edge-markings J.C. in relief within rectangular depression, and laureate male head right within 6-lobed depression (actually 5 petals and a flat base) lead the researcher to conclude the medals were struck for the Hall of Fame outside the United States or Great Britain. This is confirmed by the metallic content, engraver's signature and the edge-markings themselves.

Anton Scharff (1845-1903) was an outstanding Austrian medalist, employed by the Austrian State Mint, Vienna from 1866 on. Besides commemorative coins for Austria-Hungary, Bulgaria and Persia, he engraved many medals and plaques of merit. His normal signature was A. Scharff in script.

The head-in-petals edge-mark needs study under 50-power magnification as it is so tiny. It is an exact match with the Vienna "inspection mark" for silver adopted in the 1866-72 period (see Seymour B. Wyler's *The Book of Old Silver* published in New York, 1937; page 381, illustration number 7864).

There are tiny marks around the youthful male head: (seemingly) u at top; 2 or script 1 at right; r or Greek lepta below. Presumably the silver medals were inspected, and edge-marked, for export.

A continental provenance for the beautiful medal is also confirmed by the odd silver standard of .940 fineness. The gross weight of the silver medal is 130.32 grams, and its specific gravity is 10.384, which translates to 4.19 troy ounces of .940 fine silver, or 3.939 troy ounces of pure silver.

The clues of the Vienna inspection mark, Vienna Mint chief engraver's signature and .940 fine silver content led also to discovery of the J. C. on the edge. It was the hallmark of Joseph Christian Christelbauer (1820-1897), whose diesinking and medallic firm used his hallmark for a time after his death, and struck the Hall of Fame medal series. The famous old Christelbauer firm elicited these comments from Leonard Forrer in his *Biographical Dictionary of Medallists* (I, 427):

"Many of the works of the foremost Austrian medalists, Tautenhayn, Scharff, Breithut, Schwerdtner, Hugo Kaufmann, Hans Fischer, & c were struck at Christelbauer's establishment."

An AU specimen of E356 (silver) realized $484 in May, 1997.

HALL OF FAME 1966

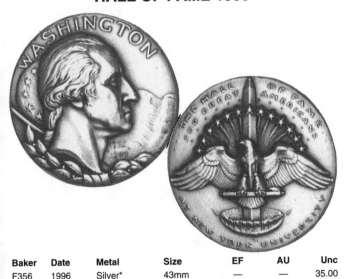

Baker	Date	Metal	Size	EF	AU	Unc
F356	1996	Silver*	43mm	—	—	35.00

* Pure silver; concave flan.

High relief Washington bust right on unfurled flag, tiny G.W. CARTER on truncation. WASHINGTON above, laurel sprays below. Small .1732. / 1799 under Washington's chin. Rv: Spread winged eagle displayed before Washington Monument, arc of 13 stars above. Around: THE HALL OF FAME / FOR GREAT AMERICANS / AT NEW YORK UNIVERSITY. Tiny C-in-circle 1966 below ground. Plain edge marked: MEDALLIC ART CO. N.Y. 999+ PURE SILVER 1602 (or another serial number).

Baker	Date	Metal	Size	EF	AU	Unc
F356A	1966	Bronze	76mm	—	—	30.00

As F356 in larger size and differing metal. Plain edge, marked: MEDALLIC ART CO. N.Y. BRONZE. Not serially numbered. (H.J. Levine report)

These are very well-executed medals with a strong Washington effigy. Were they better known, they might well command higher numismatic valuations.

There was a glut of medals produced in the 1960's and 1970's, many of which ended their careers in the melting pots of 1979-1980. Overproduction by Franklin Mint, Medallic Art Co., and a number of their imitators meant that many pieces saturated a market unwilling to retain them over a long period; the excellent and the mediocre both suffered as a result.

GREAT AND GOOD

Struck late 1870's

Baker	Date	Metal	Size	VF	EF	Unc
357	ND	WM	48mm	—	—	200.

Undraped bust left, A C M. F on truncation of bust. Around: GEORGE WASHINGTON, THE GREAT AND GOOD. Rv: Wreath of cornucopia completed at top by branches of laurel and oak, encloses blank field. Plain edge. 50 pieces struck. Rarity 7.

Engraved by Alexander C. Morin of Philadelphia, who died in 1873. According to Baker, Morin cut the obverse die in 1832, but no proper reverse was ever engraved for it. The Baker 357 reverse, obviously for award purposes received only sparing use with the obverse. All known pieces may be restrikes.

LAUER'S MEDALS

W.S. Baker considered 358 thru 358K as medals. They are in fact game counters and may be found under their original Baker numbers in Chapter 32.

1ST REGIMENT INFANTRY

Cape May, N.J.

Baker	Date	Metal	Size	VF	EF	Unc
359	1869	Bronze	60mm	—	—	75.00

Obverse as Baker 326 (undraped bust right in sunken field, Paquet. F. in script under bust; etc.). Rv: In four lines, with blank scroll at bottom: 1ST REGT. INFANTRY 1ST. DIV. P.M. GRAY RESERVES CAPE MAY JULY 1869. Two crossed flags at center of text. Plain edge. Rarity 8.

Dies were cut by Anthony C. Paquet for the Pennsylvania Militia's (?) 1st Regiment of Infantry.

PHILADELPHIA RIFLE CLUB

Struck 1870-71

Baker	Date	Metal	Size	VF	EF	Unc
360	ND	Silver	26mm	—	85.00	125.

Undraped Washington bust right. Rv: Within beaded circle: Blank scroll, above it AWARDED TO. Around: PHILADELPHIA RIFLE CLUB***. Plain edge. Rarity 8. Only 50 struck, in 1870.

Baker	Date	Metal	Size	VF	EF	Unc
360A	ND	Bronze	26mm	—	—	35.00

As 360. Plain edge. Rarity 6. (Wright 825)

Baker	Date	Metal	Size	VF	EF	Unc
360B	ND	Gold	26mm	—	—	Ex. Rare

As 360 Pure (.999 fine) gold. Plain edge. Only 8 struck, in 1871.

The Philadelphia Rifle Club was organized in 1846. It issued an attractive medallic token for its 25th anniversary in August, 1871, listed as number Pa-Ph 326 in Russ Rulau's *Standard Catalog of U.S. Tokens 1700-1900*.

THE ENGINEERS CLUB OF PHILADELPHIA

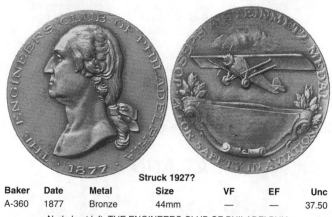

Struck 1927?

Baker	Date	Metal	Size	VF	EF	Unc
A-360	1877	Bronze	44mm	—	—	37.50

Nude bust left, THE ENGINEERS CLUB OF PHILADELPHIA around, . 1877. below. Rv: Single-engine monoplane of circa 1927 in flight above

ornamental scroll for inscribing name. Around: . JOSEPH A. STEIN METZ MEDAL. / FOR SAFETY IN AVIATION. Plain edge. (ANS collection)

The portraiture, based on the Houdon bust, is excellent.

Baker	Date	Metal	Size	VF	EF	Unc
B-360	1877	Bronze	—	—	20.00	25.0

Obverse as A-360. Rv: Laurel and oak wreath open at top encloses large blank area for engraving. Plain edge. (Kirtley June 16, 1998 sale lot B064)

The Engineers Club apparently used B-360 for awards and honors purposes engraving a recipient's name on reverse.

Baker	Date	Metal	Size	VF	EF	Unc
C-360	1877	Bronze	35mm	—	20.00	30.0

Obverse as A-360, in smaller size. Rv: LET US / RAISE / A STANDARD / TO WHICH THE / WISE & HONEST / CAN REPAIR / THE FIRST AMERICAN ENGINEER. Plain edge. (Kirtley June 16, 1998 sale, lo B063)

Baker A-360 thru C-360 were struck by Joseph Davison. Dates of issuance are uncertain.

Joseph K. Davison Sons of Philadelphia is known to have been in busines 1895 until at least 1922.

EXHIBITIONS AND FAIRS

The United States Sanitary Commission was organized June 9, 1861 to provide sanitary measures and practical relief for Union forces in camp, hospital and field, following the example of the women of Bridgeport, Conn., who organized a local group for that purpose on April 15, 1861, the day the first troops were called into the field in the Civil War. At least two-thirds of the funds the commission raised were through Sanitary Fairs, the first of which was at Chicago in autumn, 1863, and the last at Milwaukee in June, 1865.

Four of the Sanitary Fairs issued medals with Washington portraits.

Early world's fairs, such as the Exhibition of the Industry of all Nations in New York City, 1853, and other later events are also covered in this chapter. However, the Independence Centennial Exposition in Philadelphia, 1876, and Washington Inaugural Centennial in 1889 deserve - and have - chapters of their own later on. This present chapter serves as a gathering-place for some other events.

CRYSTAL PALACE
New York City

Struck 1853

Baker	Date	Metal	Size	VF	EF	Proof
361	1853	Silver	52mm	—	875.	1000.

Undraped bust left, A C M under bust. UNITED STATES OF AMERICA / GEORGE WASHINGTON. around, all within ornamental circle. Outside circle is partial olive and oak wreath, with radiant eagle with flag at top, separating E PLURIBUS - UNUM. Rv: View of Crystal Palace across center. PAQUET PHILA. on base of design. Above: THE CRYSTAL PALACE FOR THE EXHIBITION / OF THE INDUSTRY OF ALL NATIONS. / NEW YORK, 1853. Below: PRESIDENT: THEODORE SEDGWICK, ESQR. / ARCHITECTS: / MESSRS: CARSTENSEN & GILDEMEISTER, / LENGTH 365 FEET WIDTH 365 FEET, / HEIGHT OF DOME 148 FEET, / GLAZED SURFACE 206,000 SUP FEET, / OCCUPIES 5 ACRES / OF GROUND. / ESTIMATED VALUE $450,000. Plain edge. Rarity 8. (Garrett 1863; Stack's 1991, lot 160)

361A	1853	Bronze	52mm	—	—	350.

As 361. Plain edge. Rarity 6.

361B	1853	WM	52mm	100.	—	350.

As 361. Plain edge. Rarity 6.

Alexander C. Morin designed the obverse, and Anthony C. Paquet engraved the reverse of this beautiful medal.

The Crystal Palace, modeled after London's Crystal Palace Exhibition in 1851, was erected in 1853 and was destroyed by fire in October, 1858; in the space of just 30 minutes it was leveled to the ground.

CIVIL WAR SANITARY FAIRS

Great Fair, New York

Baker	Date	Metal	Size	VF	EF	Unc
362	1864	Silver	27mm	—	—	300.

Head right, GEO. WASHINGTON above, **** PRESIDENT **** around below. (Fuld CW die 1138). Rv: BLESSED IS THE GIVER. / GREAT FAIR / FOR THE / SANITARY (on scroll) / COMMISSION (on scroll) / NEW YORK / MAY, 1864. in seven irregular lines. Plain edge. Rarity 9. (Fuld CWT NY 640BJ-1fo)

George Fuld reports that 362 is struck over a French silver 1-franc coin.

362A	1864	Copper	27mm	—	—	60.00

As 362. Plain edge. Rarity 4. (Fuld NY 630BJ-1a)

362B	1864	Brass	27mm	—	—	125.

As 362. Plain edge. Rarity 8. (Fuld NY 6308BJ-1b)

362C	1864	Nickel	27mm	—	—	125.

As 362. Plain edge. Rarity 8. Magnetic. (Fuld NY 640BJ-1c)

362D	1864	WM	27mm	—	—	145.

As 362. Plain edge. Rarity 8. (Fuld NY 630BJ-1e)

362G	ND	Silver	27mm	—	—	155.

Obverse as 362. Rv: Blank. Plain edge.

The Sanitary Commission's fair in New York city was held in May, 1864.

GREAT CENTRAL FAIR

Philadelphia

Baker	Date	Metal	Size	VF	EF	Unc
363	1864	Silver	18mm	35.00	45.00	60.00

Undraped bust right. (Fuld CW die 1135). Rv: GREAT / CENTRAL / FAIR / PHILADELPHIA / JUNE 1864 in five irregular lines. Reeded edge. Rarity 5. (Fuld CWT Pa 750L-1f; Garrett 1865)

363A	1864	Copper	18mm	—	11.00	30.00

As 363. Reeded edge. Rarity 1. (Fuld Pa 750L-1a)

363B	1864	Gilt/C	18mm	—	—	100.

As 363. Reeded edge. Rarity 8. (Fuld Pa 750L-1K)

363C	1864	Brass	18mm	Unique?		

As 363. (Hirsch coll., in about Good)

These tokens were struck by a coining press located on the fair grounds. The copper pieces were sold at 10 cents, the silver at 50 cents.

There are some minute die varieties of 363, leading, with metallic combinations, to 28 varieties. For full treatment, see the detailed list by M. & G. Fuld in *The Numismatist* for Sept., 1952, page 887.

Later restrikes

Baker	Date	Metal	Size	EF	AU	Unc
363X	ND	Silver	18mm	—	—	35.00

Obverse as 363. Rv. Blank, but with rim as on obverse. (There is a carving or test mark on the Roelofs specimen reverse.) Plain edge.

Baker	Date	Metal	Size	EF	AU	Unc
363Y	ND	Platinum	18mm	—	—	100.

Obverse as 363. Rv: Blank, but with rim as on obverse. Plain edge. (Roelofs coll.)

Researcher Reigh L. Roelofs, who owns specimens of each, opines that 363X and 363Y are recent strikes off the original dies, possibly for sale to the gullible. No such specimens have been reported in the vast literature on Washingtonia.

SANITARY FAIR

Nantucket, Mass.

Baker	Date	Metal	Size	VF	EF	Unc
364	1864	Silver	24mm	—	—	250.

Obverse as Baker 362 (Fuld CW die 1138). Rv: GOD LOVETH A CHEERFUL GIVER / GREAT FAIR / IN AID OF THE / U.S. / SANITARY / COMMISSION / NANTUCKET, / MASS / AUGUST, 1864. Plain edge. Rarity 9. (Fuld CWT Mass 530A-1f)

Baker	Date	Metal	Size	VF	EF	Unc
364A	1864	Copper	24mm	—	35.00	40.00

As 364. Plain edge. Rarity 5. (Fuld Mass 530A-1a; Collins 285)

Baker	Date	Metal	Size	VF	EF	Unc
364B	1864	Brass	24mm	—	—	50.00

As 364. Plain edge. Rarity 7. (Fuld Mass 530A-1b)

Baker	Date	Metal	Size	VF	EF	Unc
364C	1864	Nickel	24mm	—	—	80.00

As 364. Plain edge. Rarity 9. (Fuld Mass 530A-1c). Magnetic!

Baker	Date	Metal	Size	VF	EF	Unc
364D	1864	WM	24mm	—	—	75.00

As 364. Plain edge. Rarity 8. (Fuld Mass 530A-1e)

The Nantucket Fair took place on the island in August, 1864.

SOLDIERS' FAIR

Springfield, Mass.

First obverse

Baker	Date	Metal	Size	VF	EF	Unc
365	1864	WM	28mm	—	50.00	65.00

Uniformed bust left, J.A. BOLEN under bust. Around: WASHINGTON. (Same obverse as Baker 92). Rv: SOLDIERS' / FAIR / DEC'/ 1864. / SPRINGFIELD, MASS. in five lines, all within olive wreath. Plain edge. Mintage: 350 pieces; of these about 15 survive; Rarity 6. (Bolen 16; Schenkman B5; Rulau Ma-Sp 65; Clark sale, lot 2122; Garrett 1865)

Baker	Date	Metal	Size	VF	EF	Unc
365A	1864	Copper	28mm	—	—	185.

As 365. Plain edge. Only 2 struck. (Bolen 16)

Second obverse

Baker	Date	Metal	Size	VF	EF	Unc
366	1864	Copper	28mm	—	—	200.

Obverse as Baker 93 (Uniformed bust left, BOLEN under bust).Rv: As reverse of 365. Plain edge. Rarity 9.

James Adams Bolen cut the dies for both 365 and 366. His Journal shows h actually struck 365. It is believed A.R. McCoy restruck 366 using the Bolen dies la er.

The Springfield Fair took place in December, 1864. There are other medall remembrances of the fair, using Bolen's reverse die. These occur with a Linco bust by Merriam and an Apollo bust by Merriam, all mulings from the 1870's. (Se Russ Rulau's U.S. Trade Tokens 1866-1889)

Besides the Sanitary Fairs enumerated here which sparked Washington effig medalets, there were other Sanitary Fairs which are remembered with tokens medals. These include: Wapakoneta, Ohio (Fuld CWT Ohio 905C); Soldiers Hom Fair, Milwaukee, Wis. in June, 1865 (Fuld NC-17a).

METROPOLITAN CARNIVAL

Washington, D.C.

Baker	Date	Metal	Size	VF	EF	Unc
367	1871	Lead	74.5mm	300.	—	—

Laureate head right. Around: METROPOLITAN CARNIVAL FEBRU ARY 20 & 21, 1871, all within olive wreath. Rv: Capitol at Washington across center. Above: BY ACT OF CONGRESS JULY16. 1790. THE SEAT OF GOVERNMENT OF THE UNITED STATES. TO BE PERMA NENTLY FIXED AT THE CITY OF WASHINGTON. in four curved lines Below the design: POPULATION OF CITY IN 1810 WAS 8298. POPU LATION IN 1871 - 109412. CORNERSTONE LAID BY GEN. WASH INGTON SEP 18 1793. COR. STONE. EXTENSION LAID BY PRES FILLMORE. JULY. 4. 1851. LENGTH 751 FT. 4 IN. HEIGHT OF DOME ABOVE TIDE 377 FT. COST ABOUT $12,000.000 in eight lines, the las four being curved. Plain edge. Rarity 9. (Collins 287)

These pieces are known only as casts, said to be from dies. The portrait re sembles no original.

The 1988 Magriel sale offered a better than VF specimen. Few sales have offered this piece in the 20th century.

This extremely rare cast from dies was recognized as a rarity by Chapman in H.P. Smith Sale in 1904. Magriel sale, 1988, lot 70 resold in Presidential 61, 11/96, as lot 158. Second specimen ex-Picker, Fuld, NNC, Brand, Hall with similar appearance to Magriel specimen. Only 3 pieces located.

NORWALK MEMORIAL

Baker	Date	Metal	Size	VF	EF	Unc
369	1869	Silver	38.6mm	—	—	300.

Uniformed bust right, KEY. F ON TRUNCATION. Around: NORWALK CONN. MEMORIAL / 1869. Rv: BOUGHT OF THE NORWAKE INDI-ANS / BY / ROGER LUDLOWE AND CAP. DANIEL PATRICK / 1640./ FOUNDED 1649./ SETTLED BY ACT OF COURT 1650. / BURNT BY BRITISH UNDER TRYON/ 1779./ BOROUGH INCORPORATION / 1836./ D. & N. R.R. OPENED 1852. / POPULATION 15.000 / I.F. WOODS MEM. SERIES in 13 lines. Plain edge. Rarity 8.

369A	1869	Copper	38.6mm	—	—	75.00

As 369. Plain edge. Rarity 6. (Bullowa-Lessin sale, lot 73)

369B	1869	Bronze	38.6mm	—	—	75.00

As 369. Plain edge. Rarity 6.

369C	1869	WM	38.6mm	—	50.00	60.00

As 369. Plain edge. Rarity 5.

Dies cut by William H. Key of Philadelphia for Isaac F. Wood

SABBATH SCHOOL JUBILEE

Struck about 1862

Baker	Date	Metal	Size	VF	EF	Unc
370	1842	Silver	32mm	—	—	125.

Obverse as Baker 264 (facing bust in civil dress, UNITY OF GOVERN-MENT, etc.) Rv: In five lines at center: SABBATH SCHOOL JUBILEE JULY 4 1842. Around: RELIGION OUR SAFEGUARD * TEMPERANCE OUR SHIELD * Plain edge. Rarity 8.

370A	1842	Copper	32mm	—	—	35.00

As 370. Plain edge. Rarity 7.

370B	1842	Nickel	32mm	—	—	35.00

As 370. Plain edge. Magnetic. Rarity 8.

370C	1842	WM	32mm	—	—	30.00

As 370. Plain edge. Rarity 7.

The dies are by Robert Lovett Jr. of Philadelphia, who according to J. Doyle DeWitt, used the obverse in combinations about 1862.

BROOKLYN SUNDAY SCHOOL

Baker	Date	Metal	Size	VF	EF	Unc
371	1876	Silver	31.4mm	—	—	85.00

Draped bust left above crossed palm branches, 12 six-pointed stars with a period at center above. WASHINGTON below. The bust divides 1776 - 1876. Around: 100TH.YEAR OF OUR NATIONAL INDEPEN-DENCE. Rv: Within olive wreath: 47th ANNIVERSARY OF THE BROOKLYN SUNDAY SCHOOL UNION, MAY, 1876 in eight lines. Plain edge. Rarity 8.

371A	1876	Copper	31.4mm	—	—	40.00

As 371. Plain edge. Rarity 7. (Collins 291)

371B	1876	Brass	31.4mm	—	—	40.00

As 371. Plain edge. Rarity 7.

371C	1876	WM	31.4mm	—	—	30.00

As 371. Plain edge. Rarity 5.

The obverse die of 371 is also used on Baker 293 and 271, but 371 is the original combination for it. By George Hampden Lovett.

JAPANESE EMBASSY

Baker	Date	Metal	Size	VF	EF	Unc
368	1860	Silver	51mm	—	Ex. Rare	—

Undraped bust right, LOVETT PHILA. beneath bust. Around: GEORGIUS WASHINGTON PRAES. PRIM. RER. CONF. AMER. MD-CCLXXXIX (same obverse as Baker 135).Rv: Within oak wreath, in seven lines: TO THE JAPANESE EMBASSY FROM BAILEY & CO. JEWELLERS, PHILADELPHIA. 1860. Plain edge. (PCAC Nov. 1994 Sale, lot 254)

368A	1860	Bronze	51mm	—	55.00	90.00

As 368. Plain edge. Rarity 5.

368B	1860	Brass	51mm	—	—	110.

As 368. Plain edge. Rarity 8.

368C	1860	WM	51mm	40.00	65.00	100.

As 368. Plain edge. Rarity 7. (Collins 288)

The first Embassy of the Empire of Japan was accredited to the U.S. and visited with President Buchanan on May 17, 1860. Members of the Embassy staff later visited Bailey & Co., the leading jewelry and silverware firm in Philadelphia, and Bailey's commissioned Robert Lovett Jr. to create these special medals to honor the occasion. A single speciman in gold was presented to the chief of the Embassy and other members were given silver specimens. The location of the gold and most silver specimens, if they still exist, is not known.

Bailey & Co. were the issuers of a lengthy series of store cards about 1860, Miller Pa 28 through 33, which give the date 1855. See Russ Rulau's *U.S. Merchant Tokens 1845-1860.*)

JERSEY CITY SUNDAY SCHOOLS

First obverse

Baker	Date	Metal	Size	VF	EF	Unc
372	1876	Silver	28mm	—	—	115.

Draped bust left, small P on truncation. Above: *IN GOD WE TRUST. * / 1776. CENTENNIAL. 1876. Rv: Within palm wreath: 21ST / ANNIVER-SARY / OF THE / JERSEY CITY / SUNDAY / SCHOOLS / MAY 22 / 1876. Plain edge. Rarity 8. (Clark sale, lot 2123)

372A	1876	Bronze	28mm	—	—	40.00

As 372. Plain Edge. Rarity 5.

372B	1876	WM	28mm	—	33.00	40.00

As 372. Plain country. Rarity 5.

Second obverse

Baker	Date	Metal	Size	VF	EF	Unc
373	1876	Silver	28mm	—	—	115.

Undraped bust left in sunken field, surrounded by raised border. Around: THE PATTERN OF PATRIOTISM, INDUSTRY AND PROGRESS (same obverse as Baker 340). Rv: As reverse of 372. Plain edge. Rarity 8.

373A	1876	Bronze	28mm	—	25.00	45.00

As 373. Plain edge. Rarity 6.

373B	1876	WM	28mm	—	—	35.00

As 373. Plain edge. Rarity 4.

Third obverse

Baker	Date	Metal	Size	VF	EF	Unc
374	1876	Silver	28mm	—	—	115

Obverse as Baker 307 (draped bust left, WASHINGTON THE FATHER OF OUR COUNTRY).Rv: as reverse as 372. Plain edge. Rarity 8.

374A	1876	Bronze	28mm	—	—	45.00

As 374. Plain edge. Rarity 6.

374B	1876	WM	28mm	—	—	45.00

As 374. Plain edge. Rarity 6.

Baker 372 through 374 were struck by George Hampden Lovett of New York. From the signature P on the bust on 372, it appears that obverse was designed by Anthony C. Paquet of Philadelphia.

BETHANY SABBATH SCHOOL

Philadelphia

Baker	Date	Metal	Size	VF	EF	Unc
375	1883	Bronze	35mm	—	30.00	40.00

Undraped bust right. Around: BETHANY SABBATH SCHOOL PHIL. Rv: In Nine lines: PRESENTED TO THE MEMBERS OF THE SCHOOL ON THE OCCASION OF THE 25TH. ANNIVERSARY MARCH 22, 1883. Plain edge. Rarity 5. (Collins 300)

375A	1883	WM	35mm	—	30.00	40.00

As 375. Plain edge. Rarity 5.

The bust on the obverse is the same as that appearing on Baker 347 by Charles E. Barber of the U.S. Mint.

PHILLIPSE MANOR BICENTENNIAL

Baker	Date	Metal	Size	VF	EF	Unc
376	1882	Bronze	33mm	—	—	75.00

Undraped bust right, LOVETT on truncation, a folded flag below. Around: YONKERS INCORP. AS A VILLAGE, 1855, AS A CITY, 1872. Rv: house in center, PHILLIPSE MANOR above, 1682 BI-CENTENNI-AL 1882 below. Plain edge. Issued with loop. Rarity 6.

376A	1882	WM	33mm	—	—	75.00

As 376. Plain edge. Rarity 6. (Collins 302)

Dies cut by Robert Lovett Jr. of Philadelphia.

N.G.P. ARMORY DEDICATED

Baker	Date	Metal	Size	VF	EF	Unc
377	1884	Bronze	32mm	—	—	50.00

Undraped bust right, GEORGE WASHINGTON around. Rv: Regimental badge at center. Around:1ST. REGT INFANTRY N.G.P. ORGAND. APRIL 19,1861/ ARMORY DEDICATED / * FEB.22 1884* Plain edge. Rarity 5. (Collins 303)

377A	1884	WM	32mm	—	—	35.00

As 377. Plain edge. Rarity 7. (Collins 304)

377E	1884	WM	30mm	—	—	35.00

Normal obverse for this medal (no Washington portrait). Rv: As reverse of 377. Plain edge. Rarity 7.

The bust used on the obverse is the same as that on Baker 279, the mint Allegiance medal portrait by Paquet. At this period the U.S. mint and the medalists and engravers of Philadelphia were particularly close, making many medallic and token products by joint effort.

The opening of the 1st infantry Regiment Armory of the National Guard of Pennsylvania in 1884 was quite a community event. There are other medallic mementoes of this armory dated 1884.

ROBERT E. LEE CAMP

CONFEDERATE VETERANS

Baker	Date	Metal	Size	VF	EF	Unc
378	1883	Bronze	30mm	—	—	90.00

Obverse as 377. Rv: Three tents, in front of which two soldiers are clasping hands; an eagle displayed at base. Around: R. E. LEE CAMP NO. 1 C.V. ORGANIZED APRIL, 1883. Plain edge. Rarity 7.

378A	1883	WM	30mm	—	—	90.00

As 378. Plain edge. Rarity 7.

The Washington bust is by Anthony C. Paquet. It is not certain who struck these medals for the Confederate Veterans, then newly organized.

INTERNATIONAL MEDICAL CONGRESS

Baker	Date	Metal	Size	VF	EF	Unc
F-378	1887	Bronze	76mm	—	—	275.

Undraped Washington bust right, C.E. BARBER F. under bust. Around: UNITED STATES OF AMERICA / *FOUNDER OF THE REPUBLIC * Rv: Group of five persons within central circle. Half-nude bearded doctor seated at left, holding staff wound with a snake, a seated woman with child at his feet, and two half-nude men in back, one with cane and the other with crutch. Below design: WASHINGTON 1887. Outside circle: Lengthy circular inscription. Plain edge. Rarity 6. (Rich Hartzog Aug. 1983 sale, lot 443; Collins 281)

Charles E. Barber, the Mint engraver, used the classic Houdon bust as his model for this obverse. This medal possesses class and style.

The Collins specimen's edge was engraved: H. CUNDELL-JULER, CINCINNATI, O.

Your authors have traced Dr. E. Cundell Juler of Cincinnati, something collector Paul Magriel apparently was unable to do. The "H." instead of "E." was either an engraver's error or a misreading of the edge inscription by the cataloger. Dr. Juler's practice was located at 12 1/2 West 9th Street in 1894; he is still listed 1903. He was the author of a book, *Ophthalmic Practice*.

OHIO CENTENNIAL EXPOSITION

Baker	Date	Metal	Size	VF	EF	Unc
G-378	1888	WM	38mm	—	25.00	40.00

Nude bust right, MURDOCK under truncation. Around: * GEORGE WASHINGTON * / BORN FEB. 22' 1732. DIED DEC. 14' 1799. Rv: Exposition buildings, CENTENNIAL EXPOSITION above, 1788 -- 1888 at sides, OF THE / OHIO VALLEY & / CENTRAL STATES / AT / CINCINNATI in exergue. Plain edge. Rarity 8. (Hibler-Kappen 146)

Struck in Cincinnati by James Murdock.

WORLDS COLUMBIAN EXPOSITION

Illustration reduced

Baker	Date	Metal	Size	VF	EF	Unc
K378	1893	Bronze	91mm	—	—	—

Two facing medallions, C. COLUMBUS head to right, G. WASHINGTON head to left. Eagle head above, in its beak a scroll inscribed E PLURIBUS UNUM. Beneath medallions (tiny lettering): C. ORSINI -- C.B. MILLEFIORI INC. At bottom edge (tiny): ROME. Rv: Female robed America gestures toward radiant cross over fairgrounds on lakeshore. Around: COLUMBIAN EXPOSITION CHICAGO/ MDCCCXCII-III. Plain edge. (Eglit 102; Kirtley May 26, 1998 sale, lot M8; Storer 9)

A magnificent medal, struck in Italy.

CENTURY OF PROGRESS EXPOSITION
Chicago, Ill.

Baker	Date	Metal	Size	EF	AU	Unc
P378	1934	Copper/WM	63mm	—	—	30.00

Civil bust 3/4 left within circle, wide ornamental border around. Rv: A CENTURY OF PROGRESS / Colonial (fancy script) Village (fancy script) /. CHICAGO 1934. Plain edge. (Kirtley May 26, 1998 sale, lot C7; Roelofs coll.)

Chapter 23

POLITICAL AND CALENDAR MEDALS

HERO OF TIPPECANOE

Struck 1861

Baker	Date	Metal	Size	VF	EF	Unc
379	ND	Silver	35mm	—	—	200.

Facing civil bust of Washington, head slightly right. Around: UNITY OF GOVERNMENT IS THE MAIN PILLAR OF INDEPENDENCE (same obverse as Baker 227 and 264). Rv: Log cabin, over which an American flag flies, a tree at either side, and a barrel of cider and a mug at left. THE PEOPLES CHOICE above, THE HERO / OF / TIPPECANOE below. Plain edge. (DeWitt WHH-G (5): Garrett 1866). Rarity 8.

379A	ND	Copper	35mm	—	—	100.

As 379. Plain Edge. Rarity 8.

379B	ND	Brass	35mm	—	—	100.

As 379. Plain Edge. Rarity 8.

379C	ND	Nickel	35mm	—	—	100.

As 379. Plain Edge. Magnetic Rarity 8.

379D	ND	WM	35mm	—	—	100.

As 379. Plain Edge. Rarity 8.

At first glance this would seem to be a medal of William Henry Harrison's presidential campaign of 1840. The Bangs Merwin Co. sale of 1862 referred to them as "from Stimpson dies, recently discovered." But in 1865, at the sale of the J.N.T. Levick collection, and at other occasions during the period, these were referred to as "modern reproductions."

J. Doyle DeWitt in his A Century of Campaign Buttons 1789-1889, listed a number of mulings made of the new log cabin-and cider barrel die. The dies were cut by Robert Lovett Jr. of Philadelphia. The fancy novelties apparently did bring good prices at first, but all are rare today. Age has given them both legitimacy and value.

BUCHANAN AND BRECKINRIDGE

First obverse

Baker	Date	Metal	Size	VF	EF	Unc
380	1856	Bronze	47mm	—	—	150.

Undraped bust left within a circle, KEY under the bust. Around: THE UNION MUST & SHALL BE PRESERVED / UNITED WE STAND DIVIDED WE FALL / 1856 / JACKSON in two concentric circles divided by a circular line. Rv: A buck leaping to right above 1856 and a cannon. In field around buck are 32 stars. Below cannon is: - AND - /BRECKINRIDGE. Plain edge. (DeWitt JB 1856-2: Satterlee 235). Rarity 8.

380A	1856	WM	47mm	—	—	150.

As 380. Plain edge. Rarity 8.

380C	1856	Lead	48.6mm	—	—	Unique?

Obverse as 380. Rv: Blank, Weight 1121.3 grains. Die trial? (Schuster coll.)

The dies are by William H. Key of Philadelphia. The reverse is a play on sounds. *Buck cannon* and Breckinridge for "Buchanan and Breckinridge," the Democrat Party's candidates - and winners - that year.

Second obverse

Baker	Date	Metal	Size	VF	EF	Unc
381	1856	Bronze	47mm	—	—	150.

Obverse as Baker 221 ('Eight Presidents' medal). Rv: As reverse of 380. Plain edge. (DeWitt JB 1856-3). Rarity 8.

The obverse die was cut by W.H. Bridgens of New York about 1840. It was re-used by Key about 1860 or later to create a rare variety to sell to collectors by muling it with his 'Buck Cannon' die.

Muling

382	1856	Bronze	47mm	—	—	600.

Obverse was 380 (Washington left). Rv: As obverse of 381 (Eight Presidents). Plain edge. Rarity 8. (DeWitt JB 1856-5; Garrett 1867; Hirsch Coll.)

382A	1856	WM	47mm	—	—	200.

As 382. Plain edge. Rarity 8.

A muling by Key of both obverses used with his 'Buck Cannon' die, including further use of the 1840 Bridgens die. All pieces 380-382 are rare.

LINCOLN AND JOHNSON

Baker	Date	Metal	Size	VF	EF	Unc
383	1864	Silver	32mm	—	—	175.

Small Washington head right against five-pointed star made up of rays, 13 small stars around. Around: FREEDOM TO ALL MEN. Below: UNION. Rv: Lincoln bust left, W. H. KEY F. under bust. Around: LINCOLN & JOHNSON UNION CANDIDATES / 1864. Plain edge. Rarity 8. (DeWitt AL 1864-5; King 77; Zabriskie 56; Garrett 1868)

383A	1864	Copper	32mm	—	—	100.

As 383. Plain edge. Rarity 5. (Zabriskie 57)

383B	1864	Brass	32mm	—	—	100.

As 383. Plain edge. Rarity 5. (Zabriskie 58)

383C	1864	WM	32mm	—	65.00	80.00

As 383. Plain edge. Rarity 3. (DeWitt AL 1864-5; King 77; Holland 205; Collins 307)

The dies were cut by William H. Key of Philadelphia and were purchased by medal publisher Isaac F. Wood of New York City.

HONEST ABE OF THE WEST

Baker 384 - 384E may now be found in Chapter 35, 19th Century Store Cards, as numbers 569M - 569R, Bramhall's "Wideawakes" Series.

CALENDAR MEDALS

Benjamin C. True

Struck 1857-59

Baker	Date	Metal	Size	VF	EF	Unc
385	1799	Brass	34mm	50.00	75.00	100.

Undraped bust right. TRUE on truncation. Around: GEORGE WASH-INGTON. BORN FEB. 22, 1732. DIED DEC. 14, 1799. Rv: Calendar, Plain edge. Rarity 6.

385A	1799	WM	35mm	—	—	100.

As 385. Plain edge. Rarity 8.
Dies cut by Benjamin C. True of Cincinnati, Ohio.

386	1799	Brass	35mm	—	75.00	100.

Washington standing full length, in uniform, with orderly in background holding horse. Around: BORN, FEB. 22, 1732. DIED DEC. 14, 1799. Rv: Calendar. Reeded edge. Rarity 8.

Peter H. Jacobus

Struck 1858

Baker	Date	Metal	Size	VF	EF	Unc
387	1799	Brass	33.8mm	45.00	75.00	100.

Equestrian figure in uniform right, a tree at left, on ground below: P H J. Around: THE FATHER OF OUR COUNTRY BORN, FEB. 22, 1732 DIED, DEC. 14, 1799. Rv: A calendar. Reeded edge. Rarity 5. (Collins 308; Bob Moffat March 1998 Sale, lot 80)

Dies cut by Peter H. Jacobus of Philadelphia in 1858. The original use of the Washington die was on the busniess card of S.J. Bestor (Baker 514, Miller PA 50-52).

For a full accounting of Baker 385-387 and all other calendar medals and store cards, see the catalog of these published in The Numismatist for May 1959 (page 55) and June 1959 (page 675) by Melvin and George Fuld.

Chapter 24

CENTENNIALS OF INDEPENDENCE, 1876-1976

DECLARATION OF INDEPENDENCE

DEMAREST-LOVETT

First reverse

Baker	Date	Metal	Size	VF	EF	Unc
388	1776	Copper	40mm	—	65.00	80.00

Undraped bust right, within ornamental border including cavalry and infantry, LOVETT on truncation of bust. Around: TO COMMEMORATE THE 100DTH, ANNIVERSARY OF THE DECLARATION OF INDEPENDENCE. Rv: Copy of Trumbull's painting of the Congress of 1776 receiving the committee's report on the Declaration of Independence. Above: THE DECLARATION. Below: OF INDEPENDENCE 1776. / DEMAREST. SC. Plain edge. Rarity 5. (Hibler-Kappen 75-77)

388A	1776	Bronze	40mm	—	20.00	—

As 388. Plain edge. Rarity 5.

388B	1776	WM	40mm	—	20.00	—

As 388. Plain edge. Rarity 5.

The obverse die was engraved by George Hampden Lovett, the reverse by Abraham Demarest.

Second reverse

Baker	Date	Metal	Size	VF	EF	Unc
389	1776	Silver	42mm	—	—	90.00

Obverse as 388. Rv: Similar to reverse of 388, but DEMAREST. SC. omitted from the die. The reverse is from a differently executed die. Plain edge. Rarity 8. (Hibler-Kappen 78 -79; Garrett 1869)

389A	1776	Bronze	42mm	—	—	60.00

As 389. Plain edge. Rarity 5. (Garrett 1869)

389B	1776	Brass	42mm	—	—	60.00

As 389. Plain edge. Rarity 5.

389C	1776	WM	42mm	—	—	60.00

As 389. Plain edge. Rarity 5.(Hibler - Kappen 79; Collins 309)

By George Hampden Lovett of New York City.

COLONIAL INDEPENDENCE

Baker	Date	Metal	Size	VF	EF	Unc
390	1876	WM	40mm	—	—	—

Obverse as 388. Rv: In nine lines: UNITED STATES OF AMERICA IN COMMEMORATION OF THE CENTENNIAL OF COLONIAL INDEPENDENCE 1876. In line at lower rim: PAT. NOV. 3. 1874 H & L. Plain edge. Rarity 6. (Hibler-Kappen 74)

390D	1876	WM	40mm	—	—	25.00

Obverse as reverse of 390 (COLONIAL INDEPENDENCE) Rv: As reverse of 389 (Declaration scene, DEMAREST omitted). Plain edge. Rarity 4.

For some reason, George H. Lovett made a fair number of the mulings, Baker 390D.

JOHN HANCOCK SIGNATURE

Struck 1876

Baker	Date	Metal	Size	VF	EF	Proof
391	ND	Silver	42mm	—	—	—

Obverse as 388. Rv: Facsimile of the signature of John Hancock. Above: WORDS SPOKEN BY JOHN HANCOCK, / AFTER SIGNING THE DECLARATION OF INDEPENDENCE / (13 stars in an arc). Below: In five lines: THERE ! JOHN BULL CAN READ THAT NAME WITHOUT SPECTACLES, NOW LET HIM DOUBLE HIS REWARD. Plain edge. Rarity 8.

391A	ND	Copper	42mm	—	—	90.00

As 391. Plain edge. Rarity 4.

391B	ND	Bronze	42mm	—	—	150.

As 391. Plain edge. Rarity 5. (Garrett 1870)

391C	ND	Brass	42mm	—	—	—

As 391. Plain Edge. Rarity 5.

391D	ND	WM	42mm	—	—	150.

As 391. Plain edge. Rarity 5. (Garrett 1870; Collins 310)

391G	1776	WM	42mm	—	—	—

Obverse as reverse of 391 (John Hancock signature). Rv: As reverse of 389 (Declaration scene, DEMAREST omitted). Plain edge. Rarity 5.

Baker 388 through 391 are die-linked through the obverse die by George Hampden Lovett. Neither the portraiture nor the reverses exhibit any particular artistic merit, as W.S. Baker pointed out a century ago.

INDEPENDENCE HALL MEDALS

Commenced 1729

Baker	Date	Metal	Size	VF	EF	Proof
392	1876	Silver	38mm	—	—	115.

Uniformed bust right, KEY F. under bust. On scroll below: BORN FEB 22 1732 / DIED DEC 14 1799 in two lines. Above: GEORGE WASHINGTON. Rv: Independence Hall, KEY F. below. 1776 INDEPENDENCE HALL 1876 above, COMMENCED 1729 / FINISHED 1734. Plain edge. Rarity 8. (Hibler-Kappen 39)

392A	1876	Bronze	38mm	—	—	50.00

As 392. Plain edge. Rarity 5. (Clark Sale, lot 2124; Garrett 1870; Collins 311)

392B	1876	WM	38mm	—	25.00	50.00

Struck by William H. Key of Philadelphia. Good portraiture on obverse.

REMEMBRANCE OF THE CENTENNIAL

Baker	Date	Metal	Size	VF	EF	Unc
393	1876	WM	32mm	—	—	—

Bust three-quarters left., Go. WASHINGTON beneath. Around: FIRST IN WAR, FIRST IN PEACE, FIRST IN THE HEARTS OF HIS COUNTRYMEN. Rv: Independence Hall and adjoining Hall. Above: IN REMEMBRANCE OF THE CENTENNIAL JULY 4TH, 1876. Below: INDEPENDENCE HALL AS IN 1776 in three lines. Plain edge. Rarity 7.

Baker 393 is of English origin.

STUBENRAUCH MEDAL

Baker	Date	Metal	Size	VF	EF	Unc
A393	1876	Bronze	40mm	—	100.	—

Standing robed female personification of Liberty placing wreath over the head of kneeling figure of Vigilance. To right is a pedestal bearing bust of Washington. Sword and American shield rest against the pedestal. Surrounding scene is the legend: ETERNAL VIGILANCE IS THE PRICE OF LIBERTY. GEO. WASHINGTON / 1776 in exergue. Legend in nine lines surrounded by a wreath with an eagle perched on a shield at top. THANK PROVIDENCE / REJOICE! / JULY 4TH / 1876. Rare medal. (PCAC June, 1990 Sale, lot 342)

Carl Stubenrauch of San Antonio, Texas 1875-1885 was a superlative medalist who was a court engraver in Germany until emigrating to St. Louis in the 1850's. He moved to Texas circa 1875 -76. For examples of his work, see Russ Rulau's *U.S. Trade* Tokens 1866-1889, numbers Mo-SL 32J and Tx-SA 173.

BIRTH PLACE OF INDEPENDENCE

Baker	Date	Metal	Size	VF	EF	Unc
394	1776	Silver	38mm	—	—	—

Undraped bust right, 1776 below, GENERAL WASHINGTON AROUND. Rv: Independence Hall and adjoining buildings. BIRTH PLACE OF AMERICAN in arc above, INDEPENDENCE / 1776 BELOW. Plain edge. Rarity 8. (Hibler-Kappen 42-45)

Baker	Date	Metal	Size	VF	EF	Unc
394A	1776	Gilt/C	38mm	—	—	60.00

As 394. Plain edge. Rarity 5.

| 394B | 1776 | Copper | 38mm | — | — | 60.00 |

As 394. Plain edge. Rarity 5.

| 394C | 1776 | WM | 38mm | — | 40.00 | 60.00 |

As 394. Plain Edge. Rarity 5. (Collins 312)

| 394 G | 1776 | — | 38mm | — | — | — |

Obverse as 394. Rv: Blank, with arabesque border. Plain edge. (Foot note in Baker)

Baker 394 was published by George B. Soley of Philadelphia.

PAQUET SERIES BY KEY

Baker	Date	Metal	Size	VF	EF	Unc
395	ND	Silver	18mm	—	—	30.00

Bust in civil dress right, AP on truncation (same obverse as Baker 156). Rv: Independence Hall. In exergue: KEY.F / INDEPENDENCE HALL. Plain edge. Rarity 7. (Bullowa - Lessin sale, lot 71)

| 395A | ND | Copper | 18mm | — | — | 15.00 |

As 395. Plain edge. Rarity 4.

| 395B | ND | Bronze | 18mm | — | — | 15.00 |

As 395. Plain edge. Rarity 4.

| 395C | ND | WM | 18mm | — | — | 15.00 |

As 395. Plain edge. Rarity 4.

Designed by Anthony C. Paquet and struck by William H. Key in Philadelphia.

Baker	Date	Metal	Size	VF	EF	Unc
396	ND	Silver	18mm	—	—	30.00

Obverse as 395. Rv: As reverse of 395, but 13 stars are added around the hall. Plain edge. Rarity 7.

| 396A | ND | Copper | 18mm | — | — | 15.00 |

As 396. Plain edge. Rarity 4. (Bullowa-Lessin 70)

| 396B | ND | WM | 18mm | — | — | 15.00 |

As 396. Plain edge. Rarity 4.

Baker	Date	Metal	Size	VF	EF	Unc
396F	ND	Silver	18mm	—	—	30.00

Obverse as Baker 155 (undraped bust right, P on truncation). Rv: As reverse of 396. Plain edge. Rarity 7.

| 396G | ND | Copper | 18mm | — | — | 25.00 |

As 396F. Plain edge. Rarity 5. (Bullowa-Lessin 69; Collins 313)

| 396H | ND | Brass | 18mm | — | — | 25.00 |

As 396F. Plain edge. Rarity 5.

| 396J | ND | WM | 18mm | — | — | 25.00 |

As 396F. Plain edge. Rarity 5.

Baker 395 through 396J were the products of Anthony C. Paquet obverses and William H. Key reverses, struck by Key. They greatly resemble the earlier U.S. Mint series medalets - a resemblance which was intended for public sale purposes during the Centennial.

INDEPENDENCE HALL

Baker	Date	Metal	Size	VF	EF	Unc
C-396	ND	Copper	25mm	—	—	40.00

Nude bust right, hair tied in a bow at back of neck. Rv: Hall, INDEPENDENCE HALL above. Plain edge.

| C-396A | ND | WM | 25mm | — | — | 40.00 |

As C-396. Plain edge.

| C-396B | ND | Silver | 25mm | — | — | 40.00 |

As C-396. Plain edge.

This series, unknown to Baker or Douglas, probably emanates from the 1876 period. In collection Dr. I.N. Schuster.

LIBERTY BELL MEDALS

PROCLAIM LIBERTY THROUGHOUT THE LAND

Baker	Date	Metal	Size	EF	Unc	Proof
397	1876	Silver	38mm	60.00	150.	—

Obverse as Baker 392. Rv: Liberty Bell, cracked, on which is visible its provenance: PASS AND STOW / PHILADA / MDCCLIII. LIBERTY BELL above, 1776 left, 1876 right, LEV. XXV VX. below. Around all: *PROCLAIM LIBERTY THROUGHOUT THE LAND UNTO ALL THE INHABITANTS THEREOF. Plain edge. Rarity 8. (Garrett 1871; Collins 314)

Baker	Date	Metal	Size	EF	Unc	Proof
397A	1876	Copper	38mm	—	35.00	—

As 397. Plain edge. Rarity 5. (Garrett 1871; Collins 314)

397B	1876	Bronze	38mm	—	35.00	—

As 397. Plain edge. Rarity 5.

397C	1876	WM	38mm	—	35.00	—

As 397. Plain edge. Rarity 5. (Collins 315)

All struck by William H. Key of Philadelphia. The medallic work is impressive. Published by J.H. Diehl of Philadelphia.

AMERICA CENTENNIAL

Baker	Date	Metal	Size	VF	EF	AU
398	1876	WM	39mm	90.00	200.	325.

Head left, on a shield. Above the head in a band: E PLURIBUS UNUM; above that, in a compartment of the shield: 1776 with 15 stars around . Around the head, in the form of a bell. FIRST IN WAR, FIRST IN PEACE, FIRST IN THE HEARTS OF HIS COUNTRYMEN. Script signatures along bottom rim. Rv: Liberty Bell on a shield, inscribed PROCLAIM LIBERTY THROUGHOUT ALL THE LAND, UNTO ALL THE INHABITANTS THEREOF in six lines. CENTENNIAL above in a band, 1776 left, 1876 right AMERICA below. Plain edge. Rarity 9.

JAMES A. BOLEN

399	1876	WM	25mm	—	—	—

Roman-mantled bust right, BOLEN under bust, WASHINGTON above. Rv: Liberty Bell surmounted by eagle with rays pointed downward, seven stars at left, six at right. CENTENNIAL above, 1776 1876 below. Plain edge. Rarity 8.

Struck by James A. Bolen, Springfield, Mass. Obverse is the same as Baker 56.

ANTHONY C. PAQUET

First obverse, First reverse

Baker	Date	Metal	Size	VF	EF	Unc.
400	1876	Silver	18mm	—	—	30.00

Obverse as 395. Rv: Liberty Bell, 1776 left, 1876 right, LIBERTY BELL below. Plain edge. Rarity 7.

400A	1876	Copper	18mm	—	—	15.00

As 400. Plain edge. Rarity 4.

400B	1876	WM	18mm	—	—	15.00

As 400. Plain edge. Rarity 4.

400C	1876	Brass	18mm	—	25.00	35.00

As 400. Plain edge. Rarity 6? (Collins 316)

Obverse cut by Anthony C. Paquet. Probably struck by William H. Key.

Second reverse

Baker	Date	Metal	Size			Unc
401	1776	Silver	18mm	—	—	30.00

Obverse as 395. Rv: Liberty Bell and supporting beam, the clapper dividing 17 - 76. Above: LIBERTY BELL. Plain edge. Rarity 7.

401A	1776	Copper	18mm	—	—	15.00

As 401. Plain edge. Rarity 4.

401B	1776	Brass	18mm	—	—	15.00

As 401. Plain edge. Rarity 4.

401C	1776	WM	18mm	—	—	15.00

As 401. Plain edge. Rarity 4.

Obverse die cut by Anthony C. Paquet- Probably struck by William H. Key of Philadelphia.

Second obverse,

First reverse

Baker	Date	Metal	Size	VF	EF	Unc
402	1876	Silver	18mm	—	—	—

Undraped bust right, similar to the bust on Baker 155- Rv: As reverse of 400. Plain edge. Rarity 8.

402A	1876	Copper	18mm	—	—	25.00

As 402. Plain edge. Rarity 4. (Collins 318)

402B	1876	Bronze	18mm	—	—	

As 402. Plain edge. Rarity 4.

402C	1876	Gilt	18mm	—	—	

As 402. Plain edge. Rarity 4.

402D	1876	Oreide	18mm	—	—	

As 402. Plain edge. Rarity 4.

Baker	Date	Metal	Size	VF	EF	Unc
402E	1876	Nickel	18mm	—	—	

As 402. Plain edge. Magnetic. Rarity 5.

402F	1876	WM	18mm	—	—	25.00

As 402. Plain edge. Rarity 4.

Dies for the obverse probably the work of Anthony C. Paquet; striking by

Key of Philadelphia.

Second obverse,

Second reverse

Baker	Date	Metal	Size			
403	1776	Silver	18mm	—	—	—

Obverse as 402. Rv: As reverse of 401. Plain edge. Rarity 7.

403A	1776	Copper	18mm	—	—	25.00

As 403. Plain edge. Rarity 4. (Collins 319)

403B	1776	Brass	18mm	—	—	35.00

As 403. Plain edge. Rarity 5.

403C	1776	Gilt	18mm	—	—	—

As 403. Plain edge. Rarity 4.

403D	1776	Oreide	18mm	—	—	—

As 403. Plain edge. Rarity 5.

403E	1776	Nickel	18mm	—	—	—

As 403. Plain edge. Magnetic. Rarity 5.

403F	1776	WM	18mm	—	—	—

As 403. Plain edge. Rarity 4.

Another Paquet-Key product.

AMERICAN COLONIES

Baker	Date	Metal	Size	VF	EF	Unc
404	1776	Silver	38mm	—	60.00	100.

Obverse as Baker 394 (undraped bust right, GENERAL WASHINGTON around, 1776 below. Rv: Officer, soldier with gun, cannon and balls, drum, staff with Liberty cap at center; at left a mill and pioneer with axe; radiant eye with 13 stars above divides AMERICAN - COLONIES; 1776 below. Plain edge. Rarity 8. (Hibler-Kappen 71-72)

404A	1776	Copper	38mm		20.00	—

As 404. Plain edge. Rarity 4.

404B	1776	Gilt/C	38mm		20.00	—

As 404. Plain edge. Rarity 4.

404C	1776	WM	38mm		20.00	—

As 404. Plain edge. Rarity 4.

Published by George B. Soley of Philadelphia.

FREE AND UNITED STATES

Baker	Date	Metal	Size	VF	EF	Proof
405	1876	Silver	38mm	—	—	100.

Obverse as 404. Rv: Liberty seated left, olive branch in her right hand, her left upon a keystone with scales and square on it. In background a ship, plow and railroad train. FREE AND UNITED STATES above, 1876 below. Plain edge. Rarity 8. (Hibler-Kappen 52-55; Garrett 1872-1873)

405A	1876	Copper	38mm			20.00

As 405. Plain edge. Rarity 4. (Garrett 1873)

405B	1876	Gilt/C	38mm			20.00

As 405. Plain edge. Rarity 4.

405C	1876	WM	38mm			20.00

As 405. Plain edge. Rarity 4.

405D	1876	Brass	38mm			20.00

As 405. Plain edge.

Published by George B. Soley of Philadelphia. Two proofs in silver were in the Garrett collection sold in 1981. These had been acquired by T. Harrison Garrett Jan. 26, 1882 (Staeblein sale by John Haseltine) and May 2, 1883 (55th sale by W. Elliott Woodward). One copper piece in proof in the Garrett sale had been acquired April 12, 1883 (Aulick sale by George W. Cogan).

AMERICAN INDEPENDENCE

Baker	Date	Metal	Size	VF	EF	Unc
406	1876	Silver	40mm	—	—	—

Head left, U. S. M. CO. below. Around: GEORGE WASHINGTON. Rv: In eight irregular lines at center: FIRST IN WAR FIRST IN PEACE, FIRST IN THE HEARTS OF THE AMERICAN PEOPLE BORN, FEB. 22, 1732 DIED, DEC. 14, 1799. Inscription around: IN COMMEMORATION OF THE 100TH. ANNIVERSARY OF AMERICAN INDEPENDENCE, 1876 *. Plain edge. Rarity 8.

406A	1876	WM	40mm	—	—	—

As 406. Plain edge. Rarity 4.

Published by the U. S. M. Company. This firm was unknown to Baker in 1885.

Possibly U.S. Manufacturing Co. of John F. W. Dorman in Baltimore, 1870-1879.

IN MEMORY OF THE CENTENARY

Baker	Date	Metal	Size	VF	EF	Unc
407	1876	Gilt/Brass	25mm	25.00	45.00	—

Draped bust left, GEORGE WASHINGTON 1876 * around. Rv: Eagle displayed surmounts a U.S. shield with 13 stars in chief; a scroll above is lettered: E PLURIBUS UNUM. Around: IN MEMORY OF THE CENTENARY. Plain edge. Very thin planchet. Rarity 7. (Collins 323).

The bust is outsize for the planchet. Baker thought this piece had a French origin. It may well have a German origin.

FIT KEYSTONE

Baker	Date	Metal	Size	VF	EF	Unc
408	1876	Silver	31mm	—	—	100.

Undraped bust right in circular panel surrounded by oak wreath on a large keystone, 1732 at left, 1799 at right, crest of Washington arms above, monogram GW at base. Rv: Arch and keystone bearing: WASHINGTON, support at left: 1776 1. F. W. DES and support at right: 1876 G. H. L FEC. In six lines: FIT KEYSTONE IN THE TRIUMPHAL ARCH WHICH SPANS THE NATION'S CENTURY. Plain edge. Rarity 8. (Collins 325)

408A	1876	Bronze	31mm	—	—	20.00

As 408. Plain edge. Rarity 5.

408B	1876	WM	31mm	—	—	20.00

As 408. Plain edge. Rarity 5.

408C	1876	Copper	31.5mm	—	—	Rare

As 408. Rarity 8? (Collins 326).

Struck by George Hampden Lovett and Published by Isaac F. Wood, both of New York.

FIRST CENTURY OF LIBERTY

Baker	Date	Metal	Size	VF	EF	Unc
409	1876	Silver	42mm	—	—	350.

Standing Washington and Grant support U.S. shield, eagle with scroll in its beak which reads E PLURIBUS UNUM. Beneath the shield: WASHINGTON 1776 - U. S. GRANT 1876. Around all are 25 stars. In exergue: CENTENNIAL / (tiny) F X KOEHLER. Rv: Within olive wreath in eight lines: DEDICATED TO THE PEOPLE OF THE UNITED STATES AS A MEMORIAL OF THE FIRST CENTURY OF LIBERTY. Plain edge. Issued holed. Rarity 9. (Wood 450; Hibler-Kappen 118)

409A	1876	Bronze	42mm		40.00	60.00

As 409. Plain edge. Rarity 8.

409B	1876	WM	42mm		27.00	45.00

As 409. Plain edge. Rarity 7. (Collins 327)

Francis Xavier Koehler of Baltimore, Md. cut the dies for these pieces, all of which are quite elusive. They are missing from most collections.

CALIFORNIA MEDAL

Baker	Date	Metal	Size	VF	EF	Proof
410	1876	Silver	41mm	—	250.	—

Small head right within olive wreath and flanked by two flags, in upper field. 1776 at left, 1876 at right. Scene below shows stagecoach rushing left, post rider in full gallop right in middle distance, sailing ship left in bay in distance. Under the design: C. F. MOHRIG - A. KUNER. F. Circle surrounds all. Outside circle: WASHINGTON THE GREAT FOUNDER OF THE UNITED STATES OF AMERICA. JULY 4TH. 1776. Rv: California arms in circle in upper field, San Francisco harbor view below show train moving right, steamship left, miners at work, all surrounded by 38 stars. Around outer circle: PROGRESS OF TIME AND FREEDOM TO ALL MANKIND. JULY 4TH. 1876 / .CALIFORNIA. Plain edge. Rarity 8. Issued with loop. (Garrett 1874)

| 410A | 1876 | WM | 41mm | — | 110. | — |

As 410. Plain edge. Rarity 6. (PCAC Nov. 1997 sale, lot 269)

Dies were cut by C. F. Mohrig and the striking was done by Albert Kuner, both of San Francisco. Kuner is famous as the maker of many California territorial gold coins. 410 is also reported in brass.

CENTENNIAL RECEPTION

New York City

First obverse

Baker	Date	Metal	Size	EF	Unc	Proof
411	1876	Silver	27mm	—	—	150.

Uniformed bust left, plain border around. Around: TO AID'ST. JOHN'S - GUILD' FLOATING - HOSPITAL / (WOOD'S SERIES "C" NO. 5). Rv: Martha Washington bust left Around: CENTENNIAL RECEPTION, BALL, & TEA - PARTY. / FEBY. 22ND. 1876 / ACADEMY OF MUSIC, N.Y. *. Plain edge. Rarity 9.

| 411A | 1876 | Copper | 27mm | — | — | 135. |

As 411. Plain edge. Rarity 9. (Wood 653)

| 411B | 1876 | WM | 27mm | — | — | 80.00 |

As 411. Plain edge. Rarity 7.

These were struck by George Hampden Lovett and published by Isaac F. Wood. Only a few pieces, mostly silver and white metal, were struck before the obverse die broke. Lovett then used the reverse die with Baker 412.

Second obverse

| 412 | 1876 | Silver | 27mm | — | — | 175. |

Undraped bust right. Around: TO AID 'ST. JOHN'S - GUILD' - FLOATING - HOSPITAL / (arc of 13 stars) / WOOD'S SERIES "C" NO. 5 / G. H. L. Plain edge. Rv: As reverse of 411. Rarity 8. (Garrett 1875; Bullowa-Lessin sale, lot 68; Clark sale, lot 2125; Collins 328)

| 412A | 1876 | Copper | 27mm | — | — | 70.00 |

As 412. Plain edge. Rarity 5. (Collins 329)

| 412B | 1876 | WM | 27mm | — | — | 50.00 |

As 412. Plain edge. Rarity 7. (Bullowa-Lessin sale, lot 67; Collins 330)

Struck by George Hampden Lovett and published by Isaac F. Wood, both of New York.

THE 100TH YEAR

First obverse

Baker	Date	Metal	Size	VF	EF	Unc
413	1876	Copper	28mm	—	—	45.00

Obverse as Baker 296 (undraped bust right, LOVETT on truncation and G. H. L. under bust. Around: GEORGE WASHINGTON). Rv: Martha Washington bust left, within olive wreath. Around: THE 100TH. YEAR OF OUR INDEPENDENCE 1876. Plain edge. Rarity 5.

| 413A | 1876 | WM | 28mm | — | — | 45.00 |

As 413. Plain edge. Rarity 5.

Second obverse

| 414 | 1876 | Copper | 28mm | — | — | 45.00 |

Draped bust left within olive wreath. Around: WASHINGTON THE FATHER OF OUR COUNTRY (same obverse as Baker 307). Rv: As reverse of 413. Plain edge. Rarity 5. (Collins 331)

| 414A | 1876 | Brass | 28mm | — | 30.00 | 45.00 |

As 414. Plain edge. Rarity 5.

| 414B | 1876 | WM | 28mm | — | — | 45.00 |

As 414. Plain edge. Rarity 6.

Muling

Baker	Date	Metal	Size	VF	EF	Unc
414M	ND	WM	28mm	—	—	45.00

Obverse as Baker 240 (undraped bust right, GEORGE WASHINGTON FIRST IN WAR, (etc.). Rv: As obverse of Baker 307 and 414. Plain edge. Rarity 6.

Baker 413 and 414 are products of George Hampden Lovett of New York City.

CHILDREN OF AMERICA

Baker	Date	Metal	Size	EF	Unc	Proof
415	1876	Silver	34mm	—	—	85.00

Draped bust left within oak and palm wreath. Around: 100TH. ANNIVERSARY OF THE DECLARATION OF INDEPENDENCE / * JULY 4, 1876 * (same obverse as Baker 271). Rv: Within oak and olive wreath joined at the top by date 1876: (in five lines) DEDICATED TO THE CHILDREN OF AMERICA. Plain edge. Rarity 8. (Hibler-Kappen 115-117)

| 415A | 1876 | Bronze | 34mm | — | — | 50.00 |

As 415. Plain edge. Rarity 5. (Hibler-Kappen 115; Collins 333)

| 415B | 1876 | Copper | 34mm | — | — | 50.00 |

As 415. Plain edge. Rarity 5.

| 415C | 1876 | WM | 34mm | — | — | 50.00 |

As 415. Plain edge. Rarity 5. (Bullowa-Lessin sale, lot 66; Collins 334)

| C-415 | 1876 | Silver | 34mm | — | — | Ex. Rare |

Obverse as Baker 415. Rv: Standing female facing right, chiseling inscription into a large rock. A globe rests upon books at her back. Plain edge. (Dr. 1. N. Schuster coll.)

DELPHOS UNION SCHOOL

Baker	Date	Metal	Size	EF	Unc	Proof
416	1876	WM	34.2mm	—	40.00	50.00

Obverse as 415. Rv: Without oak wreath, in seven lines: DEDICATED TO THE PUPILS OF THE DELPHOS UNION SCHOOL JULY 4, 1876. Plain edge. Rarity 6. (Collins 335)

The bust appearing on Baker 415 and 416 is the same as that on Baker 271, whose maker is George Hampden Lovett.

BOYS & GIRLS OF AMERICA

First obverse

Baker	Date	Metal	Size	VF	EF	Unc
417	1876	Copper	28mm	—	—	35.00

Draped bust left within olive wreath. Around: WASHINGTON THE FATHER OF OUR COUNTRY. Rv: Shield surmounted by Liberty cap atop staff, radiant, within group of six flags. Around: THE BOYS & GIRLS / .*. OF AMERICA 1876 .*. Plain edge. Rarity 5.

| 417A | 1876 | Bronze | 28mm | — | — | 35.00 |

As 417. Plain edge. Rarity 5.

| 417B | 1876 | Brass | 28mm | — | — | 35.00 |

As 417. Plain edge. Rarity 5.

| 417C | 1876 | WM | 28mm | — | — | 35.00 |

As 417. Plain edge. Rarity 5.

| 417M | ND | Bronze | 28mm | — | — | 50.00 |

Obverse as Baker 240. Rv: As obverse of 417. Plain edge.

| 417N | ND | WM | 28mm | — | — | 50.00 |

As 417M. Plain edge. (Bullowa-Lessin sale, lot 65)

Second obverse

Baker	Date	Metal	Size	VF	EF	Unc
418	1876	Copper	28mm	—	—	35.0

Obverse as 413. Rv: As reverse of 417. Plain edge. Rarity 4.

| 418A | 1876 | Bronze | 28mm | — | — | 35.0 |

As 418. Plain edge. Rarity 4.

| 418B | 1876 | WM | 28mm | — | — | 35.0 |

As 418. Plain edge. Rarity 4. (Bullowa-Lessin sale, lot 64)

Baker 417 and 418 were struck by George Hampden Lovett.

Third obverse

| A418 | 1876 | WM | 28mm | — | 75.00 | - |

FIRST IN WAR (etc.) obverse. Rv: As 417. Rarity 8. (Collins 338)

CENTENNIAL PARTY

First obverse

Baker	Date	Metal	Size	VF	EF	Un
419	1876	Silver	18mm	—	—	-

Bust right in civil dress, AP on truncation (same obverse as Baker 156 Rv: In eight lines: CHILDRENS CENTENNIAL PARTY AT LYCEU HALL POTTSVILLE PA. FEB. 22. 1876. Plain edge. Rarity 6.

| 419A | 1876 | Copper | 18mm | — | — | - |

As 419. Plain edge. Rarity 5.

| 419B | 1876 | Bronze | 18mm | — | — | 40.0 |

As 419. Plain edge. Rarity 5.

| 419C | 1876 | WM | 18mm | — | — | - |

As 419. Plain edge. Rarity 5.

AP - Anthony C. Paquet, the engraver of the dies.

Second obverse

| 420 | 1876 | Silver | 18mm | — | — | - |

Undraped bust right (same obverse as Baker 402). Rv: As reverse 419. Plain edge. Rarity 6.

| 420A | 1876 | WM | 18mm | — | — | - |

As 420. Plain edge. Rarity 5.

CHILDRENS BALL

Cape May, N.J.

Baker	Date	Metal	Size	VF	EF	Un
421	1876	Silver	18mm	—	—	45.0

Obverse as 420. Rv: CHILDREN'S / BALL / STOCKTON / HOTEL CAPE MAY N.J. / 1876 in six lines. Plain edge. Rarity 7.

| 421A | 1876 | Copper | 18mm | — | 20.00 | |

As 421. Plain edge. Rarity 5.

| 421B | 1876 | Oreide | 18mm | — | 20.00 | 25.0 |

As 421. Plain edge. Rarity 5.

| 421C | 1876 | WM | 18mm | — | 20.00 | — |

As 421. Plain edge. Rarity 5. (Rulau NJ-CM 5; Bullowa-Lessin sale, lot 63)

| 421F | 1877 | Silver | 18mm | — | — | 35.00 |

Obverse as 421. Rv: As reverse of 421, but 1877 in place of 1876. Plain edge. Rarity 7.

| 421G | 1877 | Copper | 18mm | — | — | 20.00 |

As 421F. Plain edge. Rarity 5.

| 421H | 1877 | Oreide | 18mm | — | — | 25.00 |

As 421 F. Plain edge. Rarity 5.

| 421J | 1877 | WM | 18mm | — | — | 20.00 |

As 421 F. Plain edge. Rarity 5.

SESQUICENTENNIAL EXPOSITION

Baker	Date	Metal	Size	EF	AU	Unc
F421	1926	Pure Nickel	35mm	30.00	—	40.00

Washington head right wihtin circle of 13 stars. Around: SESQUICEN-TENNIAL - INTERNATIONAL - EXPOSITION / PHILADELPHIA / 1926.

Rv: Liberty with torch riding winged Pegasus right above clouds. Faintly incused, along left rim, is ALBIN POLASEK. Magnetic. Plain edge. Rarity 4. (Hibler-Kappen 454)

| F421A | 1926 | Copper | 35mm | 40.00 | — | 60.00 |

As F421. Plain edge. These are red in color. Rarity 6. (H-K 451)

| F421B | 1926 | Gilt/Copper | 35mm | 20.00 | — | 30.00 |

As F421. Plain edge. Rarity 3. (H-K 453)

Designed by Albin Polasek, these are the official medals of the exposition. Bronze specimens were also struck, Rarity 3, in higher relief.

Struck with U.S. Mint machinery on exposition grounds.

FRENCH U.S. BICENTENNIAL

Baker	Date	Metal	Size	VF	EF	Unc
A421	1976	Bronze	81mm	—	—	20.00

Heads of Washington, Jefferson, Adams and Franklin. Around: WASH-INGTON JEFFERSON ADAMS FRANKLIN; below: BICENTENAIRE / DE L'INDEPENDANCE - DES ETATS UNIS / D'AMERIQUE Rv: JUIL-LET 1776 above a sailing vessel, cannons, the thirteen colonies listed to left, below F. ANGER, On edge: 1976 (cornucopia) BRONZE. 400 struck at Paris Mint. (Greenslet GM-255)

Engraved: Francois Anger.

| B421 | 1976 | Bronze | 86mm | — | — | 22.50 |

Around above: PROCLAMATION; below: DE L'INDEPENDANCE DES ETATS - UNIS D'AMERIQUE. Heads of Jefferson, Franklin and Wash-ington central, THOMAS / JEFFERSON / LA LOI under Jefferson, BEN-JAMIN / FRANKLIN / LA POLITIQUE under Franklin, GEORGE / WASHINGTON / LA PATRIE under Washington. Divided snake with sections labeled for the thirteen colonies. Rv: 4 JUILLET 1776 to left, thirteen-star flag, declaration in French, ship, two lanterns, minuteman, 1776 on left and 1976 on right, portion of Liberty Bell, M MOCQUOT in-cused under bell. On edge: 1976 (cornucopia) BRONZE. 400 struck at French Mint. (Greenslet GM-256)

Engraved by Magdeleine Mocquot.

Chapter 25

CENTENNIAL INTERNATIONAL EXHIBITION OF 1876

The international exhibition of arts, manufactures and products of the soil and mine, held at Philadelphia from May 10 through November 10, 1876, was the premier event in the celebration of the first centennial of existence of the American republic. Though conceived originally as an American fair, it soon became a world's fair and exhibition of the products of all nations with which the U.S. had diplomatic relations.

The fair was built in Fairmount Park and consisted of five buildings - Main Exhibition Building, Memorial Hall (or Art Gallery), Machinery Hall, Horticultural Hall and Agricultural Hall. With their annexes, the fairground buildings covered 75 acres, the Main Exhibition building alone covering 21 acres. Some 10 million visitors were recorded at the event.

An excellent contemporary account, heavily illustrated, covers 918 pages within its cloth covers. Written by James D. McCabe, it is titled *The Illustrated History of the Centennial Exhibition* and serves as a primary source-book for any account of the fair. It is especially useful in determining which products, services or companies were represented in the buildings, and deals in some length with numismatic mementos.

The crescendo of activity at the fair occurred on July 4, 1876, preceded by a great civic parade July 3 and a midnight celebration and fireworks after the parade. The vice president of the U.S., Thomas W. Ferry, presided at the morning ceremonies July 4, at which Richard Henry Lee of Virginia, a grandson of the patriot of the Revolution, read the Declaration of Independence from the original manuscript.

Medals of Washington connected with the Centennial Exhibition include some noteworthy examples of medallic art. A century ago, W.S. Baker especially liked numbers 422 and 423 by Fredrick B. Smith, 426 (the Danish medal) by Schmahlfeld and others, 428 by R. Laubenheimer, and 429, of German origin.

MEMORY OF WASHINGTON

Smith & Hartmann

Baker	Date	Metal	Size	EF	Unc	Proof
422	1876	WM	64mm	275.	—	—

Undraped bust left, F.B. SMITH & HARTMANN N.Y. on truncation. Around: GEORGE WASHINGTON (same obverse as Baker 111). Rv: Within oak and olive wreath: THIS MEDAL / IS STRUCK / TO PERPETUATE / THE MEMORY OF / WASHINGTON / AND IN HONOR OF THE PATRONS / WHO ATTEND OUR / CENTENNIAL EXHIBITION / AT / PHILADELPHIA, PA. / U.S. / 1776. 1876 in 12 LINES. At lower rim: F.B. SMITH & HORST N.Y. Plain edge. Rarity 6.

Baker	Date	Metal	Size	EF	Unc	Proof
422M	1876	WM	64mm	225.	—	—

Obverse as reverse of Baker 111 (view of mansion, RESIDENCE OF WASHINGTON MOUNT VERNON, VIRGINIA). Rv: As reverse of 422. Plain edge. Rarity 5.

Smith & Horst

Baker	Date	Metal	Size	EF	Unc	Proof
423	1876	WM	64mm	225.	—	—

Roman-mantled bust left. F.B. SMITH & HORST N.Y. under the bust. Around: GEORGE WASHINGTON. Rv: As reverse of 422. Plain edge. Rarity 4. (The 'O' in HORST on obverse was recut over an erroneous 'Y' by the diesinker) (Garrett 1877)

Baker 422 and 423 were struck by Fredrick B. Smith & Horst in New York. Smith and his earlier partner, Herman Hartmann, designed the bust on 422. The workmanship on these medals is excellent.

Baker	Date	Metal	Size	VF	EF	Unc
423M	1876	WM	64mm	—	—	125.

Obverse is as reverse of Baker 119 (F.B. Smith's tomb). Rv: As reverse of Baker 423 (Smith & Horst's MEMORY OF WASHINGTON). Plain edge. (Roelofs coll.)

Muling, designed by Frederick B. Smith and struck by Smith & Horst, New York City.

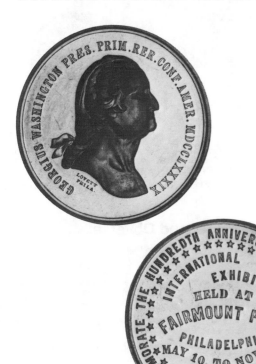

Baker	Date	Metal	Size	VF	EF	Unc
424	1876	Bronze	55mm	—	—	200.

Obverse as Baker 135 (undraped bust right, LOVETT PHILA. under bust, GEORGIUS WASHINGTON PRAES. PRIM. RER. CONF . AMER. MDCCLXXXIX around. Rv: Circle of 38 stars around 7-line inscription: INTERNATIONAL EXHIBITION HELD AT FAIRMOUNT PARK PHILADELPHIA MAY 10. TO NOV. 10. 1876. Plain edge. Rarity 5.

Baker	Date	Metal	Size	VF	EF	Unc
424A	1876	WM	55mm	—	—	100.

Robert Lovett Jr. of Philadelphia struck this medallic memorial to George Washington, utilizing one of his 1860 dies for the obverse.

UNION FOR EVER

Baker	Date	Metal	Size	EF	Unc	Proof
425	1876	Silver	39mm	—	—	—

Undraped bust right, LOVETT on truncation, within arc of 13 stars. Around: TO COMMEMORATE THE 100TH. ANNIVERSARY OF THE DECLARATION / .OF INDEPENDENCE. Rv: Radiant clasped hands divide: UNION FOR EVER, all within beaded circle. Around: INTERNATIONAL EXHIBITION AT PHILADELPHIA 1876. The whole within an oak wreath. Plain edge. Rarity 9.

Baker	Date	Metal	Size	EF	Unc	Proof
425A	1876	Bronze	39mm	—	125.	—

As 425. Plain edge. Rarity 5. (Clark sale, lot 2126)

Baker	Date	Metal	Size	EF	Unc	Proof
425B	1876	Brass	39mm	—	95.00	—

As 425. Plain edge. Rarity 5. (Kirtley 1991 list)

Baker	Date	Metal	Size	EF	Unc	Proof
425C	1876	WM	39mm	—	80.00	—

As 425. Plain edge. Rarity 5.

Dies cut by Robert Lovett Jr. of Philadelphia.

Baker	Date	Metal	Size	EF	Unc	Proof
426	1876	Silver	53mm	1500.	—	1750.

Head left in oval panel on a wreath, supported at base by an eagle with upraised wings and at either side by winged cherubs holding a circlet of 13 stars over Washington's head and a palm branch in its free hand. Around: MDCCLXXVI. / FIRST IN WAR, FIRST IN PEACE, FIRST IN THE HEARTS OF HIS COUNTRYMEN. Rv: Allegorical group of five females, America with Liberty cap at center presenting wreaths to Art and Mechanics left and Commerce and Agriculture right. Under base of design: H. OHLRIK INV. F SCHMAHLFELD FEC. At top: INTERNATIONAL EXHIBITION. In exergue: PHILADELPHIA 1876 / V. CHRISTESEN. Plain edge. Less than 6 known. (Garrett 1878)

Baker	Date	Metal	Size	EF	Unc	Proof
426A	1876	Bronze	53mm	95.00	—	250.

As 426. Plain edge. Rarity 4. (Garrett 1878-1879)

Baker	Date	Metal	Size	EF	Unc	Proof
426B	1876	WM	53mm	80.00	100.	250.

As 426. Plain edge. Rarity 4. (Garrett 1878-1879)

Second obverse

Baker	Date	Metal	Size	EF	Unc	Proof
427	1876	Silver	55mm	1500.	—	1750.

Obverse similar to 426, but the legends are changed. At top: LET US HAVE PEACE. Below: 1776. THE CENTENNIAL YEAR OF THE UNITED STATES OF AMERICA. 1876. Rv: As reverse of 427. Plain edge. Rarity 8.

Baker	Date	Metal	Size	EF	Unc	Proof
427A	1876	Bronze	55mm	80.00	100.	250.

As 427. Plain edge. Rarity 4. (Garrett 1879)

Baker	Date	Metal	Size	EF	Unc	Proof
427B	1876	WM	55mm	—	—	250.

As 427. Plain edge. Rarity 4.

The two Danish medals are the work of Danish diesinkers and medalists who prepared the pieces in the United States - F. Schmahlfeld, maker; H. Ohlrik, diesinker, and V. Christesen, publisher. They are among the most beautiful pieces struck for the 1876 Exhibition, and among the most beautiful of all Washington medals.

GRADE HEADINGS

Three grade (condition) columns appear in this catalog. Coins and tokens, which circulate, are graded down to VG (Very Good), but medals, which do not circulate, usually are graded no less than VF (Very Fine). Other abbreviations used are F (Fine), EF (Extremely Fine), AU (About Uncirculated), Unc (Uncirculated), and P-L (Prooflike). Proof is spelled out.

SEE HOW WE PROSPER

Baker	Date	Metal	Size	VF	EF	Unc
428	1876	Silver	44.8mm			250.

Undraped bust left, 1776 at left, 1876 at right, and R. LAUBENHEIMER under bust. Around: GEORGE WASHINGTON, THE FATHER OF HIS COUNTRY. / * A CENTURY ADDS LUSTRE TO HIS FAME *. Rv: Two females on a section of the globe, marked AMERICA. Europe at left has a shield ornamented with temples; America at right has a U.S. shield and staff with Liberty cap, an exhibition building with radiant eagle above. Plain edge. Rarity 8.

| 428A | 1876 | Bronze | 44.8mm | — | — | 60.00 |

As 428. Plain edge. Rarity 4.

| 428B | 1876 | WM | 44.8mm | — | — | 60.00 |

Designed by R. Laubenheimer.

MEMORIAL HALL MEDALS

GERMAN ORIGIN

Baker	Date	Metal	Size	EF	Unc	Proof
429	1876	WM	42mm	—	100.	—

Half-length bust three-quarters right, a sword resting on his right forearm. 1776 to left of head, 1876 to right, arc of 13 stars below. All within olive wreath. Rv: Memorial Hall. Above in two lines: A GOVERNMENT OF THE PEOPLE, BY THE PEOPLE, AND FOR THE PEOPLE. Below in two lines: CENTENNIAL EXHIBITION PHILADA. PA U.S.A. Plain edge. Rarity 7.

The Washington bust in civil dress on this piece is after the Gilbert Stuart portrait, and the medal is German in origin. Only a very limited number were made.

CENTENNIAL MEMORIAL BUILDING

German origin

Baker	Date	Metal	Size		Unc	
430	1876	Gilt/Cop	37mm	—	50.00	—

Undraped bust left, UNITED STATES OF AMERICA / * 1776 * around. Rv: Memorial Hall, CENTENNIAL MEMORIAL BUILDING above, 1876 PHILADELPHIA below. Plain edge. Rarity 8. (Wood 552; Collins 347)

| 430A | 1876 | WM | 37mm | | 50.00 | |

As 430. Plain edge. Rarity 7.

EXHIBITION PHILADELPHIA

German origin

| 431 | 1876 | Brass | 26mm | 10.00 | 15.00 | 25.00 |

Bust three-quarters right, a star at either side, 1776 at base. Around GEORGE WASHINGTON. Rv: Memorial Hall, EXHIBITION PHILADELPHIA above, CENTENNIAL 1876 below. Plain edge. Rarity 7.

Baker 430, 431 and 432 have a German origin which has not been traced.

Second Obverse

German origin

| 432 | 1876 | Brass | 26mm | 10.00 | 15.00 | 25.0 |

Obverse as 431, but two stars at either side of Washington's bust rather than one. Rv: As reverse of 431. Plain edge. Rarity 7.

| 432C | 1876 | Brass | 26mm | 10.00 | 15.00 | 25.00 |

Obverse as 431, but three stars at either side of the bust. Rv: As reverse of 431. Plain edge. Rarity 6.

Though scarce, Baker 431-432C have never commanded strong prices.

Baker	Date	Metal	Size	VF	EF	Un
A432	1876	Brass	36.5mm	17.50	—	–

Nude bust left, UNITED STATES OF AMERICA / 1776 around. Rv Building. Around: CENTENNIAL / MEMORIAL BUILDING / COPYRIG (sic!) SECURED / PHILADELPHIA 1876. Plain edge. Issued holed (PCAC McSorley sale Nov. 1997, lot 1174; Roelofs coll.)

Both the previous owner and 1997 cataloger overlooked the fact COPYRIGHT was misspelled on the die. Unpublished.

AMERICAN STAR

Baker	Date	Metal	Size	VF	EF	Unc
433	1876	Silver	38mm	—	—	250

Undraped bust right, 1776 beneath, GEORGE WASHINGTON around (same obverse as Baker 394). Rv: Large six-point star, radiant, enclosing 25 small stars and with 13 more stars around it, is at center of five line legend: STRUCK IN THE CENTENNIAL BUILDING IN THE ONE HUNDREDTH YEAR / OF AMERICAN INDEPENDENCE 1876. Reeded edge. Rarity 8.

| 433A | 1876 | Bronze | 38mm | — | — | 60.0 |

As 433. Reeded edge. Rarity 5.

| 433B | 1876 | Brass | 38mm | — | — | 60.0 |

As 433. Reeded edge. Rarity 5.

| 433C | 1876 | WM | 38mm | — | — | 60.0 |

As 433. Reeded edge. Rarity 5.

CENTENNIAL FOUNTAIN

Baker	Date	Metal	Size	VF	EF	Unc
434	1876	Silver	38mm	—	60.00	100

Obverse as 433. Rv: Fountain. Above: CENTENNIAL FOUNTAIN. Below, in five lines: FAIRMOUNT PARK DEDICATED TO AMERICAN LIBERTY JULY 4, 1876 PHILA. Plain edge. Rarity 8. (Hibler-Kappen 65-68)

| 434A | 1876 | Copper | 38mm | — | 20.00 | – |

As 434. Plain edge. Rarity 5.

| 434B | 1876 | Gilt/C | 38mm | — | 20.00 | 30.00 |

As 434. Plain edge. Rarity 5.

| 434C | 1876 | WM | 38mm | — | 20.00 | |

As 434. Plain edge. Rarity 4.

Baker 433 and 434 were published by George B. Soley of Philadelphia.

SEVENTH REGIMENT
NEW YORK NATIONAL GUARD

Baker	Date	Metal	Size	EF	Unc	Proof
435	1876	Silver	43mm	—	—	250.

Bust right on a pedestal inscribed 1776 - 1876 - July 4th. - PHILADEL-PHIA PA. A soldier presents arms at left, an officer salutes at right. Under the design: DEMAREST SC. N.Y. Around: IN COMMEMORATION OF THE VISIT OF THE SEVENTH REGIMENT AND THE VETERAN CORPS N.G.S.N.Y. * TO THE CENTENNIAL EXHIBITION OF 1876. Rv: Quartered shield with monogram NG script in center. Eagle on globe above, scroll with motto PRO PATRIA ET GLORIA below, and below that: ORGANIZED 1824, all within oak wreath. Around: ACTIVE MEMBERS, 1001. COL. E. CLARK * VETERANS, 1060. COL. M. LEFFERTS *. Plain edge. Rarity 9.

Baker	Date	Metal	Size			
435A	1876	Bronze	43mm	—	125.	—

As 435. Plain edge. Rarity 6. (Garrett 1880)

435B	1876	WM	43mm	125.	—	—

As 435. Plain edge. Rarity 6.

Baker 435 struck by George Hampden Lovett of New York.

FRENCH U.S. BICENTENNIAL

Baker	Date	Metal	Size	VF	EF	Unc
A435	1976	Bronze	81mm	—	—	25.00

Heads of Washington, Jefferson, Adams and Franklin. Around: WASHINGTON JEFFERSON ADAMS FRANKLIN; below: BICENTENAIRE / DE L'INDEPENDANCE - DES ETATS UNIS / D'AMERIQUE Rv: JUILLET 1776 above a sailing vessel, cannons, the thirteen colonies listed to left, below F. ANGER, On edge: 1976 (cornucopia) BRONZE. 400 struck at Paris Mint, (Greenslet GM-255)

Engraver: Francois Anger.

B435	1976	Bronze	86mm	—	—	25.00

Around above: PROCLAMATION; below: DE L'INDEPENDANCE DES ETATS - UNIS D'AMERIQUE. Heads of Jefferson, Franklin and Washington central, THOMAS / JEFFERSON / LA LOI under Jefferson, BENJAMIN / FRANKLIN / LA POLITIQUE under Franklin, GEORGE / WASHINGTON / LA PATRIE under Washington. Divided snake with sections labeled for the thirteen colonies. Rv: 4 JUILLET 1776 to left, thirteen star flag, declaration in French, ship, two lanterns, minuteman, 1776 on left and 1976 on right, portion of Liberty Bell, M MOCQUOT incused under bell. On edge: 1976 (cornucopia) BRONZE. 400 struck at French Mint. Magdeleine Mocquot. (Greenslet GM-256)

CENTENNIALS OF REVOLUTIONARY EVENTS

THE WASHINGTON ELM
CAMBRIDGE CENTENNIAL

Baker	Date	Metal	Size	VF	EF	Unc
436	1875	Copper	40mm			75.00

Undraped bust right, in depression surrounded by raised border, LOVETT on truncation. In arc above: 1775 - 100 YEARS - 1875. Below: 1. F. W. DES. G. H.L. FEC. Around: THE LOVER OF PEACE / HE ES-POUSED THE SWORD / FOR THE COLONIES' BIRTHRIGHT. Rv: House and tree in circle. Under the design: THE WASHINGTON / *** ELM *** / ISAAC F. WOOD'S SERIES "C" NO 4. Legend around: CAM-BRIDGE, MASSACHUSETTS, JUNE THIRD 1875 / * CENTENNIAL CELEBRATION * Plain edge. Rarity 5.

436A	1875	Bronze	40mm	—		75.00

As 436. Plain edge. Rarity 5. (Garrett 1880; Clark sale, lot 2127)

436B	1875	WM	40mm	—	—	75.00

As 436. Plain edge. Rarity 5. (Clark sale, lot 2127; Bullowa-Lessin sale, lot 62; Collins 349)

Struck by George Hampden Lovett and published by Isaac F. Wood, both of New York City.

Baker	Date	Metal	Size	EF	Unc	Proof
437	1875	Copper	27mm	—	50.00	

Undraped bust right, LOVETT on truncation, monogram GW below. Around: 1775 - 100 YEARS - 1875 / 1. F. W. DES. G. H. L. FEC. Rv: Undraped bust right, LOVETT on truncation and G. H. L. below. Around: GEORGE WASHINGTON. (Same obverse as Baker 296). Plain edge. Rarity 7.

437M	1875	Copper	27mm	—	—	—

Obverse as 437. Rv: As obverse of Baker 240. Plain edge. Rarity 7.

A product of George Hampden Lovett and Isaac F. Wood of New York.

ASSUMED COMMAND 1775

438	1875	Silver	27.8mm	—	—	—

Undraped bust right, within circle of 13 stars, in an oval panel. Mono-gram GW under bust. Above: 1775 JUNE 3. 1875. Below: I.F.W. left, G.H.L. right. Rv: Dress and service swords crossed, with palm branches in sunken field. Legend: HE ASSUMED COMMAND IN 1775 - AND RE-SIGNED IT IN 1785 - GRACING EACH OCCASION WITH LIKE MOD-ESTY. Plain edge. Rarity 7.

438A	1875	Gilt/C	27.8mm	—	40.00	60.00

As 438. Plain edge. Rarity 6. (Bullowa-Lessin sale, lot 61)

438B	1875	Bronze	27.8mm	—	40.00	60.00

As 438. Plain edge. Rarity 6. (Clark sale, lot 2128; Collins 350)

438C	1875	WM	27.8mm	—	40.00	60.00

As 438. Plain edge. Rarity 6. (Clark sale, lot 2128)

All Products of George H. Lovett and Isaac F. Wood.

			Second obverse			
Baker	Date	Metal	Size	EF	Unc	Proof
439	1875	Silver	28mm			

Similar to 438, but bust is uniformed. Rv: As reverse of 438. Plain edge. Rarity 8.

439A	1875	Gilt/C	28mm	—	60.00	85.00

As 439. Plain edge. Rarity 7. (Clark sale, lot 2129; Collins 351)

439B	1875	Bronze	28mm	—	60.00	85.00

As 439. Plain edge. Rarity 7.

439C	1875	WM	28mm	—	60.00	85.00

As 439. Plain edge. Rarity 7.

BATTLE SERIES MEDALS
FIRST OBVERSE

MOORE'S CREEK BRIDGE, NO. 1

Baker	Date	Metal	Size	EF	Unc	Proof
440	1876	Silver	34mm	—	175.	—

Undraped bust right within circle of 34 stars, LOVETT on truncation. Around: THE CENTENNIAL YEAR OF OUR NATIONAL INDEPEN-DENCE 1876 (same obverse as Baker 136). Rv: 1776 within star-shaped radiant circle, BATTLE OF MOORE'S CREEK BRIDGE / FEB-RUARY 27 above, 1 / NO. CAROLINA below. Plain edge. Rarity 8. (Hibler-Kappen 90-92; Garrett 1881; Collins 352)

440A	1876	Bronze	34mm	20.00	45.00	

As 400. Plain edge. Rarity 5.

440B	1876	WM	34mm	20.00	45.00	

As 440. Plain edge. Rarity 5. (Collins 353)

This medal and all other medals in this "Battle" series were struck by George Hampden Lovett of New York.

SULLIVAN'S ISLAND, NO. 2

Baker	Date	Metal	Size	EF	Unc	Proof
441	1876	Silver	34mm	—	175.	—

Obverse as 440. Rv: Inscription around star: BATTLE OF SULLIVAN ISLAND / JUNE 28 / 2 / SO. CAROLINA. Plain edge. Rarity 8. (Garrett 1881; Hibler-Kappen 93-95)

441A	1876	Bronze	34mm	20.00	45.00	

As 441. Plain edge. Rarity 5.

441B	1876	WM	34mm	20.00	45.00	

As 441. Plain edge. Rarity 5. (Bullowa-Lessin sale, lot 60; Collins 354)

LONG ISLAND, NO. 3

Baker	Date	Metal	Size	EF	Unc	Proof
442	1876	Silver	34mm	—	175.	—

Obverse as 440. Rv: Inscription around star: BATTLE OF LONG IS-LAND / AUGUST 27 / 3 / NEW YORK. Plain edge. Rarity 8. (Garrett 1881)

| 442A | 1876 | Bronze | 34mm | — | 45.00 | — |

As 442. Plain edge, Rarity 5.

| 442B | 1876 | WM | 34mm | — | 45.00 | — |

As 442. Plain edge. Rarity 5. (Collins 355)

HARLEM PLAINS, NO. 4

Baker	Date	Metal	Size	EF	Unc	Proof
443	1876	Silver	34mm	—	175.	—

Obverse as 440. Rv: Inscription around star: BATTLE OF HARLEM PLAINS / SEPTEMBER 16 / 4 / NEW YORK. Plain edge. Rarity 8. (Garrett 1881)

| 443A | 1876 | Bronze | 34mm | — | 45.00 | — |

As 443. Plain edge. Rarity 5. (Bullowa-Lessin sale, lot 59)

| 443B | 1876 | WM | 34mm | — | 45.00 | — |

As 443. Plain edge. Rarity 5.

LAKE CHAMPLAIN, NO. 5

Baker	Date	Metal	Size	EF	Unc	Proof
444	1876	Silver	34mm	—	—	Rare

Obverse as 440. Rv: Inscription around star: BATTLE OF LAKE CHAM-PLAIN / OCTOBER 11 & 12 / 5 / NEW YORK. Plain edge. Rarity 8.

| 444A | 1876 | Bronze | 34mm | 30.00 | 50.00 | — |

As 444. Plain edge. Rarity 5.

| 444B | 1876 | WM | 34mm | — | 50.00 | — |

As 444. Plain edge. Rarity 5.

WHITE PLAINS, NO. 6

Baker	Date	Metal	Size	EF	Unc	Proof
445	1876	Silver	34mm	—	175.	—

Obverse as 440. Rv: Inscription around star: BATTLE OF WHITE PLAINS / OCTOBER 28 / 6 / NEW YORK. Plain edge. Rarity 8. (Garrett 1881)

| 445A | 1876 | Bronze | 34mm | — | 45.00 | — |

As 445. Plain edge. Rarity 5. (Collins 360)

| 445B | 1876 | WM | 34mm | — | 45.00 | — |

As 445. Plain edge. Rarity 5.

FORT WASHINGTON, NO. 7

Baker	Date	Metal	Size	EF	Unc	Proof
446	1876	Silver	34mm	—	175.	—

Obverse as 440. Rv: Inscription around star: BATTLE OF FORT WASH-INGTON / NOVEMBER 16 / 7 NEW YORK. Plain edge. Rarity 8. (Garrett 1881)

| 446A | 1876 | Bronze | 34mm | — | 45.00 | — |

As 446. Plain edge. Rarity 5.

| 446B | 1876 | WM | 34mm | — | 45.00 | — |

As 446. Plain edge. Rarity 5.

TRENTON, NO. 8

Baker	Date	Metal	Size	EF	Unc	Proof
447	1876	Silver	34mm	—	175.	—

Obverse as 440. Rv: Inscription around star: BATTLE OF TRENTON / DECEMBER 26 / 8 / NEW JERSEY. Plain edge. Rarity 8. (Garrett 1881)

| 447A | 1876 | Bronze | 34mm | — | 45.00 | — |

As 447. Plain edge. Rarity 5.

| 447B | 1876 | WM | 34mm | — | 45.00 | — |

As 447. Plain edge. Rarity 5.

BATTLE SERIES MEDALS
SECOND OBVERSE

448	1876	Silver	34mm	—	175.	—

Draped bust left with oak and palm wreath. Around: 100TH ANNIVERSARY OF THE DECLARATION / OF INDEPENDENCE / * JULY 4, 1876 * (same obverse as Baker 415). Rv: As reverse of Baker 440. Plain edge. Rarity 8.

448A	1876	Bronze	34mm	20.00	45.00	—

As 448. Plain edge. Rarity 5. (Bullowa-Lessin 53)

448B	1876	Copper	34mm	20.00	45.00	—

As 448. Plain edge. Rarity 5.

448C	1876	WM	34mm	20.00	45.00	—

As 448. Plain edge. Rarity 5.

The obverse die of 448 was struck with all eight reverses of Baker 440 through 447, in silver, copper, bronze and white metal. The rarity and price of all pieces is the same as for 448. Two medals are shown here.

448M	1876	Silver	34mm	—	—	200.

Obverse as 440. Rv: As obverse of 448. A muling. Plain edge. Rarity 8.

448N	1876	Copper	34mm	—	—	60.00

As 448M. Plain edge. Rarity 7.

About the Eight Battles.....

George Hampden Lovett selected eight different 1776 battles to commemorate on his "Battle Series" of 1876, featuring two different obverses and mulings of the two obverses. Since some of these battles may sound unfamiliar to users of this catalog, we have extracted pertinent data from the authoritative 1979 book, *A Dictionary of Battles (1715-1815)* by British brigadiers Michael Calvert and Peter Young (Mayflower Books, New York).

Names and dates are as given on the medals themselves!

1. Moore's Creek Bridge, N.C., Feb. 27, 1776. Brig. Gen. Donald McDonald and Col. Donald McCleod commanded 1780 Scottish regulars and Tory volunteers who had been sent by Maj. Gen. Sir Thomas Gage to establish a British base in the rebellious colony at Fayetteville (then called Cross Creek). Three American units totaling 1000 men posed a threat and forced the British to withdraw to the coast. Col. James Moore was in overall command, with Col. Richard Caswell and his 800 Rangers and Colonels Alexander Lillington and John Ashe commanding the Yankee militia. At Moore's Creek Bridge at 1 a.m. 80 Highlanders under Capt. John Campbell charged the bridge, backed up by McCleod's troops. Campbell and 30 of his men were killed, then the Americans counterattacked. A small force under Lt. Ezekiel Slocum forded the river to attack the British rear. The battle turned into a British rout, with Col. McCleod and 30 more men killed, and the Americans took 850 prisoners. Only 2 Americans were wounded, with one dying later.

2. Sullivan's Island, S.C., June 28, 1776. Charleston (then called Charles Town) was ordered to be attacked by Sir Henry Clinton, and a British fleet of 55 warships under Commodore Peter Parker appeared off the coast in early June. On June 8 the fleet crossed the bar. Fort Moultrie on Sullivan's Island guarded the harbor entrance. Col. William Moultrie commanded the fort and Maj. Gen. Charles Lee with 1200 men was in overall command. On the morning of June 28 the 270 guns of the fleet opened fire on Fort Moultrie's 25 guns, but the island's sands and fort's palmetto logs withstood the fire. A diversionary landing assault from nearby Long Island by 100 British was repulsed. The British ships *Actaeon, Sphinx* and *Syren* all ran aground. At 9:30 p.m. the fleet retreated, having suffered 420 men killed or wounded, mostly on *Bristol and Experiment.*

3. Long Island, N.Y., August 27,1776. Maj. Gen. Sir William Howe was in overall command of a force of 22,000 British and Hessians under Maj. Gen. Sir Henry Clinton, Maj. Gen. Lord Cornwallis, Gen. Philip von Heister and Col. Grant. The American defenders under Maj. Gen. Israel Putnam numbered 10,000. On Aug. 22 British crossed from Staten Island and advanced on the Brooklyn defenses on Guian Heights. At 9 a.m. on Aug. 27 the Hessians advanced on the center, with Grant to their left. Though Col. Grant was killed, he was successful in drawing the American reserves to his flank. Then Howe launched his main assault, with 28 guns, around behind the American left flank (the British right) and the Americans were routed, Maj. Gen. John Sullivan being captured. The American rear guard under Brig. Gen. William Alexander was forced to surrender to Gen. Heister. The Americans had 1400 men killed, wounded or captured, while British casualties totaled 380. This battle forced the evacuation of Brooklyn on Aug. 29-30.

4. Harlem Plains, N.Y., Sept. 16, 1776. Also known as the Battle of Harlem Heights. Sir William Howe aimed to drive the British north from New York City, so he sent two infantry battalions plus a detachment of the Black Watch to establish a British line from Horn's Hook to Bloomingdale (now East 90th Street). A heavy skirmish resulted when 150 American Rangers under Lt. Col. Thomas Knowlton and another 150 men under Lt. Col. Archibald Crary attempted a penetration from about where East 105th Street is now. Both sides attacked, and the American of-

ficers Lt. Col. Knowlton and Major Andrew Leitch were killed. The British withdrew to their own lines, now reenforced to a total of 5000 men. Gen. Washington ordered his force to withdraw rather than risk a general engagement at this point. British casualties numbered 164; Americans 130.

5. Lake Champlain, N.Y., Oct. 11-12, 1776. Usually called Valcour Island, this was a severe American naval defeat in which 11 vessels were lost.

6. White Plains, N.Y., Oct. 28, 1776. Maj. Gen. Sir William Howe led 13,000 British troops to cross from Manhattan to the mainland at Pell's Point on Oct. 18. Gen. Washington with 6000 troops set up his defenses at White Plains. Brig. Gen. Alexander McDougall with 1600 men and two guns manned Chatterton's Hill, and an American delaying force under Maj. Gen. Joseph Spencer skirmished for an hour before returning at 9:30 a.m. to the defense lines. Three Hessian regiments under Maj. Gen. Baron Wilhelm von Knyphausen built a bridge to cross the Hudson, while two British regiments under Brig. Gen. Alexander Leslie forded it further south. Leslie's bayonet charge was repulsed, then the whole British force attacked. The Massachusetts militia on the American right gave way to assault by British dragoons, then the center collapsed and the hill was taken. British losses were 313, American 150. Washington, covered by a heavy storm on Oct. 31, was able to withdraw his whole force into Connecticut.

7. Fort Washington, N.Y., Nov 16, 1776. Maj. Gen. Howe with 7000 British and Hessians assaulted Fort Washington's 2850 men under Col. Robert Magaw, supported 1 1/2 miles south by a Yankee force of 800 under Lt. Col. John Cadwalader. A spy in the American garrison, William Demont, told of a weak spot and the Hessians under Baron von Knyphausen in hand-to-hand fighting drove the defenders back. Meanwhile British under Brig. Gen. Lord Hugh Percy, Brig. Gen. Edward Mathew and Maj. Gen. Lord Cornwallis assaulted from all sides. This was a complete British victory. British losses were 460 killed or wounded (of whom 320 were Hessians); Americans had 30 killed, 250 wounded and 2820 captured. The British were now free to advance into New Jersey.

8. Trenton, N.J., Dec. 26, 1776. This important American victory is discussed in detail in Chapter 30 following Baker 926C.

BATTLE OF LONG ISLAND

Baker	Date	Metal	Size	VF	EF	Unc
B-448	1928	Bronze	51.4mm	—	15.00	30.0

Small jugate portraits left of Washington and another man within small branch-supported medallion near top. Around: * MESSAGE FROM GENERAL GEORGE WASHINGTON TO THE AMERICAN TROOPS AT THE BATTLE OF LONG ISLAND AUGUST 27.1776. A 12-line legend occupies the center. Tiny S. SWETT below. Rv: Fancy bridge entrance, MEMORIAL / PORTAL TO BROOKLYN / BRIDGE / 1928 across scene. Lengthy 2-concentric circle inscription. Signatures LAVELLI (medalist) and J. S. GRAHAM-PRES. near bottom. Plain edge. Incused on the edge: MEDALLIC ART CO. N.Y.

Issued by the Brooklyn Bridge Plaza Association, of which J. S. Graham was then president. This is a singularly unattractive medal, with excessively "busy" design and weak portraiture.

VALLEY FORGE CENTENNIAL

Baker	Date	Metal	Size	EF	Unc	Proof
449	1878	Silver	41mm	—	—	25

Undraped bust right, BARBER under the bust, all within a circle. One side: * GEORGE WASHINGTON. * / COMMANDER IN CHIEF. Rv: Within oak and olive wreath in central circle: IN / COMMEMORATION / OF THE / DEPARTURE / OF THE CONTINENTAL ARMY / JUNE 19. Outside: VALLEY FORGE CENTENNIAL. 1778 - 1878. Plain edge. Rarity 7. Only 62 pieces struck. (Garrett 1882; Clark sale, lot 2131; Hibler-Kappen 136-137; Julian CM-48; PCAC 1988 Magriel sale, 076)

449A	1878	Red Bronze	41mm	—	60.00	

As 449. Plain edge. Rarity 4. (Garrett 1882; Clark sale, lot 2132; Julian CM-48)

449R	1878	Yellow Bronze	41mm	—	8.00	

As 499. Plain edge. Still being restruck at U.S. Mint

Designed by William Barber and struck at the U.S. Mint, Philadelphia

MONMOUTH CENTENNIAL

Baker	Date	Metal	Size	VF	EF	Unc
450	1878	Copper	34.5mm	—	—	35.00

Undraped bust right. Around: THE MONMOUTH BATTLE MONUMENT ASSOCIATION / *1878   *. Rv: THIS MEDAL IS STRUCK TO COMMEMORATE THE CENTENNIAL/OF THE/ BATTLE OF/MONMOUTH FOUGHT / JUNE 28TH.1778. Plain edge. Rarity 4. (Collins 369)

Baker	Date	Metal	Size	VF	EF	Unc
450A	1878	WM	34.5mm	—	—	50.00

As 450. Plain edge. Rarity 5.

YORKTOWN MEDALS

SOUVENIR - CENTENNIAL

by William H. Key

Baker	Date	Metal	Size	VF	EF	Unc
451	1881	Copper	33mm	—	—	35.00

Bust three-quarters left in sunken field surrounded by raised border, K on truncation. On border is an olive wreath. Rv: In nine lines: 1781 / SOUVENIR -.- CENTENNIAL / OF THE / SURRENDER / AT / YORKTOWN VA. / OCT. 19, 1881 / 1881. Plain edge. Rarity 4.

Baker	Date	Metal	Size	VF	EF	Unc
451A	1881	Bronze	33mm	—	—	35.00

As 451. Plain edge. Rarity 4. (Clark sale, lot 2133; Collins 370)

Baker	Date	Metal	Size	VF	EF	Unc
451B	1881	WM	33mm	—	—	35.00

As 451. Plain edge. Rarity 4.

Struck by Key for Sigmund Harzfeld.

SURRENDER AT YORKTOWN

by P.L. Krider

Baker	Date	Metal	Size	VF	EF	Unc
452	1881	Copper	50mm	—	125.	160.

Washington and Lafayette heads accolated right,1881   under   busts and, at the edge: DESIGN PATENTED JULY 12. 1881. Around: CENTENNIAL YORKTOWN VA. Rv: Design representing the surrender, P. L. KRIDER PHILA. at base. Around: SURRENDER AT YORKTOWN VA. / OCT. 19. 1781. Plain edge. Rarity 5.

Baker	Date	Metal	Size	VF	EF	Unc
452A	1881	Bronze	50mm	—	—	125.

As 452. Plain edge. Rarity 5.

Baker	Date	Metal	Size	VF	EF	Unc
452B	1881	Lead	50mm	—	—	175.

As 452. Plain edge. Rarity 7

Baker	Date	Metal	Size	VF	EF	Unc
452C	1881	WM	50mm	—	—	115.

As 452. Plain edge. Rarity 4.

Baker	Date	Metal	Size	VF	EF	Unc
C-452	1881	Gilt/Brass	yy	—	—	25.00

yy A 23mm medallion is mounted at center of 13-pointed star. On each point of the star, on obverse, is a 5-point star, and on reverse is the abbreviation of one of the 13 original states, with VA in the 12 o'clock position.

British officer (right) hands his sword to Washington, SURRENDER / OCT. 19. 1781 around. Rv: YORKTOWN / VA. / CENTENNIAL / 1881 / MEMORIAL. in five lines. Issued with eye loop. (ANS collection)

CHATHAM ARTILLERY

Issued 1891

Baker	Date	Metal	Size	VF	EF	Unc
E-452	1791	Bronze	45mm	—	—	55.00

Undraped bust left, GEORGE WASHINGTON around. Rv: GUNS CAPTURED AT YORKTOWN, VA. / -.- / OCT. 19,1781. / AT THE SURRENDER / (ornate cannon pointing left) / OF CORNWALLIS. PRESENTED BY / (ornate cannon pointing right) / GENERAL / -.- / GEO. WASHINGTON / TO CHATHAM ARTILLERY 1791. Plain edge.

The bust on this piece, though modeled on the Houdon sculpture, is quite different than on other Washington medals in its cut of the nude upper breast.

MONUMENT ERECTION

by George T. Morgan

Baker	Date	Metal	Size	EF	Unc	Proof
453	1881	Copper	32mm	—	—	30.00

Head right in circular panel. In a circular panel above is bust of Lafayette and in one below is bust of Admiral de Grasse. Around: WASHINGTON - DE GRASSE - LAFAYETTE. Rv: Elevation of the intended monument at Yorktown. In the field: 1781 - 1881 - OCT. - 19. Around: IN COMMEMORATION OF THE SURRENDER AT YORKTOWN. Plain edge. Rarity 5.

Baker	Date	Metal	Size	EF	Unc.	Proof
453A	1881	Bronze	32mm	—	—	30.00

As 453. Plain edge. Rarity 5.

| 453B | 1881 | WM | 32mm | — | 25.00 | 35.00 |

As 453. Plain edge. Rarity 4. (Garrett 1883)

| 453C | 1881 | Silver | 32mm | — | — | 500. |

As 453. (PCAC Magriel sale, 1988, lot 076; Ganter II, lot 261).

Dies cut by George T. Morgan, then assistant engraver at the U.S. Mint. Morgan was born in Birmingham, England in 1845 and emigrated to America in 1876.

STATE OF PENNSYLVANIA

by George T. Morgan

Baker	Date	Metal	Size	EF	Unc.	Proof
454	1881	Silver	32mm	—	150.	—

Group of four circular panels in center, containing heads of (from top): Washington, Lafayette, de Grasse and Rochambeau. On upper truncation: M. Around: WASHINGTON - DE GRASSE - LAFAYETTE - ROCHAMBEAU. Rv: Pennsylvania arms on a keystone, surrounded by band on which is: IN COMMEMORATION OF THE SURRENDER AT YORKTOWN. OCT. 19. 1781. In an outer band: PRESENTED BY THE STATE OF PENNSYLVANIA. OCT. 19. 1881. Plain edge. Rarity 8.

| 454A | 1881 | Bronze | 32mm | — | 75.00 | — |

As 454. Plain edge. Rarity 5.

| 454B | 1881 | WM | 32mm | — | 75.00 | — |

As 454. Plain edge. Rarity 5.

The state of Pennsylvania commissioned Morgan to prepare these medals for presentation to the French representatives at the centennial ceremonies at Yorktown, Va. on October 19, 1881.

Surrender of the British army at Yorktown in 1781, for all intents and purposes, ended all fighting on the North American continent during the Revolutionary War (1775-1783).

After desultory fighting in North Carolina and Virginia, Lt. General Lord Cornwallis was advised by his commander-in-chief in New York, Lt. General Sir Henry Clinton, "to take a defensive station in any healthy situation you choose, be it at Williamsburg or Yorktown." Cornwallis chose the latter port on the York River off Chesapeake Bay. Clinton's advice was rendered June 15, 1781.

Cornwallis sent a force under Lt. Colonels Banastre Tarleton and Tom Dundas across the York to secure the city of Gloucester. The Yorktown defenses were established close to the city, as the garrison was not large enough to man a perimeter longer than 1,000 yards. The inner defense line had 14 batteries, 65 guns and 10 redoubts. The principal strongpoint was the 'horn-work' to the south. Lord Cornwallis had at his disposal 9,750 British and Hessian troops.

American forces under Major Generals Marquis de Lafayette, Anthony Wayne and Baron Friedrich Wilhelm von Steuben began to bottle the British up. After a show of force against Clinton in New York, the American and French armies under General George Washington and Lt. General Comte de Rochambeau sailed via Chesapeake Bay to Yorktown by September 26. A smaller French force under Gen. de Choisy invested Gloucester.

At this point the combined French fleets under Admiral Comte de Barras and Rear Admiral Comte de Grasse arrived off Yorktown to prevent any reinforcements from reaching Cornwallis.

Washington had about 20,000 American and French troops at his disposal. The actual investment of Yorktown commenced on October 6. Bombardment began Oct. 9. Redoubt 9 under Lt. Col. McPherson was carried by bayonet charge under Col. Guillaume Deuxponts, while Lt. Col. Alexander Hamilton captured Redoubt 10. A second parallel meanwhile was being built to invest the city more closely. British under Lt. Col. Robert Abercrombie attacked the parallel at 4 a.m. on Oct. 16 with only partial success.

After Abercrombie's futile attack, Cornwallis decided to ferry his troops across the York that night (Oct. 16). He was balked by a sudden fierce storm and a shortage of boats.

On the morning of Oct. 17 a bombardment by 100 guns began against Yorktown, and at 10 a.m. Cornwallis asked Washington for a truce to discuss terms. The surrender was signed by noon on Oct. 20, and the ceremonies of surrender

took place the next day. Lord Cornwallis surrendered with 8,080 men; he had lost 600 in the siege. American and French casualties were 400.

It was the second surrender of a British army during the war (the first had been at Saratoga, N.Y. in October, 1777, when Major General John Burgoyne capitulated with about 4,400 men). When Prime Minister Lord North heard the news of Yorktown, he exclaimed, "Oh God! It is all over!" He was right, though peace needed two more years.

As a footnote to the Yorktown battle. the fleet under de Grasse sailed to the West Indies. There a fleet of 150 French and Spanish ships was assembled under de Grasse to attack Jamaica. The fleet sailed April 8, 1782 from Martinique, but was intercepted by a British fleet under Admiral George Rodney on April 12. The British had 36 ships of the line plus 5 frigates; the French and Spaniards 35 ships of the line (the rest being troop carriers, supply ships, etc.). In the Battle of The Saints (between Guadeloupe and Dominica). de Grasse was completely defeated and forced to surrender. He lost 6 ships captured and 3 more put out of action. The other French ships got away to Haiti. This footnote battle ended all fighting in the western hemisphere.

GRAND LODGE OF VIRGINIA

Baker	Date	Metal	Size	VF	EF	Unc
A454	1981	Bronze	Rect 56x76mm	—	17.50	—

In center, Yorktown monument, to left bust of Lafayette facing right and bust of De Grasse facing right, above on ribbon LAFAYETTE, below on ribbon DE GRASSE. To right: bust of Washington facing left, bust of Franklin facing left, above on ribbon WASHINGTON, below on ribbon FRANKLIN. Below monument in five lines: YORKTOWN / MONUMENT / TO THE ALLIANCE AND VICTORY / CORNERSTONE LAID BY THE M..W..GRAND LODGE OF VIRGINIA / OCTOBER 18, 1981 On edge 1981 MACO-BRONZE (Greenslet GM-266)

Struck by Medallic Art Co.

VIRGINIA SOCIETY OF THE CINCINNATI

Baker	Date	Metal	Size	EF	Unc	Proof
E-454	1931	Bronze	54mm	50.00	100.	—

Scene of the surrender of Yorktown, from a painting, with Washington at left center accepting the tendered sword of Cornwallis. On four round medallions at N-W-S-E are busts of Washington, de Grasse, Lafayette and Rochambeau. On a scroll at lower right: 1781 / YORKTOWN / 1931 Rv: Seal of the Cincinnati. On raised rim: PRESENTED BY THE SOCIETY OF THE CINCINNATI IN THE STATE OF VIRGINIA. Plain edge (Hume 16)

Designed by Edgar Erskine Hume of Virginia, then president of the Virginia society, and engraved by A. Baqueville of 5 Galerie Montpensier, Paris, and struck at the Paris Mint. The reverse has been used annually since 1925 at the College of William and Mary and the University of Virginia for excellence in history, especially Virginia history, and is known as the Cincinnati Medal.

Copies of the Yorktown 150th anniversary medal were presented to dignitaries attending ceremonies at Richmond on Oct. 19, 1931.

INDEPENDENCE ACHIEVED

F-454	1931	Gilt/B	34mm	—	7.00	—	

British officer hands sword to Washington and another officer, SUR-RENDER OF CORNWALLIS above, WHEN AMERICAN INDEPEN-DENCE WAS ACHIEVED below. Rv: YORKTOWN / SESQUI-CENTENNIAL / CELEBRATION / OCTOBER 16-19-1931. Plain edge.

BERLIN IRON PLAQUE

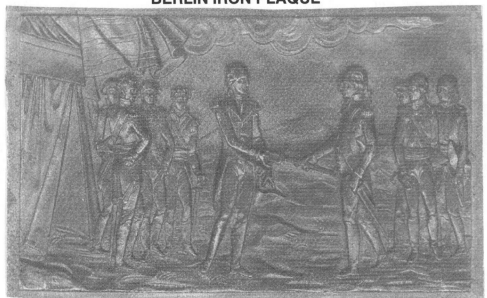

Baker	Date	Metal	Size	EF	AU	Unc
J-454	ND	Iron	Rect132.7x56.3mm—		300	—

Lord Cornwallis facing right offers his sword in surrender to General Washington, facing left, both in bareheaded full military dress. Behind Cornwallis stand four British officers before a large tent; three American or French officers stand behind Washington. A thick plain border surrounds the scene. Rv: Blank. (PCAC Nov. 15, 1997 sale, lot 270)

This cast iron plaque is unsigned and virtually unknown. Medal expert Richard Margolis determined it was listed circa 1920 on Godefroy Mayer's fixed price offering "Medallions, Medals and other Objects of Art Relating to America" as number 307, where it is described as *fonte de Berlin* (Berlin casting).

CAPITULATION DE YORK TOWN

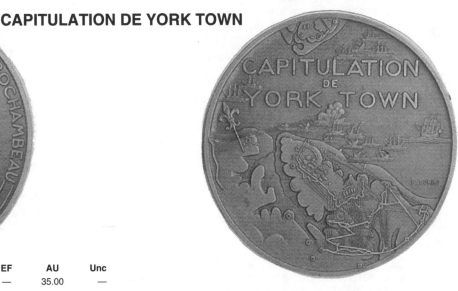

Baker	Date	Metal	Size	EF	AU	Unc
K-454	1931	Bronze	68mm	—	35.00	—

Jugate busts right of Washington, De Grasse and Rochambeau in fine style. Around: = WASHINGTON = DE GRASSE-TILLY = ROCHAMBEAU =. In exergue: MDCCLXXXI - MCMXXXI. Rv: Map of the battle plan area by sea and land, small P. TURIN at right. Above: CAPITULATION DE YORK TOWN. Edge: Plain; edge-markings not examined by authors. (Kirtley May 26, 1998 sale, lot C4)

Pierre Turin (born Aug. 3, 1891) designed French and French colonial coins 1929-1955. Struck at Paris Mint. Admiral de Grasse and General Rochambeau were the commanders of the regular French forces in America in the Revolutionary War.

Jean Baptiste Donatien de Vimeur, Comte de Rochambeau (1725-1807), entered France's navy 1742, distinguishing himself at Siege of Maastricht and, in 1756, in the expedition against Minorca. In 1780 he assumed command of all French land forces in America and was a hero at Yorktown 1781. In 1783 he was appointed royal governor of Picardy and Artois, and in 1791 promoted to marshal. He was imprisoned in the Reign of Terror and saved from the guillotine only by Robespierre's fall in 1794. His rank and estates were restored to him by Napoleon I.

Francois Joseph Paul, Comte de Grasse and Marquis de Grasse - Tilly (1722-1788) joined the Knights of Malta fleet 1734 and, in 1740, the French navy. He helped win the 1781 Battles of Chesapeake Bay and Yorktown, but was badly defeated by the British fleet at Les Saintes in 1782. Court-martialed, he was cleared but never given another command.

YORKTOWN MEMORIAL

Baker	Date	Metal	Size	F	VF	Unc
M454	1881	WM	23mm	10.00	15.00	—

Washington at left accepts sword of surrender from bowing Cornwallis. Around: SURRENDER / OCT. 19, 1781. Rv: YORKTOWN / VA. / CENTENNIAL / 1881 / MEMORIAL. Possibly issued holed for suspension. (Kirtley June 16, 1998 sale, lot B067)

The relief is low and token-like and the standing figures mere caricatures.

NEWBURGH MEDALS

CENTENNIAL OF PEACE

by Robert Lovett Jr.

Baker	Date	Metal	Size	EF	Unc	Proof
455	1883	WM	31mm	—	25.00	40.00

Undraped bust right, LOVETT on truncation, 1783 to left, 1883 to right. Around: CENTENNIAL OF PEACE BETWEEN UNITED STATES & GREAT BRITAIN. Rv: The house at Newburgh, in a circle. Around: NEWBURGH. N.Y. SETTLED IN 1719 * WASHINGTON'S HEADQUARTER'S 1783 *. Plain edge. Rarity 5.

| 455M | 1881 | Silver | 31mm | — | — | — |

Obverse as 455. Rv: As obverse as Baker 461. Plain edge. Rarity 9.

CHERRY TREE

Baker	Date	Metal	Size	VF	EF	Unc.
455N	1783	WM	31.5mm	—	—	45.00

FATHER I CANNOT TELL A LIE I DID IT around scene of young G.W. and his father in front of a fallen cherry tree, with young George holding a hatchet. Rv.: As reverse of 455, Centennial of Peace, Newburgh, N.Y. Plain edge. Holed for suspension. (PCAC Nov. 1997, McSorley, lot 1171)

CENTENNIAL CELEBRATION

by George H. Lovett

Baker	Date	Metal	Size	EF	Unc	Proof
456	1883	Silver	25mm	—	—	—

Undraped bust right (same obverse as Baker 137). Rv: The house at center. Above: CENTENNIAL * CELEBRATION OCT. 18, 1883. Below: WASHINGTON'S HEADQUARTERS NEWBURGH N.Y. Plain edge. Rarity 8.

Baker	Date	Metal	Size	EF	Unc	Proof
456A	1883	Copper	25mm	—	35.00	—

As 456. Plain edge. Rarity 4.

| 456B | 1883 | Bronze. | 25mm | — | 30.00 | — |

As 456. Plain edge. Rarity 4.

| 456C | 1883 | WM | 25mm | — | 45.00 | — |

As 456. Plain edge. Rarity 4.

FAMILY ARMS / NEWBURGH

Baker R-456 may now be found in Chapter 18!

REFUSING THE CROWN

| S-456 | 1883 | WM | 27mm | 15.00 | 30.00 | — |

Standing figure facing, GEO. WASHINGTON REFUSING THE CROWN / . NEWBURGH. Rv: Demi-female above shield, PROCLAMATION OF PEACE AND VICTORY / NEWBURGH / 1783 CENTENNIAL 1883 (legend uncertain). Plain edge. (Leon Hendrickson coll.)

EVACUATION OF NEW YORK

EVACUATION DAY CENTENNIAL

First obverse

by Morgan and Diehl

| 457 | 1883 | Bronze | 33mm | — | 35.00 | — |

Uniformed bust right, the Washington arms at left, MORGAN on truncation of bust. On a ribbon below: EXITUS ACTA PROBAT. Around: G. WASHINGTON. Rv: New York City shield of arms within olive wreath on a group of six flags, two crossed cannon below. A cluster of 13 stars above, 1783 to left, 1883 to right. Around: EVACUATION DAY CENTENNIAL NOV. 25 / . CITY OF NEW YORK. Plain edge. Rarity 4.

| 457A | 1883 | WM | 33mm | — | 35.00 | — |

As 457. Plain edge. Rarity 4.

| 457F | ND | Silver | 33mm | — | 100. | — |

Obverse as 457. Rv: Blank. Plain edge. Rarity 8.

| 457G | ND | Bronze | 33mm | — | 50.00 | — |

As 457F. Plain edge. Rarity 6

| 457H | ND | WM | 33mm | — | 50.00 | — |

As 457F. Plain edge. Rarity 6.

Second obverse

by Morgan and Diehl

Baker	Date	Metal	Size	EF	Unc	Proof
458	1883	Bronze	33mm	—	—	—

Undraped bust right in circular panel. Below are two other circular panels, containing busts of General Knox and Governor George Clinton. Around: WASHINGTON - KNOX - CLINTON. Rv: As reverse of 457. Plain edge. Rarity 5.

| 458A | 1883 | WM | 33mm | 25.00 | — | — |

As 458. Plain edge. Rarity 5.

Baker 457 and 458 were engraved by George T. Morgan and published by John H. Diehl of Philadelphia.

CENTENNIAL ANNIVERSARY

by Warner & Brother

Baker	Date	Metal	Size	EF	Unc	Proof
459	1883	Copper	44mm	—	60.00	—

Undraped bust in high relief left, GEORGE WASHINGTON around. Rv: Within laurel wreath: CENTENNIAL / ANNIVERSARY / NOV. 25, / 1883. Around: NEW YORK EVACUATED BY THE BRITISH / * NOV. 25, 1783. *. Plain edge. Rarity 4.

459A	1883	Bronze	44mm	—	60.00	—

As 459. Plain edge. Rarity 4.

459B	1883	WM	44mm	40.00	60.00	—

As 459. Plain edge. Rarity 5. (Garrett 1883)

Baker 459's forceful portrait of Washington, after the Houdon sculpture, was obtained from an original hub by Charles Cushing Wright. The wreath on reverse is the work of Anthony C. Paquet. The medals were published by Warner & Brother of Philadelphia.

NEW YORK EVACUATED

by Paquet

Baker	Date	Metal	Size	EF	Unc	Proof
460	1883	Silver	32mm	—	—	125.

Obverse as Baker 377 (undraped bust right, GEORGE WASHINGTON around). Rv: Within olive wreath: 1883 / NEW YORK / EVACUATED / BY THE / BRITISH / NOV. 25. 1783 / 1783. Plain edge. Rarity 8.

460A	1883	Bronze	32mm	—	35.00	65.00

As 460. Plain edge. Rarity 5. (Bullowa-Lessin sale, lot 52)

460B	1883	WM	32mm	—	35.00	65.00

As 460. Plain edge. Rarity 5. (Bullowa-Lessin sale, lot 51)

The obverse bust was modeled by Anthony C. Paquet for an earlier medal, the 1861 Mint Allegiance medal, and was used later (1884) for the First Regiment Armory medal - respectively Baker 279 and 377.

PEACE PROCLAIMED

by Robert Lovett Jr.

Baker	Date	Medal	Size	EF	Unc	Proof
461	1883	WM	32mm	—	25.00	35.00

Undraped bust right in a circle, LOVETT on truncation. Around: PEACE PROCLAIMED & ARMY DISBANDED IN 1783. Rv: In eight lines: 1783 CENTENNIAL 1883 CELEBRATION OF THE EVACUATION OF THE

CITY OF NEW YORK NOVEMBER 25. Half circle above, arc of 13 stars below. Plain edge. Rarity 3. (Bullowa-Lessin sale, lot 50; Collins 386)

Struck by Robert Lovett Jr. of Philadelphia.

EQUESTRIAN EFFIGY

462	1883	Copper	40mm	—	—	75.00

Uniformed equestrian figure advancing left. Around: GENERAL WASHINGTON ENTERING NEW YORK NOV. 25. 1783. Rv: British army departing. Above: 1783 - 1883 / CENTENNIAL and 13 stars Around: EVACUATION OF NEW YORK BY THE BRITISH ARMY. Plain edge. Rarity 7.

462A	1883	WM	40mm	—	25.00	—

As 462. Plain edge. Rarity 4.

NEW YORK EVACUATED

By William H. Key

Baker	Date	Metal	Size	EF	Unc	Proof
463	1883	Silver	16mm	—	35.00	—

Uniformed bust right, K on truncation. Around: GEN. GEORGE WASHINGTON. Rv: 1783 / NEW YORK / EVACUATED / NOV. 25. / 1883 in five lines, ornamentation at top and bottom. Plain edge. Rarity 7.

463A	1883	Bronze	16mm	—	20.00	—

As 463. Plain edge. Rarity 5. (Bullowa-Lessin sale, lot 49)

463B	1883	Gilt / Cop	16mm	—	20.00	—

As 463. Plain edge. Rarity 4. (Bullowa-Lessin sale, lot 49)

463C	1883	WM	16mm	—	20.00	—

As 463. Plain edge. (Roelofs Coll.)

The bust is a reduction of that on the Norwalk Memorial piece of 1869, Baker 369. The reverse die on all is blundered.

GOD AND OUR COUNTRY

by George B. Soley

464	1883	Gilt	12.5mm	7.50	10.00	—

Undraped bust right, GOD AND OUR COUNTRY around. Rv: EVACUATION DAY CENTENNIAL 1783 - 1883. Reeded edge. Rarity 3.

Published by George B. Soley of Philadelphia.

464E	1883	Gilt	13mm	—	9.00	—

Obverse as 464. Rv: Bridge, BROOKLYN BRIDGE above, 1883 in exergue. Reeded edge. (Schuster coll.)

LONGINES FAREWELL TO OFFICERS

Struck 1983?

Baker	Date	Metal	Size	EF	AU	Unc
A464	ND	Silver*	40mm	—	—	30.00

* Sterling (.925 fine) silver, antiqued finish.
Washington bidding farewell to four officers, small a at left below, JDL at right. Around: WASHINGTON'S FAREWELL TO HIS OFFICERS / 1783. Rv: DECEMBER 4, 1783 / SOON AFTER THE EVACUATION OF / THE LAST BRITISH TROOPS / GENERAL GEORGE WASHINGTON / TOOK LEAVE OF HIS KEY OFFICERS / IN NEW YORK'S FRAUNC-ES TAVERN / THUS DEPARTING THE COMMAND / THAT WON AMERICAN INDEPENDENCE / (defiant eagle right on shield.) Plain edge marked: C-in circle LONGINES SYMPHONETTE STERLING R 268 (or another serial number). (H.J. Levine report)

Baker	Date	Metal	Size	EF	AU	Unc
A464A	ND	Gold/Silver x	40mm	—	—	35.00

* 24-Karat gold plating on sterling silver.
As 464, but signature letters on bottom are small a at left and capital W at right. Plain edge is marked: C-in-circle LONGINE (sic!) SYMPHO-NETTE
24 K GOLD E.P. ON STERLING D 523 (or another serial number).

E.P. = Electroplate. The Longines Watch Co.'s symphony orchestra sponsored these handsome medals.

The authors have not determined who designed or struck these pieces.

LONGINES DELAWARE CROSSING

Baker	Date	Metal	Size	VF	EF	Unc
AA464	ND	Silver*	40mm	—	—	30.00

*Sterling (.925 fine) silver; antiqued finish.
Washington standing at prow of boat facing viewer, small a at left below, JDL at right. Around: WASHINGTON CROSSING THE DELAWARE / 1776. Rv: GENERAL GEORGE WASHINGTON'S / UNEXPECTED CROSSING OF THE DELAWARE RIVER ON CHRISTMAS NIGHT / IN THE FATEFUL YEAR OF 1776 / PRECEDED THE HESSIAN DEFEAT / IN TRENTON, NEW JERSEY / AND GAVE FRESH HOPE / TO THE AMERICAN CAUSE / (defiant eagle right on shield). Plain edge,

marked: C-in-circle LONGINES SYMHPONETTE STERLING R 268 (or another serial number). (H.J. Levine report)

This is an impressive example of the medalist's art. The unusual depiction of the famous crossing is shown head on, in high relief.

WITTNAUER "SELF MADE MAN"

Baker	Date	Metal	Size	VF	EF	Unc
AC464	1972	Silver*	40mm	—	—	27.50

* Sterling (.925 fine) silver; antiqued finish.
Mature head right, at left, looks at chopped cherry tree and ax, boy's head 3/4 left; small AM near boy's head. Around: GEORGE WASHING-TON / 1789-1797. Rv: Branches and crossed sabers below: 1732-1799 / GEORGE WASHINGTON. / A SELF-MADE MAN WHO / ROSE TO THE PRESIDENCY / OF THE UNITED STATES / WITHOUT THE BEN-EFIT OF / ANY FORMAL EDUCATION. / THROUGHLY ENJOYED ALL / LIFE'S CULTURAL PURSUITS. Plain edge, marked: C-in-circle WITT-NAUER P.M.G. 1972 STERLING E 786 (or another serial number). (H.J. Levine report)

The Longines-Wittnauer Watch Co. High relief; excellent workmanship. P.M.G.=Precious Metals Guild.

N.C.S.

(National Commemorative Society)

Baker	Date	Metal	Size	VF	EF	Unc
B-464	1974	Silver	38mm	—	—	25.00

Cloaked, uniformed standing figure of Washington faces viewer at left, Mount Vernon and crested U.S. shield at right, FIRST / PRESIDENT at right, GEORGE WASHINGTON below. Rv: Battle scene; officer plants Stars and Stripes as soldiers ready cannon and others hoist flag on pole, 1776 NCS / 1974 at sides, THE THIRTEEN ORIGINAL STATES below.

Struck by Franklin Mint, Franklin Center, Pa.

Chapter 27

CENTENNIALS OF THE CONSTITUTION, 1887-1987

CONSTITUTIONAL CONVENTION

Baker	Date	Metal	Size	EF	Unc	Proof
1800	1887	Bronze	37mm	—	30.00	—

Undraped bust right within sunken circular field. Around, on raised border: PRESIDENT OF THE CONSTITUTIONAL CONVENTION / * 1787 *. Rv: Independence Hall across center, CONSTITUTIONAL CENTENNIAL around, PHILADELPHHIA / - SEP. 17, - / 1887 in exergue. Plain edge. (Parsons 980; Bullowa-Lessin 34)

1800A	1887	WM	37mm	—	40.00	—

As 1800.

A1800	1887	Bronze	50.9mm	—	65.00	—

As Baker 1800, but larger format. Rv: Similar to Baker 1800, but legend reads in two lines around top: CENTENNIAL ANNIVERSARY OF THE / ADOPTION OF THE / CONSTITUTION OF THE UNITED STATES. Plain edge. (Schuster coll.)

1803	1887	Bronze	27mm	20.00	25.00	—

Undraped bust right, PRESIDENT OF THE CONSTITUTIONAL CONVENTION 1787. around, reading clockwise from 2 o'clock position. Rv: Independence Hall at center, CONSTITUTIONAL CENTENNIAL above, PHILADELPHIA / SEP. 17. / 1887. below. Plain edge. (Parsons 880; Bullowa-Lessin 35)

CAMP GEORGE WASHINGTON

Baker	Date	Metal	Size	VF	EF	Unc
1804	1887	WM	35mm	—	25.00	35.00

Houdon bust right in circle. Around: CAMP GEORGE WASHINGTON / * WASHINGTON, D.C. *. Rv: Sentinel standing guard over tent camp, cannon and three stacked rifles at each side, all within thick circular wreath. Around: NATIONAL PRIZE DRILL / * MAY 23 - 30, 1887. * . Issued holed. (Kirtley Dec. 5, 1995 sale, lot E073)

Baker	Date	Metal	Size	EF	Unc	Proof
A1804	1887	WM	35.1mm	—	—	60.00

Bust right, NATIONAL PRIZE DRILL above. Below: CAMP GEO. WASHINGTON / WASHINGTON, D.C. MAY 23-30, 1887. Rv: Captiol.. WASHINGTON, D.C. on scroll above. Below: 1887. Plain edge. (Irving Schuster Coll.)

PRESIDENT OF THE CONVENTION

Baker	Date	Metal	Size	VF	EF	Unc
1805	1887	Brass	25mm	10.00	15.00	—

Washington bust left. Around: PRESIDENT OF THE CONSTITUTIONAL CONVENTION / 1787. Rv: Independence Hall. Around: CENTENNIAL ANNIVERSARY OF THE / CONSTITUTION OF THE UNITED STATES / PHILADELPHIA / SEPT. 17, 1887. Issued holed for suspension. (Kirtley Dec. 5, 1995 auction, lot E074)

A1805	1887	WM	51mm	—	75.00	—

Larger version of Baker 1805. (Kirtley 1991 fixed price list)

Baker	Date	Metal	Size	F	VF	Unc
E1805	1887	Brass	25mm	—	15.00	—

Nude bust left, PRESIDENT OF THE CONVENTION / 1787 around. Tiny E A K on truncation of bust. Rv: Independence Hall, CONSTITUTIONAL CENTENNIAL / SEPT. 1887 above. In exergue: PHILA. 15-17. Plain edge. (Stewart Witham 1986 report)

E.A.K. = E. A. Kretschman, 9th and Ward Streets, Philadelphia. Issued holed for suspension.

CONSTITUTION ADOPTED

Baker	Date	Metal	Size	VF	EF	Unc
1806	1887	Brass	25mm	—	—	20.00

Washington bust right. THE CONSTITUTION ADOPTED / SEPT. 1787 around. Rv: Unknown head left, CONSTITUTION CENTENNIAL / SEPT. 1887 around. Plain edge.

Baker	Date	Metal	Size	VF	EF	Unc
1808	1887	Brass	25mm	—	—	20.00

Bust right. Around: CONSTITUION ADOPTED. 1787 SEPT. Rv: Liberty Bell at center. Around. PROCLAIM LIBERTY THROUGHOUT THE LAND / CONSTITUTION CENTENNIAL 1887.

Baker	Date	Metal	Size	VF	EF	Unc
1810	1887	WM	35mm	—	20.00	30.00

Uniformed bust right, MORGAN on truncation. PRESIDENT OF THE CONVENTION around, 1787 below. Rv: Small jugate busts of Hamilton and Madison right in medallion at top, HAMILTON - MADISON on surrounding scroll. Independence Hall on central tablet, 1787 left, 1887 right, CENTENNIAL OF THE ADOPTION / OF THE / CONSTITUTION in exergue. Plain edge. (Rich Hartzog coll.; Stewart Witham coll.)

Dies were but by George T. Morgan of the U.S. Mint.

Baker	Date	Metal	Size	EF	Unc	Proof
A1810	1887	WM	35mm	—	20.00	30.00

Bust as on 1810, EXITUS ACTA PROBAT on scroll below. Washington arms at left, G. WASHINGTON at right. Rv: As reverse of 1810. (Dr. Schuster coll.)

George T. Morgan cut the Baker A1810 dies.

SESQUICENTENNIAL 1937

Baker	Date	Metal	Size	EF	AU	Unc
1807	1937	Bronze	76mm	—	35.00	

Nude bust left, UNITED. STATES. CONSTITUTION. SESQUICEN-TENNIAL / (spray) 1787-1937 (spray) around. Rv: Furling LIBERTY OR DEATH flag amid: SEMPER FIDELIS / 1683 / THE / CITY / OF / WHITE PLAINS/ N.Y. / 1776 / 1915. Outside central circle: (laurel spray) AWARDED TO (laurel spray). Plain edge. (Kirtley May 26, 1998 sale, lo C8)

Struck by Medallic Art Co., New York.

BICENTENNIAL OF THE CONSTITUTION

Baker	Date	Metal	Size	VF	EF	Unc
1809	1987	Bronze	38mm	—	—	8.00

The COMMISSION OF THE BICENTENNIAL OF THE UNITED STATES CONTITUTION around with Franklin seated in foreground, Washington and six others at signing of the Constitution. Below: *1787 - 1987* THE UNITED STATES / CAPITOL HISTORICAL / SOCIETY under desk. Rv: divided into three sections, an eagle representing the Executive, ARTICLE II THE EXECUTIVE POWER.... VESTED IN / A PRESIDENT OF THE UNITED STATES above on ribbon. To left, eagle atop flag pole representing Legislature, ARTICLE I ALL LEGISLATIVE POWERS... VESTED / IN A CONGRESS OF THE UNITED STATES to left on ribbon. To right, scales representing the Judicial, ARTICLE III THE JUDICIAL POWER... VESTED / IN ONE SUPREME COURT on ribbon. 2,500 struck. Sculpted by Marcel Jovine, MACO. (Greenslet GM-271)

Baker	Date	Metal	Size	VF	EF	Unc
1809A	1987	Bronze	64mm	—	—	12.50

Similar to preceding, 1,000 struck.

Baker	Date	Metal	Size	VF	EF	Unc
1809B	1987	Bronze	76mm	—	—	15.00

Similar to preceding, 500 struck.

Baker	Date	Metal	Size	VF	EF	Unc
1809E	1987	18k gold	33mm	—	—	350.

Similar to preceding, 50 struck.

Baker	Date	Metal	Size	VF	EF	Unc
1809C	1987	Silver	38mm	—	Proof	20.00

Similar to preceding, 500 struck.

Baker	Date	Metal	Size	VF	EF	Unc
1809D	1987	Silver	76mm	—	—	75.00

Similar to preceding, 75 struck.

Struck by Medallic Art Co., Danbury, Conn.

Baker	Date	Metal	Size	VF	EF	Unc
1811	1987	Bronze	39mm	—	—	7.50

CONSTITUTIONAL / CONVENTION / Franklin seated in foreground, three others including Washington, standing, heads of two others in background. Rv: THE CONSTITUTION / OF THE UNITED STATES / SEPTEMBER 17, 1787 / a portion of the Preamble of the Constitution. 500 struck. Medal number 4 of the Medals of America series, sub-set Documents of Freedom (2 pieces) sponsored by The International Numismatic Agency, New York. Sculpted by Ernest Schroeder. (MAS-4; Greenslet GM-456)

Baker	Date	Metal	Size	EF	Unc	Proof
1812	1787	Gold/Silver	39mm	—	—	10.00

Franklin seated, with others at Constitutional Convention. Rv: Washington head on shield at top; double circle around PRESIDING / OVER / CONSTITUTIONAL / CONVENTION / MAY 25 - SEPTEMBER 17, 1787 within circle. 1640 struck. Medal number 10 in the Great Moments in the Life of George Washington series, sculpted by Ronald Hower. (LGW-10; Greenslet GM-541)

CENTENNIAL OF WASHINGTON'S INAUGURATION IN 1889

Baker numbers are not used in this chapter. Instead, Douglas numbers are used to correspond with the catalog by Susan Douglas of "George Washington Medals of 1889" appearing in *The Numismatist* for 1949. Pseudo-Douglas numbers are assigned on an arbitrary basis where she omitted an entry.

The arrangement of medals in this chapter is basically as Douglas initiated it. A few pieces have been moved so that they appear in a more logical position: 58 follows 17, 35 and 34 are transposed, 32 follows 42, 60 follows 61, 63 follows 51.

Douglas	Designer/Medalist	Maker	Publisher/Distributor
1-1B	Tardier/Tiffany & Co.	Philadelphia Mint	N.J. Historical Soc.
2-2B	Tardier/Tiffany & Co.	Philadelphia Mint	N.J. Historical Soc.
3-5		Childs & Co.	
6			
7-7A		George H. Lovett	N.Y. Natl. Guard
8		George H. Lovett	N.Y. Cent. Comm.
9-9B			
10-11		George H. Lovett	
12			Chas. S. Higgins
13-13B	E. A. Kretschman		
14-14U	George T. Morgan		
15			L. F.
16		Peter L. Krider	Black Starr Frost
17		Childs & Co.	
18-26		George H. Lovett	
27		George H. Lovett	A. Raymond & Co.
28		George H. Lovett	
29			
30			
31-31 B		G. P. Kato	
32		George H. Lovett	
33	Robert Lovett Jr.	P.	
34-34B		N. M. Friederich	
35-35A		N. M. Friederich	
C35		William Friederich	
36			
37		George H. Lovett	
38	George H. Lovett	P.	
39-39B			
40-40B		C. G. Braxmar	
41-41 B		Gorham Mfg. Co.	
42-43A	George T. Morgan		
44-44A			
45			
46	S.	Childs & Co.	
47		Robert Lovett Jr.	
48-48A	William H. Key		
49-49A	William H. Key		
50-50E	William H. Key		
51-51G		Childs & Co.	
52-52A	Charles C. Wright		S.H. & H. Chapman
53-53B	Philip Martiny/ Augustus St. Gaudens	Gorham Mfg. Co.	
54		Gorham Mfg. Co.	
55	George T. Morgan		O.U.A.M.
56		(5-point star)	
57			
58		Childs & Co.	
59			
60-610	Robert Lovett Jr.	P.	
62-62A			Unitarian Church
63		Childs & Co.	Cragin's friends
66			
67			
68			
70.	L.A.K.		Pa. State Fair
71			P.O.S. of A.

ABOVE ALL THINGS HOLD DEAR

Struck 1895

Douglas	Date	Metal	Size	VF	EF	Unc
1	1889	Gold	60mm	—	—	Unique

Undraped bust left. TIFFANY & CO. below bust. Around: WASHING-TON CENTENNIAL MEDAL * NEW JERSEY HISTORICAL SOCIETY / * 1789 APRIL 1889 * Rv: Seal of the NJHS within wreath below three lines of text. ABOVE ALL THINGS / HOLD DEAR / YOUR NATIONAL UNION. Plain edge, numbered 1. Only 1 struck.

1A	1889	Silver	60mm	—	900.	1200.

As 1. Plain edge, numbered.

1B	1889	Bronze	60mm	—	—	700.

As 1. Plain edge, numbered.

The medals were authorized by the New Jersey Historical Society on Jan. 22, 1889 but the committee of five reported on Jan. 23, 1894 that the medals were delayed by illness of the engraver and correction of a text error (see Douglas 2). They were finally presented on May 16, 1895. The gold medal, numbered 1, was pre-sented to former President Benjamin Harrison. Silver medal number 2 was pre-sented to former New Jersey Governor Robert S. Green. Both men were in office during the centennial observances.

Each comittee member received a silver medal and bronze copies went to per-sons who contributed to the cost of cutting the dies.

Mrs. Douglas in 1949 reported the whereabouts of bronze medals numbered 48, 52 and 71.

Bronze medal numbered 48 on edge, ex-Susan Douglas, realized $467.50 in PCAC Dec. 1988 sale and appeared again in Kirtley may 6, 1997 sale (lot AD 83) where it fetched $660. There are still only three pieces of Douglas 1B located though others are reported.

Dies were executed by Tardier and the medals struck at the U.S. Mint, Phila-delphia under direction of Superintendent Bosbyshell.

ABOVE ALL THINGS HOLD FAST

Douglas	Date	Metal	Size	VF	EF	Unc
2	1889	Silver	60mm	—	—	Unique

Obverse as 1. Rv: As reverse of 1, but second line of text reads (in er-ror), HOLD FAST. Plain edge. Only 1 struck; in N.J. Historical Society.

2A	1889	Bronze	60mm	—	—	Unique

As 2. Plain edge. In 1949 this was in the F. C. C. Boyd collection.

2B	1889	Lead	60mm	—	—	Unique

As 2. Plain edge. In 1949 this was in the Susan Douglas collection.

CHILDS ALUMINUM MEDALS

Douglas	Date	Metal	Size	VF	EF	Unc
3	ND	Aluminum	34.3mm	—	—	40.00

Undraped bust left, CHILDS CHICAGO below, all within circle. Around GEORGE WASHINGTON / *** OUR FIRST PRESIDENT ***. Rv: Within beaded circle: ALUMINUM / MALLEABLE / UNTARNISHABLE / TASTELESS / ODORLESS / DUCTILE. Around: THIS MEDAL IS MADE OF THE WONDERFUL METAL / ooOoo. Plain edge.

Manufacturers of aluminum seized the opportunity of the 1889 celebrations to advertise their new product, which had been introduced commercially only in No-vember, 1988.

	ND	Aluminum	37mm	—	35.00	50.00
4						

Undraped bust left, UNITED STATES OF AMERICA above, * IN GOD WE TRUST * below. On raised rim at bottom in tiny letters: CHILDS CHICAGO. Rv: MALLEABLE, / TASTELESS, SONOROUS, / DUCTILE, / UNTARNISHABLE. / * ALUMINUM * (in fancy letters on band across center) / CUBIC FOOT OF GOLD, 1204 LBS. / "ALUMINUM 179" / THIS MEDAL / IS PURE. / CHILDS CHICAGO (tiny letters). Plain edge. Rarity 5. (Collins 392).

Douglas	Date	Metal	Size	VF	EF	Unc
5	ND	Aluminum	37mm	—	35.00	50.00

Large undraped bust left, CHILDS * CHICAGO, under bust. Around: WASHINGTON CENTENNIAL. Rv: As reverse of 4. Plain edge. Rarity 5. (Collins (393)

Douglas 3, 4 and 5 are advertising medals of the S. D. Childs & Co. private minting establishment in Chicago, Illinois. They should, perhaps, be included under store cards rather than medals but we prefer to keep Douglas' 1889 pieces together.

SEVENTH REGIMENT N.G.S.N.Y.

Douglas	Date	Metal	Size	VF	EF	Unc
6	1889	Bronze	35mm	—	300.	450.

Undraped bust left. Around: WASHINGTON * INAUGURATION * CENTENNIAL / * 1889 * Rv: 11 lines: A SOUVENIR / OF THE / CENTENNIAL CELEBRATION / AS GUARD OF HONOR / TO THE PRESIDENT OF THE / UNITED STATES / BY THE UNIFORMED BATTALION / OF THE VETERANS OF THE / SEVENTH REGIMENT N.G.S.N.Y. / NEW YORK / APRIL 29TH, 1889. Plain edge. Issued with loop, for suspension from red ribbon and bronze bar, the latter dated 1789 1889 and with V N.G. PRO PATRIA ET GLORIA and numeral 7. (PCAC Dec. 1988 sale, Unc, realized $291.50; same piece fetched $451 in Kirtley May 1997 sale, lot AD 87).

N.G.S.N.Y. - National Guard State of New York. Rare

by George H. Lovett

Douglas	Date	Metal	Size	VF	EF	Unc
7	1889	Bronze	51.2mm	—	125.	225.

Undraped bust right, LOVETT below, withiin sunken central circle. Around, a raised border with 13 arches and stars, inscribed: FIRST PRESIDENT OF THE UNITED STATES OF AMERICA / DEO PATRIAEQUE FIDELIS. Rv: Radiant sun over Brooklyn Bridge and East River, HAEC OLIM MEMINISSE JUVABIT above, all within central circle with draped arms of New York below. Around, in two concentric lines: TO COMMEMORATE THE WASHINGTON INAUGURAL CENTENNIAL / NEW YORK CITY 1789 - APRIL 30 - 1889. Plain edge. Rarity 7. (Springfield 4073; Collins 394).

7A	1889	WM	51.2mm	—	30.00	50.00

As 7. Plain edge. Rarity 5. (Krueger sale, lot 1993; Collins 395)

Douglas	Date	Metal	Size	VF	EF	Unc
8	1889	WM	52mm	—	—	—

Obverse as 7, except the radiant sun in on reverse! Rv: As reverse of 7. Plain edge. Rarity 7. Only 18 to 20 struck; just 4-5 known.

George Hampden Lovett of New York struck Douglas 7 and 8, the latter an error since the committee wanted the radiant sun on obverse.

Douglas	Date	Metal	Size	VF	EF	Unc
9	1789	Gilt/Cop	25.5mm	—	12.50	20.00

Undraped bust right, INAUGURATED NEW YORK APRIL 30 / 1789 around. Rv: Bridge at center, NEW YORK - BROOKLYN / PROGRESS OF / 100 YEARS above. THE EIGHTH / WONDER in exergue. Plain edge. Rarity 4. (Bullowa-Lessin 33; Collins 396)

9A	1789	Brass	25mm	—	12.50	17.50

As 9. Plain edge. Rarity 4. (Springfield 4074)

9B	1789	WM	25mm	—	20.00	—

As 9.

Douglas 9 was issued holed for suspension from a blue ribbon, which was hung from a hatchet-shaped pin inscribed I CANNOT TELL A LIE. Also reported in copper.

Douglas	Date	Metal	Size		EF	Unc
13A	1889	Gilt/Bz	43.7mm	—	30.00	50.00

As 13. Plain edge.

Douglas	Date	Metal	Size		EF	Unc
13B	1889	WM	43.7mm	—	30.00	50.00

As 13. Plain edge. Rarity 5. Bullowa-Lessin 32; Springfield 4075)

Designed by E. A. Kretschman, sculptor, with studio at 9th and Ward Streets, Philadelphia.

CENTENNIAL CELEBRATION

by George H. Lovett

Douglas	Date	Metal	Size		VF	EF	Unc
10	1789	WM	40mm	—		30.00	45.00

Undraped bust right, GEORGE WASHINGTON around, within Laurel wreath at rim. Rv: Within oak wreath in 10 lines: CENTENNIAL / CELE-BRATION / OF THE / INAUGURATION / OF / GEORGE WASHING-TON / FIRST PRESIDENT / OF THE / UNITED STATES / APRIL 30, 1789. Plain edge. Rarity 4. (Kirtley report; Collins 398)

Douglas	Date	Metal	Size		VF	EF	Unc
11	1789	WM	40mm	—		30.00	45.00

Undraped bust right, G.H.L. on truncation, GEORGE WASHINGTON around. Raised band at rim. Rv: As reverse of 10. Plain edge. Rarity 4. (Collins 399)

CENTENNIAL

Higgins Toilet Soap

Douglas	Date	Metal	Size	VF	EF	Unc
12	1889	Wax	54.3mm	—	—	2 Known

Undraped bust left, PRESIDENT above, 1789 below. Rv: CENTENNIAL / CHAS. S. HIGGINS / PURE MILLED / TOILET SOAP / 1889. Plain edge. Wax impression, struck off dies. Rarity 9. (In ANS collection; Kirtley sale 156)

Higgin's German Laundry Soap was advertised on cards of the day by Charles S. Higgins, 94 Wall Street, New York City. He also advertised Pure Milled Glycerine Ball Toilet Soap from Park and Clinton Avenues in Brooklyn, N.Y.

EQUESTRIAN MEDAL

Douglas	Date	Metal	Size		VF	EF	Unc
13	1889	Bronze	43.7mm	—		60.00	115.

Civil bust right, E A K on truncation, GEORGE WASHINGTON around. Rv: Equestrian figure right, right arm extended, circled by wreath containing arms of New York City (left) and New York state (right). Around: CENTENNIAL INAUGURATION / NEW YORK APRIL 30, 1889. Plain edge. (Kirtley May 1997 sale, lot AD 94, Unc, fetched $112.20).

WASHINGTON-HARRISON

Douglas	Date	Metal	Size		EF	Unc	Proof
14	1889	WM	38mm		30.00	40.00	

Busts of Washington and Benjamin Harrison jugate right, M on truncation WASHINGTON HARRISON / 1789 - 1889 around. Rv: On a rectangular tablet surrounded by oak and olive wreath: CENTENNIAL OF THE / INAUGURATION OF / GEORGE WASHINGTON / AS FIRST PRESIDENT / OF THE UNITED STATES / NEW YORK APRIL 30. / 1789. Plain edge. Rarity 4. (Bullowa-Lessin 30)

Douglas	Date	Metal	Size		EF	Unc	Proof
14A	1889	Bronze	38mm		35.00	60.00	—

As 14. Plain edge. Rarity 7.

Douglas	Date	Metal	Size		EF	Unc	Proof
14S	1889	WM	35mm		20.00	35.00	—

As 14, in reduced size. Plain edge. Issued holed, for suspension with ribbon and pin. (Bullowa-Lessin 31)

Denver reverse

Douglas	Date	Metal	Size		VF	EF	Unc
14U	1889	WM	37mm		—	Rare	—

Obverse as 14. Rv: In five lines: AMERICAN INDEPENDENCE / CELEBRATION / JULY 4-5-6 / 1889. / DENVER, COL. Plain edge.

Engraved by M = George T. Morgan.

PATER PATRIAE

Certain Latin terms appear on medals pertaining to George Washington, the first "General of the Armies of the United States." Only one other man held this title until the 5-star rank was created in World War II, and that was John J. Pershing, U.S. commander in France in WWI.

Pater Patriae (father of his country) is the apt title frequently appearing. Many other Latin words and phrases appear on items in this catalog; in most cases we have translated these for users.

SHIELD-SHAPED MEDAL

Douglas	Date	Metal	Size	VF	EF	Unc
15	1889	Gilt	35 by 44mm	150.	185.	—

Head left within circle at center of raised U.S. shield, inscribed (in lines of varying size and direction): COP'Y'D 1889 LF / CENTENNIAL / OUR FIRST / 1789 PRESIDENT 1889 / GEORGE WASHINGTON / FIRST IN WAR, FIRST IN PEACE and FIRST IN THE HEARTS OF HIS COUNTRYMEN. Rv: Intaglio of obverse. Plain edge. (ANS collection; Kirtley May 1997 sale, lot AD 96, realized $162.80 in VF)

Publisher LF = ? An eagle-on-crossed flags hanger accompanies this piece; there was a ribbon when issued.

BLACK, STARR & FROST

Douglas	Date	Metal	Size	EF	Unc	Proof
16	1889	WM	50.6mm	35.00	50.00	50.00

Sub-Treasury building with Washington statue, 1789 - 1889 on scroll work below. Around: * THE CENTENNIAL CELEBRATION OF WASHINGTON'S INAUGURATION. Rv: Above: COMPLIMENTS / OF / BLACK, STARR & FORST / -.- / NEW YORK. Two crossed flags with standards at center, sprays around. Along bottom: P. L. KRIDER CO. PHILA. Plain edge. Rarity 6. (Collins 403)

Struck by Peter L. Krider Co. Philadelphia.

Douglas	Date	Metal	Size	EF	Unc	Proof
16A	1889	Bronze	51mm	—	250.	—

As 16. Unpublished. (Kirtley May 1997 sale, lot AD 98; fetched $242 in Unc)

DENMAN THOMPSON'S PLAY

Chicago

Douglas	Date	Metal	Size	VF	EF	Unc
17	1889	Bronze	39mm	30.00	40.00	60.00

Accolated busts of Washington and Benjamin Harrison right, CHILDS on truncation. Around: GEO. WASHINGTON 1789 BENJ HARRISON / 1889. Rv: In 12 lines: DENMAN THOMPSON'S PLAY / "TWO / SISTERS" / McVICKER'S THEATRE, CHICAGO / APRIL 30TH 1889. / CENTENNIAL / OF INAUGURATION OF / GEO. WASHINGTON / AS / PRESIDENT OF U.S.A. / AT / NEW YORK. Plain edge.

Struck by S. D. Childs & Co. Chicago

Douglas	Date	Metal	Size			Unc
58	1889	Aluminum	39mm	—	—	50.00

Obverse as 17. Rv: Blank. Plain edge.

FEDERAL HALL

by George H. Lovett

Douglas	Date	Metal	Size	EF	Unc	Proof
18	1889	WM	40mm	35.00	50.00	—

Obverse as Douglas 11. Rv: Federal Hall above FEDERAL HALL / WALL ST., within circular thick wreath. Around WASHINGTON INAUGURAL CENTENNIAL, NEW YORK. / APRIL 30, 1889. Plain edge. Rarity 5. (Collins 404)

Douglas	Date	Metal	Size	EF	Unc	Proof
19	1889	WM	40mm	45.00	60.00	—

Obverse as Douglas 11. Rv: Federal Hall, NEW YORK above, FEDERAL / HALL below, all within circle of 13 stars. Around: CENTENNIAL CELEBRATION OF INAUGURATION / APRIL 30, 1889. Plain edge. Rarity 5. (Collins 405)

Also known in copper.

Douglas	Date	Metal	Size	EF	Unc	Proof
20	1889	WM	39mm	—	50.00	—

Undraped bust right, GEORGE WASHINGTON around, all within clover-leaf cartouche. Rv: Hall at center above: FEDERAL HALL / WALL ST, all within circular wreath. Around: WASHINGTON INAUGURAL CENTENNIAL, NEW YORK. / APRIL 30, 1889. Plain edge. (Bullowa-Lessin 29)

Douglas	Date	Metal	Size	EF	Unc	Proof
20M	1889	WM	39mm	—	50.00	—

Obverse as 20. Reverse: As Douglas 18. Plain edge (Springfield 4076)

OLD FEDERAL BUILDING

Douglas	Date	Metal	Size	EF	Unc	Proof
21	1889	WM	38mm	80.00	100.	—

Undraped bust right, L on truncation, 5 stars at left, 8 stars at right. Around: 1789 CENTENNIAL INAUGURATION 1889. Rv: Federal Hall above: IN OLD FEDERAL / BUILDING. Around: WASHINGTON TAKING OATH OF OFFICE / NEW YORK 1789. Reeded edge. Rarity 6. (Collins 406)

Douglas	Date	Metal	Size	EF	Unc	Proof
21A	1889	WM	38mm	30.00	40.00	—

As 21. Plain edge. Rarity 5. (Collins 407)

Struck by George H. Lovett, New York.

FEDERAL HALL

Lovett's 32mm Series

Douglas	Date	Metal	Size	EF	Unc	Proof
22	1889	WM	32mm	30.00	50.00	—

Undraped bust right, LOVETT on truncation, GEORGE WASHINGTON around, all within border of 13 stars. Rv: Federal Hall, APRIL 30, 1889 above, FEDERAL / HALL below, all within central beaded circle. Around: Border of pattern of points inscribed: TO COMMEMORATE THE INAUGURAL CENTENNIAL IN NEW YORK / * Plain Edge. Rarity 3. (Collins 408)

23	1889	WM	32mm	30.00	50.00	—

Undraped bust right, LOVETT on truncation. Around: GEORGE WASHINGTON / 1789- 1889 / FIRST PRESIDENT OF THE UNITED STATES. Ornate border circles. Rv: Federal Hall. Above: FEDERAL HALL WALL ST. N.Y. / WHERE WASHINGTON WAS. Below: INAUGURATED / FIRST PRESIDENT / APRIL 30, 1789. Plain edge. Rarity 3. (Collins 409)

Douglas	Date	Metal	Size	EF	Unc	Proof
24	1889	WM	32mm	—	22.50	—

Undraped bust right, LOVETT on truncation, GEORGE WASHINGTON around. Around all: 1789 1889 / INAUGURAL CENTENNIAL IN NEW YORK. Rv: As reverse of 23. Plain edge. Issued suspended by a ribbon from a composition button bearing a likeness of Washington, eagle displayed and flag.

The obverse die of 24, with LOVETT removed, was used by Thomas L. Elder from circa 1902-1910 with various reverses such as MORE ENDURING THAN BOOKS, STEAM NAVIGATION and TO-COMMEMORATE-MOUGEY COLLECTION. (See Elder in the Store Cards chapter)

25	1889	WM	32mm	35.00	50.00	—

Undraped bust right, LOVETT on truncation, separating 1789 - 1889. Around: CENTENNIAL INAUGURAL CELEBRATION. NEW YORK / APRIL 30. Rv: As reverse of 23. Plain edge.

All struck by George Hampden Lovett of New York, by far the most prolific of the engravers who modeled Washington's effigy in the 19th century.

24mm Series

Douglas	Date	Metal	Size	EF	Unc	Proof
26	1889	WM	24mm	15.00	20.00	—

Undraped bust right within two concentric circles, the inner tiny dots and the outer 38 stars. Around: CENTENNIAL INAUGURAL CELEBRATION, NEW YORK / APRIL 30, 1889. Rv: Hall at center, WHERE HE WAS INAUGURATED FIRST PRESIDENT OF THE U.S. / APRIL 30, 1789 around, FEDERAL HALL / WALL ST. / N.Y. below. Plain edge. Rarity 4. (Collins 411)

A. Raymond & Co.

27	1889	WM	24mm	15.00	20.00	—

Undraped bust right, 13 stars partly around. Around: CENTENNIAL CELEBRATION / APRIL 30 1889 / GEORGE WASHINGTON / A. RAYMOND & CO. CLOTHIERS N.Y. Rv: As reverse of 26. Plain edge. Rarity 5. (Collins 412)

Douglas	Date	Metal	Size	EF	Unc	Proof
28	1889	WM	24mm	22.50	30.00	—

Draped bust right. Around CENTENNIAL CELEBRATION / APRIL 30 1889 / GEORGE WASHINGTON / *************. Rv: Federal Hall above: FEDERAL HALL / WALL ST. / N.Y. / *. Around WHERE HE WAS INAUGURATED FIRST PRESIDENT OF THE U.S. / APRIL 30, 1789. Plain edge Rarity 4. (Collins 413)

20mm Medal

Douglas	Date	Metal	Size	VF	EF	Unc
29	1889	Lead	20mm	—	Ex. Rare	—

Undraped bust right, 13 stars around. APRIL 30, 1889 above, GEORGE WASHINGTON below. Rv: Federal Hall, APRIL 30 - 1789 above. FEDERAL HALL, WALL ST. below. Plain edge. (Only reported copy was in L. Bayard Smith, then F. C. C. Boyd collection)

FIRST IN WAR, FIRST IN PEACE

Douglas	Date	Metal	Size	VF	EF	Unc
30	1889	WM	22mm	—	115.	—

Undraped bust right, GENERAL GEO. WASHINGTON above. * 1789 . 1889 * below. Rv: Within circular olive wreath: FIRST IN WAR / FIRST IN PEACE / FIRST / IN THE / HEARTS OF HIS / COUNTRYMEN. Plain edge. 4 or 5 known. Rarity 8. (Copy in ANS collection; Collins 414, ex-F.C.C. Boyd)

Also reported in gilt brass in Schuster coll., 21.9mm, 72.8 grains, holed.

LOVETT'S FEDERAL HALL

Douglas	Date	Metal	Size	EF	AU	Unc
32	1889	WM	23mm	—	30.00	—

Houdon bust right separates 1789-1889. Thick laurel wreath border, within which is: GEORGE WASHINGTON / FIRST PRESIDENT OF THE UNITED STATES. Rv: Federal Hall. Above: FEDERAL HALL WALL ST. N.Y. / WHERE WASHINGTON WAS. Below: INAUGURATED / FIRST PRESIDENT / APRIL 30, 1789. (Kirtley March 31, 1998 sale, lot AA8)

Dies cut by George Hampden Lovett.

GEN. WASHINGTON

Cast Bronze

Douglas	Date	Metal	Size	VF	EF	Unc
31	1889	Bronze	114mm	—	40.00	—

Undraped bust left, GEN. WASHINGTON, above. 1789 - 1889. Below. Rv: Blank, except maker's mark large K within diamond. Plain edge. Cast in bronze.

31A	1889	Bronze	128mm	—	40.00	—

As 31, but cast with half-inch rim around the edge with loop for hanging. Plain edge.

31B	1889	Bronze	134mm	—	60.00	—

As 31, but K in oval. (Magriel 1988 sale, lot 095)

K = G. P. Kato.

GREAT WASHINGTON LIVED FOR YOU

Douglas	Date	Metal	Size	EF	Unc	Proof
33	1889	WM	28mm	37.50	50.00	—

Undraped bust left, P under bust, square and compass framing the bust. Around: GEOPGE (sic!) WASHINGTON / 1789 1889. Rv: GREAT / WASHINGTON / HAS / LIVED FOR YOU. / MARK WELL HIS / STEPS / HIS COURSE / PURSUE. Plain edge.

Note the error in the spelling GEOPGE, by engraver P - ?

The reverse die was used with Baker 106 (by Robert Lovett Jr.) about 1860 for Charles I. Bushnell, and with two other obverse dies described by Baker in 1885 under number 106.

HARRISON-MORTON

First obverse

Douglas	Date	Metal	Size	EF	Unc	Proof
35	1889	WM	38mm	45.00	70.00	—

Washington bust in civil dress three-quarters left, within beaded oval. Below: Scroll and 1789. Rv: Bust of Benjamin Harrison and Morton in ovals facing toward center, divided by a scroll lettered: HARRISON AND MORTON, U.S. shield above, 1889 below. Plain edge. (DeWitt BH 1888-8; Springfield 4074 and 4077)

35A	1889	Bronzed/ WM	38mm	45.00	70.00	—

As 35. Plain edge. (DeWitt BH 1888-8)
All either holed as issued, or issued with ring, for suspension. They are found suspended two ways - by a ring from a metal eagle clasp pin, and from a ribbon. The red, white and blue ribbon with a bar clasp inscribed: CENTENNIAL / INAUGURAL. Reverse of the ribbon is inscribed N. M. FRIEDERICH, / MANUFACTURER, / WASHINGTON, D.C. / PAT. FEB. 1889.

C-35	1889	Copper	38mm	—	—	—

Similar to 35, but WM. FRIEDERICH, WASH. D.C. in place of scroll under the bust. Rv: Similar to reverse of 35, but PAT. JAN. / 14. in small letters above the date. Plain edge. Probably a rejected trial piece. Rarity 8. (L. B. Fauver coll.)

Second obverse

Douglas	Date	Metal	Size	EF	Unc	Proof
34	1889	WM	38mm	50.00	70.00	—

Obverse as 35, but inscription around added: GEO. WASHINGTON FIRST PRESIDENT OF THE U.S. Rv: As reverse of 35. Plain edge. Issued holed. (DeWitt BH 1888-9)

34A	1889	Bronze	38mm	50.00	90.00	—

As last. Plain edge. Rarity 6. (Collins 415)

34B	1889	Gilt/WM	38mm	—	80.00	—

As last. Plain edge.

These pieces are found suspended as are Douglas 35 pieces. Also known in silver and gold.

WASHINGTON INAUGURAL CENTENNIAL

Douglas	Date	Metal	Size	VF	EF	Unc
36	1889	WM	25mm	—	20.00	35.00

Draped bust right, encircled by thick wreath border. Rv: - / WASHING-TON / * / INAUGURAL / CENTENNIAL / * 1789. 1889 * / NEW YORK CITY. Plain edge. Rarity 6. (Rulau NY-NY 362; Collins 416)

LIBERTY ENLIGHTENING

Douglas	Date	Metal	Size	EF	Unc	Proof
37	1889	WM	38mm	—	150.	—

Obverse as Douglas 21. Rv: Statue of Liberty and view of the bay with boats; Liberty's arm extends to top of the medal. Above, in two lines: COMMEMORATIVE MONUMENT OF AMERICAN INDEPENDENCE / (36 stars). In exergue: LIBERTY ENLIGHTENING / THE WORLD. / DEDICATED OCT. 28, 1886. Plain edge. Rarity 9. Only 10 struck 2-3 known. (Collins 417)

By George Hampden Lovett. A specimen was in the F.C.C. Boyd collection.

MASONIC

Douglas	Date	Metal	Size	EF	Unc	Proof
38	ND	Bronze	28mm	25.00	40.00	—

Obverse as Douglas 33, except that the P in GEOPGE has been recut and changed to an R by the addition of a diagonal line. Rv: As reverse of Baker 307 (radiant eye above plumb, level and square). Plain edge. Rarity 5. (Collins 418)

The reverse die by George Hampden Lovett was used on Baker 307, 308 and 309.

NEW YORK, APRIL 30

Douglas	Date	Metal	Size	EF	Unc	Proof
39	1889	Gilt/Cop	20mm	12.50	25.00	45.00

Undraped bust right, GEO. WASHINGTON FIRST PRES'T U.S. around. 1789 . below. Rv: * CENTENNIAL OF HIS INAUGURATION / NEW YORK / APRIL 30. /1889. Plain edge. Rarity 5. (Rulau NY-NY 362F(

39A	1889	Bronze	20mm	12.50	25.00	—

As 39. Plain Edge. Rarity 6. (Collins 420)

39B	1889	Copper	20mm	—	—	15.00

As 39, but later restrike, circa 1960.

39C	1889	Copper	23mm	—	—	40.00

Obverse as 39B. Rv: Blank. Die splasher from 1960's strike. (Kirtley March 31, 1998 sale, lot N2; fetched $24.20 in Unc; same sale, lot AA13, fetched $40.70 in Unc)

NEW YORK CITY BADGE

Douglas	Date	Metal	Size	VF	EF	Unc
40	1889	Bronze	53.3	—	40.00	75.00

Undraped bust left within large 5-pointed star within radiant circular field. Edging the star: NEW YORK CITY APRIL 30TH. 1889 / FIRST IN WAR FIRST IN PEACE / AND FIRST IN THE / HEARTS OF HIS COUNTRYMEN. There are 13 stars scattered around the bust. Rv: Blank, except maker's mark: C.G. BRAXMAR / 86 COURTLANDT ST / NEW YORK at center. Plain edge. Issued suspended from metal bar with 2 shields, eagle and inscription 1789 CENTENNIAL 1889 / INAUGURATION.

40A	1889	Gilt/B	53.3mm*	—	—	75.00

As 40. Plain edge.

40B	1889	SLVD/Cop	53.3mm*	—	35.00	75.00

As 40. Plain edge. Rarity 6. (Collins 422)

*Point of star to point of star. The circular medal measures 50mm.

GRADE HEADINGS

Three grade (condition) columns appear in this catalog. Coins and tokens, which circulate, are graded down to VG (Very Good), but medals, which do not circulate, usually are graded no less than VF (Very Fine). Other abbreviations used are F (Fine), EF (Extremely Fine), AU (About Uncirculated), Unc (Uncirculated), and P-L (Prooflike). Proof is spelled out.

REPUBLIQUES CENTENAIRES SALUT

Douglas	Date	Metal	Size	VF	EF	Unc
41	1889	Silver	45mm	—	90.00	110.00

Winged Victory standing, facing, holding in her arms oval medallions bearing the effigies of the writer Mirabeau (left) and George Washington, 1776 at left, 1789 at right, and 18- 89 divided by her naked feet, below. Rv: Within ornate cartouche which includes shields of France and the U.S., a five-line inscription beginning SALUT and ending 1889. Above: REPUBLIQUES CENTENAIRES. Below: PROGRES LABEUR; GORHAM CO. MFG. U.S.A. in small letters along lower rim. Plain edge.

Douglas	Date	Metal	Size	VF	EF	Unc
41A	1889	Bronze	45mm		45.00	75.00

As 41. Plain edge. Rarity 5. (Collins 423)

41B	1889	Copper	45mm		45.00	75.00

As 41. Plain edge.

This attractive medal was struck by Gorham & Co. the New York silversmiths.

Honore Gabriel Riqueti Mirabeau (1749-1791) was a popular writer and a hero of the initial stage of the French Revolution in 1789. The Universal Exposition at Paris in 1889 celebrated the centennial of the French Revolution's onset.

SEAL, NEW YORK CITY

Douglas	Date	Metal	Size	EF	Unc	Proof
42	1889	Dark Bronze	34mm	40.00	75.00	—

Undraped bust right, M on truncation, GEORGE WASHINGTON around, 1789 below. Rv: Same as reverse of Douglas 43. Plain edge. Rarity 7. (Bullowa-Lessin 26; Collins 425)

42A	1889	WM	34mm	30.00	50.00	—

As 42. Plain edge. Rarity 5. Issued holed. (Bullowa-Lessin 25; Collins 426)

42C	1789	WM	34mm		75.00	

Obverse as 42. Rv: Blank. Plain edge.

Designed by George T. Morgan. A copy of Douglas 42C was in the F.C.C. Boyd collection.

A brass specimen of 42 fetched $35 in Unc.; with blue ribbon, in 1995.

CENTENNIAL PARTICIPATION BADGE

Douglas	Date	Metal	Size	EF	Unc	Proof
43	1889	WM	35mm	20.00	35.00	45.00

Military bust right, MORGAN on truncation, GEORGE WASHINGTON around, 1789 below. Rv: Shield of Arms of New York within circular wreath at center. In concentric lines around: CENTENNIAL ANNIVERSARY OF THE INAUGURATION / FIRST PRESIDENT OF THE UNITED STATES / . NEW YORK. / .APRIL 30. 1789. Plain edge. Some were issued holed. Issued suspended from red, white and blue-striped ribbon. Rarity 5. (Bullowa-Lessin sale. lot 24; Collins 427 unholed)

Douglas	Date	Metal	Size	EF	Unc	Proof
43A	1889	WM	35mm	50.00	90.00	—

As 43. Plain edge.

The reverse is the same as that used on Douglas 42. Designed by George T. Morgan.

SEAL, NEW YORK STATE

Douglas	Date	Metal	Size	EF	Unc	Proof
44	1889	Bronze	33mm	—	35.00	—

Civil bust left on shield, wreath around broken by scrolls lettered 1789 and 1889. Around: CENTENNIAL / INAUGURATION. Rv: New York state seal within circular oak wreath. Around: NEW YORK. WASHINGTON. PHILADA. NEW JERSEY. Plain edge. Issued holed.

Douglas	Date	Metal	Size	EF	Unc	Proof
44A	1889	WM	33mm	25.00	35.00	—

As 44. Plain edge. Rarity 6. (Collins 428)

Also known in Lead and Copper-plated Lead.

SOLDIERS MEDAL

Douglas	Date	Metal	Size	VF	EF	Unc
45	1889	WM	40mm	15.00	30.00	45.00

Brown's equestrian statue left, GEORGE WASHINGTON above, 1789 left, 1889 right. Around: CENTENNIAL CELEBRATION OF THE INAUGURATION OF / NEW YORK APRIL 30. Rv: SOLDIERS / MEDAL / (large blank area) / PARTICIPATED. Plain edge. Rarity 6. (Collins 429)

Douglas 45 was often engraved. The ANS specimen reads: Herbert Valentine.

SOUVENIR MEDALS

By Childs

Douglas	Date	Metal	Size	EF	Unc	Proof
46	1889	Bronze	37mm	120.00	145.00	—

Undraped bust left, S on truncation, CHILDS. CHICAGO below. Around: WASHINGTON CENTENNIAL. Rv: Above two crossed sprays: SOUVENIR / OF THE / CENTENNIAL / 1789 / 1889. Plain edge. Rarity 6. (Collins 430)

By Lovett

Douglas	Date	Metal	Size	VF	EF	Unc
47	1889	WM	40mm	—	25.00	40.00

Washington bust left, R L on truncation, 1789 - 1889. Rv: SOUVENIR / OF THE / CENTENNIAL / FESTIVAL / APRIL. 1889. Plain edge. Rarity 6. (Collins 431)

The Kurt R. Krueger sale of Aug. 13-20, 1983 offered two of these, holed, VF-EF, as lot number 1986. By Robert Lovett Jr. There are 8 pieces of 47 in Schuster Coll., all holed.

CENTENNIAL ANNIVERSARY

Doulgas	Date	Metal	Size	EF	Unc	Proof
48	1889	WM	50.6mm	50.00	85.00	—

Civil bust after Stuart in oval medallion at upper center, with oak and olive wreath. Around: GEORGE WASHINGTON FIRST PRESIDENT OF THE UNITED STATES / *1789*. Rv: Three men standing (oath of office ceremony), APRIL 30./*1889* below. Around: CENTENNIAL ANNIVERSARY OF THE INAUGURATION NEW YORK. Plain edge. Rarity 7. (Bullowa-Lessin sale, lot 22; Collins 432)

| 48A | 1889 | Bronze | 50.6mm | 50.00 | 85.00 | — |

As 48. Plain edge.

William H. Key made a reduction of this head from a print by Giuseppe Longhi of Italy for the Philadelphia numismatic dealer, Sigmund K. Harzfeld, in the 1876-81 period.

TAKING THE OATH

Douglas	Date	Metal	Size	EF	Unc	Proof
49	1889	Bronze	38mm	—	80.00	—

Undraped bust right in sunken circle. Raised band around, inscribed: GEORGE WASHINGTON FIRST PRESIDENT OF THE UNITED STATES / *1789*. Rv: Central scene is a reduction of the reverse vignette on Douglas 48. Around: CENTENNIAL ANNIVERSARY OF HIS INAUGURATION NEW YORK * / APRIL 30, 1889. Plain edge.

| 49A | 1889 | WM | 38mm | 25.00 | 35.00 | — |

As 49. Plain edge. Rarity 4. (Collins 433)

| 50 | 1889 | Bronze | 38mm | — | 45.00 | — |

The Harzfeld bust of Douglas 48 obverse in sunken circle. Raised band around, inscribed same as 49. Rv: As reverse of 49. Plain edge.

| 50A | 1889 | WM | 38mm | — | 35.00 | |

As 50. Plain edge. Rarity 4. (Collins 434)

| 50D | 1889 | Copper | 38mm | — | 300.00 | |

Obverse similar to 50, but without date. Rv: As reverse of 50. Plain edge. Rarity 6. (Collins 435)

| 50E | 1889 | WM | 38mm | 125.00 | 175.00 | — |

As 50D. Plain edge

Douglas	Date	Metal	Size	VG	F	EF
50C	ND	Brass	38mm	—	Unique?	—

Obverse die trial of Douglas 50 central circle, plain border, weakly struck. Rv: Blank. (Kirtley Feb. 10, 1998 sale, lot W055)

Douglas 50D in Unc realized $302.50 and 50E in EF fetched $132 in the Kirtley March 31, 1998 sale, lots N10 and N11.

CENTENNIAL OF OUR NATION

CHICAGO COMMEMORATION

Douglas	Date	Metal	Size	VF	EF	Unc
51	1889	WM	37mm	10.00	25.00	40.00

Obverse as Douglas 4. Rv: Oblong cartouche with APRIL 30. at center, 1789 above. 1889 below. Around: THE CENTENNIAL OF OUR NATION / * CHICAGO COMMEMORATION*. Plain edge. Rarity 3. (Rulau 11-Ch 7; Collins 436)

| 51B | 1889 | WM | 37mm | 30.00 | 40.00 | 50.00 |

Obverse as 51. Rv: As reverse of 51, but * E PLURIBUS UNUM * replaces * CHICAGO COMMEMORATION *. Plain edge. Only 5 specimens known. Rarity 8. (Rulau 11-Ch 8)

Issued with a red, white and blue suspension ribbon 4mm wide and 5 inchees long as most following varieties.

PUBLIC SCHOOL, OLNEY

Douglas	Date	Metal	Size	VF	EF	Unc
51D	1889	WM	37mm	—	1 Known	—

Obverse as 51. Rv: As reverse of 51, except WASHINGTON CENTEN-NIAL SOUVENIR appears above and PUBLIC SCHOOL OLNEY, ILL. at bottom. Plain edge. (Harvey Gamer coll.)

Issued holed for suspension from a red ribbon. The one known copy was found only in late 1983.

PERU COMMEMORATION

Douglas	Date	Metal	Size	VF	EF	Unc
51E	1889	WM	37mm	—	3 known	—

Obverse as 51. Rv: As reverse of 51, except * PERU, ILLS. COMMEM-ORATION * replaces * CHICAGO COMMEMORATION *. Plain edge. Rarity 9. (Rulau 11-Pu 4)

Only known specimens in Joseph Schmidt and Phil Klabel collections in 1983, and another dug up in 1984.

SPRINGFIELD COMMEMORATION

51G	1889	WM	37mm	—	—	Rare

Obverse as 51. Rv: As reverse of 51, but * SPRINGFIELD, ILL. COM-MEMORATION * replaces * CHICAGO COMMEMORATION * Plain edge. (Rulau 11-Sp 3). Rarity 8. Only 6 specimens known.

All struck by Childs & Co. of Chicago. It seems probable that other towns is-sued similar commemoratives as well, but Susan Douglas knew only of number 51 and the others have been recorded only in recent years. Most likely all types except Chicago Commemoration would prove rare.

All the Douglas 51 varieties except 51E read CHILDS CHICAGO in tiny letters in obverse bottom rim and COPYRIGHT 1889 BY THE CHICAGO CENTENNIAL CELEBRATION COMMITTEE in reverse bottom rim. The Peru specimen reads on obverse: CHILDS & CO. MEDALLISTS CHICAGO, but same on reverse as others.

All were issued in a pot metal, so soft it can be bent with the fingers, thus sur-vivorship is slight and many varieties which must have been struck may no longer exist.

Douglas	Date	Metal	Size	EF	Unc	Proof
63	1889	WM	68mm	—	85.00	—

Obverse and reverse of Douglas 51 (Chicago Commemoration medal) appear side-by-side across center, standing angel with wings outspread above, U.S. shield draped with six flags and crested with an eagle dis-played below. Rv: TO EDWARD F. CRAGIN / (branch) / IN RECOGNI-TION OF / HIS VALUABLE SERVICES / IN ORIGINATING AND PLANNING / THE PATRIOTIC OBSERVANCE AT / CHICAGO OF THE CENTENNIAL / OF THE NATION'S / BIRTH-DAY / ***FROM HIS FRIENDS AND COLABORERS ***. Plain edge. (Leon Hendrickson coll.)

The word "colaborers" (minus a hyphen after co) seems at first glance to be poor grammar but on reflection is a happy choice. Unknown to Susan Douglas, this medal adds a bit to the mystery surrounding the Douglas 51 series.

Struck by Childs & Co., Chicago.

THIRTEEN LINKS

OBVERSE AND REVERSE

The term Obverse refers to the "heads" or "face" side of a piece. Where there is a human head or bust, this is easy to determine, but where there is no head, the side with the "princi-pal device" is the Obverse. The opposite side is the Reverse. In some cases determining Obverse and Reverse must be arbi-trary, especially where a head is on each side.

Each piece also has a third side, the Edge, which is described as Reeded, Plain, Lettered, etc. The term Rim is not the edge, but the periphery of one face or another.

GRADE HEADINGS

Three grade (condition) columns appear in this catalog. Coins and tokens, which circulate, are graded down to VG (Very Good), but medals, which do not circulate, usually are graded no less than VF (Very Fine). Other abbreviations used are F (Fine), EF (Extremely Fine), AU (About Uncirculated), Unc (Uncirculated), and P-L (Prooflike). Proof is spelled out.

OBVERSE AND REVERSE

The term Obverse refers to the "heads" or "face" side of a piece. Where there is a human head or bust, this is easy to determine, but where there is no head, the side with the "principal device" is the Obverse. The opposite side is the Reverse. In some cases determining Obverse and Reverse must be arbitrary, especially where a head is on each side.

Each piece also has a third side, the Edge, which is described as Reeded, Plain, Lettered, etc. The term Rim is not the edge, but the periphery of one face or another.

PATER PATRIAE

Certain Latin terms appear on medals pertaining to George Washington, the first "General of the Armies of the United States." Only one other man held this title until the 5-star rank was created in World War II, and that was John J. Pershing, U.S. commander in France in WWI.

Pater Patriae (father of his country) is the apt title frequently appearing. Many other Latin words and phrases appear on items in this catalog; in most cases we have translated these for users.

COMMITTEE OF THE CELEBRATION
NEW YORK

Douglas	Date	Metal	Size	EF	Unc	Proof
52	1889	Bronze	54mm	175.	275.	—

Undraped bust left, C.C. WRIGHT S C. below, Above: GEORGE WASHINGTON. Below: FIRST PRESIDENT OF THE UNITED STATES / INAUGURATED APRIL 30. 1789. Rv: Radiant sun on 11-pointed star encircled by chain of 13 links. each bearing initials of one of the 13 original states. Around: CENTENNIAL OF THE INAUGURATION OF THE FIRST PRESIDENT OF THE UNITED STATES APRIL 30. 1889. Around the rim are 42 stars spaced evenly. Plain edge. Rarity 7. (Collins 437)

52A	1889	WM	54mm	50.00	75.00	—

As 52. Plain edge.

The coin dealer brothers, Samuel Hudson & Henry Chapman, published this medal in April, 1889, utilizing an unpublished Washington portrait by the late master engraver Charles Cushing Wright, said to be "his finest work" and the best reproduction on a medal of the Houdon bust.

The die was reworked from the die for Baker E96.

Douglas	Date	Metal	Size	EF	Unc	Proof
53	1889	Bronze	112mm	—	115.	—

Half-length civil bust left. Under bust: PHILIP. MARTINY. MODELED. DESIGN. AND./COPYRIGHT. BY. AVGVSTVS. SAINT. GAVDENS. To left of bust:. PATER. / M.D.CC. L. to right: Fasces divides PAT - RAIE. / XX - XIX. Above: GEORGE WASHINGTON. Around rim are 13 stars. Rv: Eagle with outspread wings above 12-line inscription: THE IN-AVGVRATION / OF. GEORGE. WASHINGTON / AS. FIRST. PRESI-DENT. OF THE / UNITED STATES OF AMERICA / AT. NEW. YORK. APRIL. XXX / M.D.C.C.LXXXIX. / BY. AVTHORITY. OF / THE COM-MITTEE / ON. CELEBRATION / NEW. YORK. APRIL / .XXX. / M.D.C.C.C.LXXXIX. A shield of arms is at lower left. Around all is a border of 5-point stars at the rim. Plain edge. (Clark sale, lot 2141)

53A	1889	Silver	112mm		4 or 5 known	—

As 53. Edge marked: GORHAM MFG. CO. and three hallmarks: Lion right, Anchor, English G and STERLING. Struck in .925 fine silver. (ANS collection)

| 53B | 1889 | Gold | 112mm | — | — | 2 known |

As 53. Edge marked: GORHAM MFG. CO. 18K. Struck in .750 fine gold. (ANS collection; Norweb, ex-Fuld, J.P. Morgan)

Douglas 53 is the official medal of the committee on the inaugural centennial celebration in New York City. The designs were modeled by Philip Martiny and the dies cut by Augustus St. Gaudens, who later designed the Standing Liberty $20 gold coin of the U.S. The large medal was cast in bronze and sold to the public. Also cast in gold and silver. On all, the pieces were cast and the shells joined.

| 54 | 1889 | Copper | 35mm | 100. | 175. | — |

Somewhat similar to 53, but in reduced size and struck rather than cast. Plain edge. Rarity 5. (Springfield 4080; Collins 438)

Douglas 54 is very rare; it was presented only to celebration officials and to members of the New York state legislature. It was issued suspended from a yellow ribbon hung from a bronze bar. A single specimen in silver is known.

VIRTUE LIBERTY PATRIOTISM

Douglas	Date	Metal	Size	EF	Unc	Proof
55	1789	WM	34mm	25.00	40.00	—

Obverse as Douglas 42. Rv: Open shield encloses square and compass framing arm and hammer. Around: VIRTUE . LIBERTY . PATRIOTISM / -.-. Plain edge.

The central insignia is that of the Order of the United American Mechanics (OUAM).

WASHINGTON-HARRISON BUTTONS

Douglas	Date	Metal	Size	VF	EF	Unc
56	1889	Bronze	22mm	—	40.00	60.00

Conjoined Washington and Harrison busts, that of Washington to left and that of Harrison facing slightly left. Around: ****** 1789 ****** / 1889. Rv: Blank, but star-shaped maker's mark on attachment for lapel button. Plain edge. Rarity 7. (DeWitt BH 1888-77)

| 57 | 1889 | WM | 22mm | — | 40.00 | 60.00 |

Accolated busts left, WASHINGTON 1789 HARRISON around, 1889 below. Rv: Blank, except for pin attachment for stickpin. Plain edge.

WASHINGTON CENTENNIAL

Douglas	Date	Metal	Size	VF	EF	Unc
59	1889	Brass/Tin	47mm	—	50.00	—

Large undraped bust left in high relief on pebbled field. Around: WASH-INGTON CENTENNIAL / 1789 - 1889. Rv: Blank, lead-filled shell coated

with brass-over-tin. Plain edge. Rare. (Kirtley March 10-14, 1998 sale, lot U085)

In 1949 Susan Douglas reported this from the N. J. Hoffman collection.

WHILE WE ENJOY THE FRUIT

Douglas	Date	Metal	Size	EF	Unc	Proof
61	1889	WM	28mm	35.00	70.00	—

Draped bust left, P on truncation, WASHINGTON INAUGURAL CEN-TENNIAL / 1789 - APR. 30 - 1889 above, arc of 13 stars and NEW YORK below. Rv: WHILE / WE ENJOY / THE FRUIT, LET / US NOT FORGET / HIM / THAT PLANTED / THE TREE. Plain edge. (Bullowa-Lessin sale, lot 20)

The reverse of 61 is the same as that of Baker 107, used about 1860.

| 61D | 1889 | Brass | 28mm | — | Rare | — |

Obverse as Douglas 61. Rv: Wreath encloses empty central area. Plain edge. Rarity 9. (L. B. Fauver coll.)

Douglas	Date	Metal	Size	EF	Unc	Proof
60	1889	WM	28mm	60.00	75.00	—

Obverse as Douglas 33 (GEOPGE error die). Rv: As reverse of Douglas 61. Plain edge.

See Baker number 107 for earlier uses of this reverse die by Robert Lovett Jr. The diesinker P must be identified.

UNITARIAN CONFERENCE

PHILADELPHIA

Douglas	Date	Metal	Size	EF	Unc	Proof
62	1889	Silver	25mm	30.00	50.00	—

Civil bust left, on a plain field. Rv: Open book at center lettered HOLY BIBLE, branch behind. Around: UNITARIAN NATIONAL CONFER-ENCE / PHILA OCT. 29 - 31 1989. Plain edge.

| 62A | 1889 | Bronze | 25mm | 20.00 | 35.00 | — |

As 62. Plain edge.

It could not have been by coincidence that the Unitarians chose a Washington portrait for their conference medal in the Inauguration Centennial year.

NINTH WARD PIONEER CORPS

66	1889	Bronze	**	—	—	—

** Maltese cross-shaped badge, 34 by 38mm. Radiant acorn within circle, .ORGANIZED / * 1876 * around at center of cross. On cross arms, NINTH / WARD / PIONEER / CORPS. Rv: Blank. On metal hanger: CENTENNIAL / 1789 INAUGURATION 1889. Plain edge. (L. B. Fauver coll.)

CHRISTIAN ENDEAVOR

Douglas	Date	Metal	Size	EF	Unc	Proof
67	1889	WM	25mm	12.50	20.00	—

Civil bust left. Rv: Large monogram CE at center; around 8TH NATIONAL C. E. CONFERENCE PHILADA JULY 9-11 1889. Plain edge. (L. B. Fauver coll.)

Just as with the Unitarians (Douglas 62), it would not have been by coincidence that the Christian Endeavor organization chose a Washington portrait for their conference medal in the Inauguration Centennial year.

KNIGHTS TEMPLAR

Douglas	Date	Metal	Size	VF	EF	Unc
68	1889	Gilt/Lead	**		35.00	

** Maltese cross-shaped, 34 x 34mm. Bust left in oval at cross' center. On four arms of cross (T-R-B-L) are: WASHINGTON / D.C.; CONCLAVE; OCT / 1889; TRIENNIAL. Suspended from hanger inscribed: KNIGHTS TEMPLAR. (Collins 442)

PENNSYLVANIA STATE FAIR

Douglas	Date	Metal	Size	EF	Unc	Proof
70	(ca 1889)	Bronze	25mm	—	—	35.00

Obverse as Douglas 62 and 67 (civil bust left on plain field, L A K on truncation of bust). Rv: SOUVENIR within wreath of agricultural products, PENNSYLVANIA STATE FAIR above. BETHLEHEM, PA. below. Plain edge.

P.O.S. OF A.

(PATRIOTIC ORDER SONS OF AMERICA)

Douglas	Date	Metal	Size	EF	AU	Unc
71	1889	WM	36mm	—	80.00	—

Bust left on star within shield, on top arm of shield being: P.O.S. of A. (The order's logo). Around: GOD OUR COUNTRY AND OUR ORDER. Rv: Capitol, WASHINGTON D.C. above. Holed for suspension from red-white-blue ribbon, which is lettered in gold: 19TH NATIONAL / CAMP / JUNE 17 TO 23, / 1889. The brass hanger has a Washington head within circle, flanked on each side by three stars. (Kirtley March 31, 1998 sale, lot N16; realized $77 in AU)

CENTENNIAL OF DEATH, 1899

WASHINGTON MONUMENT ASSOCIATION

Struck 1904

Baker	Date	Metal	Size	VF	EF	Unc
1825	ND	Bronze	40.3mm	—	30.00	40.00

Undraped bust after Houdon right, WASHINGTON / MONU-MENT / ASSOCIA / -TION in four lines to right, ALEXAN / -DRIA VA. in two lines under bust. Around: STRUCK BY ORDER OF CONGRESS TO COMMEMORATE THE CENTENARY OF WASHINGTON'S DEATH. Rv: Winged female holding torch of liberty aloft in flight over beehive, plow, etc. Inscription on scroll along left and lower rim: WASHINGTON. FOREMOST. FARMER. OF. HIS. DAY. Plain edge. Rarity 4. (Bullowa-Lessin sale, lot 9; Collins 443)

Also known in silver.

Baker	Date	Metal	Size	VF	EF	Unc
1826	1749	Bronze	40.3mm	—	30.00	40.00

Obverse as last. Rv: Surveyor's instrument divides: WASHI -NGTON / 17 - 49/ SURVEYED - ALEXANDRIA. All within continuous oak wreath along rim. Plain edge. Rarity 4. (Bullowa-Lessin sale, lots 10 and 11; Collins 444)

The Washington Monument Association series was struck at the U.S. Mint, Philadelphia, in 1904.

Also known in silver.

1828	1773	Bronze	40.3mm	—	30.00	40.00

Obverse as last. Rv: 18th century hand-pumper fire wagon to left, WASHINGTON above, 1773 / MEMBER OF FRIENDSHIP FIRE CO. below. Around the rim is a thick border of oak branches. Plain edge. Rarity 4.(Leon Hendrickson coll.; Collins 445)

Also known in silver, Rarity 6.

Struck 1904

Baker	Date	Metal	Size	VF	EF	Unc
1829	1788	Silver	40mm	—	100.	175.

Obverse as 1825. Rv: Compass, square and G on Masonic apron, WASHINGTON above, MASTER / ALEXANDRIA LODGE NO 22 A.F. & A.M. 1788 below. Plain edge. Rarity 6. (Hartzog coll.)

| 1829A | 1788 | Bronze | 40mm | — | 20.00 | 50.00 |

As 1827. Plain edge. Rarity 4. (Collins 446)

Robert Julian reported that Baker 1825 thru 1829 were authorized by Congress in 1899 to honor the centennial of Washington's death, but that the medals were not struck at the U.S. Mint until 1904. They were struck in both bronze and silver.

The bronze specimens occur in auction sales occasionally, the silver very seldom.

U.S. Mint reports that 206 silver medals were struck, but does not specify the numbers of each of the four. Assuming that equal numbers were struck of each of the four types, either 51 or 52 pieces would have been made, or Rarity 6. Silver specimens have been reported of types 1825, 1826, and 1829 in recent years, and most likely 1828 also exists. The silver medals' value in Unc. should be in the $100 to $175 range, but there are no recent sales records to back this up.

Baker 1826 in silver was lot 204 in AU condition in the PCAC May 16, 1997 sale, but was withdrawn before the auction.

MASONIC FRATERNITY

Baker	Date	Metal	Size	EF	Unc	Proof
1831	1899	Bronze	32mm	—	40.00	—

Undraped bust right within central depression: thick stippled border around rim. Rv: Compass-square-G at center. Around: CENTENNIAL OF WASHINGTON'S DEATH BY MASONIC FRATERNITY./ MT. VERNON VA. / DEC. 14. 1899. Plain edge. (Marvin 1189; Bullowa-Lessin sale, lot 12)

| 1831A | 1899 | WM | 32mm | — | 35.00 | — |

As 1831. Plain edge. (Collins 447)

Baker	Date	Metal	Size	EF	Unc	Proof
B1831	1899	WM	32mm	27.50	—	—

Obverse as 1831. Rv: Amid Flourishes: 1749 / SESQUI/ CENTENNIAL / OF/ ALEXANDRIA VA./ OCT.12./ 1899. Unpublished. (Kirtley March 31, 1998 sale, lot Q7)

1832	1901	Bronze	32mm	—	30.00	—

Obverse as 1831. Rv: 125TH / ANNIVERSARY / OF THE / BATTLE / OF / TRENTON N.J. / DEC.26. 1901. Plain edge.

1833	1902	Bronze	32mm	—	30.00	—

Obverse same as last. Rv: SESQUI-CENTENNIAL / + AND + / 4TH OF JULY / CELEBRATION / WINCHESTER, VA. / + 1902 +. Plain edge. (Parsons 1022; Bullowa-Lessin sale, lot 7)

These four medals have an unusually fine obverse. One 1899 and the 1901 and 1902 pieces, not connected with Washington's death centenary, are included here because of die linkage.

Leonard Forrer identifies the diesinker of Baker 1831 as Robert Sneider & Co. of New York.

WOR. BRO. GEO. WASHINGTON

Baker	Date	Metal	Size	VF	EF	Unc
1835	1899	Bronze	27.5mm	—	25.00	35.00

Nude bust left arising from laurel branch, tiny . R. Sneider. F. below. Around: MEMORIAL OBSERVANCE / . MT. VERNON, DEC. 14. 1899. . Rv: Compass, square and G at center, 100TH ANNIVERSARY / OF THE DEATH OF above, . WOR. BRO. GEO. WASHINGTON. below. Plain edge. Thick (3.5mm) flan. (Hartzog coll.; Kirtley March 31, 1998 sale, lot Q88).

"Worshipful Brother" is a term of respectful salutation in the Masonic fraternity.

Struck by Robert Sneider & Co. of New York, founded in 1866. In 1895 Sneider absorbed the medallic business of George Hampden Lovett.

ALEXANDRIA VA. LODGE A.F.A.M.

Baker	Date	Metal	Size	EF	Unc	Proof
1836	1899	Bronze	37.7mm	—	50.00	—

Undraped bust right, GEORGE WASHINGTON around, all within central circle. Around, in concentric lines: MASONIC CELEBRATION IN COMMEMORATION OF THE CENTENNIAL / OF THE DEATH OF WASHINGTON MOUNT VERNON, VA. / * DECEMBER 14. * / * 1899 *. Rv: Compass and square enclose G and radiant eye, 17 - 88 at top, A.F. - A.M. at bottom, all within circle. Around: GEORGE WASHINGTON MASTER OF ALEXANDRIA, VA. / * LODGE NO. 22 *. Plain edge. Rarity 6. (Marvin 1142; Bullowa-Lessin sale, lot 13; Collins 448)

1836A	1899	WM	37.7mm	—	35.00	—

As 1836. Plain edge. Rarity 6. (Collins 449)

1837	1899	Bronze	38mm	20.00	35.00	—

Washington standing alongside oath table, GEORGE WASHINGTON MASTER 1788 around, . * . below. Rv: Tomb at center, MT VERNON VA. 1799 - 1899 * around, tiny COPYRIGHTED 1899 / ALEXA-WASHN-LODGE 22 below. Plain edge. Suspended from ribbon, with metal hanger lettered: ALEXANDRIA WASHINGTON / LODGE 22. A.F.&A.M. (Dr. I. Schuster collection; Collins 450)

KEY'S DEATH CENTENNIAL SERIES

Baker	Date	Metal	Size	VF	EF	Unc
1840	1899	Gilt/Brass	16.5mm	—	—	25.00

Uniformed bust right, K on truncation, GEN. GEORGE WASHINGTON around. Rv: CENTENNIAL / OF HIS / DEATH / MOUNT VERNON, VA. / DEC. 14. 1899 amid scrollwork. Plain edge. Thin (1.4mm) flan.

1840A	1899	Gilt/Brass	16.6mm	—	—	25.00

As 1840, but Thick (1.9mm) flan.

1840B	1899	Bronze	16.5mm	—	—	20.00

As 1840. Thin flan.

1840C	1899	WM	16.5mm	—	—	25.00

As 1840. Plain edge. (PCAC McSorley 1997 sale, lot 1178)

1841	1776	Gilt/Brass	16.5mm	—	12.50	25.00

Obverse as 1840. Rv: Liberty bell, LIBERTY BELL around, JULY 4TH. 1776 below. Plain edge. (Hartzog coll.)

Dies cut by William H. Key of Philadelphia. The obverse die is the same as used on Baker 463.

OUR GREATEST PATRIOT

Struck 1899?

Baker	Date	Metal	Size	VF	EF	Unc
1845	ND	WM	32mm	25.00	35.00	50.00

Nude bust right, GEORGE WASHINGTON above, arc of 13 stars below. Rv: Trophy of arms binds open-top wreath, within which is: IN MEMORY / OF OUR / GREATEST PATRIOT. Plain edge. Scarce. (H. J. Levine report)

Chapter 30

BICENTENNIAL OF WASHINGTON'S BIRTH, 1932

United States Commission
for the Celebration of the Two Hundredth Anniversary of the Birth of
George Washington

1732   1932

COMMISSIONERS
PRESIDENT OF THE UNITED STATES, CHAIRMAN
VICE PRESIDENT OF THE UNITED STATES
SPEAKER OF THE HOUSE OF REPRESENTATIVES

UNITED STATES SENATE
SIMEON D. FESS   OHIO

VICE CHAIRMAN

ARTHUR CAPPER   KANSAS
CARTER GLASS   VIRGINIA
MILLARD E. TYDINGS   MARYLAND

HOUSE OF REPRESENTATIVES
WILLIS C. HAWLEY   OREGON
JOHN Q. TILSON   CONNECTICUT
JOSEPH W. BYRNS   TENNESSEE
R. WALTON MOORE   VIRGINIA

ASSOCIATE DIRECTORS
REPRESENTATIVE SOL BLOOM

PRESIDENTIAL COMMISSIONERS
MRS. ANTHONY WAYNE COOK   PENNSYLVANIA
MRS. JOHN DICKINSON SHERMAN COLORADO
HENRY FORD   MICHIGAN
GEORGE EASTMAN   NEW YORK
C. BASCOM SLEMP   VIRGINIA
WALLACE McCAMANT   OREGON
ALBERT BUSHNELL HART   MASSACHUSETTS
BERNARD M. BARUCH   NEW YORK

EXECUTIVE COMMITTEE
THE SENATE AND HOUSE COMMISSIONERS
C. BASCOM SLEMP
MRS. ANTHONY WAYNE COOK
BERNARD M. BARUCH

HISTORIAN
PROF. ALBERT BUSHNELL HART

WASHINGTON BUILDING,
WASHINGTON, D. C.

March 5, 1932.

My dear Madam: (Refer to File SCT)

We are desirous of having specimen letterheads which
are being used by the City Committees, as well as two samples
of such medals or badges they may issue, or any other souvenirs,
such as programs, etc. Will you please supply us with your own
for exhibition purposes, and also that they may become a part of
the permanent record of the joint activities of the various City
Committees and this Commission.

We are anxious, also, to receive two or more copies of
newspapers containing accounts of your February 22 exercises, or
other exercises, in order that we may have as complete a record as
possible of your activities for the permanent Government records.

We have already expressed to you our thanks for your
splendid efforts. We count it a privilege to work with you
heartily in this the greatest project which has ever been under-
taken by any nation at any time in the history of the world.

Kindly let me have a reply at your earliest convenience.

Sincerely yours,

Sol Bloom

Sol Bloom,
Associate Director.

Mrs. M.W. Cave,
Topeka,
Kansas.

SB-A-C-City

The 1932 Bicentennial of Washington's birth celebrations were coordinated to an extent by the federal government, as the foregoing letter attests. Note some of the well-known Americans serving on the United States commission -- Senators Carter Glass and Millard Tydings, business giants Henry Ford, George Eastman and Bernard M. Baruch, and the commission chairman, President Herbert C. Hoover.

The listing of medals honoring the bicentennial of George Washington's birth 1732-1932 is based in part on the catalog prepared contemporaneously by Harvey L. Hansen in the January 1934 issue of *The Numismatist*. Hansen's work, prepared through the narrow prism of all such works, without the value of hindsight, was supplemented and corrected by three later writers: Melvin Fuld's "Hansen supplement" in the *Token and Medal Society Journal* for December 1966; H. Joseph Levine's Washington catalog in *The Numismatist* for April 1979; and Jack Collins' remarkable 1991 fixed price listing.

Your authors have expended much effort to meld these four works, cull out the unimportant, add fresh listings and rearrange some of the material. In our 1985 Centennial edition of Baker, the 1932 listings were admittedly inadequate, but the thrust of the overall work was not to be diminished by inclusion of too much of this vast 1932 output of medallic material. The original 1885 Baker was, after all, a catalog of **classic** Washingtonia.

Some of the pieces listed in the catalog by Hansen and his supplementers are tokens rather than medals, and these may be found in Chapter 36, Twentieth Century Store Cards.

In general, the 1932 medallic memorials do not carry the fine style of the medals issued on other anniversaries, e.g. in 1876

or 1889. With a few notable exceptions such as issues of the U.S. Mint and Medallic Art Co., the 1932 output was pedestrian. Collectors have managed to avoid most of this material, even though some legitimacy has been achieved in the 67 years intervening. The modest prices of most listings reflect this situation. With much haste medallic firms such as Bastian, Whitehead-Hoag, Robbins, Grammes, Greenduck, Childs, Noble and others turned out hordes of indifferently-executed low-relief medals as a commercial venture. Both medallic art and commerce suffered, as many of these products did not sell.

Today's collector must understand that the year 1932 was a low point of the Great Depression of the 1930s. Following the October 1929 Massacre on the New York stock market, America's economy rapidly tattered. Jobs, bank accounts and houses were lost, and Americans could not rise to the "feel-good" Bicentennial in February 1932. (A contrast: Thousands of the destitute flocked to Chicago's Century of Progress Expo in 1933!)

Does this mean Washingtonia enthusiasts should avoid the 1932 issues? We think not. Quality and scarcity are only two elements of collectibility; demand is perhaps the most important element. Who knows what the numismatists of 2032 will think on the Tricentennial? Our advice: Collect what you wish, enjoy what you collect, and worry only a little about investment potential.

PROCLAIM LIBERTY

shape separates 1732-1932. Rv: Standing Liberty facing, holding a torch in right hand, sheathed sword in her left. Above, an eagle in flight and 13 scattered stars. Liberty separates legend: PROCLAIM - LIBERTY / THROVGHOVT - ALL THE LAND. Plain edge. (Hansen 1)

Baker	Date	Metal	Size	EF	Unc	Proof
900A	1932	Bronze	76mm	50.00	75.00	—

As 900. Plain edge. (Hansen 2)

Baker	Date	Metal	Size	EF	Unc	Proof
900B	1932	Silver	76mm	550.	750.	—

As 900. Presentation piece inscribed on the edge. (Kirtley March 14, 1988 sale, lot 1166)

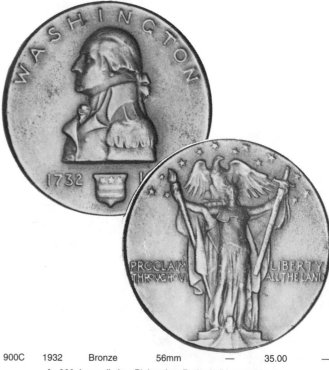

Baker	Date	Metal	Size	EF	Unc	Proof
900C	1932	Bronze	56mm	—	35.00	—

As 900, in small size. Plain edge. Rarity 2. (Hansen 3)

The single platinum piece (Baker 900) was presented to President Herbert C. Hoover on Dec. 1, 1932, by the U.S. Commission for the Celebration of the 200th Anniversary of the birth of George Washington, of which Hoover was chairman. The 76mm bronze strikes were used by the Commission as an award medal in connection with national essay, oratorical and declamatory contests. The 56mm bronze medals were sold by the U.S. mint to the public.

Designed by sculptress Laura Gardin Fraser and struck at the Philadelphia Mint.

(See *The Numismatist* for Oct., 1931, page 738)

Baker	Date	Metal	Size	EF	Unc	Proof
900	1932	Platinum	76mm	—	Unique	—

Uniformed bust left, LAURA GARDIN FRASER, SCULPTOR under bust. Above: WASHINGTON. Below: Washington coat of arms in shield

BICENTENNIAL COMMISSION

Baker	Date	Metal	Size	EF	Unc	Proof
901	1932	**	37 by 41mm	100.	Rare	—

Shield-shaped flan. ** Gold-filled copper.

Nude Bust right within circle, with Mount Vernon and two medallions above, scroll lettered GEORGE WASHINGTON BICENTENNIAL below, and 1732 1932 at bottom. Rv: Aerial view of the Capitol, blank scroll below, and below that: UNITED STATES / GEORGE WASHINGTON / BICENTENNIAL / COMMISSION. Plain edge. Issued with loop for suspension from yellow-blue-yellow ribbon, with the hanger blank for entry of a name. (Leon Hendrickson coll.; Fuld NLH-117)

Issued for official guests at a Commission function. The illustrated specimen is engraved on reverse: HON. WILLIAM L. FIESINGER / REP. FROM OHIO / 72ND CONGRESS /PRESENTED BY THE. The hanger on obverse is inscribed: HON. WM. L. FIESINGER / OHIO.

Baker	Date	Metal	Size	EF	Unc	Proof
901A	1932	**	37by41mm	100.	Rare	—

Similar to 901 for HON. DUNCAN FLETCHER of FLORIDA. (Fuld NLH-117-Gf: Collins 451, ex-Fuld)

The Collins specimen was offered at $165 in 1991.

Baker 901-901B were made by Bailey, Banks & Biddle of Philadelphia. The Kirtley March 14, 1998 sale, lot 1168, offered a version of 901 in AU, named to the Pennsylvania commissioner.

Baker	Date	Metal	Size		Unc	
901B	1932	Bronze	37 by 41mm	—	60.00	—

Similar obverse. Rev: PRESENTED BY THE / UNITED STATES / GEORGE WASHINGTON / BICENTENNIAL / COMMISSION in exergue. Suspended on a ribbon. Rarity 6. (Levine 1, not in Fuld: Collins 452)

PHILADELPHIA MINT

Baker	Date	Metal	Size	VF	EF	Unc
901C	1932	Golden bronze	51mm	—	—	25.00

Civilian bust facing right withint a cameo, dividing birth and death dates at left and right. Above: field view of Mount Vernon flanked on the sides with trees, MOUNT * VERNON at top. Rv: Elevation of entrance to Philadelphia Mint within a round panel, the top corners of the facade and flag bleeding over onto the raised peripheral border, MINT OF THE UNITED STATES * PHILADELPHIA, PA. *

(Unlisted in Hansen: Fuld NLH72-BoGmf: Collins 455)

See Baker A-348, where Fraser's obverse is used for the Mint's 1932 Annual Assay medal.

MILITARY ORDER OF THE PURPLE HEART

PARIS MINT MEDAL

Baker	Date	Metal	Size	VF	EF	Unc
902	ND	Gilt/Enamel	Heart-shaped 35x44mm	—	—	165.

Relief bust of Washington in uniform of a general of the Continental Army on center of purple enamel; gold-bordered. Rv: Gold, inscribed FOR MILITARY MERIT. Plain edge. Rarity 2. (Hansen 4; Collins 457)

This decoration, awarded for wounds received in warfare, is not generally thought of in connection with the Washington Bicentennial. However, it was revived in connection with that 1932 event.

The original Purple Heart was not a medal, but was a silk badge of purple edged with a narrow silver binding and the word MERIT stitched in silver across its face. It was designed by Washington and first mentioned in his signed order of August 7, 1782.

President Hoover ordered its revival and it was announced in War Department general order 3, Feb. 22, 1932 (Washington's 200th birthday). The Washington coat of arms is incorporated in the ring which attaches the medal to a purple ribbon bordered with white. The name of the recipient is engraved on the reverse.

Decorations bearing names of well-known recipients, or as part of a group of medals for the same person, may bring higher prices.

GRADE HEADINGS

Three grade (condition) columns appear in this catalog. Coins and tokens, which circulate, are graded down to VG (Very Good), but medals, which do not circulate, usually are graded no less than VF (Very Fine). Other abbreviations used are F (Fine), EF (Extremely Fine), AU (About Uncirculated), Unc (Uncirculated), and P-L (Prooflike). Proof is spelled out.

OBVERSE AND REVERSE

The term Obverse refers to the "heads" or "face" side of a piece. Where there is a human head or bust, this is easy to determine, but where there is no head, the side with the "principal device" is the Obverse. The opposite side is the Reverse. In some cases determining Obverse and Reverse must be arbitrary, especially where a head is on each side.

Each piece also has a third side, the Edge, which is described as Reeded, Plain, Lettered, etc. The term Rim is not the edge, but the periphery of one face or another.

Baker	Date	Metal	Size	VF	EF	Unc
903	1799	Silver	68mm	—	475.	525.

Civil bust left, around: GEORGE WASHINGTON, 1732 1799 and 13 stars in groups. Rv: Replica of Mount Vernon as erected at French Colonial Exposition in Paris, 1931. Below, in three lines: PATRIAE LIBERATOR / ET DECVS / 1732-1932. Plain edge, marked ARGENT. (Hansen 8)

Baker	Date	Metal	Size	VF	EF	Unc
903A	1799	Bronze	68mm	—	135.	200.

As 903. Plain Edge.

Engraved by Lucien Bazor and struck at the Paris Mint in France. (See *The Numismatist* for March 1932, page 169)

GOOD LUCK MEDAL

Baker	Date	Metal	Size	VF	EF	Unc
A903	1932	Gilt/Cop	33mm	—	15.00	17.50

Obverse of Baker 907A. Rv: Defiant eagle facing left, perched within a round panel, five stars left, four right, TAKE ME / FOR LUCK around the periphery. (Fuld NLH78-2BoGf: Collins 511)

GERMAN DELAWARE CROSSING MEDAL

Baker	Date	Metal	Size	VF	EF	Unc
904	1932	Bronze	60 by 87mm	—	90.00	125.

Civil bust of Washington left within circular medallion in upper two-thirds of the plaquette. Inscribed around circle: 22 2 1732-14 12 1799. Medallion separates 19-32. Washington crosses the Delaware in lower third. Plain edge. Rarity 8. (Hansen 6; Collins 459)

Made by Mayer & Wilhelm, Rotebuhlstrasse 119-B, Stuttgart, Germany. These pieces saw very limited distribution in the U.S. Collins in 1991 offered an Unc specimen at $75.

BICENTENNIAL FOB

Baker	Date	Metal	Size	VF	EF	Unc
A904	1932	Golden bronze	36mm	—	15.00	—

Bust right in circular panel, GEORGE WASHINGTON BICENTENNIAL / * 1732-1932 * around. Rv: Blank (Fuld NHL-90-Bo; Collins 468). Issued looped. Rarity 7.

Baker	Date	Metal	Size	VF	EF	Unc
A904A	1932	Gilt/Cop	35mm	—	15.00	—

Similar to preceding, but integral fob at top. (Fuld NLH90-BoGf)

Struck by F.H. Noble Co.

BICENTENNIAL LAPEL BUTTON

Baker	Date	Metal	Size	VF	EF	Unc
C904	1932	Golden bronze	Scal 20mm	—	7.50	—

Nude bust right within a round panel, GEORGE WASHINGTON BICENTENNIAL / *1732-1932* around periphery. Scalloped border, with shank and clasp on back. Rarity 8. (Hansen 62)

INDEPENDENT ORDER OF FORESTERS
York, Pa.

Baker	Date	Metal	Size	VF	EF	Unc
D904	1932	Bronze	32mm	—	15.00	—

Similar obverse to Baker 910. Rv: 109th ANNUAL SESSION GRAND LODGE OF PENNSYLVANIA I.O.O.F. YORK JUNE 1932 in seven lines. Suspended from hanger, consisting of a horizontal bar with the inscription REPRESENTATIVE; pin attached on back, along with a red silk ribbon, gilt stamped.

PIN

Baker	Date	Metal	Size	VF	EF	Unc
E904	ND	WM	15mm	—	—	7.50

Die struck pin. Periwigged civilian bust facing one-quarter left, birth and death years flanking either side of the neck, GEORGE WASHINGTON BICENTENNIAL around periphery. Rv: Manufacturer's signature. (Hansen 56)

EQUESTRIAN PLAQUETTE

Struck 1932-1955

Baker	Date	Metal	Size	VF	EF	Unc
F904	1799	Bronze	Rect 57x92mm	—	100.	200.

Full-length military figure of Washington facing left astride his horse, name above, and 1732 1799 directly below. In exergue HE WENT TO WAR / A COLONIAL VIRGINIAN / HE RETURNED A CITIZEN / OF THE / UNITED STATES in five lines, enclosed by fasces at left and right, and Washington's coat-of-arms integrated into the inscription at lower center, thirteen stars across border below. Uniface. (Fuld H57-1-Bo; Hansen 57)

This plaque was available on special order from Medallic Art Co. as late as 1955. Only 30 pieces struck in 1932. Designed by Fraser. An AU piece fetched $302.50 in March, 1998.

BICENTENNIAL FOB

Baker	Date	Metal	Size	VF	EF	Unc
G904	1932	Svd/Copper	Oval 30x42mm	—	—	12.50

Periwigged nude bust facing right, name halfway around above, birth and death years below: fasces wreath around periphery. Union shield at top, five-pointed star at bottom. Rv. Incuse impression of obverse. Integral fob of two eagles at top. (Hansen 60, Levine 34). Rarity 5.

WASHINGTON, D.C. SOUVENIR

Baker	Date	Metal	Size	VF	EF	Unc
J904	1799	Svd/Copper	Rect 23x65mm	—	12.50	—

Periwigged civilian bust facing one-quarter left within an oval panel, coat-of-arms in exergue * GEORGE * WASHINGTON * BICENTENARY * around the raised peripheral border. Rv: Torch and elongated sconce dividing birth and death years, laurel wreath halfway around from base. Suspended from the ring and hanger, consisting of an ornate bar inscribed SOUVENIR / WASHINGTON, / D.C. in three lines, pin attached to back. (Hansen 65-66, Fuld NLH109-Bo-Afg)

Baker	Date	Metal	Size	VF	EF	Unc
K904	1799	Svd/Copper	Rect 23x65mm	—	25.00	—

Bicentennial plaquette, same design as last from different die. Eagle on union shield at top, garlands of flowers and leaves draped on either side over the oval medallion, EXITUS ACTA PROBAT; on banner the family coat-of-arms, laurel branches on either side, 1732 1799 on a shelf face below, FEB. 22 on a banner in exergue. Uniface. With integral standing bracket. (Fuld NLH110-Bo-Agf).

FIRST IN WAR

Baker	Date	Metal	Size	VF	EF	Unc
L904	1799	Antique Brz	69mm	—	—	70.00

Periwigged nude bust left, name around above, 1732-1799 below, laurel branches at either side. Rv: FIRST IN WAR / FIRST IN PEACE / FIRST IN THE HEARTS / OF HIS COUNTRYMEN in four lines, vertical fasces on either side. Rarity 6. (Hansen 69; Collins 584)

Baker	Date	Metal	Size	VF	EF	Unc
L904A	1799	Bronze	32mm	—	—	15.00

Reduction in size of Baker L904 Rv: Blank except for three line imprint: MEDALLIC / ART CO. / NEW YORK. (Fuld H69-1-Bo)

Baker	Date	Metal	Size	VF	EF	Unc
M904	1932	Gilt/Cop	32mm	—	—	10.00

Periwigged nude bust right, laurel branch under truncation, within a round panel, banner bearing name around below, laurel branches on either side. Cartouche in exergue with BICENTENNIAL flanked by 1732--1932. Rv: COMMEMORATING / THE / BICENTENNIAL / OF / BIRTH OF / GEORGE WASHINGTON in six lines with decorative divider in upper half, blank below. (Fuld NLH91-BoBf)

Baker	Date	Metal	Size	VF	EF	Unc
N904	1932	Gilt/Cop	31mm	—	—	10.00

Periwigged nude bust right, 1732/1932 at lower right within a round panel, name around above, laurel wreath two-thirds around. Rv: BICENTENNIAL / (two crossed flats on standards) / OF THE BIRTH OF / GEORGE / WASHINGTON / 1732 / 1932, laurel wreath around the latter. (Fuld NLH94-BoGf: Collins 589)

ENAMELED PIN

Baker	Date	Metal	Size	VF	EF	Unc
Q904	ND	**	**	—	15.00	17.50

** Shield-shaped, 15x17mm. Gilt copper, enameled blue.

Periwigged nude bust right, field in blue enamel, frame held from above by a spread eagle, its legs dividing WASHINGTON / BICENTENNIAL on a banner. Rv APPROVED DESIGN / A. KAHN INC. / WASH. D.C. / PAT APPL'D FOR in four lines at center. (Fuld NLH108-BoEf)

Baker	Date	Metal	Size	VF	EF	Unc
Q904A	ND	Copper	15x17mm	—	12.50	—

Similar to preceding, from different dies. (Fuld NLH108-BoBrf)

Baker	Date	Metal	Size	VF	EF	Unc
Q904B	ND	Golden bronze	15x17mm	—	10.00	—

Nearly identical to last obverse. Rv: Same legend as above, in four lines. (Fuld NLH108-Bo)

Baker	Date	Metal	Size	VF	EF	Unc
Q904C	ND	Svd/Copper	15x17mm	—	10.00	—

Similar to Q904B, different finish. (Fuld NLH108-BoAgf)

LONG-NECKED BUST

Baker	Date	Metal	Size	VF	EF	Unc
R904	1932	Brass	33mm	—	—	20.00

Periwigged nude bust facing left, above, GEORGE WASHINGTON BICENTENNIAL around the periphery. Rv: Birth, presidential and death dates in seven lines within an olive wreath, Union shield at bottom. (Levine 23)

Maker's name at bottom of reverse; D&C NY.

BIRTHDAY ASSOCIATION

Alexandria, Va.

Baker	Date	Metal	Size	VF	EF	Unc
S904	1932	Gilt/Cop	32mm	—	10.00	15.00

Periwigged bust right. Fancy typed header marked STAFF, yellow-blue-yellow ribbon inscribed GEORGE/WASHINGTON/BIRTHDAY/ASS'N/BICENTENNIAL/CELEBRATION/ALEXANDRIA/FEB'Y22,1932. PCAC sale Dec. 1993, lot 918)

FREDERICKSBURGH LODGE

Baker	Date	Metal	Size	EF	Unc	Proof
905	1932	Bronze	32mm	10.00	—	

Undraped bust right, GEORGE WASHINGTON around, * 1732 G Washington (signature) 1932 *. Rv: Washington standing, facing, on a Masonic mosaic on which are a table and three pillars, 1732 / 1932 at right, GEORGE WASHINGTON BICENTENNIAL above. Plain edge. (Hansen 40/33; Bullowa-Lessin sale, lot 2)

This medal was issued by the Fredericksburgh, Va. lodge of the Masons, which was also responsible for Baker 297.

Struck by Bastian Brothers Co., Rochester, N.Y.

Baker	Date	Metal	Size	VF	EF	Unc
906	1932	Yellow Bronze	32mm	—	10.00	

Obverse as reverse of 905 (Washington standing before altar table). Rv: Masonic jewel surrounded by scroll reading WASHINGTON AS A MASON, trowel and sprig of acacia below. At center, in eight lines: ENTERED / FREDERICKSBURG LODGE / NOV. 4, 1752 / APPOINTED / FIRST MASTER / ALEXANDRIA LODGE / NO. 22 / APRIL 28 1788. In tiny letters, under trowel: WHITEHEAD-HOAG. Plain edge. (Hansen 25)

Baker	Date	Metal	Size	VF	EF	Unc
A906	1932	Copper	33mm	—	10.00	—

Obv. same as following, Baker 907. Rv: Masonic square and compass dividing scrolls bearing WASHINGTON / THE MASON; INITIATED / FREDERICKSBURG / LODGE NO. 4 / NOV. 4TH 1752 / APPOINTED / FIRST MASTER / ALEXANDRIA LODGE / NO. 22 / APRIL 28TH 1788 in nine lines. Struck by Robbins Co. (Fuld H33-1-Bo; Collins 516)

MASONIC NATIONAL MEMORIAL

Baker	Date	Metal	Size	VF	Ef	Unc
907	1932	Bronze	32mm	—	7.50	—

Obverse similar in all important respects to obverse of Baker 906 (reverse of 905), but from different dies. Rv: Building at center, on scroll above and around: THE. GEORGE. WASHINGTON. MASONIC. NATIONAL. MEMORIAL. Below: ALEXANDRIA, VA. / DEDICATED / MAY 12, 1932. Plain edge. (Hansen 33)

Struck by Robbins Co. Attleboro, Mass.

Baker	Date	Metal	Size	VF	EF	Unc
907A	1932	Bronze	32mm	—	7.50	—

Very similar to Baker 907, same inscription. The apron on obverse has different treatment. Manufactured by Whitehead-Hoag. (Fuld sub 1, H33-Bo)

Baker	Date	Metal	Size	VF	EF	Unc
A907		Golden bronze	32mm	—	10.00	—

Obverse is reverse of Baker 907. Rv: Same as reverse of Baker A906. (Levine 16)

Baker	Date	Metal	Size	VF	EF	Unc
908	1932	Bronze	32mm	—	—	10.00

Standing, facing Washington has right hand on bible resting on a pedestal, PRESIDENT WORSHIPFUL MASTER above, WASHINGTON below. Rv: Building with tall central tower. Above: WASHINGTON MASONIC MEMORIAL ALEXANDRIA. Below: MAY 12, 1932. Radiant compass, square and G at right. Plain edge.

Baker	Date	Metal	Size	VF	EF	Unc
A908	1932	Gilt/Cop	33mm	—	10.00	15.00

Nude bust right. GEORGE WASHINGTON BICENTENNIAL around above. Rv: Corner elevation of the Masonic Hall, ALEXANDRIA, VA. on a scroll in exergue. Masonic emblem, in right field, GEORGE / WASHINGTON / MASONIC / NATIONAL / MEMORIAL in left field. (Fuld NLH78-BoBrf; Collins 509). Struck by Grammes Co.

PATER PATRIAE

Certain Latin terms appear on medals pertaining to George Washington, the first "General of the Armies of the United States." Only one other man held this title until the 5-star rank was created in World War II, and that was John J. Pershing, U.S. commander in France in WWI.

Pater Patriae (father of his country) is the apt title frequently appearing. Many other Latin words and phrases appear on items in this catalog; in most cases we have translated these for users.

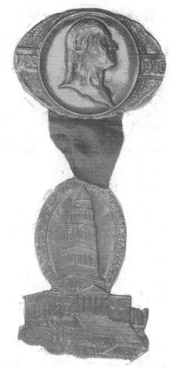

Baker	Date	Metal	Size	VF	EF	Unc
A909	1932	VV	Overall 35x97mm	—	25.00	32.50

VV Antiqued bronze, 2 pieces with ribbon between.

Nude bust in a round medallion, flanked by 1732-1932 right on raised cartouches, surmounted on an oval with scalloped edges. Uniface. Suspended below are one-and-a-half inches of yellow-blue-yellow silk ribbon, and a medal depicting the corner facade of the entrance to Masonic Hall, GEO. WASHINGTON MASONIC HALL MEMORIAL ALEXANDRIA VA on a raised oval surrounding the steeple. (Levine 10; Collins 518). Rarity 7.

Baker	Date	Metal	Size	VF	EF	Unc
B909	1932	Gilt/Cop	32mm	—	15.00	—

Full length civilian figure in Masonic apron standing beside an altar with his hand on a bible, a hat in his other hand, chair in the background; PRESIDENT WORSHIPFUL MASTER / WASHINGTON around. Rv: Corner elevation of Masonic Hall, their emblem in right field; WASHINGTON MASONIC MEMORIAL ALEXANDRIA / MAY 12, 1932, around. Initials B.B&B (Bailey, Banks & Biddle) on reverse. (Hansen 51; Collins 564)

Bailey, Banks & Biddle of Philadelphia was a high quality, oldline manufacturing jeweler and medallic firm tracing its roots to Joseph T. Bailey in 1833.

YORKTOWN CHAPTER 304

Baker	Date	Metal	Size	VF	EF	Unc
909	1932	Bronze	32mm	—	—	15.00

Obverse as 908. Rv: YORKTOWN ROYAL ARCH CHAPTER / NO. 304 / PAST HIGH / PRIEST'S NIGHT / NOVEMBER 17, 1932. Plain edge.

SHARON ELKS LODGE

Baker	Date	Metal	Size	EF	Unc	Proo
910	1932	Bronze	32mm	10.00	—	—

Obverse as 905. Rv: Building at center. Around: SHARON LODGE B.P.O.E. ELKS' HOME / DEDICATED / MARCH 30TH 1932 / BASTIAN BROS CO ROCH N.Y. Plain edge. (Hansen 40)

The building shown is the Benevolent & Protective Order of Elks' home in Sharon, Pennsylvania.

KNIGHTS OF PYTHIAS ENCAMPMENT
West Haven, Conn.

Baker	Date	Metal	Size	VF	EF	Unc
911	1932	Gilt/Cop	Oct 32mm-	—	20.00	—

Obv. of Baker 935. Rv: Seal of the Knights of Pythias within a beaded border, NATIONAL ENCAMPMENT AND SUPREME ASSEMBLY WEST HAVEN; JULY 17*23, 1932 around. Around seal: UNIFORM RANK / K. OF P. (Levine 11; Collins 535)

Struck by Whitehead & Hoag, Newark, N.J.

ROTARY CLUB
Eaton, Ohio

Baker	Date	Metal	Size	VF	EF	Unc
A911	1932	Golden bronze	32mm	—	15.00	—

Same obverse die as M904. Rv: COMMEMORATING / THE / BICENTENNIAL / OF THE / BIRTH OF / GEORGE WASHINGTON / ROTARY CLUB OF EATON, OHIO / NO. 2570 / 2-22-32 in ten lines. (Fuld NLH92-BoBf; Collins 588)

PHILIPPINE ISLANDS MASONIC
GRAND LODGE

Baker	Date	Metal	Size	VF	EF	Unc
C911	1932	Copper	50.8mm	50.00	150.	250

Washington Monument superimposed upon a radiant sun, partly concealed by the horizon; banner across the obelisk near the summit bearing GEORGE WASHINGTON / 1753 / *1732 / 1789 / 1932* / 19 MARCH 1932 in a cartouche above, surveyor's scope in left field, cornerstone and trowel in right. In exergue: "LET THOSE FOLLOW THE PURSUIT OF AMBITION & FAME WHO HAVE A KEENER RELISH FOR THEM ... I SEE A PATH CLEAR & DIRECT AS A RAY OF LIGHT, WHICH

LEADS TO - HAPPINESS FOR MY COUNTRY", facsimile signature below, all within a round panel, COMMEMORATIVE * OF * THE * BICENTENARY * OF * THE * BIRTH * OF * A * GREAT MAN * AND * MASON * around the periphery. Rv: Masonic lodge seal, GRAND LODGE OF FREE AND ACCEPTED MASONS / * PHILIPPINE ISLANDS * around the periphery. Rarity 8 or 9. (Hansen 55; Aldo Basso 748; Collins 571)

Supposedly 300 struck, but extremely rare today. Collins in 1991 knew of only 3 specimens, one corroded. The Collins piece is illustrated.

Signature seems to read L.B. BAUER FEC.(?)

FORT NECESSITY, PA

Baker	Date	Metal	Size		
912	1932	Bronze	32mm	20.00	—	40.00

Obverse as 905. Rv: View of fort. Above: FORT NECESSITY NEAR UNIONTOWN PA / 1754 - JULY 3-4-1932. Plain edge. (Hansen 41)
This medal was issued by the Fort Necessity Memorial Committee and struck by Bastian Brothers Co., Rochester, N.Y.

The medal commemorates Washington's first important military action. Then only 22, he was appointed Lieutenant Colonel by Virginia Governor Robert Dinwiddie and sent with a force of 500 colonial militia to secure the area near what is now Pittsburgh. Finding the French had already built Fort Duquesne there, he withdrew to Great Meadows and built Fort Necessity there. He had left in Feb., 1754 with his force. The French sent a 900-man force under Col. Coulon de Villiers to dislodge him, and on July 3 forced Washington to surrender the fort. The British casualties were 70, the French 20. Far from tarnishing Washington's military reputation, the action at Fort Necessity enhanced it, and just a year later he heroically led part of Braddock's defeated force from the field safely after the French and Indian ambush of 1755.

Baker 912 is also known in Golden Bronze, same values.

FRIENDSHIP FIRE CO.
Alexandria, Va.

Baker	Date	Metal	Size	VF	EF	Unc
A912	1932	XX	Overall 33x114mm	—	30.00	—

XX Hanger, red ribbon, shield-shaped medal. Metallic parts in golden bronze. Nude bust right separates 1732-1932, facsimile signature on

scroll above. Fob attached to top. Rv: GEORGE WASHINGTON MEMBER OF FRIENDSHIP FIRE COMPANY ALEXANDRIA, VA. 1773, manufacturer's shield logo in exergue. Suspended from the original ornate hanger, 18th century hand pump within panel, THE / FIREMAN'S ASS'N OF / PENNA on three scrolls above, LANCASTER, PA. On scroll in exergue, the latter superimposed over a keystone: 53RD CONVENTION / OCT 4-6, 1932 in left and right fields respectively. Rv: Bastian Bros. seal, two pins attached, the lower one with 1-1/2 inches of red silk ribbon. (Fuld H48-2-Bo)

VIRGINIA FIREMAN'S CONVENTION
Alexandria, Va.

Baker	Date	Metal	Size	VF	EF	Unc
913	1932	Copper	**	—	—	20.00

** Cross-shaped, 48x48mm. Overall height 96 mm.

Periwigged nude bust right, * GEO. WASHINGTON BICENTENNIAL * / 1732-1932 around within a round panel on a Maltese cross; two crossed axes on top arm, hook and ladder on right arm, fireman's hat on bottom arm, and fireplug on left arm. Rv: Incuse impression of portrait, VIRGINIA 46TH ANNUAL STATE AND around above, 31ST ANNUAL VALLEY ASS'N on left arm, CUMBERLAND FIREMEN'S CON'S on right arm, ALEXANDRIA, VA. AUG. 10-12 1932 on lower arm. Suspended from pinback hanger, inscribed GUEST with two inches of red-white-blue ribbon. Integral loop at top. (Fuld NLH114-Bo; Collins 600)

VIRGINIA'S GREATEST SON

Baker	Date	Metal	Size	EF	Unc	Proof
914	1932	Bronze	32mm	10.00	15.00	—

Obverse as 905. Rv: In eight lines: FOUNDER OF THE REPUBLIC FATHER OF THE FATHERLAND VIRGINIA'S GREATEST SON / BASTIAN BROS CO ROCHESTER N.Y. Plain edge. (Hansen 42)

Struck by the Bastian Brothers Co., Rochester, N.Y., and distributed by various Virginia organizations. Hansen in 1934 reported his specimen was distributed by the newspaper Richmond News Leader.

P.O.S. OF A.

915   1932   Bronze   32mm   —   —   —

Obverse as 905. Rv: In seven lines: 200TH ANNIVESARY BIRTH OF GEORGE WASHINGTON VIRGINIA STATE CAMP / P.O.S. OF A. (on scroll) / BASTIAN BROS. COMPANY, ROCHESTER, N.Y. Plain edge. (Hansen 43)

P.O.S. OF A. = Patriotic Order, Sons of America.

NEW JERSEY P.O.S. OF A.

A915   1932   Gilt/Cop   32mm   —   25.00   —

Same obverse as Baker 925. Rev: 200TH / ANNIVERSARY / BIRTH OF / GEORGE WASHINGTON / NEW JERSEY / STATE CAMP in six lines, shield and banner in exergue, each bearing P.O.S. of A. (Fuld H17-2-BoGf; Collins 488)

Another dreary medallic product of Whitehead & Hoag, who were capable of better execution.

PENNSYLVANIA P.O.S. OF A.

Baker	Date	Metal	Size	VF	EF	Unc
B915	1932	Golden bronze	Oval,29x33mm	—	25.00	35.00

Periwigged civilian bust right, name above, seal of Patriotic Order Sons of America superimposed over truncation, bleeding over border, * 67TH ANNUAL SESSIONS PENNA. STATE CAMP .P.O.S.OF A. * / PHILA-

DELPHIA / AUG. 23-25, 1932 around the raised peripheral border, integral fob at top. Rv: Manufacturer's signature in two lines. The hanger depicts Independence Hall, flanked to left and right by scrolls, banner in exergue inscribed PHILADELPHIA. Liberty Bell below, with arabesques at sides; with pin attached on back of hanger together with two inches of red-white-blue silk ribbon. (Levine 39; Collins 606)

RICHMOND LIGHT INFANTRY BLUES
Connecticut

Baker	Date	Metal	Size	VF	EF	Unc
C915	1932	Bronze	32mm	—	—	—12.50

Obverse as 918. Rv: PRESENTED BY / RICHMOND / LIGHT INFANTRY BLUES / JUNE 1932 / CONNECTICUT'S BICENTENNIAL / CELEBRATION. (Kirtley Dec. 5, 1995 auction; lot E071; Collins 548)

Struck by Bastian Bros., Rochester, N.Y.

This famous old militia regiment, raised in 1798, issued a membership medalet circa 1830, cataloged as Rulau-E Conn 40 (formerly Va 8).

BASTIAN AWARD MEDALS

Baker	Date	Metal	Size	VF	EF	Unc
916	1932	Gilt/Brz	32mm	—	10.00	—

Obv. of Baker 905. Rv: Plain except for small shield with MPB / PIU around. Below: BASTIAN BROS. CO. ROCHESTER, N.Y. Made with a loop through which is a red, white and blue ribbon, attached a bar 44by12mm which is engraved: 1ST AWARD. (Fuld H40-5-BoGf)

| 916A | 1932 | Svd/Brz | 32mm | — | 10.00 | — |

Identical to preceding, but bar is engraved 2ND AWARD. (Fuld H40-6-Bo Agf)

The reverse carries Bastian's official seal.

WASHINGTON BICENTENNIAL

Baker	Date	Metal	Size	VF	EF	Unc
918	1932	Bronze	32mm	—	—	8.00

Obverse is 905. Rv: In seven lines: WASHINGTON BICENTENNIAL CELEBRATION 1932 BASTIAN BROS. COMPANY, ROCHESTER N.Y. Plain edge. (Hansen 44)

This and the next, 919, were sold to the general public and thus are the commonest of the Bastian Brothers series. Also issued in Copper. Rarity 1.

APPLETON JUBILEE

Baker	Date	Metal	Size	VF	EF	Unc
D919	1932	Brass	32mm	—	15.00	—

Washington on his horse, holding an extended sword. Below: WASHINGTON. Rv: Around, CITY OF APPLETON, WISCONSIN, DIAMOND JUBILEE. Inscription in six lines within, AND / BICENTENNIAL / CELEBRATION / APR. (?) MAY 7 / 1932 / SOUVENIR. (Levine 24)

DAUGHTERS OF THE AMERICAN REVOLUTION

Baker	Date	Metal	Size	VF	EF	Unc
F919	1932	Bronze	32mm	—	7.50	—

Bust right similar to Baker 925. Above: FOR HOME AND COUNTRY. Rv: At top: CITIZENSHIP MEDAL. In field: PRESENTED / BY / N.S.D.A.R. / TO followed by a bar for engraving below lamp of knowledge, and below in three scrolls, LOYALTY / HONOR / SERVICE Equipped with a loop and red-white-blue ribbon with bar and pin. On back of bar in three lines, W & H CO / PAT. / APPLIED. (Fuld NLH89-Bo)

Baker	Date	Metal	Size	VF	EF	Unc
919	1932	Yellow Bronze	30mm	—	—	8.50

Undraped bust right, GEORGE WASHINGTON around, * 1732 G Washington (signature) 1932 * below. Rv: WASHINGTON / BICENTENNIAL / CELEBRATION / 1932 / (shield) / (tiny) BASTIAN BROS. CO. ROCHESTER, N.Y. Plain edge. Suspended from a yellow and deep blue ribbon; hanger on reverse of medal. (Hansen 45)

REPUBLICAN NATIONAL CONVENTION

A919	ND	Svd/Copper	Rect, 34x54mm	—	15.00	—

Periwigged military bust in high relief facing right, facsimile signature on raised cartouche in exergue. Uniface, except for manufacturer's signature at bottom of reverse. (Hansen 39; Collins 541)

A919A	ND	Copper	Rect, 34x54mm	—	15.00	—

We have not examined A919 or A919A, thus do not know the maker's name. Collins in 1991 exaggerated their value at $40 to $45, we believe

B919	1932	Bronze	VV	—	12.50	—

VV Shield-shaped, 33x47mm.

Periwigged nude bust right, head dividing 1732-1932, facsimile signature on scroll above. In exergue, narrow shield in center, superimposed over a vertical word and horizontal fasces, laurel branches on each side. Rv: Bastian Bros. seal. Fob attached at top. (Hansen 48; Collins 558)

G919	1932	Bronze	VV	—	25.00	35.00

Same medal as Baker B919, with fob and ribbon attached. PRESS on a cartouche, eagle atop a shield above, the figure dividing banners inscribed REPUBLICAN / NATIONAL CONVENTION on a banner across the shield. In exergue, two draped flags on standards superimposed on a banner inscribed CHICAGO / 1932, two pins attached on back, the lower one with one-and-three-quarters inches of red-white-blue silk ribbon. (Fuld H48-1-Bo)

H919   1932   Golden Bronze   VV   —   35.00   —

As G919, but ASS'T SGT. AT-ARMS in the cartouche. (Hansen 49)

The convention in the summer of 1932 renominated President Herbert C. Hoover, who was overwhelmed in the November balloting by Franklin Delano Roosevelt.

GRADE HEADINGS

Three grade (condition) columns appear in this catalog. Coins and tokens, which circulate, are graded down to VG (Very Good), but medals, which do not circulate, usually are graded no less than VF (Very Fine). Other abbreviations used are F (Fine), EF (Extremely Fine), AU (About Uncirculated), Unc (Uncirculated), and P-L (Prooflike). Proof is spelled out.

OBVERSE AND REVERSE

The term Obverse refers to the "heads" or "face" side of a piece. Where there is a human head or bust, this is easy to determine, but where there is no head, the side with the "principal device" is the Obverse. The opposite side is the Reverse. In some cases determining Obverse and Reverse must be arbitrary, especially where a head is on each side.

Each piece also has a third side, the Edge, which is described as Reeded, Plain, Lettered, etc. The term Rim is not the edge, but the periphery of one face or another.

PATER PATRIAE

Certain Latin terms appear on medals pertaining to George Washington, the first "General of the Armies of the United States." Only one other man held this title until the 5-star rank was created in World War II, and that was John J. Pershing, U.S. commander in France in WWI.

Pater Patriae (father of his country) is the apt title frequently appearing. Many other Latin words and phrases appear on items in this catalog; in most cases we have translated these for users.

Baker	Date	Metal	Size	VF	EF	Unc
J919	1932	XX	Overall 39x126mm	—	50.00	70.00

XX Gold-filled copper.

Same bust design as on last, facsimile signature in exergue, flanked by 1732-1932, within a round medallion. On banners around below: REPUBLICAN / NATIONAL, CONVENTION below on a horizontal banner superimposed over a sword upon a shield; above the medallion is an integral spread eagle, suspended by loops and rings from a blue enameled gold bar inscribed CHICAGO. The upper piece depicts a side view of the United States Capitol within an oval, laurel branches on either side, horizontal fasces partly behind the top of frame, flanked at left and right by red-white-blue enameled flags, DELEGATE on a blue enameled cartouche at top, date 1932 on a banner above; with pin attached on back of hanger, together with five inches overlapped with one-and-a-half inches of red-white-blue silk ribbon. Two part hanging badge. (Levine 35; Collins 561)

K919   1932   XX   As J919   —   40.00   —

As J919, but hanger reads: ALTERNATE. (Levine 36)

CHICAGO COMMISSION

Baker	Date	Metal	Size	VF	EF	Unc
M919	1932	Gilt/Cop	32mm	—	15.00	—

Periwigged nude bust left, GEORGE III WASHINGTON *** around. Rv: City seal inscribed CITY OF CHICAGO / INCORPORATED 4th MARCH 1837. Around: CHICAGO GEORGE WASHINGTON BICENTENNIAL COMMISSION / 1732 * 1932. (Collins 566)

Baker	Date	Metal	Size	VF	EF	Unc
N919	ND	Gilt/Cop	32mm	—	—	25.00

Obverse as M919. Rv: Blank, but tiny GREENDUCK CO. at bottom. (Collins 565). Rarity 7.

Baker	Date	Metal	Size	VF	EF	Unc
Q919	ND	Svd/Cop	29mm	—	—	25.00

As N919 in smaller size, without maker's name. Rarity 6. (Collins 567)

N919 and Q919 may have been maker's samples issued as early as 1911. The Q919 obverse appears on 1912-dated Baker 761 and 1911-dated Baker K700.

HISTORIC ST. PAUL'S

Baker	Date	Metal	Size	EF	Unc	Proof
920	1932	Bronze	32mm	20.00	—	—

Obverse as 905. Rv: St. Paul's Church at top center, WASHINGTON BI-CENTENNIAL / CELEBRATION above. Below, in 10 lines: HISTORIC ST. PAUL'S CHURCH (EPISCOPAL) / WHERE WASHINGTON AT-TENDED / CHURCH SERVICES WHILE IN / NORFOLK, VA. / THIS MEDAL ISSUED BY / TOURIST BUREAU / NORFOLK-PORTS-MOUTH / CHAMBER OF / COMMERCE / BASTIAN BROS CO ROCH-ESTER N.Y. Plain edge. (Hansen 46)

NEW BRITAIN EAGLES CONVENTION

921	1932	Bronze	32mm	20.00	—	—

Obverse as 905. Rv: In seven lines: FRATERNAL ORDER OF EAGLES BOOST OLD AGE PENSIONS / BASTIAN BROS CO ROCHESTER, N.Y. Plain edge. (Hansen 47). Issued suspended from red, white and blue ribbon reading: 26TH ANNUAL CONVENTION F.O.E. JUNE 17-18-19, 1932. NEW BRITAIN, CONN. A clasp at top of ribbon reads: DELEGATE.

LITERARY DIGEST AWARD

A921	1932	XX	Irreg	18mm	10.00	—

XX Naked bust of Washington in bronze medallion surrounded by laurel branches, below on blue enamel. 1732 LITERARY DIGEST AWARD 1932. Pin back for wearing. Used by the Literary Digest as first prize award. (Hansen 54)

Baker	Date	Metal	Size	VF	EF	Unc
922	1932	Bronze	64mm	—	45.00	65.00

Civil bust of Washington facing, in high relief. Rv: Within laurel wreath joined at bottom by cartouche lettered STATE / OF / RHODE ISLAND is: IN / COMMEMORATION / OF THE / GEORGE WASHINGTON / BI-CENTENNIAL / 1732-1932. Plain edge. Rarity 6. (Hansen 38; Collins 540)

Baker 922 was struck by the Robbins Co., Attleboro, Mass., whose signature appears in tiny letters at bottom of reverse, and was authorized as an official issue of the Rhode Island state legislature.

923	1932	Bronze	32mm	—	—	20.00

Obverse as 922 in smaller size. Rv: Same as reverse of Baker 907 (Masonic national memorial). Plain edge. (Hansen 34)

924	ND	Bronze	32mm	—	—	25.00

Obverse as 923. Rv: Blank, except ROBBINS CO ATTLEBORO, MASS, in tiny letters. Plain edge. Issued holed for suspension. (Hansen 35)

924A	ND	Gold/Brz	32mm	—	—	35.00

As 924, but heavy gold plating. (Magriel sale, lot 659)

WAKEFIELD RESTORED

Baker	Date	Metal	Size	VF	EF	Unc
925	1932	Bronze	32mm	—	7.50	—

Undraped bust right, 1732 / 1932 at right, GEORGE WASHINGTON BI-CENTENNIAL around. Rv: Home across center, WASHINGTON'S BIRTHPLACE above. In exergue: WAKEFIELD (RESTORED) / AT POPE'S CREEK / POTOMAC RIVER / WESTMORELAND COUNTY / VIRGINIA / (tiny) WHITEHEAD-HOAG. Plain edge. (Hansen 17; Bullowa-Lessin sale, lot 3)

Baker	Date	Metal	Size	VF	EF	Unc
925A	1932	Gilt/B	32mm	—	7.50	—

As last. Plain edge. (Bullowa-Lessin 3). Several die varieties exist. Struck by Whitehead & Hoag Co., Newark, N.J. The bronze in the first piece is oxidized. Used by newspapers for awards in crossword puzzle contests, essays, etc.

Baker	Date	Metal	Size	VF	EF	Unc
925C	1932	Gilt/Cop	32mm	—	10.00	—

Similar to Baker 925, different die. Rv: Corner elevation of Washington's birthplace, flanked on either end by trees, plume of smoke streaming upward from the forefront chimney, title above, WAKEFIELD in exergue, 13 stars around lower border. (Fuld NLH75-BoGf)

Baker	Date	Metal	Size	VF	EF	Unc
925D	1932	Gilt/Brz	32mm	—	10.00	—

Obv. of Baker 925. Rv: Almost identical to 925 'Wakefield' reverse, but differences in alignment and spacing. In very small letters at the bottom: METAL ARTS CO. ROCH. N.Y. (Levine 4)

Baker	Date	Metal	Size	VF	EF	Unc
929	1932	Gilt/Cop	32mm	—	17.50	—

Similar to 925. Rv: Similar to 925, but arc of 13 stars forms lower border, and WAKEFIELD is under facade of the home. (Collins 499)

Struck by Whitehead & Hoag Co., Newark, N.J.

CROSSING THE DELAWARE

Baker	Date	Metal	Size	VF	EF	Unc
926	1932	Bronze	32mm	7.50	—	25.00

Similar to last, from different die. Rv: Washington and his men crossing the Delaware River in a boat, WASHINGTON CROSSING THE DELA-WARE above, BORN FEB. 22. 1732. / PRESIDENT OF THE UNITED STATES / 1789-1797 / DIED DEC. 14, 1799 in exergue. Plain edge. (Hansen 16; Bullowa-Lessin 4)

Baker	Date	Metal	Size	VF	EF	Unc
926A	1932	Brass/Bz	32mm	7.50	—	25.00

As 926. Plain edge. Rarity 4. (Bullowa-Lessin, lot 4)

Baker	Date	Metal	Size	VF	EF	Unc
926B	1932	Gilt/Bz	32mm	7.50	—	—

As 926. Plain edge. (Hansen 16)

Baker	Date	Metal	Size	VF	EF	Unc
926C	1932	Nickel/Bz	32mm	9.00	—	30.00

As 926. Plain edge.

Baker 926 thru 926C, with rather routine artistry, and Baker 904, with much better effect, celebrate Washington's Christmas crossing of the Delaware River under cover of a night snowstorm in the early hours of Dec. 26, 1776. This led to the Bat-

tle of Trenton, where Washington's 2400 men attacked a drunken Hessian garriso at 8 a.m. while the German mercenaries were still asleep.

Colonel Johann Rall commanded his own and the Lossberg regiments, som 1400 men. The Americans in three detachments under Washington, Maj. Ger Nathanael Greene and Maj. Gen. John Sullivan attacked simultaneously from three directions, forcing the garrison from the town into open fields eastward. Co Rall was killed. The Hessians had 105 men killed or wounded, and 920 of them were taken prisoner; only about 375 escaped the rout.

American casualties were two men wounded, though three died from exposure during the ensuing retreat. The British referred to "that unhappy affair at Trenton as changing the course of the war. Trenton and the followup Battle of Princeto (Jan. 3, 1777) did in fact alter the dynamics of the Revolutionary War toward even tual American Victory.

YORKTOWN SESQUICENTENNIAL

Baker	Date	Metal	Silver	VF	EF	Unc
D926	1932	Gilt/Cop	Oct 32mm	—	15.00	17.50

Nude bust right, 1931 / 1932 in exergue, GEORGE WASHINGTON BI-CENTENNIAL COMMISSION around. Rv: Obelisk, dates 1781 / 1931 at right, three lines below, lawn and shrubs in exergue. (Hansen 30; Collins 532)

EASTERN STATES EXPOSITION

Baker	Date	Metal	Size	VF	EF	Unc
927	1932		32mm	10.00	15.00	

Obverse as Baker 925. Rv: Church at Storrowton, clouds around tower. Around: EASTERN STATES EXPOSITION. At right: WEST / SPRING-FIELD, / MASS. Below, in four lines: STORROWTON THE OLD NEW ENGLAND VILLAGE / WHITE-HEAD-HOAG. Plain edge. (Hansen 18; Collins 493)

Struck by Whitehead & Hoag Co., Newark, N.J. in connection with the New England Colonial Village display. (See *The Numismatist* for Nov., 1932, page 712)

INDEPENDENT ORDER OF FORESTERS

Baker	Date	Metal	Size	VF	EF	Unc
928	1932	Bronze	32mm	—	10.00	—

Obverse as 925. Rv: I.O.F. insignia at top. Below, in seven lines: MEM-BERSHIP TOKEN PRESENTED TO THE MEMBERS AND SPON-SORS OF THE GEORGE WASHINGTON BICENTENNIAL CLASS OF INITIATES. In tiny letters below: WHITEHEAD-HOAG. Plain edge. (Hansen 21)

NEW YORK CITY

Baker	Date	Metal	Size	EF	Unc	Proof
929F	1932	Gilt/Bz	32mm	—	10.00	—

Obverse as 925. Rv: 1779 /PLANNED SULLIVAN / CLINTON CAMPAIGN / 1782 / NEWBURGH TEMPLE HILL / REFUSED A CROWN / 1789 APRIL 30TH / NEW YORK CITY / INAUGURATED FIRST / PRESIDENT OF THE / UNITED STATES / WHITEHEAD-HOAG (tiny). Plain edge. Issued holed for suspension from ribbon; metal hanger is labeled NEW YORK. (Leon Hendrickson coll.)

TREE SHIELD

Baker	Date	Metal	Size	VF	EF	Unc
930	1932	Copper		—	—	25.00
		Shield-Shaped	48mm			

Head right, 1732 at left, 1932 at right. Above: A / GEORGE / WASHINGTON. Below: BICENTENNIAL TREE. Rv: Blank, Plain edge. Issued with holes at top and bottom for mounting.(Hansen 13; Collins 471)
The Amercian Tree Association, Washington D.C., distributed these shields through various garden magazines for attachment to trees planted in the Bicentennial year as part of the celebrations. The authors do not have a report on how these copper shields weathered.

SWASTIKA BADGE

Baker	Date	Metal	Size	VF	EF	Unc
B-930	1932	Hard Rubber	**	—	—	35.00

** Shield-shaped hard rubber flan, 35 by 48mm. Nude bust right, GEORGE WASHINGTON BICENTENNIAL around, 1732 / 1932 at right, all within circle. Rv: Large swastika on plain field. Plain edge. Issued holed for suspension. (Dr. Schuster coll.)

JANOWSKY/SCULPTURE MEDALS

Baker	Date	Metal	Size	VF	EF	Unc
931	1932	Bronze	127mm	—	—	20.00

In center, clothed bust of Washington facing right, surrounded by GEORGE WASHINGTON, each letter separated by a star, scroll work at bottom. Rv: Blank. (Hansen 7)

Baker	Date	Metal	Size	VF	EF	Unc
931A	1932	Bronze	228mm	—	—	30.00

Similar to preceding, but enlarged.

Baker	Date	Metal	Size	VF	EF	Unc
931B	1932	Bronze	265mm	—	—	40.00

Similar to preceding, but enlarged.
These huge medals were designed by Janowsky and struck by Sculpture Sales Association.

BETHANY SUNDAY SCHOOL

Baker	Date	Metal	Size	VF	EF	Unc
932	1932	Bronze	Oct 25mm	—	—	6.50

Undraped bust right, 1732 / 1932 at right, GEORGE WASHINGTON below (same obverse as Baker 787). Rv: At top, in five lines: TO COMMEMORATE THE BICENTENNIAL OF THE BIRTH OF GEORGE WASHINGTON. Horizontal fasces separate upper text from: BY THE BETHANY SUNDAY SCHOOL PHILADELPHIA WHITEHEAD-HOAG in five lines. Plain edge. (Hansen 28)

Struck by the Whitehead & Hoag Co., Newark, N.J.

ORDER UNITED AMERICAN MECHANICS

Baker	Date	Metal	Size	VF	EF	Unc
C933	1932	Golden Bronze	**	—	15.00	—

** Shield-shaped, 28x31mm.

Periwigged nude bust right, olive branch below, name flanking neck at right, 1732 / 1932 above. Rv: Masonic seal at center, JR.O.U.A.M. above, NEW JERSEY below. (Fuld NLH111-BoLf; Collins 598)

| A933 | 1932 | Bronze | Irreg 33x48mm | — | 15.00 | — |

Periwigged nude bust right, 1732 / 1932 in exergue within an oval fasces wreath, vertical fasces on either side, integral fob at top consisting of a spread eagle with a shield on its breast, banner draped across bottom bearing name. Rv: GEORGE / WASHINGTON / BICENTENNIAL / MEMBERSHIP / CAMPAIGN / JR. O.U.A.M. in six lines, seal of order below (Levine 30; Collins 599)

KU KLUX KLAN LU LU TEMPLE

Baker	Date	Metal	Size	VF	EF	Unc
C933	1932	Gilt/Cop	32mm	75.00	100.	—

Nude bust right, LU LU TEMPLE * PHILADELPHIA. Tiny GREEN DUCK CO. CHI. at lower rim. Rv: Equestrian figure left of a hooded klansman holding a flaming torch within a KLONVOKATION * / KU KLUX KLAN 1932 around the raised peripheral border. (Birdsall 232, Levine 21) Rarity 8.

Carried as pocket pieces, C933 is not found in mint state.

GRAMMES SAMPLE MEDAL

| E933 | 1932 | Gilt/Cop | 32.8mm | — | 15.00 | — |

Obverse similar to A908. Rv: Blank, but tiny GRAMMES, ALLENTOWN, PA. at lower rim. Rarity 6. (Collins 508)

VETERANS ORGANIZATIONS
American Legion

Baker	Date	Metal	Size	VF	EF	Unc
934	1932	Bronze	Oct. 31.7mm	—	—	75.00

Undraped bust right, laurel branch under bust. Around: GEORGE WASHINGTON BICENTENNIAL. To right: 1732 / 1932. Along bottom, in tiny letters: WHITEHEAD-HOAG. Rv: American doughboy bust in

WWI steel helmet left, American Legion insignia superimposed over lower part of bust. Issued holed. Plain edge. Rarity 8. (Hansen 31; Collins 533)

| 934A | 1932 | Bronze | 35by43mm | — | 30.00 | — |

Small bust of Washington right in oval frame. In background is a town scene with home and factories. The bottom: 1732 PITTSBURGH 1932. Rv: Blank except for manufacturers imprint, ROBBINS CO. / ATTLEBORO. Attached to the top loop of medal is a brown and blue ribbon, 14TH ANNUAL / CONVENTION / AMERICAN / LEGION / DEPARTMENT / OF PENNSYLVANIA / AUGUST 20TH 1932 / PITTSBURGH, PA. The ribbon is suspended by a top bar showing rows of crosses and poppies. At top, IN FLANDERS FIELD. In center is the American Legion insignia, the outer circle of which is enameled in blue. (Levine 37)

| 934C | 1932 | Bronze | 32x43mm | — | 30.00 | — |

Rv: in nine lines, ST / ALBANS / ORGANIZED / AS A TOWN 1788 / AS A VILLAGE 1859 / AS A CITY 1897 / SCENE OF ST. ALBANS RAID / OCT. 19, 1864 / VT. Below is a small shield which is divided into two parts. IN the upper part are the letters MP.B In the lower part are letters P.I.U. Below in small letters BASTIAN BROS. CO. ROCHESTER, N.Y. Attached to badge is a ribbon, inscribed 14TH ANNUAL / CONVENTION / AMERICAN LEGION / AND / AUXILIARY / DEPT. OF / VERMONT / JULY 27 * 30, 1932 / ST. ALBANS / VT.

| 934D | 1932 | Bronze | 21mm | — | 30.00 | — |

Nude bust right, GEORGE WASHINGTON BICENTENNIAL / 1732-1932. Rv: Building. GADSBY's TAVERN. AMERICAN LEGION POST 24. Suspended from ribbon labeled DEPT. OF VIRGINIA / AUGUST 1-2-3 / 1932. (Kirtley March 31, 1998 sale, lot N19)

934D struck by Whitehead & Hoag, Newark, N.J.

Plewacki Post 799

Baker	Date	Metal	Size	EF	AU	Unc
934G	1932	Bronze	Oct 32mm	—	25.00	—

Bust right, WASHINGTON BI-CENTENNIAL / *1732 (G. Washington signature) 1932*. Rv: American Legion seal, NO. 799 above, FEB. 1932 below. Around: ADAM PLEWACKI POST / DEDICATION OF NEW CLUB ROOMS / (tiny) BASTIAN BROS. CO, ROCHESTER, N.Y. (Kirtley May 26, 1998 sale, lot C64)

Veterans of Foreign Wars

Baker	Date	Metal	Size	VF	EF	Unc
935	1932	Bronze	Oct 32mm	—	—	60.00

Obverse as 934. Rv: Insignia of Veterans of Foreign Wars of the United States. Plain edge. Rarity 7. (Hansen 32; Collins 534)

The two principal veterans' organizations active in 1932 were the American Legion, founded in 1920 as a result of World War I, and the Veterans of Foreign Wars, founded in 1899 following the Spanish-American War. These are still the leading veteran groups, though Disabled American Veterans, Marine Corps League, Reserve Officers Association, Vietnam Veterans of America and others also share today's limelight.

The 19th century veteran groups, the Grand Army of the Republic (G.A.R.) and the United Confederate Veterans (U.C.V.) were barely a memory 67 years after the Civil War ended in 1865. The hereditary veteran groups (such as the Society of the Cincinnati) were active in 1932, though small in membership.

Your author Russ Rulau is a life member of the VFW and a longtime member of the American Legion, 11th Airborne Division Association and other veteran groups, having served in World War II, Korean War and various crises 1955-1962. With fondness I can recall old friends in VFW Post 2903 (Collins-Meyer, Milwaukee, 1947-48) and Post 568 (Stevens Point, Wis., 1982-85). It was my privilege to be founding commander of VFW Post 9748 (Iola, Wis.) in 1985, an off-on duty which ended in 1998 after six terms.

None of the small group of veterans' Washingtonia above is common, yet lack of demand has held down prices. Jack Collins called Baker 934 one of the rarest of all 1932 Washington issues. My father, an Army veteran of WWI, once owned one but it disappeared years since.

GUSTAVUS ADOLPHUS

Baker	Date	Metal	Size	VF	EF	Unc
936	1932	Bronze	38mm	—	32.50	45.00

Washington bust right. Around: GEORGE WASHINGTON BICENTENNIAL 1732-1932. Rv: Gustavus Adolphus bust right. Around: Plain edge. (Kurt R. Krueger Aug. 1983 sale, lot 1995; Hansen 23)

This medal commemorates the 200th anniversary of birth of George Washington and 300th anniversary of death of Sweden's hero-king, Gustavus Adolphus, at the Battle of Lutzen, Nov. 16, 1632.

Struck by Whitehead & Hoag Co., Newark, N.J.

Baker	Date	Metal	Size	VF	EF	Unc
936A	1932	Gilt/Bz	38mm	—	—	—

As 936. Plain edge. (Dr. Schuster coll.)

Baker	Date	Metal	Size	VF	EF	Unc
936B	1932	Silver	38mm	—	—	60.00

As 936. Plain edge. Rarity 6. (Dr. Schuster coll.; Collins 503) Baker 936B is hallmarked STERLING on obverse, to right of 1932. This is Whitehead-Hoag's workmanship at its best, unlike much other of its 1932 output.

Baker	Date	Metal	Size	VF	EF	Unc
A936	1932	Gilt/Cop	31.7mm	—	—	20.00

Obverse as Baker 927-928. Rv: Bust of the king one-quarter right, banners with 1632 and 1932 at either side. Around: GUSTAVUS ADOLPHUS / TRICENTENNIAL. (Levine 7; Collins 502). Rarity 6.

Struck by Whitehead & Hoag. A larger version (38mm) is reported by George Fuld, worth $15 in EF.

Baker	Date	Metal	Size	VF	EF	Unc
A936A	1932	Gilt/Brz	32mm	—	15.00	—

Obverse similar to 936, in reduced size. Rv: As reverse of A936, with word DENVER added. (Levine 8)

CASIMIR PULASKI

Baker	Date	Metal	Size	VF	EF	Unc
C936	1932	Gilt/Cop	31.8mm	—	15.00	20.00

Obverse as Baker 927-928. Rv: Military bust right. Around: COUNT CASIMIR PULASKI. Rarity 6. (Levine 9; Collins 501).

General Pulaski was killed at the 1779 Battle of Savannah while leading a combined French-American force. He was a skilled Polish cavalry officer.

Struck by Whitehead-Hoag for the Washington-Pulaski Celebration in Philadelphia, Oct. 16, 1932. Issued holed, they were suspended from celluloid buttons.

MILITARY TOURNAMENT

Baker	Date	Metal	Size	VF	EF	Unc
937	1932	Bronze	32mm	—	—	—

Undraped bust right, GEORGE WASHINGTON BICENTENNIAL / MILITARY TOURNAMENT around. Rv: U.S. seal at center with **** OFFICIAL SOUVENIR *** above and 1932 / JUNE 24TH TO JULY 4TH / SOLDIERS FIELD CHICAGO below. Plain edge. (Hansen 26)

Baker	Date	Metal	Size	VF	EF	Unc
937A	1932	Nickel/B	32mm			

As 937. Plain edge. (Hansen 26)

Baker	Date	Metal	Size	VF	EF	Unc
937B	1932	WM	32mm			

As 937. Plain edge. (Hansen 26)

Struck by Whitehead & Hoag Co., Newark, N.J.

BOROUGH OF MACUNGIE, PA.

Baker	Date	Metal	Size	VF	EF	Unc
939	1932	Copper	32mm	—	15.00	—

Obverse similar to Baker 915, but different die. Rv: Log cabin with fence and shrubs, WESCOE MEETING HOUSE on lawn, INCORPORATED / 1857 / FOUNDED AS / MILLERTOWN / 1776 in five lines within a round beaded panel, scrolls at left and right borders bearing 1857 / 1932 respectively; BOROUGH OF MACUNGIE / 75TH ANNIVERSARY around periphery. (Levine 6)

CITY OF GREEN BAY

Baker	Date	Metal	Size	VF	EF	Unc
940	1932	Brass	38mm	—	—	—

Undraped bust right, CITY OF GREEN BAY, WISCONSIN above, SOUVENIR COIN, below. Rv: ISSUED TO A SPONSOR OF / GEORGE / WASHINGTON / BICENTENNIAL / (panel for engraving name) / 1932 / GREEN BAY, WIS. Plain edge. (Hansen 11)

Baker	Date	Metal	Size	VF	EF	Unc
940A	1932	Svd/Cop	38mm	—	—	55.00

As 940. Plain edge. (Hansen 11)

Struck by F.H. Noble & Co., Chicago, Ill. Occurs engraved with names.

DETROIT COIN CLUB

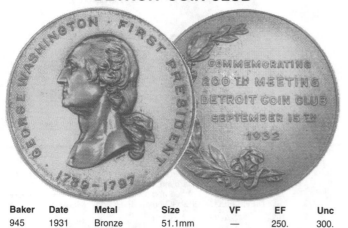

Baker	Date	Metal	Size	VF	EF	Unc
945	1931	Bronze	51.1mm	—	250.	300.

Periwigged nude bust left, tiny FRANK under truncation. Around: GEORGE WASHINGTON. FIRST PRESIDENT / 1789-1797. Rv: Thick laurel branch tied with ribbon bow at left border. In field: COMMEMO-RATING/200TH MEETING / DETROIT COIN CLUB / SEPTEMBER 15TH 1932. The bronze is antiqued. About 28 pieces struck. Rarity 8. (Hansen 59; Collins 574; ex-F.C. C. Boyd; Kirtley March 14, 1998, lot 1174)

Baker	Date	Metal	Size	VF	EF	Unc
95A	1932	Silver	51.1mm	Ex.Rare	—	—

As 945. Rarity 8 (6-8 struck).

Harry Rapp, chairman of the club's medal committee, was authorized by the club board to have off-metal impressions struck as trial pieces. There were 12 such pieces made, respectively in silver, vulcanite and leather. The few silver pieces were sold to board members at $2 each, while bronze medals were sold to all members at $1 each. August C. Frank Co., Philadelphia, struck these handsome and very rare medals, which were missing from the Hansen, Levine and Fuld collections.

The Frederick C.C. Boyd specimen is illustrated. The Frank firm had used this bust punch over many years and it is referred to occasionally as the "Baker 945" bust in this catalog.

After Rapp's death his estate sold all the trial impressions to Harold Bowen, a Detroit coin dealer, who resold all to a Michigan collection who by 1991 had traded away half of them. There are no known public sales of any but the bronze pieces.

CITY OF BUFFALO

Baker	Date	Metal	Size	VF	EF	Unc
946	1932	Gilt/Brz	36mm	—	12.50	

Nude bust right separates 1732 - 1932, GEORGE WASHINGTON / BI-CENTENNIAL around. Rv: City Hall facade separates 1832 - 1932. Around: CENTENNIAL OF CITY OF BUFFALO / 100 YEARS A CITY / NEW CITY HALL. Plain edge. Issued with two loops for suspension from metal pinback hanger inscribed SOUVENIR. (Leon Hendrickson coll.)

CITY OF NEW YORK

Baker	Date	Metal	Size	VF	EF	Unc
947	1932	Gilt/Cop	Oct. 25mm	—	7.50	—

Nude bust right, 1732 / 1932 at right, GEORGE WASHINGTON below Rv: PRESENTED / BY THE / CITY OF NEW YORK / GEORGE WASH-INGTON / BICENTENNIAL / COMMISSION / COMMEMORATING / NEW YORK CITY'S TRIBUTE / TO THE / FATHER / OF OUR COUN-TRY / 1732 - 1932. Plain edge. Rarity 4. (Collins 525)
Point of the bust near right end of G of GEORGE.

Baker	Date	Metal	Size	VF	EF	Unc
947A	1932	Gilt/Cop	Oct. 25mm	—	7.50	—

As 947, but point of bust is left of the G. (Collins 528). Rarity 4.

Baker	Date	Metal	Size	VF	EF	Unc
947B	1932	Copper	Oct. 25mm	—	10.00	—

As 947A. (Collins 529). Rarity 4.

Jack Collins identified about seven minor die rarities of Baker 947-947B in 1991; all are Rarity 4 or 5 and of little numismatic consequence.

MASSACHUSETTS SCHOOL CHILDREN

Baker	Date	Metal	Size	VF	EF	Unc
948	1932	Gilt/Cop	22mm	—	—	10.00

Reduced facsimile of Hansen 17. Rev. I HAVE CONTRIBUTED / TO THE / MASSACHUSETTS / SCHOOL / CHILDREN'S / MEMORIAL in seven lines. G of GEORGE cut too low and corrected. (Fuld H17-6-GoGf)

WORLDS FAIR IN 1939

The Trylon and Perisphere became the symbols of the New York Worlds Fair, held in 1939-40, and the Tower of the Sun became the landmark and hallmark of the Golden Gate International Exposition (San Francisco Worlds Fair) in 1939. The fairs signaled, hopefully, the end of the Depression, though it was only vaguely understood at that time that they also heralded the end of an innocent era as World War II broke out on September 1, 1939.

The year 1939 saw the introduction of two of the greatest silver screen masterpieces of all time - *Gone with the Wind* starring Clark Gable and Vivien Leigh and *The Wizard of Oz* starring Judy Garland. Both movies, just as the Washington medallic remembrances of that year, are with us still.

Only a handful of the 1939-1940 medals are cataloged here, just enough to permit the user of this volume to know that the modern pieces featuring George Washington are still largely an unexplored arena needing research. We are grateful to Dr. Irving Schuster of Long Island for assistance with this chapter.

Other mementos of the New York Worlds Fair may be found in the chapter on 20th Century Store Cards.

The year 1939 also was the 150th anniversary of the inauguration of George Washington as first president of the United States. This event is reflected on the magnificent American Numismatic Society medal (Baker 3000) and several medalets.

AMERICAN NUMISMATIC SOCIETY

WASHINGTON HALL

Baker	Date	Metal	Size	VF	EF	Unc
3001	1939	Bronze	63mm	—	—	40.00

Facing civil bust three-quarters left fills most of the field. The portrait is after Gilbert Stuart. View of Colonial structure at top. Below: "WASHINGTON HALL" / NEW YORK WORLD'S FAIR 1939 / ERECTED TO COMMEMORATE / THE 150TH ANNIVERSARY / OF THE INAUGURATION OF / GEORGE WASHINGTON / AS FIRST PRESIDENT OF THE U.S. / BY / MESSMORE KENDALL / PRES.-GEN. S.A.R. Plain edge.

INAUGURATION

Baker	Date	Metal	Size	VF	EF	Unc
3000	1939	Silver	62mm	—	—	400.

Military caped bust in three-cornered hat left, oak leaf and ANS (symbol of the society) at bottom. Around: ONE, HUNDRED. AND. FIFTIETH. ANNIVERSARY. / .1789. .1939. Rv: TO. /.COMMEMORATE. / .THE. INAUGURATION. / .OF. GEORGE. / .WASHINGTON / .FIRST PRESIDENT. / .OF. THE. UNITED. STATES. / .APRIL. 30TH. / .1789. Thirteen stars around the rim enclose the inscription. Plain edge. Only 38 struck, each numbered on its edge. (PCAC July 1998 sale, lot 252)

| 3000A | 1939 | Bronze | 62mm | — | — | 125. |

As 3000. Plain edge. Only 95 struck, each numbered on its edge. (PCAC Nov. 1997 sale, lot 305)

Engraver Albert Stewart and maker Medallic Art Co. produced here one of the 20th Century's best innovative Washington effigies.

World's Fair

Baker	Date	Metal	Size	VF	EF	Unc
3002	1939	Gilt/Bz	30mm	—	—	6.00

Washington takes oath before three men on a balcony. SOUVENIR OF THE 150TH ANNIVERSARY above, GEORGE WASHINGTON'S / INAUGURATION below. Rv: Sunrise behind Trylon and Perisphere encloses IN 1939 / NEW YORK / WORLD'S FAIR. In exergue, in tiny letters: DES. PAT. 187424 / EPCO. Plain edge.

Issued by Etched Products Corporation, Long Island City, N.Y., on a die-cut 43 by 60mm card (as shown above).

3002A	1939	Gilt/Bz	30mm	—	—	6.00

As 3002, but with raised center dot. (Weidhaas 53)

3002B	ND	Gilt/Bz	30mm	—	—	8.00

As 3002, but no date. (Weidhaas 54)

I Am An American

3003	1939	Gilt/Bz	30mm	—	—	5.00

Obverse as 3002. Rv: THIS SOUVENIR COIN COMMEMORATES MY 21ST BIRTHDAY / I / AM AN / AMERICAN / (winged shield) / MY FRANCHISE TO VOTE / IS MY MOST VALUABLE / POSSESSION ...... / PRESENTED ON / CITIZENSHIP DAY / JUNE 25 1939 / BY THE NEW YORK JOURNAL-AMERICAN. Plain edge.

PEACE AND FREEDOM

Baker	Date	Metal	Size	VF	EF	Unc
3004	1940	Silver	32mm	—	—	20.00

Facing statue of Washington divides GEORGE - WASHINGTON. Around: ** ** FOR PEACE AND FREEDOM ** **. Rv: Trylon and Perisphere dominate center, NEW YORK / WORLD'S FAIR / 1940 above, ETCHED PRODUCTS below. Plain edge.

3004A	1940	Gilt/Bz	32mm	—	—	5.00

As 3004. Plain edge.

POLAND EXHIBITION

Baker	Date	Metal	Size	VF	EF	Unc
3005	1939	Svd/Copper	31mm	—	—	30.00

Oval medallion portraits of Washington, Kosciusko and Pulaski on a wreath, WHITEHEAD.HOAG below. Rv: Building, 1939 at right. In exergue: REPUBLIC OF POLAND / EXHIBITION / NEW YORK WORLD'S FAIR. Plain edge. (Weidhaas 31)

3005A	1939	Bronze	31mm	—	—	10.00

As 3005. Plain edge.

3005B	1940	Bronze	31mm	—	—	20.00

As 3005, but dated 1940.

Germany invaded and conquered Poland beginning September 1, 1939, with the Russians overrunning the country's eastern half. The sunny summer of '39 turned wintry early for the Poles manning this exhibition.

Casimir Pulaski gave his life for America at the 1779 Battle of Savannah during the Revolution, and Tadeusz Kosciusko fought through the war, then returned to lead his countrymen in a desperate attempt to throw off the Russian yoke in 1795. They were the two ranking and best known Poles fighting on the American side during the Revolution.

Other foreigners who loaned their swords to America at this time included the Frenchmen Marquis de Lafayette and Baron de Kalb, the German Baron von Steuben, and the regular French officers Count de Grasse and General Rochambeau.

AMERICAN JUBILEE

Struck 1939

Baker	Date	Medal	Size	VF	EF	Unc
3006	ND	Gilt/B	31mm	—	—	4.50

Nude bust left, AMERICAN JUBILEE above, GEORGE WASHINGTON / * WORLD'S FAIR * below. Rv: Statue of Liberty radiant at center, STATUE OF LIBERTY above, 13 stars around and below. Plain edge. Issued holed for suspension.

N.Y.W.F.

3007	1939	Gold/Br	13mm	—	—	6.50

Facing civil bust in circle, WASHINGTON'S 150TH ANNIVERSARY / 1789 N.Y.W.F. 1939 around. Rv: Blank. Plain edge. Looped for suspension.

N.Y.W.F. = New York World's Fair.

OFFICIAL FAIR MEDAL

Baker	Date	Metal	Size	VF	EF	Unc
3008	1939	Bronze	77mm	—	—	35.00

Trylon and Perisphere. At upper right, a full length figure of Washington in the clouds. In two lines below: NEW YORK WORLD'S FAIR/1939. Rv: Horizontally divided into three parts, top panel, THE WORLD OF TOMORROW, with a rising sun and 13 rays, a small Trylon and Perisphere in foreground, middle panel, TODAY, lower Manhattan, bottom panel, YESTERDAY, New Amsterdam. Small KILENYI at right below center panel. Made by Robbins Company. Plain edge. (Weidhaas 7)

3008A	1939	Bronze	64mm	—	—	25.00

As 3008. Plain edge. (Weidhaas 8)

3008B	1939	Bronze	32mm	—	—	25.00

As 3008. Plain edge. (Weidhaas 9a)

3008C	1939	Brass	32mm	—	—	15.00

As 3008. Plain edge. (Weidhaas 9b)

GAME COUNTERS, or SPIEL MARKEN

Many of the counters in this chapter carry the "General Washington" bust by Ludwig Christian Lauer of Nuremberg, Germany, the famous token and counter maker. The bust faces slightly right, with the head three-quarters left. This awkward pose is a rather faithful rendering of a well-known Washington portrait.

The portrait is taken from a print by Giuseppe Longhi, the Italian engraver, executed in 1817 from his own sketch - a combination of the Trumbull and Stuart heads - and known in Germany through an extremely close copy engraved by G. G. Felsing in 1824, while a student under Longhi.

Lauer produced two basic types of General Washington bust design, referred to in this chapter as Type I and Type II.

Type I: Washington bust in civil dress facing (as described above). Bust is not truncated, but extends to the border. GENERAL WASHINGTON above bust.

Type II: Similar, but bust is truncated and ends away from the lower border.

OBVERSE TYPE I

Struck 1850's

Baker	Date	Metal	Size	F	VF	Unc
608	ND	Brass	18mm	—	—	35.00

Obverse: Type I. Rv: Eagle displayed, head turned left, shield on its breast. SPIELMARKE below. Plain edge. Rarity 8. (Kurth 37; R-F Gnw-1)

| 608B | ND | Brass | 18mm | — | — | 35.00 |

Obverse as 608. Rv: SPIEL / MARKE in two lines in oak wreath; bow of the wreath has two loops. Plain edge. Rarity 7. (Kurth 38; R-F Gnw-2)

| 608C | ND | Brass | 18mm | — | — | — |

Similar to 608B, but bow of the wreath has only one loop. Plain edge. Rarity 8. (Kurth 38; R-F Gnw-3)

| 608D | ND | Brass | 18mm | — | — | — |

As 608C, but prominent die break extends across reverse from rim to rim through MARKE. Plain edge. Rarity 9. (R-F Gnw-3A)

Baker	Date	Metal	Size	F	VF	Unc
608F	ND	Brass	19mm	—	—	35.00

Obverse as 608. Rv: Similar to 608B, but bow has two loops overlapping each other. Ends of the wreath are farther apart. SPIEL / MARKE is in smaller letters. Plain edge. Rarity 8. (R-F Gnw-4)

| 607 | ND | Brass | 19mm | 17.50 | 25.00 | 35.00 |

Obverse as 608. Rv: Eagle with shield on breast, head turned left, holding arrows and olive branch. IN UNITATE FORTITUDO above, SPIEL MUNZE below. Plain edge. Rarity 2. (Kurth 40; R-F Gnw-5)

NOTE: While the term Spiel Marke means Play, or Game Counter, the term Spiel Munze indicates Play Coin.

| 607A | ND | Brass | 19mm | — | 15.00 | — |

As 607. Reeded edge. Rarity 2. (Kurth 40; R-F Gnw-5A)

Baker	Date	Metal	Size	F	VF	Unc
607D	ND	Brass	19mm	—	15.00	—

Similar to 607, but no shield on eagle's breast. Plain edge. Rarity 2. (R-F Gnw-6)

| 607E | ND | S/Brass | 19mm | — | — | — |

As 607D. Plain edge. Rarity 3. (R-F Gnw-6A)

| 607E | ND | Copper | 19mm | — | 15.00 | — |

As 607D. Plain edge. Rarity 2. (R-F Gnw-6B)

| 607J | ND | Brass | 19mm | — | — | — |

As 607D, only arrows are thicker and in different location. Plain edge. Rarity 4. (R-F Gnw-7)

| 607L | 1855 | Gilt/B | 19mm | — | — | — |

As 607, but SPIELMUNZE / 1855. under eagle on reverse. Period after date. Plain edge. Rarity 8. (R-F Gnw-8)

| 606 | ND | | | — | 20.00 | — |

Obverse as 608, but W of WASHINGTON closer to the wig. Rv: As reverse of 607D (no shield on eagle's breast). Plain edge. Rarity 1. (Kurth 40A; R-F Gnw-9)

NOTE: There are at least 15 trifling die varieties of Baker 606, one of which was listed as Kurth 40C and six of which were listed as Rulau-Fuld Gnw-9A through 9F.

Baker	Date	Metal	Size	F	VF	Unc
606G	ND	Brass	18mm	—	35.00	—

Obverse as 608. Rv: Eagle with shield on its breast, COMPOSITIONS-SPIEL-MARKE above, JETON below. Plain edge. Rarity 8. (R-F Gnw-10)

| 606H | ND | Copper | 18mm | — | 18.00 | — |

As 606G. Plain edge. Rarity 8. (R-F Gnw-10A)

| 604 | ND | Gilt/B | 19mm | — | — | — |

Obverse as 608. Rv: Coronet Liberty head left, LIBERTY on coronet, COMPOSITIONS-SPIEL-MARKE around. LAUER in script below head. Plain edge. Rarity 4. (Kurth 41; R-F Gnw-11)

| 605 | ND | Gilt/B | 19mm | 5.00 | 20.00 | 25.00 |

As 604, but COMPOSITS SPIEL-MARKE around head. Plain edge. Rarity 3. (Kurth 41A; R-F Gnw-12)

Baker	Date		Size	F	VF	Unc
609	ND	Brass	19mm	—	—	35.00

Obverse as 608. Rv: JETON within olive wreath. Plain edge. Rarity 9. (Kurth 42; R-F Gnw-13)

| 629 | ND | Brass | 19mm | — | 20.00 | 25.00 |

25.00Obverse as 608. Rv: City Hall in New York, the sun's darting rays above. Below: CITY HALL / NEW YORK. Plain edge. Rarity 4. (R-F Gnw-15)

| 629A | ND | Gilt/B | 19mm | — | 15.00 | 17.50 |

As 629. Plain edge. Rarity 2. (Kurth 43; R-F Gnw-15B)

| 629B | ND | Copper | 19mm | — | — | 25.00 |

As 629. Plain edge. Ratity 3. (R-F Gnw-15A)

| 599 | ND | Gilt/B | 27.5mm | — | — | — |

Obverse as 608, in larger size. Rv: Eagle with no shield on its breast. COMPOSITIONS-SPIEL-MARKE above, 6-pointed star below. Plain edge. Rarity 4. (Kurth 55B; R-F Gnw-16)

OBVERSE TYPE II

Struck 1850's

Baker	Date	Metal	Size	F	VF	Unc
602	ND	Brass	22mm	—	13.00	—

Obverse Type II. Rv: Eagle with U.S. shield on its breast. IN UNITATE FORTITUDO above, SPIEL MUNZE below in large letters. Plain edge. Rarity 2. (Kurth 48; Bushnell 105; R-F Gnw-20)

| 602A | ND | Brass | 22mm | — | — | — |

As 602. Reeded edge. Rarity 2. (Kurth 48; Bushnell 105; R-F Gnw-20A)

| 602C | ND | Gilt/B | 22mm | 20.00 | 30.00 | 40.00 |

Obverse as 602, but letters are spaced more widely and bust is larger. W of WASHINGTON to right of line between wig and face. Rv: Eagle, no shield on its breast. IN UNITATE FORTITUDO above, SPIEL MUNZE in very small letters below. Plain edge. Rarity 3. (Kurth 48A; R-F Gnw-21)

| 602E | ND | Gilt/B | 22mm | — | — | 10.00 |

As 602C, but SPIEL MUNZE in larger letters. Plain edge. Rarity 4. (R-F Gnw-22)

| 602G | ND | Gilt/B | 22mm | — | — | — |

Obverse as 602 but no heading around rim. Rv: As reverse of 602 (shield on eagle's breast) but SPIEL MUNZE in tiny letters. Reeded edge. Rarity 4. (R-F Gnw-23)

| 602J | ND | Brass | 22MM | — | 100. | — |

Obverse as 602. Rv: JETON within oak wreath. Plain edge. Rarity 9. (R-F Gnw-24)

| 602K | ND | WM | 22mm | — | 110. | — |

As 602J. Plain edge. Rarity 9. (R-F Gnw-24A)

| 603 | ND | Brass | 22mm | — | 10.00 | — |

Obverse as 602. Rv: Eagle with shild on breast, olive branch and arrows in talons. COMPOSITIONS-SPIEL-MARKE above, 6-pointed star below. Plain edge. Rarity 3. (Kurth 47; R-F Gnw-25)

Baker	Date	Metal	Size	F	VF	Unc
600	ND	Gilt/B	22mm	15.00	25.00	35.00

Obverse as 602. Rv: Coronet Liberty head left in circle of 10 large stars, SP. MARKE below. Plain edge. Rarity 3. (Kurth 49; R-F Gnw-26)

601	ND	Gilt/B	22mm	20.00	30.00	40.00

Obverse as 602. Rv: Coronet Liberty head left in circle of 10 small stars, SPIEL MUNZE in small letters below. Plain edge Rarity 3. (Kurth 49A; R-F Gnw-27)

601B	ND	Brass	22mm	—	—	—

As 601, but with recut lettering on obverse. Plain edge. Rarity 5. (R-F Gnw-27A)

597	ND	Brass	27.5mm	—	—	—

Obverse as 602, in large size. Rv: SPIEL / MARKE within oak wreath. Plain edge. Rarity 7. (Kurth 56; R-F Gnw-29)

Baker	Date	Metal	Size	F	VF	Unc
628	ND	Brass	27.5mm	20.00	30.00	40.00

Obverse as 602, in larger size. Rv: City Hall in New York, the sun darting rays above. In exergue: CITY HALL / NEW YORK. Plain edge. Rarity 4. (Kurth 58; R-F Gnw-30)

598	ND	Gilt/B	27.5mm	20.00	30.00	40.00

Obverse as 602, in larger size. Rv: Eagle with shield on its breast, COMPOSITIONS *** SPIEL-MARKE *** around. Plain edge. Rarity 4. (Kurth 55; R-F Gnw-31)

598C	ND	Brass	27.5mm	25.00	32.50	45.00

Similar to 598, but no shield on eagle's breast. Plain edge. Rarity 5. (R-F Gnw-32)

Baker	Date	Metal	Size	F	VF	Unc
598E	ND	Brass	27.5mm			

Similar to 598C, but much larger neck on eagle. Plain edge. Rarity 4. (Kurth 57A; R-F Gnw-33)

598M	ND	Gilt/B	27.5mm	—	—	—

Obverse as 598, but bust is further away from border. Plain edge. Rarity 4. (Kurth 55A; R-F Gnw-35)

595	ND	Gilt/B	27.5mm	40.00	60.00	80.00

Obverse as 602, in larger size. Rv: Coronet Librty head left in arc of 8 large stars, COMP. S. MARKE completing circle below. Plain edge. Rarity 4. (Kurth 57; R-F Gnw-37)

TOKENS OF ESTEEM

Struck circa 1890

Baker	Date	Metal	Size	VF	EF	Unc
C-599	ND	Brass	25mm	6.50	12.00	20.00

Crude, laureate head right within open-ended oak wreath tied at the bottom. Rv: Crowned shield of arms above oak wreath, letter C at left, N at right and P beneath. Around top: TOKEN OF ESTEEM. Plain edge. (Parsons 1029; R-F Can-2)

C-599A	ND	Gilt/B	25mm	7.50	15.00	25.00

As C-599. Plain edge. (Parsons 1029; Bullowa-Lessin 18)

C-599B	ND	Copper	25mm	7.50	15.00	25.00

As C-599. Plain edge.

These 'Tokens of Esteem' are included here for completeness because Parsons attributed this bust as George Washington. In fact it more nearly resembles George III. The crowned arms on reverse do not resemble in any way the Wash-

ington family arms (seen on Baker 284). The book *American Game Counters* (Rulau-Fuld, 1972) called these pieces Canadian counters for lack of a better niche to fit them into.

The Token of Esteem arms are divided per fess. In chief they are divided per pale. Dexter side: Divided per fess; in chief three 6-pointed stars on field gules; in base two (hens?) on field or. Sinister side: a bend purple divides three rounded crosses on field azure from a mullet (5-point star) on field argent. The chief is argent (silver) without ornamentation.

Four distinctly different die varieties of these tokens are in the Rulau collection; no attempt has been made to gather enough of them to study how many varieties may exist.

The Token of Esteem series received wide attention during the 1960's in the Collectors Clearinghouse section of *Coin World*, without any result in determining their origin. They remain a mystery.

NO GOOD

Baker	Date	Metal	Size	VF	EF	Unc
C-599E	ND	GS	23mm	—	50.00	—

Bust resembling George Washington left, with 13 stars around. Rv: Maple leaf wreath with crown in opening at top enclosing: (ornament) / NO / GOOD / -o-. Reeded edge. Rarity 8. (Kurth 85A; R-F Can-1)

Nothing is know of this piece or its origin. The reverse resembles vaguely the reverse of Canadian quarters of Queen Victoria.

Baker	Date	Metal	Size	F	VF	Unc
C-609	1944	Brass	21mm	—	25.00	—

Crude imitation of a Washington quarter dollar of 1944. Plain edge. Rarity 8. (R-F Wsq-1)

D-609	ND	Gilt/B	14mm	—	15.00	—

Washington head left, 7 stars at left, an illegible word at right. Rv: Eagle with shield on breast, no inscription. Issued with loop. Thick flan. Plain edge. Rarity 4. (R-F Wsm-1)

GEORGIO WASHINGTON

Baker	Date	Metal	Size	VF	EF	Unc
358	ND	Brass	31mm	—	70.00	—

Undraped Washington bust right, Lauer in script beneath bust. Around: GEORGIO WASHINGTON. Plain edge. Rarity 7. (R-F Gio-1A)

358A	ND	S/Brass	31mm	—	70.00	—

As 358. Plain edge. Rarity 8. (R-F Gio-1)

358D	ND	Brass	21mm	—	100.	—

Obverse as 358. Rv: Crowned imperial Austrian double eagle. Plain edge. Rarity 9. (R-F Gio-2; PCAC Nov. 1997 sale, lot 1128)

358G	ND	Brass	21mm	—	100	—

Obverse as 358 in smaller size, but no Lauer under bust. Rv: Within wreath: SPIEL MARKE. Plain edge. Rarity 9. (R-F Gio-3)

358H	ND	Brass	22mm	—	100.	—

As 358G, but broken reverse die has left two small humps in field below MARKE. Plain edge. Rarity 9. (R-F Gio-3B)

Baker	Date	Metal	Size	VF	EF	Unc
358J	N	Gilt/B	22mm	—	70.00	—

Obverse as 358. Rv: JETON within wreath. Plain edge. Rarity 8. Originally issued Gilt.

358K	ND	Copper	22mm	—	70.00	—

As 358. Plain edge. Rarity 8.

Baker 358 and its varieties are products of the Ludwig Christian Lauer minting facility in Nuremberg, Germany. All were considered counters or reckoning markers by Rulau-Fuld in *American Game Counters*.

All the Georgio Washington pieces are rare. Previously they had been listed in Chapter 21.

BUTTONS AND COUNTERSTAMPS

In this chapter are treated Washington Inaugural buttons, effigies of Washington counterstamped on various coins and tokens, and similar items. Although very early, this subject was ignored by both W.S. Baker and Wayte Raymond in their references on George Washington pieces.

Several George Washington inaugural buttons carry the date March 4, 1789 as the first president's inauguration date. For example, Baker 1010 and 1013.

March 4, 1789 was the date appointed for the organization of the new government under the Constitution to replace the government under the Articles of Confederation. Travel at that time was slow and difficult and it was not until April 6 that a quorum of Congress reached New York, then the capital of the United States, to count the electoral votes.

After the ceremonial counting of the electoral votes, a messenger was sent by Congress to Mount Vernon, Virginia to notify George Washington that he had been elected unanimously to the presidency.

Washington began his journey to New York April 16 and it was not until April 30, 1789 that he actually took the oath of office as the nation's first chief executive.

Buttons had to be prepared in advance, and the accepted date March 4 appears on several of them. Most Washington inaugural buttons begged the issue and no date appears on them.

It is recorded that Washington wore a set of specially made metal buttons with an eagle on them for his inaugural ceremony.

Dr. Edmund Sullivan speculated that Washington buttons were also worn in celebration of the president's trip through New England later in his first term of office.

Author J. Harold Cobb, who cataloged 30 such buttons, theorized that "the reason (little factual information) is known is that these buttons were considered at the time in the same category as we consider a fine pair of cufflinks and a tie pin today -- accessories for the well groomed gentleman and not considered as unusual possessions requiring historic reference or picturization."

Like our cufflinks, the buttons were removed from the greatcoats and put away for the next garment.

Alphaeus H. Albert, the foremost authority on Washington buttons, cataloged 27 varieties in 1949 that he believed dated from Washington's first inaugural or from his first term, 1789-1793. The first edition of our Rulau-Fuld revision of Baker cataloged 30 pieces, including two dating from the centennial in 1889. The present edition catalogs 37 pieces, including modern replicas.

INAUGURAL BUTTONS, 1789

Baker	Date	Metal	Size	F	VF	EF
1000	ND	Brass	36.5mm	—	2000.	—

Script monogram GW in center circle. Around is a circular band with: LONG LIVE THE PRESIDENT. Small ornament below. Rv: Blank, but eye-shank for sewing on clothing at center (most shanks have been removed). Plain edge. (DeWitt GW 1789-1)

Replica, ca. 1974

Baker	Date	Metal	Size	EF	AU	Unc
1000R	ND	Brass	37mm	—	—	12.00

Strike off replica dies. The workmanship is modern, and these are normally encountered in Unc. condition. (Hirsch coll.)

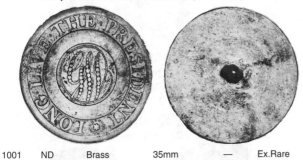

| 1001 | ND | Brass | 35mm | — | Ex.Rare | — |

Script monogram GW in central circle. On circular band near rim: LONG LIVE THE PRESIDENT (6-pointed star enclosed by circle of 13 tiny stars). All design in depressions. Rv: Blank, with button shank (usually removed). Plain edge. (DeWitt GW 1789-2; Garrett 1904.)

Baker	Date	Metal	Size	F	VF	EF
1002	ND	Brass	36.5mm	1025.	2300.	—

As 1000, but intaglio of obverse on reverse. (Albert W-9A1; Sullivan GW 1789-1; Kirtley Dec. 30, 1997 sale, lot A064)

In the Dec. 1997 sale, Baker 1002 in holed VF (shown above) realized $1017.50.

Baker	Date	Metal	Size	F	VF	EF
1003	ND	Brass	34mm	—	1375.	1800.

Script monogram GW in central circle, surrounded by a ring on which is: LONG LIVE THE PRESIDENT. Around all is an endless chain of 13 links, each enclosing the script initials of one of the 13 original states, with NH in the 12 o'clock position. The motto LONG LIVE etc. is incused. Rv: Blank, with button shank. Plain edge. (DeWitt GW 1789-9; Snowden pg 63 item 3; Garrett 1903)

| 1003A | ND | S/Copper | 34mm | — | — | — |

As 1003. Plain edge.

| 1003C | ND | Lead | 47mm | | Unique? | |

As 1003, struck on large blank planchet. (Fuld coll.)

Restrikes of 1003-1003A were made in 1889.

Struck 1889

Baker	Date	Metal	Size	VF	EF	Unc
1003R	ND	Brass	34mm	—	75.00	—

Obverse as 1003. Rv: Mark of J. R. Gaunt around button shank. Plain edge.

Baker 1003R was restruck in 1889 by J. R. Gaunt and Sons Ltd., British but-tonmakers who had a factory at Rouse's Point, N.Y., for use in connection with the centennial celebration of Washington's inaugural.

Replica, ca. 1885-1900

Baker	Date	Metal	Size	VF	EF	Unc
1003S	ND	Silver	34mm	70.00	90.00	—

Strike off replica dies, supposedly sold at Smithsonian Institution. No sil-ver originals were ever made. (David Hirsch coll.)

Original

Baker	Date	Metal	Size			Unc
1004	1776	S/Copper	34mm	—	—	Rare

Similar to 1003, but smaller script monogram GW and date 1776 are hand-engraved in the central circle. (DeWitt GW 1789-10)

Baker 1004 was first published in the *National Button Bulletin* for May, 1950, as number 13.

PIETZ VICTORY BUTTON

Struck ca. 1920?

Baker	Date	Metal	Size	VF	EF	Unc
A1004	ND	Silver	35mm	—	45.00	—

Laureate female head left, tiny A. PIETZ S.A. under truncation. At left, VICTORY. Rv: Replica of Baker 1003 obverse in fine style. Probably rare. (Kirtley May 26, 1998 sale, lot C78)

Adam Pietz (1873-1961) was assistant engraver at the Philadelphia Mint 1927-1946. He was born in Offenbach, Germany and was an established medalist be-fore his appointment to the U.S. Mint. He designed the U.S. 1946 Iowa half dollar, a masonic medal in 1931, the ANA Medal of Merit, and the reverse die for the Con-gressional Medal of Honor.

Baker	Date	Metal	Size	F	VF	EF
1005	1789	Copper	34mm	—	—	—

At center, G.W. and pyramid of 13 stars enclosed by inscription: LONG LIVE THE PRESIDENT 1789. The design and lettering are incused. Rv: Blank, with button shank at center (usually removed). Plain edge. (De-Witt GW 1789-11)

| 1012 | ND | Brass | 34mm | — | — | — |

At center, a radiant meridian sun circled by 13 stars, with inscription around: UNITY PROSPERITY & INDEPENDENCE in a depressed channel. Rv: Blank, with shank. Plain edge. (DeWitt GW 1789-12)

Baker	Date	Metal	Size	F	VF	EF
1006	ND	Copper	34mm	—	—	—

At center, script monogram GW enclosed by inscription LONG LIVE THE PRESIDENT in raised letters in a depressed channel. Rv: Blank. Plain edge. Overstruck on a 1797 British Cartwheel 2-pence coin. (De-Witt GW 1789-13)

Baker	Date	Metal	Size	F	VF	EF
1006G	ND	Copper	34mm	—	—	—

Similar to 1006, but central device is encircled by 13 stars and a floral sprig, and a reeded border has been added. Plain edge. (DeWitt GW 1789-14)

| 1006H | ND | Copper | 34mm | — | — | — |

Similar to 1006, but central device is encircled by 15 stars and a floral sprig, and a reeded border has been added. Plain edge. (DeWitt GW 1789-15)

| 1006J | ND | Copper | 34mm | — | — | — |

Similar to 1006H, but two floral sprigs. Plain edge. (DeWitt GW 1789-16)

| 1007 | ND | Brass | 31mm | — | — | — |

Same central device as 1006 enclosed by decoration of 23 ornamental, pyramidal flames extending outward from the central device. Rv: Blank, with button shank. Plain edge. (DeWitt GW 1789-17)

Baker	Date	Metal	Size	G	F	VF
1009	ND	Brass	34mm	350.	400.	800.

Scrawny-looking eagle displayed with heart-shaped U.S. shield on its breast, an olive branch in the right talon and three arrows in left, a radi-ant meridian sun above. All design elements are incused. Rv: Blank, with button shank (usually removed). Plain edge. (DeWitt GW 1789-3; David Hirsch coll. in AG cost $334; PCAC July 1998 sale, lot 245, fetched $770 in dark VF)

| 1009A | ND | S/Copper | 34mm | | | |

As 1009. Plain edge. (DeWitt GW 1789-3)

| 1010 | 1789 | Brass | 34mm | 440. | 800. | 1450. |

Similar but smaller eagle and sun than on 1009, and with legend around rim: MEMORABLE ERA MARCH THE FOURTH 178.9. Rv: Blank, with shank at center. Plain edge. (DeWitt GW 1789-4; PCAC Nov. 16, 1996 sale, lot 235; PCAC July 1998 sale, lot 246, realized $1457.50 in EF)

| 1010A | 1789 | S/Copper | 34mm | | | 800. |

As 1010. Plain edge. (DeWitt GW 1789-4)

A gold specimen has been reported.

Replica, ca. 1974

Baker	Date	Metal	Size	EF	AU	Unc
1010R	1789	Brass	34mm	—	—	12.00

Strike off replica dies. The workmanship is modern, and these are nor-mally encountered in Unc. condition. (David Hirsch coll.)

Baker	Date	Metal	Size	F	VF	EF
1011	ND	Brass	34mm	—	Ex. Rare	

Eagle displayed, with heart-shaped U.S. shield on breast, surmounted by meridian sun and 13 stars in field. In eagle's beak is a scroll reading: E PLURIBUS UNUM. Rv: Blank, with button shank. Plain edge. (DeWitt GW 1789-5)

| 1013 | 1789 | Brass | 34mm | — | — | — |

Washington bust left. Around: REMEMBER MARCH FOURTH, 1789. Rv: Blank, with button shank (usually removed). Plain edge. (DeWitt GW 1789-6; Snowden, pg. 56). A specimen is in the Washington Cabi-net of the U.S. Mint.

| 1013A | 1789 | S/Copper | 34mm | — | — | — |

As 1013. Plain edge. (DeWitt GW 1789-6)

Baker	Date	Metal	Size	F	VF	EF
1014	ND	—	25mm	—	Very Rare	

Military bust of Washington facing three-quarters left, GENERAL WASHINGTON around, PATER PATRIAE on a bar below. All design and lettering incused. Rv: Blank. Plain edge. (Fuld coll.)

Baker	Date	Metal	Size	VG	F	VF
1015	1792	S/Copper	35mm	—	1000.	—

LONG LIVE THE PRESIDENT* in relief within circular depression at center of smoothed reverse of counterfeit Spanish-American 1792 4-re-ales. Ctsp type of Alphaeus Albert's button W-101. Heavy flan crack at 10 o/clock on only reported specimen. (Kirtley May 9, 1992 sale, lot 1508)

| 1016 | ND | Brass | 34mm | — | — | 800. |

GW in relief Roman letters in stippled oval depression at center of a blank field. In an arc-shaped depression around upper half rim, in relief letters, is: LONG LIVE THE PRESIDENT. Rv: Blank, with shank at center. Plain edge. (DeWitt GW 1789-7; Alphaeus Albert 11A)

| 1016A | ND | S/Copper | 34mm | | 1300. | — |

As 1016. Plain edge. (DeWitt GW 1789-7)

Baker	Date	Metal	Size	F	VF	EF
1017	ND	Brass	34mm	—	1200.	1600.

As 1016, but letters GW are more widely spaced. Plain edge. (DeWitt GW 1789-8; Alphaeus Albert 11C); PCAC July 1998 sale, lot 248, fetched $1540 in VF-EF)

| 1017A | ND | S/Copper | 34mm | — | — | — |

As 1017. Plain edge. (DeWitt GW 1789-8)

Baker	Date	Metal	Size	F	VF	EF
1019	ND	Brass	31mm	—	—	—

Hand-engraved script monogram GW and star at center of circle made up of 18 ornamental pyramidal flames. At rim is a thick border of arrow-like dentilations. Rv: Blank. Plain edge. (DeWitt GW 1789-18)

| 1020 | ND | S/Copper | 15mm | — | — | — |

Open olive wreath enclosed by inscription LONG LIVE THE PRESIDENT. All devices incused. Rv: Blank. Plain edge. (DeWitt GW 1789-25)

Baker	Date	Metal	Size	F	VF	EF
1022	ND	Copper	29mm	—	—	—

Same central device as on Baker 1006, but with added border of dots. Rv: Blank. Plain edge. (DeWitt GW 1789-19)

| 1023 | (1789) | Copper | 20mm | 750. | — | — |

WASHINGTON above, with eagle incuse below. 16 stars around above. Very rare. (PCAC Dec. 1995, lot 287)

The uniface button has all incused designs.

GEORGE WASHINGTON WILL
BLAKSLEE BARNS

Shown above is a rough sketch of the "touch" (maker's mark) of pewterer George Washington Will, who was active in Philadelphia 1798-1807. No relation to the president, he was the son of one of America's best early pewterers, Henry Will of New York City, active 1761-75 and 1783-93 (also in Albany, N.Y. 1775-83). Henry Will was an admirer of George Washington, under whom he served in the Revolutionary War, and named his son after him.

It is possible that George Washington Will, whose touch closely matches the "GW" buttons, may have created some of them. Pewterer Blakslee Barns of Philadelphia, active 1812-17 also used Will's touch as well as his own, and may also have some connection to the buttons.

George Washington Will may have worked for a time in Cincinnati after 1807.

Metalsmiths such as pewterers were certainly capable of working in other base metals such as brass, as well as the precious metals. (References: Carl Jacobs' and Ralph Kovel's works on American pewterers.)

BRASS PORTRAIT BUTTON

Baker	Date	Metal	Size	VG	F	VF
A1023	ND	Brass	37mm	—	—	75.00

Nude bust right on plain field. Circular border of large beads. Rv: Blank, with shank. Unpublished. (Kirtley May 28, 1996 sale, lot F043; fetched $72.60 in VF)

The workmanship appears to be early 19th century.

1889 BUTTON

Baker	Date	Metal	Size	VF	EF	Unc
1024	1889	**	28mm	—	65.00	—

** Apparently imitation bone affixed to a gilt brass frame; button shank on reverse. Undraped head left, WASHINGTON above, *** 1789 * 1889 *** below, all on the white portion of the button. The brass frame around is ornamented. Rv: Blank, button shank at center. Plain edge. (Dr. I Schuster coll.)

INAUGURAL
COUNTERSTAMPS, 1789
POSSIBLE FANTASIES

Baker	Date	Metal	Size	F	VF	EF
1030	ND	Copper	29mm	—	—	—

Same central device as on Baker 1022 (script monogram GW, LONG LIVE THE PRESIDENT, circle of dots) ctsp over various American Colonial cents. Examined: Connecticut, New Jersey, Vermont. (DeWitt GW 1789-20; Brunk 15470)

| 1030A | ND | Silver | 39mm | — | — | — |

As 1030, ctsp over Spanish-American 1794-Mo-FM 8-reales coin. (Fuld coll.)

| 1031 | ND | Copper | 29mm | — | — | — |

Central device as 1030 circled by 13 stars and three floral sprigs ctsp on Vermont cent. (DeWitt GW 1789-21)

Baker	Date	Metal	Size	F	VF	EF
1032	ND	Copper	28mm	—	—	—

Same central device as 1030 circled by 13 stars, ctsp on Connecticut cent. (DeWitt GW 1789-22)

| 1032A | ND | Copper | Oct27mm | — | — | — |

As 1032, ctsp on octagonal blank planchet. (DeWitt GW 1789-23)

| 1032C | ND | Silver | 25mm | — | — | — |

As 1032, ctsp on British 1790 shilling. (DeWitt GW 1789-24)

J. Doyle DeWitt indicates that the use of dies such as 1032 struck over 1790 (and later) coins proves that the counterstamps were not contemporaneous with the 1789 Inaugural, but were commemorative strikings after the event. Brunk concludes they are merely fantasies.

OTHER 'GW' COUNTERSTAMPS

POSSIBLE FANTASIES

Baker	Date	Metal	Size	F	VF	EF
1036	ND	Silver	21mm	—	15.00	25.00

GW in relief within rectangular depression ctsp on Spanish-American 1-real coins. (Examined: 1791-NG-M)

| 1037 | ND | Silver | 27mm | — | 15.00 | 25.00 |

Similar ctsp on Spanish-American 2-reales. (Dates examined: 1780; 1792)

| 1038 | ND | Copper | 29mm | — | 30.00 | 50.00 |

Similar ctsp on Washington cent of 1783. (Brunk 15470-O)

| 1039 | ND | Copper | 29mm | — | 10.00 | 25.00 |

Similar ctsp on U.S. Large cents. (Dates examined: 1801)

| 1040 | ND | Silver | 20mm | — | 10.00 | 25.00 |

Similar ctsp on early U.S. dime.

| 1041 | ND | Silver | 27mm | — | 15.00 | 25.00 |

Similar ctsp on U.S. Bust quarters. (Dates examined: 1818)

| 1042 | ND | Silver | 40mm | — | 125. | 175. |

Similar ctsp on U.S. Bust dollars. (Dates examined: 1802)

The counterstamp of Baker types 1036 through 1042 was supposedly applied in 1824 at the time of the Lafayette visit to the United States. They are occasionally found on the same pieces as a small medallic bust of Lafayette.

In his book on American and Canadian counterstamps Dr. Gregory G. Brunk says of Baker 1036 through 1042: "These pieces are apparent fantasies supposedly issued for Lafayette's visit to the U.S. in 1824. "GW" allegedly stands for George Washington. Unlike the legitimate issues of this period (Baker 198-198D), some of which show extensive circulation, all examples of the "GW" mark which I have traced show no wear to the countermark.

"Such fantasy countermarks substantially reduce the value of the few scarce or rare coins upon which they are found. It is common, however, to find a few rare coins countermarked with such a fantasy stamp. This is one means by which counterfeiters attempt to give their fantasy issues legitimacy."

WASHINGTON BUST COUNTERSTAMPS

Baker	Date	Metal	Size	F	VF	EF
1050	ND	Copper	28mm	300.	—	—

Military bust of Washington right, in relief, within 12 by 15mm oval depression, ctsp on Ireland imitation 1766 halfpenny. (Rulau-E Non 100; in Kovacs coll.)

| 1053 | ND | Silver | 19mm | | 265. | 400. |

Washington bust right, GEORGE WASHINGTON at right, in tiny 5mm oval depression ctsp on U.S. dimes (Dates examined: 1820, 1821)

| 1053AA | ND | Silver | 27mm | | | 400. |

Similar ctsp on Spanish-American 1794 2-reales.

| 1053AB | ND | Copper | 29mm | | | 275. |

Similar ctsp on counterfeit Ireland 1766 halfpenny.

| 1053AC | ND | Copper | —mm | | | 200. |

Similar ctsp on England penny. (David Hirsch coll.)

Enlargement on left

| 1053A | ND | Silver | 25mm | 265. | 400. | — |

Similar ctsp on British shillings. (Dates examined: 1818) (Garrett 1906)

| 1053B | ND | Silver | 27mm | 265. | 400. | — |

Similar ctsp on U.S. quarter. (Dates examined: 1818)

Type 1053 was possibly struck in 1824 in honor of the visit of Marquis de Lafayette to the United States.

Funeral Medal hub

Baker	Date	Metal	Size	F	VF	EF
1054	ND	Copper	29mm	—	600.	

Bust left within upright oval, 11 by 16mm, ctsp on U.S. Large cent. (Fuld coll.; Rulau-E Non 101)

Struck from the hub of the Funeral medal, Baker 169.

Baker 1055-1056 are now relocated in Chapter 11 as Baker 198C-198F (Washington & Lafayette, 1824)

| 1056 | ND | Silver | 35mm | — | 10,000. | — |

Washington military bust left within circular depression ctsp on planed-off silver coin. Rv: Engraved script monogram APS (?) on reverse of coin. This is similar to the famed 'Stickney' Perkins dollar.

Baker	Date	Metal	Size	VF	EF	Unc
1057	ND	Copper	33mm	Rare	—	—

Washington bust, GEORGE WASHINGTON around, within 4.5mm circular depression ctsp on British 1807 penny. (Clark sale, lot 2137; Elder 5.1.1920 sale, lot 1242)

Baker 1053-1053B were countermarked in 1824 for Lafayette's visit. (NOTE: For more bust countermarks, see Baker numbers 198-198D in Chapter 11, Medals with Historic Figures)

RECENT FANTASIES

All Struck 1959-1960

Leon Hendrickson specimen

Dr. I. Schuster specimen

Baker	Date	Metal	Size	VG	VF	EF
1058	ND	Copper	42mm	50.00	—	75.00

Civil bust right, GEORGE WASHINGTON and beaded rim around, within 14mm circular depression ctsp on British 1797 Cartwheel twopence. (Brunk 41940; B&M March, 1985 sale, lot 1738)

Dr. George Fuld specimen

1059	ND	Gold	38mm	800.	—	1200.

Same ctsp as 1058, applied to a Spanish-American gold doubloon (8-escudos), 1790-NR-JJ.

In his new book on U.S. and Canadian counterstamps (not yet published at press time), Dr. Gregory G. Brunk says of Baker 1058-1059: "These pieces were made around 1960. All examples of the counterstamp I have examined are uncirculated. These pieces are very artistic and quite collectible, but should be recognized as fantasies."

George Fuld adds that 1058-1059 were made in 1959-1960 by the late Robert Bashlow.

MISCELLANY

W.S. Baker closed his 1885 opus with a chapter titled Miscellaneous. We have chosen to place a number of Baker's numbers in this chapter (610 through 651) in other chapters, where they seemed to fit better.

CALENDAR MEDAL MULINGS

Under this grouping are mulings of the George Washington calendar medal obverse (Baker 386) with obverses of four similar calendar medal obverses representing four different states. None of the pieces are actually calendars. See M. & G. Fuld's series in *The Numismatist* on calendars, April 1958, Sept. 1958, Jan. 1959 and Feb. 1959.

NEW YORK

Baker	Date	Metal	Size	VF	EF	Unc
610	1855	Brass	36.6mm	—	75.00	100.

Obverse as Baker 386. Rv: New York state arms, motto EXCELSIOR. Around: NEW YORK. / 46000 SQUARE MILES POPULATION 3,097,394 / * 1855 *. Plain edge. Rarity 6. (Garrett 1900)

PENNSYLVANIA

Baker	Date	Metal	Size	VF	EF	Unc
611	1855	Brass	36.6mm	—	75.00	100.

Obverse as 610. Rv: Pennsylvania arms, motto: VIRTUE LIBERTY INDEPENDENCE. Around: .PENN. / 46,000 SQUARE MILES POPULATION 2,300,000 / * 1855 *. Plain edge. Rarity 6. (Garret 1900; Collins 686)

Baker	Date	Metal	Size	VF	EF	Unc
M-611	1855	Brass	36.6mm	—	1000.	—

Obverse resembles the obverse die of Baker 32E, a Colonial piece in the Liberty and Security series. It may be struck from the partial die from which 32E was prepared. Rv: As reverse of 611 (Pennsylvania arms). Plain edge. Possibly unique. (Dr. I.N. Schuster coll.)

But there is still this large body of medallic pieces which defy compartmentalization - some are mulings but most are just pieces which stand alone.

Examination of M-611 in comparison with 32E and other Colonial pieces, may give some evidence of when and where these specimens were made.

OHIO

612	1855	Brass	36.6mm	—	50.00	75.00

Obverse as 610. Rv: Ohio arms, date 1802. Around: .OHIO. / 40,000 SQUARE MILES POPULATION 2,000,000 / * 1855 *. Plain edge. Rarity 6. (Garrett 1900; Collins 687)

ILLINOIS

Baker	Date	Metal	Size	VF	EF	Unc
613	1855	Brass	36.6mm	—	50.00	100.

Obverse as 610. Rv: Illinois arms, motto: STATE SOVEREIGNTY NATIONAL UNION. Around: ILLINOIS. / 55,400 SQUARE MILES POPULATION 851,470 / * 1855 *. Plain edge. Rarity 6. (Garrett 1900)

These mulings are all scarce. T. Harrison Garrett obtained the four pieces in his collection from John Haseltine's 70th auction, lot 401, the dispersal of the Sylvester S. Crosby collection.

NEW YORK MEDALET

Baker	Date	Medal	Size	VF	EF	Unc
614	1799	WM	25mm	—	95.00	125.

Undraped bust right, GEORGE WASHINGTON BORN 1732. DIED 1799. around. Rv: New York state arms, DAVIS at base. In exergue: N.Y. Plain edge. Rarity 8.

Struck by Davis of Birmingham, England.

NUMISMATIC SOCIETY MEDALS

These may now be found in Chapter 21 beginning with Baker 617.

ORATION BY EVERETT

618	1860	WM	32mm	—	—	75.00

Undraped bust right, MERRIAM under bust. Around: GEORGE WASHINGTON BORN FEBRUARY 22, 1732. (same obverse as Baker 122). Rv: In six lines within olive wreath: BOSTON JULY FOURTH 1860 ORATION * BY * EVERETT. At bottom: MERRIAM. Plain edge. Rarity 8. (Collins 689)

Struck by Joseph H. Merriam of Boston.

A LITTLE MORE GRAPE

Struck about 1860

Baker	Date	Metal	Size	VF	EF	Unc
619	ND	Bronze	32mm	—	—	—

Washington head left. Rv: A LITTLE MORE GRAPE / CAPT: BRAGG. / * / PALO-ALTO. / RESACA DE LA PALMA / MONTEREY. / BUENA-VISTA. Plain edge. Rarity 9. (Bushnell 1476)

A specimen resides in the Western Reserve Historical Society. Cleveland, Ohio. This is a muling of DeWitt ZT 1848-12 reverse with a Washington obverse, though not listed by DeWitt. Restrikes of the 1848 campaign medal were made about 1860, and it is believed these mulings occurred then.

CIVIL WAR DOG TAGS

Baker	Date	Metal	Size	VF	EF	Unc
620	186.	Brass	31mm	—	45.00	70.00

Head right in circle of 34 stars joined at base by word UNION. Rv: CO = REG = VOLUNTEERS = ENTERD SERVICE = 186 = (with blank spaces for name and other particulars). Plain edge. Rarity 7.

620A	186	Gilt copper	31.9mm	—	40.00	—

Obverse as 620. Rv: Blank. Plain edge. Rarity 5.

620B	1862	Brass	31mm	—	40.00	60.00

As 620A, but reverse has been incused with: EMANCIPATION BILL PASSED APRIL 16 1862. WASHINGTON D.C. Plain edge.

Baker 620 is very collectible. It can be found incused with the names and regiments of men from every state represented in the Union army. Issued (named) specimens bring $250 to $350 and up.

Struck 1861

Baker	Date	Metal	Size	VF	EF	Unc
621	ND	Silver	32mm	—	50.00	75.00

Obverse as Baker 269 (undraped bust right, LOVETT on truncation, R.L. beneath bust, GEORGE WASHINGTON / * SECURITY * around). Rv: NAME / (line) / CO. (line) / REGT. (line) / STERLING (incused). Plain edge. Rarity 7.

621A	ND	Gilt/B	32mm	—	37.50	60.00

As 621. Plain edge. Rarity 5. (Collins 690)

Robert Lovett and some successors made wide use of this obverse die down to 50 years after its appearance.

MONITOR

Baker	Date	Metal	Size	EF	Unc	Proof
624	1862	WM	28mm	—	—	—

Obverse as Baker 217. Rv: Ironclad vessel, MONITOR. * above, 1862 below, all within olive wreath. Plain edge. Rarity 8.

SURRENDER OF LEE

Baker	Date	Metal	Size			
625	1865	WM	28mm	—	—	—

Obverse as Baker 219. Rv: In oak and olive wreath in 7 lines: SURRENDER OF GEN LEE TO GEN. GRANT APRIL 9TH 1865. Plain edge. Rarity 8.

Baker 624 and 625 are mulings by William H. Key of Philadelphia.

CITY HALL, N.Y.

Struck 1860

Baker	Date	Metal	Size	EF	Unc	Proof
627	1812	Copper	31mm	—	—	—

Obverse as Baker 50 (equestrian figure uniformed, on an eminence, head facing). Rv: View of old City Hall, small L in foreground. Above: CITY HALL, WALL ST. N.Y. Below: ERECTED IN 1700 DEMOLISHED 1812. Reeded edge. Rarity 7.

Struck by George Hampden Lovett of New York.

NOTE: Baker 628 and 629, also depicting City Hall, are game counters and may be found in that chapter.

ST. PATRICK'S CATHEDRAL

First Obverse

Baker	Date	Metal	Size	EF	Unc	Proof
630	ND	Copper	28mm	—	40.00	—

Obverse as Baker 296 (undraped bust right, LOVETT on truncation, G.H.L. beneath, GEORGE WASHINGTON around). Rv: View of the cathedral. Around: ST. PATRICK'S CATHEDRAL NEW YORK. Plain edge. Rarity 6.

630A	ND	WM	28mm	27.50	40.00	—

As 630. Plain edge. Rarity 6.

Second obverse

631	ND	Copper	28mm	—	—	—

Obverse as Baker 437 (undraped bust right, LOVETT on truncation, monogram GW beneath. Rv: As reverse of 630. Plain edge. Rarity 8.

Baker 630 and 631 are the work of George Hampden Lovett of New York.

PARSONS FAMILY ARMS

First obverse, circa 1876

Baker	Date	Metal	Size	VF	EF	Unc
639	ND	Copper	28mm	—	—	—

Obverse as Baker 630. Rv: Parsons coat of arms. Around: EDWARD - WILLIS PARSONS OF FLUSHING, NEW YORK. Plain edge. Rarity 7.

639A	ND	WM	28mm	—	—	—

As 639. Plain edge. Rarity 7.

639M	ND	WM	28mm	—	—	—

Obverse as 639. Rv: As obverse of Baker 240. Plain edge. Rarity 7.

Second obverse, about 1876

640	ND	Copper	28mm	—	—	—

Draped bust left within olive wreath. Around: WASHINGTON THE FATHER OF OUR COUNTRY (same obverse as Baker 417). Plain edge. Rarity 8.

640A	ND	WM	28mm	—	—	—

As 640. Plain edge. Rarity 8.

Baker 639 and 640 struck by George Hampden Lovett of New York, probably to the order of Isaac F. Wood, a close friend of Parsons.

The Parsons arms reverse also was muled with an obverse for Mary-Ferris Taber of Throg's Neck, N.Y. dated Oct. 5, 1876. (PCAC Nov. 1997 sale, lot 1580)

SHELDON FAMILY ARMS

Struck 1876

Baker	Date	Metal	Size	VF	EF	Unc
641	1870	Bronze	39.8mm	—	—	110.

Obverse as Baker 425 (undraped bust right, LOVETT on truncation. TO COMMEMORATE THE 100TH. ANNIVERSARY OF THE DECLARATION OF INDEPENDENCE). Rv: Sheldon coat of arms, - HOPESHELDON on scroll beneath. Around: H.L.S. 1821 + H.A.S. 1870 / + AUG. 15. +. Plain edge. Rarity 7. (Garrett 1902)

Baker	Date	Metal	Size	VF	EF	Unc
641A	1870	WM	39.8mm	—	—	110.

As 641. Plain edge. Rarity 7. (Collins 696)

Struck by Robert Lovett Jr. of Philadelphia. Collins reports 641 struck in copper as his number 697, $50 in AU.

MCPHERSON

Baker	Date	Metal	Size	EF	Unc	Proof
642	1864	Brass	20mm	17.00	27.50	—

Roman-mantled bust left, PATER PATRIAE around. Rv: Equestrian figure in uniform right, McPHERSON above, 1864 below. Tiny GHL at rim at 8 o'clock. Plain edge. Rarity 8.

Struck by George Hampden Lovett. The McPherson die has also been muled with the SOCIETY ARMY OF THE TENNESSEE WASHINGTON CITY 1876 die, listed as Rulau DC-Wa 27 to 27B in *United States Trade Tokens 1866-1889*.

BIGGER ARMY & NAVY

Illustration enlarged
Issued 1916

Baker	Date	Metal	Size	VF	EF	Unc
M-642	ND	Alum	32mm	—	—	100.

Obverse similar to Baker 269 in larger size (Undraped bust right, R L under bust, GEORGE WASHINGTON above, * SECURITY * below). Rv: WANTED! / A BIGGER / ARMY & NAVY. / NOT WANTED! / PACIFISTS / FORDS - BRYANS. Plain edge. (Delorey 101)

Baker	Date	Metal	Size	VF	EF	Unc
M642A	ND	Red Fiber	32mm	—	—	30.00

As M642. Plain edge (Roelofs coll.)

Issued by Thomas L. Elder of New York, utilizing an old Robert Lovett Jr. design for the obverse, to attack pacifism in the World War I period before the entry of the U.S. into the war (in April, 1917). The Ford and Bryan referred to are Henry Ford and William Jennings Bryan, apostles of pacifism in 1916.

GRANT RECEPTION

Baker	Date	Medal	Size	VF	EF	Unc
N-642	1879	WM	36mm	—	25.00	35.00

Ulysses S. Grant bust right, WASHINGTON LINCOLN / THE FATHER THE MARTYR above, GRANT / THE PRESERVER / * OF OUR COUNTRY *. Rv: E PLURIBUS UNUM / *** / CHICAGO / MEMORIAL OF / -*- / + GRANT + / RECEPTION / NOV. 12. TO 17. / + 1879 + / IN GOD WE TRUST. Plain edge. Rarity 7. (Schmidt Chicago G72; ANS collection)

These pieces were made of a very soft pot metal, probably by Childs & Co. of Chicago, and due to the pocket-piece circulation they received, very few survived.

VIGILANCE

Bushnell Series

Baker	Date	Metal	Size	EF	Unc	Proof
643	ND	Silver	28mm	—	—	—

Obverse as Baker 151. Rv: Crowing cock. VIGILANCE. Plain edge. Unique, as are all pieces in this Bushnell series.

Baker	Date	Metal	Size	EF	Unc	Proof
643A	ND	Copper	28mm	—	—	—

As 643. Plain edge. Unique.

Baker	Date	Metal	Size	EF	Unc	Proof
643B	ND	Brass	28mm	—	—	—

As 643. Plain edge. Unique.

Baker	Date	Metal	Size	EF	Unc	Proof
644	ND	Silver	28mm	—	—	—

Obverse as Baker 152. Rv: As reverse of 643. Plain edge. Unique. (Also 644A Copper, 644B Brass, 644C white metal)

Baker	Date	Metal	Size	EF	Unc	Proof
645	ND	Silver	28mm	—	—	—

Obverse as Baker 153. Rv: As reverse of 643. Plain edge. Unique. (Also 645A Copper, 645B Brass, 645C White Metal)

Baker	Date	Metal	Size	EF	Unc	Proof
646	ND	Silver	28mm	—	—	—

Obverse as Baker 154. Rv: As reverse of 643. Plain edge. Unique. (Also 646A Copper, 646B Brass, 646C White Metal)

Baker 643-646 were supposedly struck in 1 copy each after the designs of Charles Cushing Wright for collector Charles I. Bushnell, in 1860.

THE TWELVE STARS

Baker	Date	Metal	Size	VF	EF	Unc
647	ND	Silver	14mm	—	—	—

Washington head right. Rv: Circle of 11 stars, surrounding one in the center. Plain edge. Rarity 8.

Baker	Date	Metal	Size	VF	EF	Unc
647A	ND	Copper	14mm	—	—	—

As 647. Plain edge. Rarity 8

Baker	Date	Metal	Size	VF	EF	Unc
647B	ND	Brass	14mm	—	—	—

As 647. Plain edge. Rarity 8.

KETTLE

Baker	Date	Metal	Size	F	VF	EF
648	ND	Brass	14mm	—	—	—

Washington bust right, KETTLE beneath the bust. Around: G. WASHINGTON. Rv: Blank. Rarity 9. (Appleton 285)

The signature Kettle belonged to a father-and-sons token-making firm in Birmingham, England founded by Henry Kettle in the late 1780's. Henry Kettle used this signature 1793-1804 and Kettle & Sons used it 1812-1837. It is most likely from the latter period that this rare medalet emanates.

Kettle is best remembered in America as the maker of the 1803-dated brass game counters in imitation of the gold $2.50 and $5 coins, but he also made many of the rare early store cards of America, including the Wolfe, Spies & Clark pieces of New York which feature a Washington effigy.

OVAL SHELL

Baker	Date	Metal	Size	VF	EF	Unc
649	ND	SilverOval	16 by 21mm	—	450.	—

Washington head right, LANDER on truncation. Rv: Intaglio of obverse (struck as a shell). Plain edge. Rarity 9.

649A	ND	Bronze	Oval 16 by 21mm—		350.	—

As 649. Plain edge. Rarity 9.

The dies were cut in the late 1840's by Louisa Lander. In 1847 Lander engraved the dies for the beautiful William J. Mullen store card, Miller NY 616.

M-649	ND	Silver	Oval, 18.5 by 24mm—		100.	—

Obverse similar to 649, but bust faces left and the shell was cut by another, unsigned, artist. Rv: Intaglio of obverse. Plain edge. Of apparently later work than the Lander shell. (Dr. I. N. Schuster coll.)

NAKED BUST IN INCUSE CROSSES

Baker	Date	Metal	Size	VF	EF	Unc
N-649	1783	Copper	25mm	—	—	165.

Small naked bust right, in relief, within a circle of 18 incuse crosses, the incuse date 1783 below, all on a plain field. Rv: Both sides have neatly dentilated raised rims. Plain edge. Thick (2.8mm) flan. Rarity 10 (unique). (Rich Hartzog coll.)

The style and workmanship on the bust resemble that on Baker 517, the Brimelow store card of New York City. It is not known what purpose was intended for Baker N649, or when it was made. A most unusual piece.

THE LORD'S PRAYER

by William Key

Baker	Date	Metal	Size	VF	EF	Unc
650	ND	Silver	16mm	—	50.00	75.00

Uniformed bust right, K on truncation, GEN. GEORGE WASHINGTON around (same obverse as Baker 463). Rv: Lord's Prayer in 15 lines. Plain edge. Rarity 8.

650A	ND	Bronze	16mm	—	10.00	20.00

As 650. Plain edge. Rarity 4.

650B	ND	Gilt/B	16mm	—	10.00	20.00

As 650. Plain edge. Rarity 4. (Bullowa-Lessin 39)

by George B. Soley

651	1880-90's	Gilt/C	13mm	—	10.00	20.00

Obverse as Baker 464 (undraped bust right, GOD AND OUR COUNTRY). Rv: Lord's Prayer in 15 lines, star at the top. Plain edge. Rarity 4. (Eglit 255; Collins 698)

561A	ND	Copper	13mm	—	—	—

As 651. Plain edge. Rarity 8.

Published by George B. Soley of Philadelphia. Sold at Columbian Exposition in Chicago, 1893, as souvenirs for 25 cents.

GEORGE WASCHINGTON MEDALLION

Struck 1850-70

Baker	Date	Metal	Size	VF	EF	Unc
C651	ND	Svd/Bz	44.8mm	—	—	Rare

Unusual Washington head left in beaded oval, GEORGE WASCHINGTON (sic!) at right, and initials G.H. at lower left. Around oval is wide border consisting of 14 ovals of various sizes, each enclosing fancy scriptlike initials. U.S. Rv: Blank. (PCAC Nov. 15, 1997 sale, lot 271)

Due to the misspelling Waschington, this piece never eventuated into a completed medal. First offered anywhere, apparently, in 1997.

UNIFACE IRON MEDALLION

Baker	Date	Metal	Size	VF	EF	Unc
M-651	ND	Iron	84mm	—	—	—

Washington bust in civil dress three-quarters left, after the portrait by Gilbert Stuart. Rv: Blank, incused. Plain edge. (Garrett 1909)

This piece is cast in "Berlin iron." It was listed by Snowden plate 3, number 2 (page 30). Actual size 4 1/4 inches (84mm).

CAST SHELL PLAQUE

Baker	Date	Metal	Size	VF	EF	Unc
N-651	ND	Iron	107mm	—	150.	250.

Washington bust. Shell plaque cast in Berlin iron. Rv: Blank, Plain edge. (Springfield 4072; Snowden plate ill; figure 2)

OCTAGONAL MEDAL

Baker	Date	Metal	Size	Ef	Unc	Proof
M-652	ND	Bronze	Oct 25mm	—	—	—

Bust in civil dress three-quarters left, within oval frame at center of plain field. Rv: Blank. Each side has a beaded rim. Plain edge. Extremely rare. (Garrett 1911)

This medal was described by Snowden in his *Washington Medals*, page 36, number 27, plate 9. Also listed in William Sumner Appleton's articles on Washingtonia in *American Journal of Numismatics*, 1873, page 40, number CCXCII. (The Garrett specimen was obtained from the Haseltine sale of the Sylvester S. Crosby collection).

N-652	ND	Copper	Oct. 24 by 27mm—			—

Nude bust right, small R.L. under truncation. ornate border at rim. Rv: Blank. Plain edge. By Robert Lovett Jr. (Dr. Schuster coll.)

EARLY CASTING

Baker	Date	Metal	Size	VF	EF	Unc
P-652	ND	Copper	48mm	—	Rare	—

Nude bust left on plain field. The rim is raised as much as on the British 1797 Cartwheel twopence coins. Rv: Blank. Plain edge. Thick flan. Cast in copper, probably early 19th century. (Dr. I.N. Schuster coll.)

COLONIAL BARRACKS, TRENTON

Baker	Date	Metal	Size	EF	Unc.	Proof
653	1920	Bronze	30mm	—	—	—

Washington crossing the Delaware. Below: NJ 1776 (shield) 1920. Rv: COLONIAL BARRACKS / AT / TRENTON at center; around: COMMEMORATING THE SIGNING / OF THE / DECLARATION OF INDEPENDENCE / AT / PHILA. Plain edge. (Kurt Krueger Aug. 1983 sale, lot 2002)

CAPITOL CORNERSTONE

Baker	Date	Metal	Size	EF	Unc	Proof
654	1893	Silver	50.7mm	—	170.	—

Three-quarters left facing bust of Washington in oval above scene of the cornerstone laying, 15 stars in arc above the oval; all within circle. Around: LAYING OF THE CORNER STONE OF THE CAPITOL / . SEPTEMBER 12 1793. .Rv: View of the Capitol, CENTENNIAL CEREMONIES above, AT THE UNITED STATES CAPITOL below, all within circle. Around: Border made up of stars, with SEPT. 8, 1893. at bottom. Plain edge. (Springfield 4081)

Baker	Date	Metal	Size	EF	Unc	Proof
654A	1893	WM	50.7mm	35.00	55.00	—

As 654. Plain edge.

Baker	Date	Metal	Size	EF	Unc	Proof
654B	1893	Bronzed copper	50.7mm	—	65.00	—

As 654. Plain edge. Rarity 5.

These medals are found suspended from a ribbon with fasces bar clasp. The silver pieces, very rare, were for ceremony officials, the white metal for participants.

BASHLOW RESTRIKES

Struck ca. 1961

Baker	Date	Metal	Size	EF	AU	Unc
A654	1789	Copper	21.9mm	—	—	20.00

Nude periwigged bust right. Around: GEO. WASHINGTON FIRST PRES'T U.S. / * 1789 *. Rv: Blank. Struck without a collar. (H.J. Levine inventory)

Baker	Date	Metal	Size	EF	AU	Unc
B654	ND	WM	**	—	—	27.50

** 9-sided flan, 23.2mm.
Nude periwigged bust right, within dentilated circular border. Impression sunk beneath nonagonal framing. Rv: Blank. Struck without a collar. (H.J. Levine inventory)

In the early 1960's the late Robert Bashlow caused to be restruck many private dies of the second half of the 19th century, primarily from Philadelphia diesinkers' hubs and dies. His most famous restrike was the Robert Lovett Jr. Confederate cent from broken dies.

H. Joseph Levine of Presidential Coin & Antique Co. believes the two items above are also Bashlow experimental (non-commercial) trials off original dies. Bashlow's restrikes caused great concern in the 1960's as he openly advertised them in numismatic periodicals, but over time they have proven to be a small factor in medal and token collecting. Other examples of his work are the fantasy counterstamps listed in this catalog in Chapter 33.

Bashlow, still a young man, died in a hotel fire in Spain only a few years after his restriking activities began.

WASHINGTON STATE DIAMOND JUBILEE

Baker	Date	Metal	Size	EF	Unc	Proof
675	1964	CN	35mm	—	2.00	—

Undraped bust right, WASHINGTON STATE DIAMOND JUBILEE above, 75 YEARS OF STATEHOOD below. Rv: Large numeral 75, with 1889 - 1964 on upper arm of each numeral, above and behind capitol building. Stylized trees at either side, fish right below. Around: COMMEMORATIVE MEDAL / WASHINGTON WELCOME INC. Plain edge.

FREEDOMS FOUNDATION

Valley Forge, Pa.

Struck 1960's

676	ND	Bronze	104mm	—	35.00	50.00

Uniformed Washington kneeling in prayer left, FREEDOMS FOUNDATION AT VALLEY FORGE around, HONORING incused on his cape. Rv: Arc of 13 stars above eagle at top. .IMPRESS.ON.THE.MIND.OF.EVERY.MAN.FROM. / FIRST.TO.LOWEST.THE.IMPORTANCE.OF.THE.CAUSE. / .AND.WHAT.IT.IS.THEY.ARE. CONTENDING.FOR. below, all above building facade. In lower field: FOR OUTSTANDING ACHIEVEMENT / IN BRINGING ABOUT A / BETTER UNDERSTANDING / OF THE / AMERICAN WAY OF LIFE. Plain edge.

676A	1952	Bronze	32mm	10.00	15.00	—

Obverse similar to 676, differing legend. Rv: BOY SCOUTS OF AMER-ICA / HONOR / RECOGNITION / GET OUT THE VOTE / CAMPAIGN / FORWARD ON / LIBERTY'S TEAM / 1952 / * (Fleur) *.

Illustrated above under Baker 676 and 676A are two of a number of medals is-sued by Freedoms Foundation. The foundation was begun 1949 and since that date it has honored more than 50,000 individuals and organizations. The awards are selected by an independent jury and given to those who promote, through words or deeds, an understanding of responsible citizenship and its relationship to a free society.

Below is the very first type of medal, listed as Baker 676C.

Struck 1949-1950

Baker	Date	Metal	Size	EF	Unc	Proof
676C	ND	Copper	100.5mm	—	50.00	65.00

Kneeling figure of Washington at prayer to left, HONORING in relief let-ters on his cape. Above: FREEDOMS FOUNDATIONS INC. VALLEY FORGE, PA. Below is hand engraved name of awardee. Rv: Border of 13 stars. Eagle displayed above: FOR OUTSTANDING / ACHIEVE-MENT IN / BRINGING ABOUT A / BETTER UNDERSTANDING / OF THE / AMERICAN / WAY OF LIFE. Plain edge.

Versions of 676C in the H. Joseph Levine inventory are engraved: DAN HEIL-MAN / 1949 and DAN HEILMAN / 1950, respectively. In 1952 Dan Heilman and Nick Dallis created the comic strip "Judge Parker."

Later versions of the medal were struck by Medallic Art Co. in bronze. 101.5mm, 1951, and gold-plated bronze, 1953, and again by Medallic Art Co. from a slightly different die in matte finish bronze, 102mm in 1961.

A specimen of Baker 676 in the Levine inventory is engraved: NATIONAL BROADCASTING CO. / "I PLEDGE ALLEGIANCE" / 1967.

Baker	Date	Metal	Size	Unc	P-L	Proof
A676	ND	Gold/Silver	39mm	—	20.00	—

Bust facing forward, BENJAMIN FRANKLIN. Rv: Washington facing left praying, above around: FREEDOMS FOUNTAIN AT VALLEY FORGE . 253 struck, medal number 12 of the Patriots Hall of Fame series sponsored by the Freedoms Foundation, Valley Forge, Pa. A series of 100 medals. Sculpted by Philip Nathan. (PHS-12; Greenslet GM-462)

Baker	Date	Metal	Size		VF	EF	Unc
A676A	ND	Silver	39mm		—	20.00	22.50

As A676. 2648 struck in Proof.

COLUMBIAN EXPOSITION

Baker	Date	Metal	Size	VF	EF	Unc
677	1893	Aluminum	52mm	—	100.	150.

Imitation souvenir admission ticket to the World's Columbian Exposition featuring a facing Washington vignette at left, encased in an aluminum medal. COLUMBIAN / 1893 above, PAT. PENDING / SOUVENIR below. Rv; Facing Columbus bust separates 1492 - 1892, COLUMBUS under truncation. Around: WORLD'S COLUMBIAN EXPOSITION / * CHICAGO *. Plain edge.

PARIS MINT

Struck 1975

Baker	Date	Metal	Size	VF	EF	Unc
678	1975	Bronze	82mm	—	40.00	50.00

Busts overlapping, facing approximately three-quarters left, of Washington, Jefferson, Adams and Franklin. WASHINGTON JEFFERSON ADAMS FRANKLIN around, BICENTENAIRE / L INDEPENDANCE / DES ETATS UNIS / D'AMERIQUE below. Rv: Sailing ship and three cannon at right, names of 13 original states at left and center (French spellings, e.g. GEORGIE, VIRGINIE etc.) Designer's name F. ANGER along lower rim. Plain edge, on which is incused 1975 BRONZE and Paris mintmark.

Baker	Date	Metal	Size	VF	EF	Unc
678A	1975	Silver	82mm	—	—	80.00

At last. Edge plain but stamped 1975 ARGENT and Paris mintmark.

OBVERSE AND REVERSE

The term Obverse refers to the "heads" or "face" side of a piece. Where there is a human head or bust, this is easy to determine, but where there is no head, the side with the "principal device" is the Obverse. The opposite side is the Reverse. In some cases determining Obverse and Reverse must be arbitrary, especially where a head is on each side.

Each piece also has a third side, the Edge, which is described as Reeded, Plain, Lettered, etc. The term Rim is not the edge, but the periphery of one face or another.

SONS OF THE AMERICAN REVOLUTION

Baker	Date	Metal	Size	VF	EF	Unc
CA-678	1883	Gold *	vv	—	250.	350.

* Oval medallion and eagle crest are struck in 14K (.585 fine) gold. Set in blue enamel scalloped border with gold stars. Pinback ribbon is colored blue and gold (gold-blue-gold vertical).

vv Overall height 70mm; badge-eagle height 44.6mm. Naked Houdon bust of Washington right, SONS OF THE REVOLUTION above, 1883 (spray) below. On back of eagle crest above: BAILEY, BANKS & BIDDLE / PHILA in circular format. The numeral 1572 is engraved to left of the BB&B signature. Rv: Continental soldier standing, facing, his musket slung across his back. In exergue: 1775. (Kirtley Dec. 4, 1990 sale, lot A158; Stack's Jan. 14-15, 1998 Sale, lot 101; PCAC Nov. 15, 1997 sale, lot 223)

The 1998 Stack's specimen is engraved around obverse frame in script: Alexander L. Porter Jr. Feb. 1894. The numeral 2093 is engraved on the eagle's reverse. These must have been serially numbered, most likely by BB&B before delivery.

The Nov. 1997 PCAC specimen has its eagle marked on reverse: 14K CENTER BB&B / 14K. The obverse is hand engraved: Lloyd Cabot Briggs April 26, 1945.

Baker	Date	Metal	Size	VF	EF	Unc
CA-678A	1883	xx	vv	—	125.	200.

xx Oval Central medallion is made of gilt silver; frame, eagle and ribbon same as on CA-678. Reverse of eagle bears BB&B logo plus serial number 2450.

As CA-678. It is difficult to distinguish CA-678 from CA-678A visually, but gold is much heavier than silver. The eagle and frame on 678A are 14K gold and blue enamel. (PCAC May 16, 1997, sale, lot 205; fetched $115.50 in AU with frayed ribbon)

Engraved specimens tell us these badges were in use at least 1894-1945.

Baker	Date	Metal	Size	VF	EF	Unc
E-678C	1889	Copper	27mm	—	—	30.00

Badge of the SOTAR (exactly as seen on C-678, minus the ribbon) at center. Around: SONS OF THE AMERICAN REVOLUTION. Rv: Minuteman with rifle at the ready, 13 stars in arc above, ORGANIZED APRIL 30, 1889, below. Plain edge. Round medal. Thick (3.1mm) flan. (Rich Hartzog collection)

GRADE HEADINGS

Three grade (condition) columns appear in this catalog. Coins and tokens, which circulate, are graded down to VG (Very Good), but medals, which do not circulate, usually are graded no less than VF (Very Fine). Other abbreviations used are F (Fine), EF (Extremely Fine), AU (About Uncirculated), Unc (Uncirculated), and P-L (Prooflike). Proof is spelled out.

Baker	Date	Metal	Size	VF	EF	Unc
C-678	1898	Bronze	**			35.00

** Maltese cross-shaped flan, 39mm wide. Head left within central circle, LIBERTAS ET PATRIA around at center of Maltese cross, a laurel wreath behind and a folded-wing eagle, head left, surmounting. Rv: PRESENTED TO SONS OF THE AMRERICAN REVOLUTION * / WAR WITH SPAIN / 1898 / .*. Plain edge. Issued suspended from ribbon for wear as a badge. (ANS collection)

Baker	Date	Metal	Size	EF	Unc	Proof
660	1913	Bronze	91mm	60.00	—	—

Undraped head right in high relief, wreath above flat field. Rv: Lettering incused. FEBRUARY 22ND, 1913. SONS OF THE REVOLUTION. Plain edge. Weight 1 pound! Round medallion.

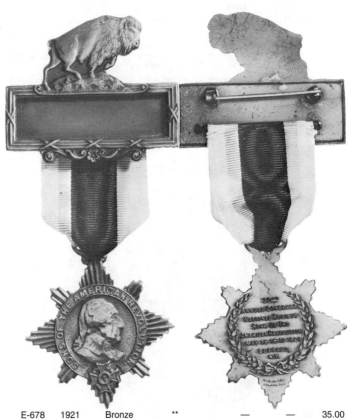

E-678	1921	Bronze	**	—	—	35.00

** Six-pointed star shaped flan, 41mm. Military bust right, SONS OF THE AMERICAN REVOLUTION above, Maltese cross device below, all superimposed on 6-pointed ornate star. Rv: Within wreath: 32ND / ANNUAL CONGRESS / NATIONAL SOCIETY / SONS OF THE / AMERICAN REVOLUTION / MAY 15-16-17 1921 / BUFFALO, / N.Y. / W & H CO / NEWARK N.J. Plain edge. Suspended from ribbon with hanger surmounted by a buffalo right. (ANS collection)

SWAMPSCOTT CONGRESS

D-678	1919	Bronze	32mm	—	—	22.50

Maltese cross badge of SOTAR as on last, 1776 1783 above. 1917 1919 below. Rv: Within wreath: PRESENTED / TO / COMPATRIOT / (tablet) / BY THE / SONS OF THE AMERICAN / REVOLUTION / -.- / FOR SERVICE / IN WORLD WAR. Plain edge. Issued with eye for suspension from ribbon. (ANS collection)

PATER PATRIAE

Certain Latin terms appear on medals pertaining to George Washington, the first "General of the Armies of the United States." Only one other man held this title until the 5-star rank was created in World War II, and that was John J. Pershing, U.S. commander in France in WWI.

Pater Patriae (father of his country) is the apt title frequently appearing. Many other Latin words and phrases appear on items in this catalog; in most cases we have translated these for users.

Baker	Date	Metal	Size	EF	AU	Unc
EA-678	1925	Bronze	63mm	—	—	—

Obverse as Baker 922 (no legend or signature). Rv: Sons of the American Revolution / 36th / Annual Congress / of the / National Society / 1775 - 1925 / Swampscott, Mass / Compliments / of the / - Massachusetts State Society - Plain edge. (Kirtley May 26, 1998 sale, lot C3)

Struck by Robbins Company, Attleboro, Mass. This medal also honors the 150th anniversary of the Battles of Lexington and Concord in April, 1775. The organization, Sons of the American Revolution, was founded April 30, 1889.

AWARD MEDAL

Baker	Date	Metal	Size	EF	AU	Unc
EB-678	1922	Bronze	63mm	—	—	—

Eagle atop Washington-portrait Maltese cross seal of the society. Around: MASSACHUSETTS SOCIETY / .SONS OF THE AMERICAN REVOLUTION. Rv: Washington and Franklin medal for excellence in study of U.S. History. (Kirtley May 26, 1998 sale, lot C14)

Struck in excellent style by Whitehead & Hoag Co., Newark, N.J. The Kirtley sale specimen was engraved to a 1922 recipient; other dates must exist.

NATIONAL SOCIETY PAPERWEIGHT

Illustration reduced

Baker	Date	Metal	Size	VF	EF	Unc
EC-678	ND	Bronze	83mm	—	55.00	—

Maltese cross-Washington bust seal of the society. Around: NATIONAL. SOCIETY. SONS.OF.THE.AMERICAN.REVOLUTION. Rv: Blank but MACO logo. Thick. (Kirtley May 26, 1998 sale, lot C13)

Struck by Medallic Art Co., New York.

ORDER OF WASHINGTON

Baker	Date	Metal	Size	VF	EF	Unc
F-678	ND	SilverOval	25x32mm	—	600.	1000.

Nude bust left after the Houdon bust. Heavily beaded rim. Rv: ORDER OF WASHINGTON / (sprays) enclose blank central portion for entering of a name. Plain edge. Issued with eye for suspension from ribbon. The ribbon is blue-white-red-white-blue, from left. (ANS collection; Kirtley March 5-8, 1996 sale, lot 1232)

Gold-plated specimens were made also, according to BB&B records.

The Kirtley specimen in AU fetched only $132 in March, 1996. It lacked the ribbon.

The Order of Washington, the only U.S. order so named, was founded at Mobile, Alabama in 1895. Aside from the Order of the Cincinnati, it is America's only order of quasi-nobility. In the case of the Society of the Cincinnati, that was considered a veterans' hereditary organization, the ancestor of a member having served as an officer in the Revolutionary War of 1775-1783.

Membership in the Order of Washington was far more restricted. To become a Companion of the Order, one must have descended in the male or female line from a male ancestor who assisted the Colonies in attaining independence. This ancestor must have descended in the male line from someone in the Colonies arriving prior to 1750, and, in addition, must have been a landowner or founder of a town, and served in some official, military, naval or ministerial position in the Colonies, or been a clergyman. A son of the qualifying ancestor would be acceptable for the revolutionary service.

The stated objective of the founders was to "institute an order of patriotism and chivalry."With such restrictive membership rules, it is not surprising that the order remained in abeyance for a time. It was reorganized and a charter adopted at Philadelphia on May 13, 1908, under the guidance of J. G. B. Bulloch, M.D., of Philadelphia, John Eyerman of Easton, Pa., and others. Eyerman designed the order's insignia, which was struck by Bailey, Banks & Biddle of Philadelphia, probably during or shortly before 1908.

Reference: Bailey, Banks & Biddle Co., "American Orders & Societies and their Decorations." Philadelphia, 1913. Bulloch's title in 1908 was "chancellor-general."

Enlarged to show detail

BOY SCOUTS OF AMERICA

Baker	Date	Metal	Size	VF	EF	Unc
G-678	1950	Bronze	39mm	—	—	15.00

Washington kneeling in prayer left, NATIONAL JAMBOREE VALLEY FORGE * 1950 / B.S.A. around Rv: (Fleur de lis) / SCOUTING's / RE-UNION / WITH / HISTORY (Fleur de lis). Plain edge.

Baker	Date	Metal	Size	VF	EF	Unc
H-678	1957	Bronze	38mm	—	—	15.00

Washington left kneeling in prayer, ONWARD FOR GOD AND MY COUNTRY above, all with central circle. Around: NATIONAL JAMBO-REE VALLEY FORGE 1957 / * B*S*A *. Rv: ON / THIS HOLLOWED / GROUND WHERE / WASHINGTON AND HIS / ARMY SPENT THE BITTER / WINTER OF 1777-8 / THE BOY SCOUTS OF / AMERICA / REDEDICATE THEMSELVES / TO THE AMERICAN IDEALS / OF DE-MOCRACY WITH A / FIRM RESOLUTION TO GO ONWARD FOR GOD / AND COUNTRY. Plain edge.

Baker	Date	Metal	Size	VF	EF	Unc
J-678	1981	Bronze	38mm	—	—	15.00

Washington in tricornered hat at left faces toward outline of a Scout at right, NATIONAL SCOUT JAMBOREE around, 1981 to right of Washington, VIRGINIA below. Rv: Similar to reverse of last, two lines are replaced by these three lines: STRENGTHEN THE ARM / OF / LIBERTY. Plain edge.

All three Scouting medals illustrated from the collection of the American Numismatic Society, New York, courtesy of Dr. Richard G. Doty, curator.

TRIESTE

Baker	Date	Metal	Size	EF	AU	Unc
K-678	1841	Silver	46mm	—	1000.	1500.

American eagle displayed, shield on breast, ribbon with E PLURIBUS UNUM in its beak. Around: * GEO. WASHINGTON BORN FEBY 22, 1732 * / TRIESTE FEBY 22, 1841. Rv: LIBERTY / PRESENTED / TO / ANDREW CANEL / BY / THE AMERICANS / FOR HIS GENTLEMANLY / HOSPITALITY / ON THE FOREGOING / OCCASION/ (arc of 26 stars). Plain edge. (ANS coll., ex-1878 Fonrobert sale, lot 566; Stack's Historical Medals 1991 fixed price list, ex-John Haseltine 1879, Isaac Wood 1884, Chapman Bros. 1849). Only 2 specimens are known. The Stack's piece in AU-prooflike was offered at $800 in 1991. Rarity 9.

Baker	Date	Metal	Size			Unc
K-678A	1841	WM	46mm	—	—	800.

As K-678. Rarity 9. (NASCA April 1981 sale)

It is reported that a copper specimen of K-678 from the same dies exists, but the authors have not examined it, nor is there proof that such was struck. The B&R Garrett sale specimen may have been K-678B.

Baker	Date	Metal	Size	EF	AU	Unc
K-678B	1841	Copper	46mm	—	—	700.

Obverse similar to K-678, from different die. The eagle is smaller. On K-678 the scroll almost touches the B of BORN. On K-678B the scroll is well away from BORN, as the illustration shows. Rv: Similar to K-678 reverse, from different dies. Plain edge. Rarity 9. (B&R Garrett sale; Johnson & Jensen 1982 sale; PCAC 1994 Ganter sale, lot 266, Hirsch coll.)

In 1841 Trieste was a principal seaport of the Austrian Empire at the head of the Adriatic Sea. An American consulate operated there. Andrew Canel has not as yet been identified.

This enigmatic rarity in any version was unknown to William S. Baker in his 1885 opus. K-678 was published for the first time in the 1985 Centennial issue of this Baker revision. The excellent die work may be European.

It is very difficult to understand why a second obverse die (K-678B) was necessary to cut, since the pieces are so rare they are virtually unknown in the hobby. It is possible K-678B is a trial strike off rejected dies.

L.A.W.

(League of American Wheelmen)

Baker	Date	Metal	Size	VF	EF	Unc
B-678	1892	Brass	31.6mm	—	45.00	65.00

Nude bust right within central circle. L A W above, ornament at either side, 13TH ANNUAL MEET below. Rv: Symbol of the League of American Wheelmen, script initials L A W and three wings joined at center against the spoked wheel of a bicycle. Around: WASHINGTON, D.C. / JULY 18-20, 1892. Plain edge. Rarity 6.

Baker	Date	Metal	Size	VF	EF	Unc
B-678A	1892	WM	31.6mm	—	45.00	65.00

As last. Plain edge. Rarity 6.

NEW YORK POLICE RESERVE

Baker	Date	Metal	Size	VF	EF	Unc
L-678	ND	Silver	37.2mm	—	75.00	125.

Civil bust left, .OUR LIVES. OUR FORTUNES. OUR SACRED HON-OR. around. Rv: Defiant eagle with folded wings perched on a baton, CITY OF NEW YORK above, POLICE RESERVE below. Plain edge. (ANS collection)

Baker	Date	Metal	Size	VF	EF	Unc
L-678A	ND	Bronze	37.2mm	—	75.00	125.

As L-678. (Collins 702)

SESQUI-CENTENNIAL INTERNATIONAL EXPOSITION

Baker	Date	Metal	Size	VF	EF	Unc
M-678	1926	Bronze	32mm	—	25.00	—

Houdon head of Washington right, GEORGE WASHINGTON above arc of 13 stars below. Rv: Liberty bell within wreath, 1776 1926 below. Around: SESQUI - CENTENNIAL - INTERNATIONAL - EXPOSITION PHILADELPHIA -. Plain edge. (Russell Sears collection)

5TH UNIVERSAL POSTAL CONGRESS

Baker	Date	Metal	Size	VF	EF	Unc
N-678	1897	Bronze	36mm	—	—	45.00

Nude bust right, UNITED STATES OF AMERICA around. Rv: Within oak wreath: MEMBER / FIFTH / UNIVERSAL / POSTAL CONGRESS WASHINGTON / MDCCCXCVII. Plain edge. Issued with hanger for suspension from a ribbon. (ANS collection).

WASHINGTON ARTILLERIE COMPAGNIE

Baker	Date	Metal	Size	VF	EF	Unc
P-678	1842	Svd/Brass	33mm	—	450.	—

Washington bust right of unusual, strong appearance. Engraved in script around: General Washington. Rv: Engraved in three lines under flourishes: Gewidmet dem besten / Schutzen der Washington / Artillerie Compagnie. Separate brass cartouche affixed below is engraved: Octr 31st 1842. Holed for suspension. Was originally gilded. (Stack's Inc 1991 fixed price listing, lot 150; Hirsch coll.)

This marksmanship medal of the "Washington Artillery Company" was unpublished until 1991.

Researcher David Hirsch has concluded, after some eight years' contact with various historical societies, that the Washington Artillery Company was a Wisconsin militia unit raised by German-speaking volunteers in Milwaukee during the territorial period. Wisconsin was admitted to statehood only in 1848.

The same unit was apparently still in existence when the Civil War broke out and became known as 2nd Battery, Wisonsin Light Artillery, part of the Wisconsin Light Artillery, part of the Wisconsin Volunteer Militia. The adjutant general of Wisconsin's records beginning in 1858 recorded that a Washington Artillery trained in Milwaukee, and was made up primarily of German - speaking immigrants. German immigration into Southern Wisconsin was well under way in the 1830's.

Many pre-Civil War militia units used "Washington" in their titles, but only Pennsylvania and South Carolina were other possibilities Hirsch considered in his research. Further information is sought. The medal is extremely rare.

Our long-time collaborator Frederick Borgmann, an expert on state and local military decorations, found in an obscure reference, "History of Milwaukee" by Gregory, some information not in the Wisconsin adjutant general's archives:

The Washington Guards were organized 1845 by German-speaking residents of Milwaukee. A "Washington Artillery", a company of miners and sappers, was organized 1856 by German immigrants and its founding officers were Captain J.A. Liebhaber, 1st Lt. L. Hess and 2nd Lt. C.F. Herzberg.

This information might indicate that the Washington Artillery Company medal of 1842 was too early to be Wisconsin, but it might mean just the opposite, as early American militia units were very loosely organized entities and frequently grew into other units. Wisconsin Territory had no set standards for militia units, they were truly a "people's army" answerable only to themselves but created for good patriotic and defense purposes.

Another reference by Gen. Charles King says the "Washington Artillery" with two 6-pounder Bronze cannon grew out of the City Guard's (made up of Irish immigrants) rivalry with Germans just after the Mexican war of 1848.

DISTINGUISHED MARKSMAN

Baker	Date	Metal	Size	EF	AU	Unc
Q-678	ND	Silver	31mm	45.00	—	—

Nude bust left, PRO PATRIA above. Tiny CHILDS CHICAGO under truncation. Rv: Kneeling rifleman in Civil War uniform, DISTINGUISHED MARKSMAN around. Unpublished (Kirtley March 10, 1990 sale, lot 2612)

BICENTENNIAL '76

Baker	Date	Metal	Size	VF	EF	Unc
682	1976	Gilt/Brass	39mm	—	—	6.00

Facing civil bust, GEORGE WASHINGTON around. Rv: Whole side arranged in wheel of 10 spokes, with hub at center. Superimposed on the spokes are: BICENTENNIAL / '76, eagle on serpent, Liberty bell, circle of 13 stars, cannon. Plain edge. Issued with loop.

PRESIDENTS OF THE UNITED STATES

Struck 1972

Baker	Date	Metal	Size	VF	EF	Proof
683	ND	Gold/Silver	44.5mm	—	—	28.00

Facing civil bust, GEORGE / WASHINGTON / GW monogram at left. Rv: Eagle perches atop shield, on which is: GEORGE WASHINGTON / 1ST PRESIDENT / OF THE UNITED STATES / BORN IN FEBRUARY 22, 1732 / WESTMORELAND COUNTY, VA. / SERVED AS PRESIDENT 1789-1797 / DIED: DECEMBER 14, 1799. Tiny FM monogram left of shield. Plain edge. Incused on edge: 24 KT GOLD ELECTROPLATE ON STERLING and hallmarks C, FM monogram, 72 and P (meaning: copyright Franklin Mint 1972, proof)

This was the first in a series of medals honoring presidents.

Chapter 35

19th CENTURY STORE CARDS

MOBILE JOCKEY CLUB *
Mobile, Ala.
Struck ca. 1860

Baker	Date	Metal	Size	VF	EF	Unc
633	1860	Silver	28mm	—	95.00	225.

Obverse as Baker 94 (undraped bust left, KEY under bust, PATRIAE PATER 1732 around). Rv: Cupid on a dolphin, in ornamental border. In exergue: 1860. Plain edge. Rarity 9.

633A	1860	Copper	28mm	—	35.00	75.00

As 633. Plain edge. Rarity 7.

633B	1860	Bronze	28mm	—	35.00	75.00

As 633. Plain edge. Rarity 7.

633C	1860	Brass	28mm	—	35.00	75.00

As 633. Plain edge. Rarity 7.

633D	1860	WM	28mm	—	35.00	75.00

As 633. Plain edge. Rarity 7.

634	1860	Silver	28mm	—	—	225.

Obverse as Baker 211 (similar to 633 but arched frame). Rv: In six lines, within palm wreath: DEDICATED / TO / COIN / AND / MEDAL / COLLECTORS. At bottom: 1860. Plain edge. Rarity 9. (Garrett 1901)

634A	1860	WM	28mm	—	—	75.00

As 634. Plain edge. Rarity 7.

635	ND	Copper	28mm	—	50.00	125.

Obverse as 634. Rv: Witch riding a broomstick left, WE ALL HAVE OUR HOBBIES above, G H L below. Plain edge. Rarity 8.

635A	ND	Brass	28mm	—	35.00	75.00

As 635. Plain edge. Rarity 7.

635B	ND	WM	28mm	—	35.00	75.00

As 635. Plain edge. Rarity 7.

636	1853	Copper	28mm	—	—	100.

Obverse as 634. Rv: NOT / TRANSFERABLE / 1853. Plain edge. Only 4 struck. (Miller Ala 26A)

636A	1853	Brass	28mm	—	—	100.

AM 636. Plain edge. Only 4 struck. (Miller Ala 26B)

636B	1853	WM	28mm	—	—	100.

As 636. Plain edge. Only 15 struck.

Struck about 1860

637	1732	Copper	28mm	—	—	275.

Undraped bust left in arched frame, KEY under the bust. PATER PATRIAE above, 1732 below (same obverse as Baker 211). Rv: Racehorse standing left, MOBILE JOCKEY CLUB above, * MEMBERS MEDAL * below. Plain edge. Rarity 8.

637A	1732	WM	28mm	—	—	275.

As 337. Plain edge. Rarity 8.

Struck by Key of Philadelphia, 637 and 637A were probably made to the order of Joseph N.T. Levick for his own collection. They are mulings of two unconnected Key dies, and undoubtedly have no other connection than that to the Mobile Jockey Club. Other similar mulings are listed as Baker 633, 634, 635 and 636.

True membership medalets of the Memphis Jockey Club are listed in Russ Rulau's *U.S. Merchant Tokens 1845-1860* as numbers Ala 2 thru 5.

* These might better have been placed under GEORGE HAMPDEN LOVETT of New York., N.Y., who seems to have done the muling of his own and Key dies, indiscriminately, at the order of Joseph N.T. Levick, the coin dealer and collector. But Adams and Miller placed these under the Mobile Jockey Club, for which there is some justification as Baker 636 uses the reverse of this membership medalet. Baker 637 uses the actual membership medal obverse.

I. L. ELLWOOD
De Kalb, Ill.

Baker	Date	Metal	Size	VF	EF	Unc
533	1863	Copper	19.8mm	25.00	40.00	110.

Obverse as Baker 508 (Fuld CW die 1137). Rv: I.L. ELLWOOD / HARDWARE / (small eagle) / TIN & STOVES / DE KALB ILL. Plain edge. Rarity 5. (Fuld Ill 200A-1a; H-G 2332)

533A	1863	Brass	19.8mm	—	Rare	—

As 533. Plain edge. Rarity 9. (Fuld Ill 200A-1b; H-G 2333)

J. L. LOVEDAY & CO.
Waukegan, Ill.

Baker	Date	Metal	Size	VF	EF	Unc
555	1863	Copper	20mm	25.00	40.00	110.

Head right, 1863. within circular olive wreath, DRY GOODS, GROCERIES & C. around, small G. G. N. Y. at lower rim (Fuld cw die 1142). Rv: J.L. LOVEDAY & CO. / DRY GOODS / ++ / AND / ++ / . GROCERIES . / * WAUKEGAN ILL. *. Plain edge. Rarity 5. (Fuld Ill 890B-2a; H-G 2466)

555A	1863	Brass	20mm	—	—	275.

As 555. Plain edge. Rarity 8.

555B	1853	WM	20mm	—	—	300.

As 555. Plain edge. Rarity 9. (Fuld Ill 890B-2e; H-F 2468)

555C	1853	Silver	20mm	—	—	350.

As 555. Plain edge. Rarity 9.

Diesinker - G.G., probably Glaubrecht

W. GREAVES & SONS
New Orleans, La.

Baker	Date	Metal	Size	VG	F	EF
538	ND	Brass	25mm	—	Unique ?	—

Washington head right. Around: EXPORTED SOLELY BY: W. GREAVES & SONS. SHEAF. . WORKS. Rv: Blank. (Rulau Z35 in *U.S. Merchant Tokens 1845-1860*)

The only traceable specimen was in the Garrett collection of Johns Hopkins University and was a cast.

This was the head of a saw blade bolt-enclosed picture in a registered package. Not a token at all. Sheaf Island Works of S. C. Wragg, knife makers. Greaves not yet traced.

HESS & SPEIDEL
Boston, Mass.

Struck circa 1870

Baker	Date	Metal	Size	VF	EF	Unc
540	ND	WM	28mm	—	55.00	110.

Obverse as Baker 92 (uniformed bust left, J.A. BOLEN under bust, WASHINGTON above). Rv: APOLLO GARDENS / 576 / WASHINGTON ST. / GOOD FOR / 6 /CENTS. / * HESS & SPEIDEL *. Plain edge. Rarity 9. (Rulau Ma-Bo 36; Miller Mass 12)

540A	ND	Copper	28mm	—	50.00	100.

As 540. Plain edge. Rarity 9. (Rulau Ma-Bo 37)

540E	ND	WM	28mm	—	—	135.

Obverse as 540. Rv: Apollo bust right within laurel wreath, MERRIAM BOSTON below bust. Above: APOLLO. Plain edge. Rarity 9.

541	ND	Copper	28mm	—	55.00	110.

Uniformed bust left, BOLEN under bust. Around: THE FATHER OF OUR COUNTRY (same obverse as Baker 93). Rv: As reverse of 540. Plain edge. Rarity 9. (Miller Mass 13)

541A	ND	Copper	28mm	—	55.00	110.

As 541. Plain edge. Rarity 9.

The Apollo Garden is listed in the 1863 Boston city directory as a restaurant and billiard saloon at 576 Washington Street, under the proprietorship of Charles Hess and Leopold Speidel.

All of the Hess & Speidel mulings were apparently made from Merriam dies in or after 1870 in extremely limited number. Another, not mentioning Hess & Speidel, follows:

Baker	Date	Metal	Size	VF	EF	Unc
623	1864	Copper	27mm	—	—	Rare

Head right within oak wreath, WASHINGTON above. Rv: MADE FROM A COPPER BOLT / TAKEN FROM / - THE - / WRECK OF THE / FRIGATE CONGRESS / - BY - / G. W. WILLIAMS / - / CO. C. 25. REG. M.V. / JAN. 1. 1864. Plain edge. Rarity 9. (Rulau Ma-Bo 41; Schenkman B28)

623M	1864	Copper	27mm	—	—	Rare

Obverse as Baker 622. Rv: As reverse of Baker 623. Plain edge. Rarity 9.

Supposedly, according to Bolen, he made only 2 copies of 623 before destroying the reverse die. One wonders, then, how many of 623M (not mentioned by Bolen) were made, and when.

JOS. H. MERRIAM
Boston, Mass.

Struck ca. 1859

Baker	Date	Metal	Size	VF	EF	Unc
560	1850	Copper	27mm	25.00	35.00	50.00

Head right within olive wreath, WASHINGTON above, small M at lower rim (obverse as Baker 88). Rv: JOS. H. MERRIAM / -*- / MEDALIST / DIE SINKER / - AND - / LETTER CUTTER / ESTABLISHED 1850 / NO.

18 / BRATTLE SQUARE / BOSTON, MASS. Plain edge. Rarity 5. (Miller Mass 55)

560A	1850	Brass	27mm	25.00	35.00	55.00

As 560. Plain edge. Rarity 7. (Miller Mass 56)

560B	1850	WM	27mm	20.00	30.00	45.00

As 560. Plain edge. Rarity 5. (Miller Mass 57)

Struck 1867-70

561	1732	Copper	32mm	—	—	60.00

Undraped bust right, MERRIAM under bust. Around: GEORGE WASHINGTON. BORN FEBRUARY 22, 1732. (same obverse as Baker 122). Rv: In eight lines: JOS. H. MERRIAM / (Liberty head coin in ornamental frame) / DIE SINKER / 18 BRATTLE SQUARE / BOSTON / MEDALS STRUCK IN / - GOLD - / SILVER, COPPER OR TIN. Plain edge. Rarity 7.

561A	1732	Brass	32mm	—	—	60.00

As 561. Plain edge. Rarity 7.

561F	1732	Bronze	32mm	—	—	70.00

Obverse as 561. Rv: As reverse of 561, but name MERRIAM is missing from die. Plain edge. Rarity 7. (Fuld coll.)

Joseph H. Merriam established his medallic business in 1850. He first appears in Boston directories in 1854, at 147 1/2 Washington St. In 1857 he removed to 18 Brattle Square, the address identified with his tokens in succeeding years. Some of his 1863-dated Civil War cards give his address as 19 Brattle Square, though others give 18.

Merriam & Co. (partners John C. Merriam and William N. Weeden) are at 18 Brattle Square 1865-69. Then the firm again becomes Joseph H. Merriam 1869-70. In 1871 a successor firm, W. C. Brigham & Co., appears in the directories. The Brigham firm gave way in 1893 to William H. Pretat.

Baker	Date	Metal	Size	VF	EF	Unc
622	1862	Copper	27mm	—	—	Rare

Obverse as 560. Rv: MADE FROM COPPER / - TAKEN FROM - / THE RUINS OF / - THE - /TURPENTINE WORKS / NEWBERN / - N.C. - / DESTROYED BY THE REBELS / MARCH 14, 1862. Tiny MERRIAM at lower rim. Plain edge. Rarity 9. (Rulau Ma-Bo 81)

621	1862	Copper	27mm	—	—	85.00

Obverse as Baker 88 (head right within olive wreath, letter M. at lower rim. Rv: As reverse of 622. Plain edge. Rarity 9.

621M	1862	Copper	27mm	—	—	85.00

Obverse as Baker 93. Rv: As reverse of 622. Plain edge. Rarity 9.

C. F. TUTTLE
Boston Mass.

Struck ca. 1860

Baker	Date	Metal	Size	VF	EF	Unc
581	ND	WM	27mm	50.00	75.00	100.

Obverse as Baker 525 (head right within olive wreath, WASHINGTON above, small M at lower rim). Rv: C. F. TUTTLE. / PAY AT THE / (stamped numeral) / COUNTER / NO.130 WASHINGTON ST. Plain edge. Rarity 7. (Miller Mass 91)

581A	ND	Brass	27mm	—	100.	125.

As 581. Plain edge. Rarity 7. (Miller Mass 92)

Numbers stamped at the center of Baker 580 which are known include: 11, 13, 17, 19, 20, 23, 24, 25, 30, 37, and no number. (See Russ Rulau's *U.S. Merchant Tokens 1845-1860*)

Charles F. Tuttle operated a restaurant, according to the 1863 Boston directory, at 1 Water Street. Yet his Civil War store cards (Fuld Mass 115G-1a) also bear the same address as on Baker 581 - 130 Washington St. The latter cards (which do not depict Washington) are not dated, though it has been assumed they were issued in 1863, possibly earlier.

J. A. BOLEN
Springfield, Mass.
Struck ca. 1862

Baker	Date	Metal	Size	VF	EF	Unc
626	ND	Silver	28.3mm	—	—	250.

Obverse as Baker 194 (uniformed bust left, surrounded by border ornamented with star and semicircles. Rv: View of Springfield Arsenal, J. A. BOLEN under design. Around: U.S. ARSENAL. Plain edge. Rarity 9.

Baker	Date	Metal	Size	VF	EF	Unc
626A	ND	WM	28.3mm	—	—	175.

As 626. Plain edge. Rarity 8.

M. A. ABRAHAMS
Independence, Mo.

Struck 1852

Baker	Date	Metal	Size	F	VF	Unc
507	ND	Brass	28mm	400.	750.	—

Undraped bust right, M. A. ABRAHAMS / *** 10 *** around. Rv: THE PEOPLES OUTFITTING STORE / INDEPENDENCE / MO. / * Reeded edge. Rarity 8. (Wright 2A; Miller Mo 40)

Abrahams' outfitting depots at Independence (Baker 507) and Weston (Baker 506) were at the heads, respectively, of the Sante Fe Trail and the Missouri River route to the West. The depots contained everything the overland prairie schooners were likely to need from an oxen yoke to a side of bacon, from wagon wheels to cotton cloth. For background details, see Russ Rulau's *U.S. Merchant Tokens 1845-1860*. It is believed about 10 to 11 Independence pieces and more than 100 Weston tokens exist.

M. A. ABRAHAMS
Weston, Mo.

Issued 1853-54

Baker	Date	Metal	Size	F	VF	Unc
506	ND	Brass	28mm	80.00	125.	500.

Undraped bust right, M. A. ABRAHAMS / *** 10 *** around. Rv: THE PEOPLES OUTFITTING STORE / WESTON / MO. / *. Reeded edge. Rarity 5. (Wright 2; Miller Mo 41)

JOHN ENGEL
Elizabeth Port, N.J.

Baker	Date	Metal	Size	VF	EF	Unc
534	ND	Copper	20mm	12.00	15.00	30.00

Obverse as Baker 509 (Fuld CW die 1265). Rv: JOHN ENGEL / MERCHANT / TAILOR / -52- / FIRST ST. / ELIZABETH PT/ NJ. Plain edge. Rarity 3. (Fuld NJ 220A-3a; H-G 4733)

J. L. AGENS & CO.
Newark, N.J.

Baker	Date	Metal	Size	F	VF	Unc
508	1863	Copper	19mm	—	100.	150.

Head right, THE WASHINGTON TOKEN. above, 1863 below (Fuld CW die 1137). Rv: J.L. AGENS & CO / -NO 1 - / COMMERCE ST. / NEWARK, N.J. / NEWSPAPERS. Plain edge. Rarity 9. (Fuld NJ 555A-3a; H-G 4754)

Baker	Date	Metal	Size	F	VF	Unc
508A	1863	Brass	19mm	—	75.00	

As 508. Plain edge. Rarity 7.

Baker	Date	Metal	Size	F	VF	Unc
508B	1863	CN	19mm	—	—	200.

As 508. Plain edge. Rarity 9.

Baker	Date	Metal	Size	F	VF	Unc
508C	1863	WM	19mm	—	—	200.

As 508. Plain edge. Rarity 8.

Baker	Date	Metal	Size	F	VF	Unc
508D	1863	Silver	19mm	—	—	300.

As 508. Plain edge. Rarity 9. (Fuld NJ 555A-3f; H-G 4758)

Baker	Date	Metal	Size	F	VF	Unc
509	ND	Copper	20mm	6.00	8.00	15.00

Numeral 1 between vertical PURE - COPPER with radiant circle at center, tiny Washington head left at either side, -I-O-U- / -CENT- around (Fuld CW die 1265). Rv: As reverse of 508. Plain edge. Rarity 3. (Fuld NJ 555A-6a; H-G 4764)

Baker	Date	Metal	Size	F	VF	Unc
509A	ND	Silver	20mm	—	—	300.

As 509. Plain edge. Rarity 9. (Fuld NJ 555-A-6f; H-G 4769)

J. WIGHTMAN
Newark, N.J.

Baker	Date	Metal	Size	VF	EF	Unc
585	ND	Copper	19mm	—	—	100.

Obverse as Baker 543 (Fuld CW die 1132 by Emil Sigel). Rv: J. WIGHTMAN / 188 / WASHINGTON / ST. / NEWARK, N.J. Plain edge. Rarity 9. (Fuld NJ 555C - 5a; H-G 4810)

Baker	Date	Metal	Size	VF	EF	Unc
585A	ND	Brass	19mm	—	—	100.

As 585. Plain edge. Rarity 9.

Baker	Date	Metal	Size	VF	EF	Unc
585B	ND	Nickel	19mm	—	—	200.

As 585. Plain edge. Rarity 9. Magnetic.

Baker	Date	Metal	Size	VF	EF	Unc
585C	ND	CN	19mm	—	—	150.

As 585. Plain edge. Rarity 9.

Baker	Date	Metal	Size	VF	EF	Unc
585D	ND	WM	19mm	—	—	100.

As 585. Plain edge. Rarity 8. (Fuld NJ 555C-5e; H-G 4814)

COUTTS & BRO.
Perth Amboy, N.J.

Baker	Date	Metal	Size	VF	EF	Unc
528	ND	Copper	20mm	10.00	12.00	20.00

Observe as Baker 509 (Fuld CW die 1265). Rv:COUTTS & BRO. / DRY GOODS / -&- / GROCERIES / P. AMBOY, N.J. Plain edge, Rarity 4. (Fuld NJ 690A-1a; H-G 4855)

BRAUN & SCHELLWORTH
Brooklyn, N.Y.

Baker	Date	Metal	Size	F	VF	Unc
515	ND	Copper	20mm	6.00	8.00	15.00

Obverse as Baker 509 (Fuld CW die 1265). Rv: BRAUN & SHELLWORTH'S / 132. 134. 136 / COURT ST. / -*- / BROOKLYN / PAVILION. Plain edge. Rarity 2. (Fuld NY 95A- 2a; H-G 4953)

Baker	Date	Metal	Size	F	VF	Unc
515A	ND	Silver	20mm	—	—	250.

As 515. Plain edge. Rarity 9. (Fuld NY 95A-2f)

T. IVORY

Baker	Date	Metal	Size	VF	EF	Unc
547	1863	Copper	19mm	8.00	10.00	20.00

Obverse as Baker 508 (Fuld CW die 1137). Rv: T. IVORY. / COR. / FULTON & ORANGE / -STS- / BROOKLYN / BILLIARD SALOON. Plain edge. Rarity 3. (Fuld NY 95D-2a; H-G 4963)

Baker	Date	Metal	Size	VF	EF	Unc
547A	1863	Brass	19mm	—	—	75.00

As 547. Plain edge. Rarity 7.

Baker	Date	Metal	Size	VF	EF	Unc
547B	1863	Brass	19mm	—	—	90.00

As 547A, but obverse struck over reverse. Plain edge. Rarity 9. (Fuld NY 95D-2bo)

DANIEL WILLIAMS
Brooklyn, N.Y.

Baker	Date	Metal	Size	VF	EF	Unc
586	1863	Copper	19mm	6.00	8.00	15.00

Obverse as Baker 508 (Fuld CW die 1137). Rv: DANIEL WILLIAMS / -.-/ GROCER / CORNER / COURT & WARREN / STS / BROOKLYN. Plain edge. Rarity 2. (Fuld NY 95F-2a; H-G 5009)

| 586A | 1863 | Brass | 19mm | — | — | Unique |

As 586. Plain edge. Rarity 10.

| 586B | 1863 | CN | 19mm | — | — | Unique |

As 586. Plain edge. Rarity 10.

| 586C | 1863 | WM | 19mm | — | — | 100. |

As 586. Plain edge. Rarity 9.

| 586D | 1863 | Silver | 19mm | — | — | 300. |

As 586. Plain edge. Rarity 9. (Fuld NY 95F-2f)

| 586G | ND | Copper | 20mm | — | 8.00 | 15.00 |

Obverse as Baker 509 (Fuld CW die 1265). Rv: As reverse of 586. Plain Edge. Rarity 2. (Fuld NY 95-F-3a; H-G 5015)

A. KILLEEN
Greenpoint, N.Y.

Baker	Date	Metal	Size	VF	EF	Unc
552	1863	Copper	19mm	—	175.	225.

Obverse as Baker 508 (Fuld CW die 1137). Rv: A. KILLEEN / -+- / NO 1 & 16 / FERRY / -ST- / GREEN POINT. Plain edge. Rarity 6. (Fuld NY 330-A-2a; H-G 5160)

| 552F | ND | Copper | 20mm | — | 20.00 | 35.00 |

Obverse as Baker 509 (Fuld CW die 1265). Rv: As reverse of 552. Plain edge. Rarity 5. (Fuld NY 330A-6a; H-G 5168)

** Greenpoint is now part of Broolyn.

ATWOOD'S RAILROAD HOTEL
New York, N.Y.

Issued about 1835-38

Baker	Date	Metal	Size	F	VF	EF
510	ND	Copper	26.5	250.	500.	1250.

Equestrian figure advancing right, hat in his left hand held forward. GEORGE WASHINGTON above: BALE & SMITH / N-Y in exergue. Rv: CARRY ME TO / ATWOOD'S RAILROAD HOTEL / 243 BOWERY / AND MY FACE / IS GOOD FOR / 3 CENTS. Reeded edge. Rarity 6. (Miller NY 45; Low 200; HT 220)

| 510A | ND | Copper | 25mm | 300. | 500. | 1000. |

As 510, but smaller planchet. Reeded edge. Rarity 6. (Low 201; HT 221)

| 510B | ND | Brass | 26.5mm | 650. | 1500. | 1800. |

As 510. Reeded edge. Rarity 8. (Miller NY 46; Low 203; HT 223)

| 510C | ND | Brass | 20mm | — | — | 3000. |

As 510B on much smaller planchet; only the central portion of design shows. Plain edge. Rarity 10. (Fuld coll.; Low 2o2; HT 222)

| 510D | ND | WM | 26.5mm | 800. | 2000. | — |

As 510, but rim dentilations are thicker. Reeded edge. Rarity 8. (Miller NY 48; Low 204; HT 224)

| 510E | ND | Silver | 26.5mm | — | — | Rare |

As 510. Reeded edge. Rarity 9. May not exist.(HT 224A)

Struck by James Bale and Frederick B. Smith, who also used the same obverse die for their own contemporary store card. The reference to Low numbers is to Russ Rulau's *Hard Times Tokens*, as the original Lyman H. Low reference in

1899 did not recognize the Atwood pieces as Hard Times-era store cards. (See Bale & Smith entry under New York City)

BALE & SMITH
Issued 1835-38

Baker	Date	Metal	Size	F	VF	Unc
512	ND	Copper	26mm	700.	1450.	2250.

Obverse as Baker 510 (BALE & SMITH / N-Y in exergue). Rv: in 11 lines: BALE & SMITH ENGRAVERS & DIE CUTTERS 68 NASSAU STREET PLATES & ROLL FOR EMBOSSING DIES & SEALS OF EVERY DESCRIPTION N.YORK (the first two and last three curved). Reeded edge. Rarity 7. (Miller NY 51; Low 207; HT 227)

| 512A | ND | WM | 26mm | — | 2000. | 3000. |

As 512. Reeded edge. Rarity 9.(Miller NY 52; Low 208; HT 227A)

| 513 | ND | Copper | 26mm | 800. | 1800. | 3500. |

Equestrian figure advancing right (as on 512) but inscriptions changed. GENL GEORGE WASHINGTON around, B & S N-Y in exergue. Rv: As reverse of 512. Plain edge. Rarity 7. (Miller NY 53; Low 209; HT 228)

| 513A | ND | WM | 26mm | — | 2500. | 3500. |

As 513. Plain edge. Rarity 9. (Miller NY 54; Low 210; HT 228A)

The firm of James Bale and Frederick B. Smith was formed in 1838. Bale had been the apprentice of Richard Trested when that diesinker died in 1829, and he formed the firm of Wright & Bale with Charles Cushing Wright. This broke up in the fall of 1833 and the partnership with Smith came after Bale operated two years on his own.

| 547C | 1863 | Nickel | 19mm | — | — | 70.00 |

As 547. Plain edge. Rarity 8. Magnetic!

| 547D | 1863 | CN | 19mm | — | — | 85.00 |

As 547. Plain edge. Rarity 9.

| 547E | 1863 | WM | 19mm | — | — | 70.00 |

As 547. Plain edge. Rarity 8.

| 547F | 1863 | Silver | 19mm | — | — | 200. |

As 547. Plain edge.

| 547G | 1863 | Silver | 18mm | — | — | 350. |

As 547f, but struck over U.S. dime. Reeded edge. (Fuld NY 95D-2fo)

JOHN BARKER
New York, N.Y.
Issued 1829-33

Baker	Date	Metal	Size	VG	F	EF
511	ND	Brass	19mm	750.	1500.	3000.

Head right within olive wreath. Around: AMERICAN REPOSITORY OF FINE ARTS. Rv: JOHN BARKER / 16 MAIDEN LANE / DEALER IN / MUSIC PRINTS / & / FANCY / STATIONERY in seven lines, all curved but the fourth. Plain edge. About 3 or 4 pieces known. (Levick 243: Miller NY 57; Rulau-E NY 57; Low 338)

Barker, a stationer, is listed at 16 Maiden Lane 1829-30 in the city directories. The card was cut by the firm of Wright & Bale, active 1829-33.

BRIDGENS
New York, N.Y.

Baker	Date	Metal	Size	F	VF	Unc
516	1863	Copper	19mm	20.00	30.00	50.00

Obverse as Baker 508 (Fuld CW die 1137). Rv: BRIDGENS./ METAL TOKENS / -&- / STORE CARDS / -189- / WILLIAM ST. N.-Y. Plain edge. Rarity 3. (Fuld NY 630J-2a; H-G 5250)

| 516 | 1863 | Brass | 19mm | 30.00 | 40.00 | 60.00 |

As 516. Plain edge. Rarity 5. (Fuld NY 630J-2b; H-G 5251)

| 516B | 1863 | Brass | 19mm | — | — | 60.00 |

As 516A, but on thick planchet. Plain edge. Rarity 5. (Fuld Ny 630J-2b1)

| 516C | 1863 | Nickel | 19mm | — | — | 300. |

As 516. Plain edge. Unique (Fuld NY 630J-2c). Magnetic!

| 516D | 1863 | CN | 19mm | — | — | 100. |

As 516. Plain Edge. Unique. (Fuld NY 630J-2d; H-G 5253).

Non-magnetic.

| 516E | 1863 | WM | 19mm | — | — | 100. |

As 516. Plain edge. Rarity 7. (Fuld NY 630J-2e; H-G 5254)

| 516F | 1863 | Silver | 19mm | — | — | 300. |

As 516. Plain edge. Rarity 9. (Fuld NY 630J-2f)

William H. Bridgens was in business from at least the 1840's making medals and tokens. His skill level was low but his output large.

T. BRIMELOW, DRUGGIST

Baker	Date	Metal	Size	VF	EF	Unc
517	1863	Copper	23.5mm	8.00	10.00	20.00

Head right, GEO. WASHINGTON above, ****PRESIDENT **** below. Rv: Mortar and pestle divide 18 - 63 within olive wreath at center, numeral 1 in wreath opening at top. Around: T. BRIMELOW, DRUGGIST, / 432 THIRD AVENUE N-Y. Plain edge, rounded (as are all in the Brimelow series). Rarity 3. (Fuld Ny 630K-1a; H-G 5264; Miller NY 87)

Baker	Date	Metal	Size	VF	EF	Unc
517A	1863	Brass	23.5mm	—	—	200.

As 517. Plain edge. Rarity 8.

| 517B | 1863 | Nickel | 23.5mm | — | — | 275. |

As 517. Plain edge. Magnetic. Rarity 8.

| 517C | 1863 | WM | 23.5mm | — | — | 275. |

As 517. Plain edge. Rarity 9.

| 517D | 1863 | Silver | 23.5mm | — | — | 300. |

As 517. Plain edge. Rarity 9. (Fuld NY 630K-1f; H-G52b9; Miller NY 92)

The workmanship on most Brimelow cards is superior to that found on most Civil War store cards. It seems obvious they were intended less for commerce than for advertising or collector usage; their large size also indicates that intent, as the small cent of the day measured only 19mm. Only Baker 522 was of cent size.

Baker	Date	Metal	Size	VF	EF	Unc
518	ND	Copper	23.5mm	—	—	175.

Obverse as Baker 517 (Fuld CW die 1138). Rv: GOOD FOR/ (ornament) / ONE GLASS/ (ornament) / OF SODA, within border at rim made up of 31 stars. Plain edge. Rarity 9. (Fuld NY 630K-4a; Miller NY 93)

Baker	Date	Metal	Size	VF	EF	Unc
518A	ND	Brass	23.5mm	—	—	175.

As 518. Plain edge. Rarity 9. (Fuld NY 630K-4b)

| 518B | ND | Nickel | 23.5mm | — | — | 250. |

As 518. Plain edge. Magnetic. Rarity 9.

| 518C | ND | WM | 23.5mm - | — | 250. | — |

As 518. Plain edge. Rarity 9.

| 518D | ND | Silver | 23.5mm | — | — | 300. |

As 518. Plain edge. Rarity 9. (Fuld NY 630K-4f; Miller NY 98)

The Baker 518 type does not mention Brimelow by name, but he issued these as part of his series. There are 12 types of Brimelow tokens in all, six of which depict George Washington.

Baker	Date	Metal	Size	VF	EF	Unc
519	ND	Copper	23.5mm	12.00	20.00	35.00

Obverse as Baker 517 (Fuld CW die 1138). Rv: Bust of Franklin left within olive and palm wreath , T. BRIMELOW, DRUGIST, above, 432 THIRD AVENUE, N.Y. below. Plain edge. Rarity 5. (Fuld NY 630K-5a; H-G 5280; Miller NY 99)

Baker	Date	Metal	Size	VF	EF	Unc
519A	ND	Brass	23.5mm	—	—	35.00

As 519. Plain edge. Rarity 5.

| 519B | ND | Nickel | 23.5mm | — | — | 80.00 |

As 519. Plain edge. Rarity 7.

| 519C | ND | CN | 19mm | — | — | 375. |

As 519, but struck over a U.S. cupronickel cent. Rarity 10 (unique). Fuld NY 630K-5do)

| 519D | ND | WM | 19mm | — | — | 100. |

As 519. Plain edge. Rarity 8.

| 519E | ND | Silver | 23.5mm | — | — | 300. |

As 519. Plain edge. Rarity 8. (Fuld NY 630K-5f; H-G 5284; Miller NY 103)

Baker	Date	Metal	Size	VF	EF	Unc
520	1863	Copper	23.5mm	7.00	10.00	25.00

Undraped bust with a stern countenance left, GEO. WASHINGTON above, ****** PRESIDENT****** / (Fuld CW die 1139). Rv: As reverse of Baker 517. Plain edge. Rarity 3. (Fuld NY 630K-2a; H-G 5270; Miller NY 119)

Baker	Date	Metal	Size	VF	EF	Unc
520A	1863	Brass	23.5mm	—	—	75.00

As 520. Plain edge. Rarity 8.

| 520B | 1863 | Nickel | 23.5mm | — | — | 200. |

As 520. Plain edge. Magnetic. Rarity 9.

| 520C | 1863 | WM | 23.5mm | — | — | 100. |

As 520. Plain edge. Rarity 9.

| 520D | 1863 | Silver | 23.5mm | — | — | 300. |

As 520. Plain edge. Rarity 9. (Fuld NY 630K-2f; H-G 5274; Miller NY 123)

The obverse die used on Baker 520-521 is unlike any other in the Civil War token series.

Baker	Date	Metal	Size	VF	EF	Unc
521	ND	Copper	23.5mm	—	—	200.

Obverse as 520 (Fuld CW die 1139). Rv: Large numeral 2 within olive and palm wreath, T. BRIMELOW, DRUGGIST, above, 432 THIRD AVENUE, N.Y. below. Plain edge. Rarity 8. (Fuld NY 630K- 8a; H-G 5297; Miller NY 124)

Baker	Date	Metal	Size	VF	EF	Unc
521A	ND	Brass	23.5mm	—	—	18.00

As 521. Plain edge. Rarity 7.

| 521B | ND | Nickel | 23.5mm | — | — | 50.00 |

As 521. Plain edge. Magnetic. Rarity 9.

| 521C | ND | WM | 23.5mm | — | — | 50.00 |

As 521. Plain edge. Rarity 8.

| 521D | ND | Silver | 23.5mm | — | — | 250. |

As 521. Plain edge. Rarity 9. (Fuld NY 630K-8f; H-G 5301; Miller Ny 128)

| 522 | 1864 | Copper | 19mm | — | — | 18.00 |

Head right, L.R. under head, 13 stars around (Fuld CW die 1133). Rv: Mortar and pestle divide the date 18-64 within olive wreath. T. BRIMELOW, DRUGGIST, above, 432 THIRD AV. N.Y. below. Plain edge. Rarity 7. (Fuld NY 630K-9a; H-G 5303; Miller NY 129)

Baker	Date	Metal	Size	VF	EF	Unc
522A	1864	Brass	19mm	—	—	18.00

As 522. Plain edge. Rarity 7.

| 522B | 1864 | Nickel | 19mm | — | — | 60.00 |

As 522. Plain edge. magnetic, Rarity 8.

| 522C | 1864 | CN | 19mm | — | — | 50.00 |

As 522. Plain edge. Rarity 8.

| 522D | 1864 | WM | 19mm | — | — | 50.00 |

As 522. Plain edge. Rarity 9.

| 522E | 1864 | Silver | 19mm | — | — | 150. |

As 522. Plain edge. Rarity 8. (Fuld NY 630K-9f; H-G 5308; Miller NY 133)

Apparently all the Brimelow cards except 522 were good for one glass of soda water rather than one cent, except that Baker 521 with a numeral 2 may have been good for two glasses. The brimelow card dies of type 522 were cut by the New York diesinker, Louis Roloff, and probably were intended as cents.

BROAS BROTHERS

Baker	Date	Metal	Size	VF	EF	Unc
523	1963	Copper	19mm	—	—	6.00

Undraped bust right over crosses flags, UNITED WE STAND around, 1863 below (Fuld CW die 1143). Rv: OUR / COUNTRY within circular olive wreath, BROAS BROTHERS above, * PIE BAKERS. * below. Plain edge. Rarity 3. (Fuld NY 630M-13a; H-G 5368)

Baker	Date	Metal	Size			
523A	1863	Brass	19mm	—	—	8.00

As 523. Plain edge. Rarity 4.

| 523B | 1863 | Nickel | 19mm | — | — | 45.00 |

As 523. Plain edge. Rarity 9.

| 523C | 1863 | Silver | 19mm | — | — | 200. |

As 523. Plain edge. Rarity 9. (Fuld NY 630M-13f)

| 523D | 1863 | Lead | 19m | — | — | 45.00 |

As 523. Plain edge. Rarity 9. (Fuld NY 630M-13g)

JOHN K. CURTIS
New York, N.Y.

Baker	Date	Metal	Size	F	VF	Unc
529	1861	Silver	32mm	—	—	500.

Military bust left. Around: GEORGE WASHINGTON, THE CINCINNATUS OF AMERICA. Below: B. 1732 D. 1799. Rv: Within corded circle: *****/ JOHN K. CURTIS / WATCH-MAKER / & MANUFACTURING / JEWELER / 83/ BLEECKER ST & / 882 BROADWAY / NEW YORK. / ***Outside circle: "SAVE MY COUNTRY HEAVEN" / 1861. Reeded edge. Rarity 9. (Miller NY 171)

| 529A | 1861 | Copper | 32mm | 15.00 | 25.00 | 70.00 |

As 529. Reeded edge. Rarity 7. (Miller NY 172)

| 529B | 1861 | Brass | 32mm | 15.00 | 25.00 | 70.00 |

As 529. Reeded edge. Rarity 7. (Miller NY 173)

| 529C | 1861 | WM | 32mm | 15.00 | 25.00 | 70.00 |

As 529. Reeded edge. Rarity 7. (Miller NY 174)

George Hampden Lovett cut the dies for the Curtis cards. Other Curtis cards show busts of Johannes Allan and "The Antiquary" (an elderly coin collector) or a view of the steamer *Great Eastern*.

C. DOSCHER

Baker	Date	Metal	Size	VF	EF	Unc
532	1863	Copper	19mm	6.00	8.00	15.00

Head right, C. DOSCHER 241 WASHN. ST. N.Y. around , 1863. below. Rv: NOT / ONE / CENT / H within olive wreath (Fuld CW die 1254).Plain edge. Rarity 2. (Fuld NY 630V-6a; H-G 5420)
There is one dot beneath the T of ST. on 532. On 532B, there are two dots under the T.

| 532B | 1863 | Copper | 19mm | 6.00 | 8.00 | 15.00 |

Obverse similar to 532, but date 1863, is much smaller. Plain edge. Rarity 2. (Fuld NY 630V-7a; H-G 5421)

| 532C | 18.. | Copper | 19mm | — | 20.00 | — |

As 532B but struck from broken die which has obscured part of the date on obverse. (Fuld NY 630V-7a1)

| 532D | 18.. | Lead | 19mm | — | — | Unique |

As 532C. Plain edge. Rarity 10. (Fuld NY 630V-7g; H-G 5423)
Struck by Charles D. Horter of New York.

A. GAVRON

Baker	Date	Metal	Size	VF	EF	Unc
535	1863	Copper	19mm	—	—	100.

Obverse as Baker 508 (Fuld CW die 1137). Rv: A. GAVRON / -213- / BOWERY / -&- / 102 PITT ST. / -N.Y.- / SAUSAGES. Plain edge. Rarity 9. (Fuld NY 630AB-2a; H-G 5463)

| 535A | 1863 | Brass | 19mm | — | — | 75.00 |

As 535. Plain edge. Rarity 7. (Fuld NY 630AB-2b; H-G 5464)

| 535B | 1863 | Nickel | 19mm | — | — | 150. |

As 535. Plain edge. Rarity 7. Magnetic

| 535C | 1863 | CN | 19mm | — | — | 175. |

As 535. Plain edge. Rarity 8. (The German silver version reported by Baker does not exist;it is actually copper-nickel alloy)

| 535D | 1863 | WM | 19mm | — | — | 200. |

As 535. Plain edge. Rarity 9.

| 535E | 1863 | Silver | 19mm | — | — | 300. |

As 535. Plain edge. Rarity 9. (Fuld NY 630AB-2f)

| 535J | ND | Copper | 20mm | 6.00 | 8.00 | 15.00 |

Obverse as Baker 509 (Fuld CW die 1265). Rv: As reverse of 535. Plain edge. Rarity 2. (Fuld NY 630AB-6a; H-G 5483)

H. D. GERDTS

Baker	Date	Metal	Size	VF	EF	Unc
537	1863	Copper	19mm	10.00	12.00	20.00

Obverse as 508 (Fuld CW die 1137). Rv: H.D. GERDTS / BROKER / -&- / COIN DEALER / -240- / GREENWICH ST. N.Y. Plain edge. Rarity 3. (Fuld NY 630AD-la; H-G 5508)

| 537A | 1863 | Brass | 19mm | — | — | 50.00 |

As 537. Plain edge. Rarity 7.

| 537B | 1863 | Nickel | 19mm | — | — | 150. |

As 537. Plain edge. Rarity 9. Magnetic.

| 537C | 1863 | CN | 19mm | — | — | 250. |

As 537. Plain edge. Rarity 9. Struck over U.S. cent.

| 537D | 1863 | WM | 19mm | — | — | 200. |

As 537. Plain edge. Rarity 9. (Fuld NY 630AD-1e; H-G 5512)

| 537E | 1863 | Silver | 18mm | — | 225. | 375. |

As 537. Reeded edge. Rarity 9. Struck over U.S.dime. (Fuld NY 630AD-1fo)

E. HILL
New York, N.Y.

Baker	Date	Metal	Size	EF	Unc	Proof
542	1860	Silver	28mm	150.	250.	—

Obverse as Baker 211 (undraped bust left, KEY under bust, PATRIAE PATER/ 1732 around. Rv: E. HILL, / DEALER IN / COINS, MEDALS,/ MINERALS / AUTOGRAPHS / ENGRAVINGS, / OLD CURIOSITIES & C / NO. 6 / BLEECKER ST. N. YORK / 1860. Plain edge. Rarity 8. (Miller NY 305)

| 542A | 1860 | Copper | 28mm | 25.00 | 50.00 | — |

As 542. Plain edge. Rarity 6. (Miller NY 307)

| 542B | 1860 | Brass | 28mm | 25.00 | 50.00 | — |

As 542. Plain edge. Rarity 6. (Miller NY 306)

| 542C | 1860 | WM | 28mm | 25.00 | 50.00 | — |

As 542. Plain edge. Rarity 6. (Miller NY 308)

GEORGE HYENLEIN

Baker	Date	Metal	Size	VF	EF	Unc
543	ND	Copper	19mm	6.00	8.00	15.00

Head right in oval frame, on a large 5-pointed star, classic wreath around. below: E. SIGEL 177 WILLIAM N.Y. (same obverse as Baker 471, Fuld CW die 1132). Rv: GEORGE HYENLEIN / * / 23 / CHRYSTIE ST. / N.Y. Plain edge. Rarity 2. (Fuld NY 630AL-3a; H-G 5614)
Tokens struck by Emil Sigel of New York, located at this Civil War period at 177 William Street.

H. M. LANE

Baker	Date	Metal	Size	VF	EF	Unc
554	ND	Copper	19mm	6.00	8.00	15.00

Obverse as Baker 543 (Fuld CW die 1132). Rv: H.M. LANE / LAMPS / KEROSENE OIL & C / 18 /SPRING ST. N.Y. Plain edge. Rarity 1. (Fuld NY 630AP-5a; H-G 5661)

| 554A | ND | Brass | 19mm | — | — | 50.00 |

As 554. Plain edge. Rarity 7.

| 554B | ND | Nickel | 19mm | — | — | 150. |

As 554. Plain edge. Rarity 8. Magnetic.

Baker	Date	Metal	Size	VF	EF	Unc
554C	ND	CN	19mm	—	—	175.

As 554. Plain edge. Rarity 9.

| 554D | ND | GS | 19mm | — | — | 225. |

As 554. Plain edge. Rarity 9.

| 554E | ND | WM | 19mm | — | — | 150. |

As 554. Plain edge. Rarity 9. (Fuld NY 630AP-5e; H-G 5665)

The Lane tokens were struck by Emil Sigel of New York.

C. MAGNUS

Baker	Date	Metal	Size	VF	EF	Unc
557	ND	Copper	19mm	—	—	75.00

Small undraped bust right in circle at center. Around: 100 ENTITLE TO A $2.00 VIEW / OF / *NEW YORK CITY.*. RV: Eagle and scroll on Shield, NEW YORK. above. Around: C. MAGNUS; NATIONAL PRINTING ESTABLISHMENT. Plain edge. Rarity 7.(Fuld NY 630AS-1a; H-G 5763

| 557A | ND | Brass | 19mm | 8.00 | 10.00 | 20.00 |

As 557. Plain edge. Rarity 3.

| 557B | ND | WM | 19mm | — | — | 175. |

As 557. Plain edge. Rarity 9. (Fuld NY 630AS-1e; H-G 5765)

| 557F | ND | Copper | 19mm | — | — | 150. |

Bust and central circle as on 557, but all inscriptions are missing (Fuld CW die 1141). Rv: As reverse of 557. Plain edge. Rarity 9. (Fuld NY 630AS-2a; H-G 5768)

J. MAHNKEN

Baker	Date	Metal	Size	VF	EF	Unc.
558	ND	Copper	20mm	8.00	10.00	20.00

Obverse as Baker 509 (Fuld CW die 1265). Rv; J. MAHNKEN / 19 & 22 / WEST ST. / -N. Y. - / LIQUORS & SEGARS. Plain edge. Rarity 3. (Fuld NY 630AT-4a; H-G 5772)

MONK'S METAL SIGNS

Baker	Date	Metal	Size	VF	EF	Unc
562	1863	Copper	19mm	6.00	8.00	15.00

Undraped bust right within olive wreath, 399 B'WAY. N.Y. above, *** 1863 ***. Rv: MONK'S / *** / METAL /-*- / SIGNS. surrounded by circle of 34 stars and a small eagle at bottom completing the star-chain. Plain edge. Rarity 3. (Fuld NY 630BB-7a; H-G 5827)

| 562A | 1863 | Copper | 19mm | — | — | 50.00 |

As 562, but on thick flan. Plain edge.

| 562B | 1863 | Brass | 19mm | 25.00 | 35.00 | 60.00 |

As 562. Plain edge. Rarity 4.

| 562 C | 1863 | Brass | 19mm | 25.00 | 35.00 | 60.00 |

As 562B, but on thick flan. Plain edge.

| 562D | 1863 | Nickel | 19mm | — | — | 175. |

As 562. Plain edge. Rarity 8. Magnetic.

| 562E | 1863 | CN | 19mm | — | — | 150. |

As 562. Plain edge. Rarity 8.

| 562F | 1863 | CN | 19mm | — | — | 250. |

As 562E, but struck over U.S. small cent. Rarity 9.

| 562G | 1863 | WM | 19mm | — | — | 150. |

As 562. Plain edge. Rarity 9.

| 562H | 1863 | Silver | 19mm | — | — | 300. |

As 582. Plain edge. Rarity 9. (Fuld Ny 630BB-7f; H-G 5832)

| 469 | 1863 | Copper | 19mm | 25.00 | 35.00 | 60.00 |

Obverse as 562. Rv:1 / O.U./1/ CENT within oak and olive wreath (Fuld CWdie 1267). Plain edge. Rarity 4. (Fuld NY630BB-14a; H-G 5858)

| 469A | 1863 | Copper | 19mm | — | — | 60.00 |

As 469, but on thick flan. Plain edge.

| 469B | 1863 | Brass | 19mm | — | — | 75.00 |

As 469. Plain edge. Rarity 7.

| 469C | 1863 | Nickel | 19mm | — | — | 175. |

As 469. Plain edge. Magnetic. Rarity 9.

| 469D | 1863 | CN | 19mm | — | — | 100. |

As 469. Plain edge. Rarity 8.

| 469E | 1863 | WM | 19mm | — | — | 150. |

As 469. Plain edge. Rarity 9.

| 469F | 1863 | Silver | 19mm | — | — | 300. |

As 469. Plain edge. Rarity 9. (Fuld Ny 630BB-14f)

Baker	Date	Metal	Size	VF	EF	Unc
470	1863	Copper	19mm	—	—	75.00

Obverse as 562.Rv: NOT / ONE / CENT within olive wreath (Fuld CW die 1253). Plain edge. Rarity 7. (Fuld NY 630 BB-13a; H-G5853)

| 470A | 1863 | Copper | 19mm | — | — | 75.00 |

As 470, but on thick flan. Plain edge.

| 470B | 1863 | Brass | 19mm | — | — | 75.00 |

As 470. Plain edge. Rarity 7.

| 470C | 1863 | Nickel | 19mm | — | — | 175. |

As 470. Plain edge. Rartiy 8. Magnetic.

| 470D | 1863 | CN | 19mm | — | — | 100. |

As 470. Plain edge. Rarity 8.

| 470E | 1863 | GS | 19mm | — | — | 175. |

As 470. Plain edge. Rarity 8.

| 470F | 1863 | WM | 19mm | — | — | 150.00 |

As 470. Plain edge. Rarity 9. (Fuld NY 630BB-13e)

NOTE: The obverse die Baker 562, used in the Monk's Metal Signs series, was also muled with all these other Fuld Civil War numbered dies: 1000 (Liberty head in Phrygian cap left , 13 stars around, 1863 below); 1218 (eagle and scroll on shield UNITED STATES OF AMERICA around, 1863 below); 1219 (eagle and scroll on shield, UNITED STATES MEDAL around, 1863 below); 1236 (shield in wreath / OUR / COUNTRY / -*- within circular wreath); 1252 (similar) to reverse of Baker 470, from differing die); and 1277 (UNITED / -*- / COUNTRY within oval, all surrounded by border of stars).

Each of these mulings is struck in multiple metals and listing them would be tedious. Specialists in this series may refer to *U.S. Civil War Store Cards* by George and Melvin Fuld for full details.

G. PARSONS
New York, N.Y.

Baker	Date	Metal	Size	VF	EF	Unc
565	ND	Copper	19mm	—	—	150.

Obverse as Baker 543 (Fuld CW die 1132 by Emil Sigel). Rv: G. PARSONS / 24 / JOHN ST. / N.Y. / * FIREWORKS * Plain edge. Rarity 9. (Fuld NY 630BE-4a; H-G 5899)

| 565A | ND | Brass | 19mm | — | — | 150. |

As 565. Plain edge. Rarity 7.

| 565B | ND | Nickel | 19mm | — | — | 200. |

As 565. Plain edge. Rarity 9.

| 565C | ND | WM | 19mm | — | — | 150. |

As 565. Plain edge. Rarity 8. (Fuld NY 630BW-4e; H-G 5903)

| 565F | 1863 | Copper | 19mm | — | — | 150. |

Obverse as Baker 508 (Fuld CW die 1137) Rv: As reverse of 565. Plain edge. Rarity 9. (Fuld NY 630BE-5a; H-G 5905)

JOHN QUINN

Baker	Date	Metal	Size	VF	EF	Unc
567	1863	Copper	19mm	—	—	150.

Obverse as Baker 508 (Fuld CW die 1137). Rv: JOHN QUINN / (eagle displayed) / GROCER / COR 26 STS. / LEXINGTON AV. Plain edge. Rarity 9. (Fuld NY 630BG-2a; H-G 5964)

| 567A | 1863 | Brass | 19mm | — | — | 125. |

As 567. Plain edge. Rarity 8. (Also known on thin planchet).

| 567B | 1863 | Nickel | 19mm | — | — | 200. |

As 567. Plain edge. magnetic. Rarity 9.

| 567C | 1863 | CN | 19mm | — | — | 200. |

As 567. Plain edge . Rarity 9.

| 567D | 1863 | WM | 19mm | — | — | 150. |

As 567. Plain edge. Rarity 8.

| 567E | 1863 | Silver | 19mm | — | — | 300. |

As 567. Plain edge. Rarixy 9. (Fuld NY 630BG-2f; H-G 5970)

| 567J | ND | Copper | 20mm | 6.00 | 8.00 | 15.00 |

Obverse as Baker 509 (Fuld CW die 1265). Rv: As reverse of 567. Plain edge. Rarity 2. (Fuld NY 630BG-6a; H-G 5983)

ROBBINS, ROYCE & HARD

Struck 1859

Baker	Date	Metal	Size	VF	EF	Unc
568	ND	Silver	19mm	—	150.	250.

Undraped bust left. Around: REPRESENTED BY / WM. LEGGETT BRAMHALL. Rv: ROBBINS ROYCE & HARD / WHOLESALE / DEALERS IN/ DRY GOODS/ 70 / READE ST. NEW YORK. Plain edge. Only 7 struck. (Miller NY 666)

Baker	Date	Metal	Size	VF	EF	Unc
568A	ND	Copper	19mm	—	25.00	45.00

As 568. Plain edge. Only 52 struck. (Miller NY 667)

| 568B | ND | Brass | 19mm | — | 25.00 | 45.00 |

As 568. Plain edge. only 52 struck. (Miller NY 668)

| 568C | ND | Nickel | 19mm | — | 35.00 | 55.00 |

As 568. Plain edge. Rarity 6.

| 568D | ND | CN | 19mm | 15.00 | 25.00 | 45.00 |

As 568. Plain edge. 250 pieces struck. (Miller NY 669)

| 568E | ND | WM | 19mm | — | — | 125. |

As 568. Plain edge. Only 15 struck. (Miller NY 670)

Struck 1860

Baker	Date	Metal	Size	VF	EF	Unc
569	ND	Silver	19mm	—	175.	350.

Obverse of 568. Rv: ROBBINS, ROYCE & HARD / JOBBERS / OF / STAPLE / & FANCY / DRY GOODS, 70 READE & / 112 DUANE STS. / NEW YORK. Plain edge. Only 20 struck. (Miller NY 671)

| 569A | ND | Copper | 19mm | — | — | 100. |

As 569. Plain edge. Only 35 struck. (Miller NY 672)

| 569B | ND | Brass | 19mm | — | — | 100. |

As 569.Plain edge. Only 35 struck. (Miller NY 673)

| 569C | ND | Nickel | 19mm | — | 50.00 | 80.00 |

As 569. Plain edge. Magnetic. Several hundred struck. (Miller NY 675)

| 569D | ND | CN | 19mm | — | 50.00 | 80.00 |

As 569. Plain edge. Rarity 6.

| 569E | ND | WM | 19mm | — | 100. | 125. |

As 569. Plain edge. Only 15 struck. (Miller NY 674)

During the winter of 1858-59, on the order of William Leggett Bramhall, the Robbins , Royce and Hard cards of type Baker 568 were executed by George Hampden Lovett. The cupronickel variety was struck on planchets secured at the U.S. Mint at Philadelphia by Lovett. Bramhall was under the impression that his was possibly the first token issued of the size of the cupronickel cent , struck in that metal.

As the reverse of Baker 568 did not suit his purpose, he next issued Baker 569.

During the autumn of 1860, Bramhall was persuaded by some of his friends to issue a limited number of mulings in different metals using his dies. The number of these was very limited. Most of the Bramhall mulings are outside the scope of this work, but one at least is in it:

Struck 1860

Baker	Date	Metal	Size	VF	EF	Unc
569M	ND	Silver	19mm	—	—	275.

Obverse as 568. Rv: Shield, WIDEAWAKES. Plain edge. Only 3 struck.

| 569N | ND | Copper | 19mm | — | — | 150. |

As 569M. Plain edge. Only 15 struck.

| 569P | ND | Brass | 19mm | — | — | 150. |

As 569M. Plain edge. Only 15 Struck.

| 569Q | ND | CN | 19mm | — | — | 150. |

As 569M Plain edge. Only 15 struck.

| 569R | ND | WM | 19mm | — | — | 150. |

As 569M. Plain edge. Only 15 struck.

See Russ Rulau's *U.S. Merchant Tokens 1845-1860*, pages 75-76 for full data on the Robbins, Royce and Hard series of cards and medalets.

William Leggett Bramhall was the first curator of the American Numismatic Society museum in Manhattan. Part of his collection was sold at auction by Bangs, Merwin & Co. on May 4-5, 1859.

569M - 569R were cataloged previously as Baker 384 - 384E in Chapter 23.

A. B. SAGE & CO.
New York, N.Y.

Baker	Date	Metal	Size	VF	EF	Unc
570	1859	WM	16mm	—	20.00	45.00

Roman-mantled bust right, above crossed palm branches, GEORGE WASHINGTON above. Rv: A. B. SAGE & CO. / DEALERS / IN / COINS, MEDALS, / AUTOGRAPHS / & ENGRAVINGS / 24 DIVISION ST./ N. 1859 Y. Plain edge. Rarity 6. (Miller NY 768)

| 570A | 1859 | Copper | 16mm | — | — | Unique |

As 570. Plain edge. Rarity 9.

| 570B | 1859 | Brass | 16mm | — | 40.00 | 75.00 |

As 570. Plain edge.

Baker	Date	Metal	Size	VF	EF	Unc
572	1859	Silver	21mm	—	150.	250.

Roman-mantled bust left, PATER PATRIAE around (same obverse as Baker 244). Rv: GOOD FOR ONE CHANCE / IN / RAFFLE / FOR NUMISMATIC / BOOKS / AT / A. B. SAGE & CO. / N.Y./ NOV. 1859. Plain edge. Rarity 8. (Miller NY 761)

| 572A | 1859 | Copper | 21mm | — | 25.00 | 45.00 |

As 572. Plain edge. Rarity 6. (Miller NY 762)

| 572B | 1859 | Brass | 21mm | — | 25.00 | 55.00 |

As 572. Plain edge. Rarity 7. (Miller NY 763)

| 572C | 1859 | WM | 21mm | — | 25.00 | 60.00 |

As 572. Plain edge. Rarity 6. (Miller NY 764)

Baker	Date	Metal	Size	VF	EF	Unc
571	1860	Silver	21mm	—	150.	250.

Obverse as 572. Rv: A.B. SAGE & CO'S / CIRCULATING / LIBRARY / 24 / DIVISION ST. N.Y. / TERMS / 1 YEAR $2.00 / 6 MONTHS 1.00 / 3 MONTHS.50 / 1860. Plain edge. Rarity 8. (Miller NY 757)

| 571A | 1860 | Copper | 21mm | — | 15.50 | 40.00 |

AS 571. Plain edge. Rarity 6. (Miller NY 758)

| 571B | 1860 | Brass | 21mm | — | 15.50 | 40.00 |

As 571. Plain edge. Rarity 6. (Miller NY 759)

| 571C | 1860 | WM | 21mm | — | 15.50 | 40.00 |

As 571. Plain edge. Rarity 6.(Miller NY 760)

| 571D | 1860 | CN | 21mm | — | 30.00 | 60.00 |

As 571. Plain edge. Rarity 7. (Miller NY 760A)

Augustus B. Sage was a prolific issuer of store cards, historical tokens, medalets and other numismatic items in an era when such activities were spurred by sales to interested people. George Hampden Lovett, a workman noted more for his prodigious output than his artistic diesinking and engraving, did Sage's striking in New York City.

H. G. SAMPSON
New York, N.Y.

Baker	Date	Metal	Size	VF	EF	Unc
573	1876	Silver	42mm	—	—	500.

Undraped bust right, TO COMMEMORATE THE 100TH ANNIVERSA-RY OF THE above, DECLARATION OF / INDEPENDENCE below, all within a circular ornamental border. LOVETT on truncation of bust. (Same obverse as Baker 388.) Rv: stamping machine lettered H. G. SAMPSON at center. Around it: H. G. SAMPSON, DEALER IN RARE AMERICAN & FOREIGN COINS, MEDALS & STAMPS. / COR. BROADWAY & FULTON ST. NEW YORK / 1876 / CENTENNIAL / LIN-EN MARKER / WHOLESALE & RETAIL/ MANUFACTORY / *81 BUSH-WICK AV. , BROOKLYN.* / E. D. Plain edge. Rarity 8. (Rulau NY-NY 270; Miller NY 774)

Baker	Date	Metal	Size	VF	EF	Unc
573A	1876	Copper	42mm	—	—	150.

As 573. Plain edge. Rarity 7. (Rulau NY-NY 270A; Miller NY 775)

Baker	Date	Metal	Size	VF	EF	Unc
573B	1876	Brass	42mm	—	—	150.

As 573. Plain edge. Rarity 7. (Rulau NY-NY 270B; Miller NY 776)

Baker	Date	Metal	Size	VF	EF	Unc
573C	1876	WM	42mm	—	—	150.

As 573. Plain edge. Rarity. 7. (Rulau NY-NY 270C; Miller NY 778)

N. J. SCHLOSS & CO.

Circa 1885

Baker	Date	Metal	Size	VF	EF	Unc
696	1778	Brass	36mm	8.50	10.50	16.00

Undraped bust right within beaded circle. Around: GEORGE WASH-INGTON / *COMMANDER IN CHIEF* Rv: Within oak and olive wreath: IN / COMMEMORARTION / OF THE / DEPARTURE / OF THE / CON-TINENTAL / ARMY / JUNE 19/ 1778, all within a beaded circle. Around: N. J. SCHLOSS & CO. BOYS CLOTHING / *NEW YORK* Plain Edge.

STORY & SOUTHWORTH

First reverse

Baker	Date	Metal	Size	VF	EF	Unc
575	ND	Brass	19mm	—	—	100.

Obverse as Baker 543 (Fuld CW die 1132 by Emil Sigel). Rv: STORY & SOUTHWORTH / GROCERS / 53 / VESEY / ST. / * N.Y. * (On this first reverse type, the legend STORY & SOUTHWORTH ends above the word VESEY). Plain edge. Rarity 8. (Fuld NY 630BV-5b; H-G 6110)

Baker	Date	Metal	Size	VF	EF	Unc
575A	ND	Nickel	19mm	—	—	200.

As 575. Plain edge. Rarity 9.

Baker	Date	Metal	Size	VF	EF	Unc
575B	ND	CN	19mm	—	—	200.

As 575. Plain edge. Rarity 9.

Baker	Date	Metal	Size	VF	EF	Unc
575C	ND	WM	19mm	—	—	200.

As 575. Plain edge. Rarity 9.

Baker	Date	Metal	Size	VF	EF	Unc
575D	ND	Silver	19mm	—	—	300.

As 575. Plain edge. Rarity 9. (Fuld NY 630BV-5f; H-G 6114)

Second reverse

Baker	Date	Metal	Size	VF	EF	Unc
575H	ND	Copper	19mm	—	—	Unique

Obverse as 575. Rv: Similar to reverse of 575, but STORY & SOUTH-WORTH name ends below word VESEY. Plain edge. Rarity 10. (Fuld NY 630BV-20a; H-G 6177)

Baker	Date	Metal	Size	VF	EF	Unc
575J	ND	Brass	19mm	—	—	100.

As 575H. Plain edge. Rarity 8.

Baker	Date	Metal	Size	VF	EF	Unc
575K	ND	Nickel	19mm	—	—	175.

As 575H. Plain edge. Rarity 9.

Baker	Date	Metal	Size	VF	EF	Unc
575L	ND	CN	19mm	—	Unique	—

As 575H. Plain edge. Rarity 10.

Baker	Date	Metal	Size	VF	EF	Unc
575M	ND	Wm	19mm	—	—	150.

As 575H. Plain edge. Rarity 8. (Fuld NY 630BV-20e; H-G 6181)

Emil Sigel of New York struck the Story & Southworth cards, some of which were intended only for the collector market.

STRASSBURGER & NUHN
New York, N.Y.
Struck 1850s

Baker	Date	Metal	Size	VF	EF	Unc
576	ND	Brass	22mm	20.00	35.00	70.00

Bust in civil dress facing slightly right, head three-quarters left, GENER-AL WASHINGTON around. Rv: Capitol at Washington. Above: STRASSBURGER & NUHN / CORNER, MAIDEL LANE / & WILLIAM STREET. In exergue: CAPITOL AT WASHINGTON. Plain edge. Rarity 4. (Miller NY 846; R-F 237; Kurth 52)

Baker	Date	Metal	Size	VF	EF	Unc
576D	ND	Brass	22mm	20.00	35.00	70.00

Obverse similar to 576, but head is smaller and the legend in larger let-ters. Rv: As reverse of 576. Plain edge. Rarity 4. (Miller NY 847; R-F 237A; Kurth 52A; Bushnell 103)

Probably struck by Ludwig Christian Lauer in Nuremberg, Germany. Strass-burger & Nuhn issued a lengthy series of game counter-type store cards for use in their business; Baker 576 is a $5 gold piece-sized counter.

WM. F. WARNER
New York, N.Y.

Baker	Date	Metal	Size	VF	EF	Unc
584	ND	Copper	20mm	6.00	8.00	15.00

Obverse as Baker 509 (Fuld CW die 1265). Rv: WM, F. WARNER / -104- / BARCLAY / -ST- / NEW-YORK. Plain edge. Rarity 3. (Fuld NY 630CB-2a; H-G 6266)

C. WOLF CLARK & SPIES
New York, N.Y.
Issued 1829

Baker	Date	Metal	Size	VG	F	EF
588	ND	Brass	26mm	500.	800.	1400.

Head right, WASHINGTON curving above, within oval frame. Around: C. WOLFE CLARK & SPIES NEW YORK / HARDWARE & / * . MILI-TARY STORE . *. Rv: Military bust of Andrew Jackson facing three-quarters left, JACKSON curving above, within oval frame. The field is plain. Reeded edge. Rarity 8. (Rulau-E NY 958)

Baker	Date	Metal	Size	VG	F	EF
588C	ND	Copper	26mm	—	—	100.

As 586. Reeded edge. (All known pieces in copper are counterfeits) (Hirsch coll.)

At this late juncture, it seems unlikely we'll find out why this firm proceeded to change the ranking of its partners to C. Wolfe, Spies & Clark as in the examples which follow.

Baker 588 was struck by Thomas Kettle of Birmingham, England, apparently.

C. WOLFE, SPIES & CLARK
Struck 1829

Baker	Date	Metal	Size	VG	F	EF
591	1823	Brass	26mm	550.	1200.	—

Central oval as on obverse of 588, and legend is the same except first line now reads: C. WOLFE SPIES & CLARK. Rv: Eagle with wings dis-played. U.S. shield on its breast, grasping olive branch and arrows. NEW YORK GRAND CANAL around, OPENED / 1823 below. Plain edge- Rarity 8. (Rulau-E NY 961)

Baker	Date	Metal	Size	VG	F	EF
589	ND	Brass	26mm	500.	800.	1200.

Obverse as 591. Rv: Central oval as on reverse of 588, but inscription added in field: CUTLERY, PLATED WARE / GUNS &C / 193 / * . PEARL ST. N.Y. . *. Reeded edge. Rarity 7. (Rulau-E NY 962)

Baker	Date	Metal	Size	VG	F	EF
589A	ND	S/Brass	26mm	550.	900.	—

As 589. Reeded edge. Rarity 8.

Baker	Date	Metal	Size	VG	F	EF
590	ND	Brass	26mm	750.	1000.	1500.

Obverse as 591. Rv: Uniformed Jackson bust facing three-quarters left in upright octagonal frame, JACKSON curving around head inside frame. The field is plain. Plain edge. Rarity 8. (Rulau-E NY 959)

| 590C | ND | Copper | 26mm | — | — | — |

As 590. Plain edge. (All known pieces in copper are counterfeits)

| 592 | ND | Brass | 26mm | 750. | 2000. | — |

Obverse as 591. Rv: George IV head left, GEORGE IV KING OF GREAT BRITAIN. around. Plain edge. Rarity 8. (Rulau-E NY 963)

The origins of the firm which issued Baker 588 through 592 go back before the War of 1812. Christopher and John Dash Wolfe sold military and naval supplies, hardware and cutlery under the firm name C. & J. D. Wolfe (it reads C. & 1. D. WOLFE on their own tokens, which do not exhibit a Washington portrait). The firm was located at 87 Maiden Lane opposite Clark & Brown's Coffee House, at the corner of Maiden Lane and Gold Street. John D. Wolfe married Miss Lorillard of the tobacco family and was reputed to be very wealthy.

C. & J. D. Wolfe appear in the New York directories 1821 to 1828. About 1829 the firm dissolved. Christopher Wolfe joined with Adam W. Spies and R. Smith Clark to form C. Wolfe, Clark & Spies in 1829, quickly changing the name to C. Wolfe, Spies & Clark, hardware, cutlery and military goods, at 193 Pearl Street, listed there 1829 through 1833.

John Dash Wolfe formed J. D. Wolfe, Bishop & Co., hardware and military goods, still located at the 87 Maiden Lane address 1829-1833.

Though dated 1823, Baker 591 could not have been issued before 1829, as directory evidence shows. All the tokens of this firm are very rare and all were struck in Birmingham, England by Thomas Kettle. (See Russ Rulau's Early American Tokens, and Coin Collector's Journal for January, 1935 for additional details.)

WOODGATE & CO.

Baker	Date	Metal	Size	VF	EF	Unc
593	1860	Silver	27mm	-	200.	300.

Obverse as Baker 211 (undraped bust left in arched frame, KEY under bust, PATRIAE PATER 1732 around). Rv: WOODGATE & CO. / IMPORTERS / OF / BRANDIES / WINES, 83 GINS &C / WATER STREET, / NEW-YORK / 1860. Reeded edge. Rarity 8; only 5 pieces struck. (Miller NY 972A)

| 593A | 1860 | Copper | 27mm | — | 25.00 | 60.00 |

As 593. Reeded edge. Rarity 6. (Miller NY 972)

| 593B | 1860 | Brass | 27mm | — | 25.00 | 60.00 |

As 593. Reeded edge. Rarity 6. (Miller NY 973)

| 593C | 1860 | WM | 27mm | — | 25.00 | 70.00 |

As 593. Reeded edge. Rarity 6. (Miller NY 974)

WRIGHT & BALE
New York, N.Y.
Issued 1832-33

Baker	Date	Metal	Size	F	VF	Unc
594	ND	Copper	19mm	150.	300.	750.

Obverse as Baker 539 (head right within large oak wreath). Rv: WRIGHT & BALE / ENGRAVERS / & DIE / CUTTERS / 68 NASSAU STREET / PLATES & ROLLS / FOR EMBOSSING / DIES & SEALS OF / EVERY / DESCRIPTION / NEW-YORK. Plain edge. Thick planchet. Rarity 6. (Wright 1275; Low 331; Rulau-E NY 1002)

| 594A | ND | Copper | 19mm | 200. | 300. | 800. |

As 594, but Thin planchet. Plain edge. Rarity 7. (Low 332; Rulau-E NY 1003)

The firm of Charles Cushing Wright and James Bale was founded in May, 1829, buying out the Richard Trested medallic business from Trested's widow, Ann. Bale had been Trested's apprentice. The partnership broke up sometime before October, 1833.

HENDERSON & LOSSING
Poughkeepsie, N.Y.

Struck ca 1832-33

Baker	Date	Metal	Size	VF	EF	Proof
539	ND	Copper	19mm	500.	700.	1200.

Head right, within oak wreath open at the top. Rv: HENDERSON & LOSSING / CLOCK & WATCH MAKERS / & DEALERS IN / WATCHES / JEWELLERY SILVER / W&B POKEEPSIE NY. Plain edge. Rarity 8. (About 10 specimens known, most in proof condition). (Rulau-E NY 1017; Low 317)

This was a partnership between Adam Henderson and Benson J. Lossing, apparently founded about 1832. Henderson appears in the 1830 census, but not Lossing. Lossing gave up the cares of business in 1835, at age 22, to study art and literature; he became a well known historian.

I. J. KNAPP
Utica, N.Y.

Baker	Date	Metal	Size	VF	EF	Unc
553	ND	Copper	20mm	8.00	15.00	30.00

Obverse as Baker 509 (Fuld CW die 1265). Rv: I. J. KNAPP—NO 8- / LIBERTY ST / UTICA / -N. Y.- / WINES & LIQUORS. Plain edge. Rarity 4. (Fuld NY 905B-1a; H-G 6358)

STONER & SHROYER
Adamsville, Ohio
Struck 1870's

Baker	Date	Metal	Size	VF	EF	Unc
574	1799	Copper	19mm	50.00	75.00	125.

Obverse as Baker 559 (Fuld CW die 1134). Rv: STONER & SHROYER / DRY GOODS / ADAMSVILLE / (ornament) OHIO. Plain edge. Rarity 7. (Fuld Ohio 5A-2a; H-G 6406)

| 574A | 1799 | Copper | 19mm | — | — | 150. |

As 574, but on flan 2mm thick. Plain edge.

| 574B | 1799 | Brass | 19mm | — | — | 75.00 |

As 574. Plain edge. Rarity 6.

| 574C | 1799 | Brass | 19mm | — | — | 75.00 |

As 574, but on flan 2mm thick. Rarity 7. Plain edge.

| 574D | 1799 | Nickel | 19mm | — | — | 200. |

As 574. Plain edge. Rarity 9. Magnetic.

| 574E | 1799 | CN | 19mm | — | — | 200. |

As 574. Plain edge. Rarity 9.

| 574F | 1799 | WM | 19mm | — | — | 150. |

As 574. Plain edge. Rarity 8.

| 574G | 1799 | Silver | 19mm | — | — | 400. |

As 574. Plain edge. Rarity 9. (Fuld Ohio 5A-2f; H-G 6411)

There is considerable doubt that the Stoner & Shroyer pieces were struck during the Civil War. They seem to emanate from about 1870-1876. See also Baker 559 and 76. For a full discussion, see "The Stoner & Shroyer Tokens" by Waldo C. Moore in *The Numismatist* for Jan., 1943 and "A New View of the Stoner & Shroyer Tokens" by Max M. Schwartz in The Numismatist for May, 1943.

F. B. ORR
Mansfield, Ohio

Baker	Date	Metal	Size	VF	EF	Unc
564	1863	Copper	19mm	—	—	125.

Obverse as Baker 508 (Fuld CW die 1137). Rv: F. B. ORR. / DEALER IN / HARDWARE / IRON & NAILS / MANSFIELD. 0. Plain edge. Rarity 8. (Fuld Ohio 505B-2a; H-G 8551)

| 564A | 1863 | Brass | 19mm | — | — | 100. |

As 564. Plain edge. Rarity 7.

| 564B | 1863 | Brass | 19mm | — | — | Unique |

As 564A, but struck over double-struck New York CW token. Plain edge. (Fuld Ohio 505B-2bo)

| 564C | 1863 | Nickel | 19mm | — | — | 150. |

As 564. Plain edge. Rarity 7.

Baker	Date	Metal	Size	VF	EF	Unc.
564D	1863	CN	19mm	—	—	200.

As 564. Plain edge- Rarity 9.

| 564E | 1863 | WM | 19mm | — | — | 150. |

As 564. Plain edge. Rarity 7.

| 564F | 1863 | Silver | 19mm | — | — | 300. |

As 564. Plain edge. Rarity 9. (Fuld Ohio 505B-2f; H-G 8556)

| 564F | 1863 | Silver | 18mm | — | — | 350. |

As 564, but struck over U.S. dime. Reeded edge. Rarity 9. (Fuld Ohio 505B-2fo)

PETERSEN'S JEWELLERS
Honesdale, Pa.

Baker	Date	Metal	Size	VF	EF	Unc
566	1863	Copper	19mm	—	—	75.00

Obverse as Baker 508 (Fuld CW die 1137). Rv: PETERSEN'S / HONESDALE. / SCRANTON / & PITTSTON. / -PA- / JEWELLERS. Plain edge. Rarity 8. (Fuld Pa 464A-2a; H-G 9256)

| 566A | 1863 | Brass | 19mm | — | — | 75.00 |

As 566. Plain edge. Rarity 8.

| 566B | 1863 | Nickel | 19mm | — | — | 150. |

As 566. Plain edge. Magnetic. Rarity 7.

| 566C | 1863 | CN | 19mm | — | — | 150. |

As 566. Plain edge. Rarity 8.

| 566D | 1863 | CN | 19mm | — | — | 250. |

As 566C, but struck over U.S. small cent. Plain edge. Rarity 9.

| 566E | 1863 | WM | 19mm | — | — | 150. |

As 566. Plain edge. Rarity 9.

| 566F | 1863 | Silver | 19mm | — | — | 300. |

As 566. Plain edge. Rarity 9. (Fuld Pa 464A-2f; H-G 9261)

MT. HOLLY PAPER CO.
Mt. Holly Springs, Pa.

Baker	Date	Metal	Size	VF	EF	Unc.
563	1860	Silver	20.5mm	—	250.	525.

Uniformed Washington bust left, F. K. on truncation. Around: MT. HOLLY PAPER CO. MT. HOLLY SPRINGS PA. (the PA. is inverted). Rv: 1860 within open-end olive wreath. Plain edge. Rarity 9. (Miller Pa 4)

| 563A | 1860 | Brass | 20.5mm | — | 300. | — |

As 563. Plain edge. Only 1 struck. (Miller Pa 5)

| 563B | 1860 | Copper | 20.5mm | — | 150. | 300. |

As 563. Plain edge. Rarity 7. (Miller Pa 7; Wright 732)

| 563C | 1860 | WM | 20.5mm | — | 200. | 300. |

As 563. Plain edge. Rarity 7. (Miller Pa 6)

These pieces, designed by F. Key, are all rare. Supposedly only 20 pieces in all metals were struck, including a single specimen in brass. Edward Cogan, in his March 25-26, 1862 sale catalog, noted the uniqueness of the brass strike. Apparently both dies broke. The 1860-in-wreath reverse is the same used by Cogan on his own store cards.

There were four owners of the Mount Holly Paper Co. One of them, Sylvester Magargee, lived in Philadelphia. Edward Cogan, ever the entrepreneur, may have had the 20 pieces made as samples to sell the idea of tokens to Magargee, but the latter rejected them. This scenario was envisioned by Elizabeth Steinle, South Charleston, W. Va. collector.

Mt. Holly Paper Co. built its plant on Mountain Creek in 1856. The original owners were the Given Brothers, Mullins, Kempton and Sylvester Magargee. This firm made fine letter and general writing paper, and patented "Commercial Safety Paper," designed to eliminate alterations on checks and documents. It is still in business, now known as Eaton-Dikeman Co., and uses the original building.

Confederate troops captured the plant briefly in 1863 on their way to the Battle of Gettysburg, and some CSA documents have turned up on paper bearing the firm's imprint, which evidently was taken by the invading army.

(See "Trolley to Holly" by Elizabeth W. Steinle in the *TAMS Journal* for Dec., 1978)

S. J. BESTOR
Philadelphia, Pa.
Struck 1858

Baker	Date	Metal	Size	VG	F	EF
514	1799	Silver	33mm	—	—	800.

Uniformed equestrian figure right, a tree at left; on the ground beneath: P H J. Around: THE FATHER OF OUR COUNTRY BORN, FEB. 22, 1732. DIED, DEC. 14, 1799. (same obverse as Baker 387). Rv: Seated female figure points to clock face, TIME IS MONEY above. Around: S. J. BESTOR, IMPORTER OF WATCHES & JEWELRY / * PHILADELPHIA, PA. *. Reeded edge. Rarity 8. (Miller Pa 50)

| 514A | 1799 | Copper | 33mm | 100. | 200. | 400. |

As 514. Reeded edge. Rarity 7. (Miller Pa 51)

| 514B | 1799 | Svd/Cop | 33mm | — | — | 400. |

As 514. Reeded edge. Rarity 7. (Wright 75; Miller Pa 52)

See Baker 387 for a muling of the 514 obverse with a calendar reverse. Peter H. Jacobus of Philadelphia, a diesinker, cut these token dies in 1858. The portraiture, Baker pointed out, is fictitious and not based on an actual portrait of Washington.

CENTENNIAL ADVERTISING MEDAL CO.
Struck 1875

Baker	Date	Metal	Size	VF	EF	Unc
524	ND	Copper	19mm	7.50	11.50	25.00

Obverse as Baker 522 (Fuld CW die 1133). Rv: CENTENNIAL ADVERTISING MEDAL CO. / 1029 / CHESTNUT / ST. / PHILADA. Plain edge. Rarity 6. (Rulau Pa-Ph 15; Fuld NC -10a; Miller Pa 85)

| 524A | ND | Brass | 19mm | 7.50 | 11.50 | 25.00 |

As 524. Plain edge. Rarity 6.

| 524B | ND | WM | 19mm | — | 17.50 | 35.00 |

As 524. Plain edge. Rarity 6.

| 524C | ND | CN | 19mm | — | 17.50 | 35.00 |

As 524. Plain edge. Rarity 9. (Rulau Pa-Ph 19; Fuld not listed)

| 524D | ND | Brass | 22mm | — | — | 50.00 |

As 524, but struck on an oversized brass planchet of irregular shape.

The Centennial Advertising Medal Co., which took over the Lingg token-making operations in 1875, resurrected a Louis Roloff token obverse of the Civil War to make their own store card. The firm was set up to sell medals and tokens during the Independence Exhibition at Philadelphia in 1876.

EDWARD COGAN

Baker	Date	Metal	Size	VF	EF	Unc
527	1859	Copper	32mm	15.00	25.00	50.00

Undraped bust right, LOVETT on truncation. Around: GEORGE WASHINGTON (obverse as Baker 136). Rv: In seven lines: EDWARD COGAN / DEALER IN BOOKS, / COINS, MEDALS / AND / ENGRAVINGS. / 1859 / PHILADELPHIA. Reeded edge. Rarity 5. (Miller Pa 89)

| 527A | 1859 | Bronze | 32mm | 15.00 | 25.00 | 50.00 |

As 527. Reeded edge. Rarity 5.

| 527B | 1859 | WM | 32mm | 17.50 | 27.50 | 60.00 |

As 527. Reeded edge. Rarity 5. (Miller Pa 89A)

| 527C | 1859 | Silver | 32mm | 100. | 250. | 350. |

As 527. Reeded edge. Rarity 7. (Miller Pa 89B)

Cogan became known as the "English daddy of the American coin trade." He closed his flourishing coin business in Philadelphia in 1865 and moved to Brooklyn, N.Y. By 1872, he was a broker at 100 William Street.

Struck 1860

Baker	Date	Metal	Size	VF	EF	Unc
527F	ND	Copper	21mm	—	25.00	50.00

Obverse similar to Baker 527. Rv: EDWARD COGAN / COIN / DEALER / 48 / N. TENTH ST. / PHILADELPHIA. Plain edge. (Miller Pa 92)

| 527G | ND | Brass | 21mm | — | 25.00 | 50.00 |

As 527F. Plain edge. (Miller Pa 93)

Baker	Date	Metal	Size		VF	EF	Unc
527H	ND	Brass	21mm	—		25.00	50.00

As 527F. Plain edge. (Miller Pa 94)

527J	ND	WM	21mm	20.00	30.00	60.00

As 527F. Plain edge. (Miller Pa 91) (Adams Pa 91 and 96)

527K	ND	WM	21mm	—	25.00	50.00

As 527F. Reeded edge. (Miller Pa 95)

527L	ND	CN	21mm	—	25.00	50.00

As 527F. Plain edge. (Miller Pa 97)

527M	ND	CN	21mm	—	25.00	50.00

As 527F. Reeded edge. (Miller Pa 98)

527N	ND	Silver	21mm	—	75.00	150.

As 527F. (Miller Pa 98A)

DICKESON'S COIN & MEDAL SAFE
Philadelphia, Pa.

Circa 1869

Baker	Date	Metal	Size	EF	Unc	Proof
530	ND	Silver	33mm	—	175.	300.

Undraped bust right, LOVETT on truncation and R. L. beneath bust. Around: GEORGE WASHINGTON / * SECURITY *. Rv: Ornate double-door safe at center. Around, in four lines: DICKESON'S COIN & MEDAL SAFE / EVANS & WATSON / * MAKERS.* / 304 CHESTNUT ST. PHILADELPHIA. Plain edge. Less than 10 struck; rarity 8. (Rulau Pa-Ph 30; Miller Pa 142)

530A	ND	Copper	33mm	50.00	85.00	—

As 530. Plain edge. Rarity 6. (Rulau Pa-Ph 31; Miller Pa 143)

530B	ND	Brass	33mm	50.00	85.00	—

As 530. Plain edge. Rarity 6. (Rulau Pa-Ph 32; Miller Pa 144)

530C	ND	CN	33mm	60.00	90.00	—

As 530. Plain edge. Rarity 6.

530D	ND	WM	33mm	60.00	90.00	—

As 530. Plain edge. Rarity 6. (Rulau Pa-Ph 33; Miller Pa 145)

Baker notes that the Dickeson reverse was also struck with the obverse of Baker 160, an 1832 birth centennial medal, but he gives no other information. Fuld in 1965 added that this was probably struck in all metals. No other source gives details and we have not seen it, but a tentative listing follows:

Baker	Date	Metal	Size	EF	Unc	Proof
530J	ND	Copper	33mm			

Obverse as Baker 160. Rv: As reverse of 530. Plain edge.

530K	ND	WM	33mm			

As 530J. Plain edge.

Type 530J was probably muled by Robert Lovett Jr. in 1869 or later; it may also exist in brass, silver and cupronickel versions.

Dr. Montroville Wilson Dickeson, a medical doctor, spent most of his life studying antiquities and archeology. He is responsible for Sommer Islands and Continental Dollar struck copies and authored the *American Numismatic Manual* in 1859. Born in 1813, he died in 1882. See Russ Rulau's U.S. Trade Tokens 1866-1889, pages 124-125, for more of Dickeson's store cards, and see Richard D. Kenney's *Struck Copies of Early American Coins* for some of his better-known imitations of Colonials.

Struck 1870's

Baker	Date	Metal	Size			Unc
615	ND	Copper	33mm	—	—	75.00

Obverse as 530. Rv: Hog standing left, XII above it, all within beaded circle. Around: SOMMER * ISLANDS * (a copy of the Sommer Islands or Bermuda shilling). Plain edge. Rarity 7.

615A	ND	WM	33mm	—	—	75.00

As 615. Plain edge. Rarity 7.

616	ND	Copper	33mm	—	—	75.00

Obverse as 530. Rv: Ship under sail to left, flag flying from each of her four masts. At the side, four guns, one of which is firing. (Copy of the reverse of the Sommer Islands shilling coin). Plain edge. Rarity 7.

616A	ND	WM	33mm	—	—	75.00

As 616. Plain edge. Rarity 7.

GEO. DOLL & CO.
Philadelphia, Pa.

Issued 1850's

Baker	Date	Metal	Size	F	VF	Unc
531	ND	Brass	22mm	15.00	25.00	55.00

Bust facing, GENERAL WASHINGTON above. Rv: GEO. DOLL & CO. / IMPORTERS OF / FANCY GOODS &C / NO. 14, NORTH 6TH ST., PHILADELPHIA. Plain edge. Rarity 4. (Wright 258; R-F Spe-1; Kurth 50; Miller Pa 126)

531A	ND	Brass	22mm	—	—	125.

Obverse as 531. Rv: Blank. Plain edge. Rarity 9. (Miller Pa 126A)

The head on 531 is similar to that on Baker 286, indicating it was probably struck for Doll by Ludwig Christian Lauer of Nuremberg, Germany in the 1850s.

FRANKLIN FIRE CO. NO. 12

Baker	Date	Metal	Size	VF	EF	Unc
S-531	1872	Silver	45mm	—	900.	—

Undraped bust left on a plain field. Rv: Engraved in four lines with many flourishes: FRANKLIN FIRE CO. / NO. 12 / 1792 TO 1872 / GEORGE W. PALMER (or another name). Plain edge. Rarity 7. (Rulau Pa-Ph 85)

The entire strike of these pieces consisted of 29 specimens in silver. A similar specimen appearing in the 1965 Baker revision by Fuld is named to Edward P. Turner. The engraver is not known, though the obverse is good work.

J. HENRY GERCKE
Struck 1875-76

Baker	Date	Metal	Size	F	Unc	Proof
536	ND	Copper	19mm	20.00	35.00	60.00

Obverse as Baker 522 (Fuld CW die 1133). Rv: J. HENRY GERCKE / WATCHMAKER / AND / JEWELER / 1206 PINE ST. PHILA. Plain edge. Rarity 6. (Fuld Pa 750K-1a; H-G not listed; Rulau Pa-Ph 104)

Baker	Date	Metal	Size	F	Unc	Proof
536A	ND	Brass	19mm		75.00	—

As 536. Plain edge. Rarity 6. (Fuld Pa 750K-1 b)

Baker	Date	Metal	Size	F	Unc	Proof
536B	ND	WM	19mm		75.00	—

As 536. Plain edge. Rarity 6. (Fuld Pa 750K-le)

There has always been some question whether the Gercke pieces are in fact Civil War issues. The Gercke card die was muled with the New Masonic Hall, Philadelphia die (Centennial die Z, Fuld NC-14a) which was not prepared until 1874. Recent evidence shows that Gercke was not in business during the Civil War at all, and that the Centennial Advertising Medal Co. of Philadelphia made these mulings in 1875 or 1876.

The Gercke card, in larger size (23mm) was also struck with the Libertas Americana die (Centennial die A) in about 1875.

WILLIAM IDLER

Struck 1860

Baker	Date	Metal	Size	VF	EF	Unc
544	1792	Silver	32mm	200.	250.	400.

Obverse as Baker 24 (uniformed bust left, G. WASHINGTON. PRESIDENT. I. around,1792 below. Rv: WILLIAM IDLER / DEALER IN / COINS, / MINERALS, / STATIONERY / & FANCY ARTICLES. / NO. 111 NORTH 9TH. ST. / PHILADELPHIA, Plain edge. Rarity 9. (Miller Pa 210)

Baker	Date	Metal	Size	VF	EF	Unc
544A	1792	Copper	32mm	50.00	75.00	160.

As 544. Plain edge. Rarity 7. (Miller Pa 211)

Baker	Date	Metal	Size	VF	EF	Unc
544B	1792	Brass	32mm	50.00	75.00	180.

As 544. Plain edge. Rarity 7. (Miller Pa 212)

Baker	Date	Metal	Size	VF	EF	Unc
544C	1792	WM	32mm	50.00	75.00	175.

As 544. Plain edge. Rarity 7. (Miller Pa 212A)

Baker	Date	Metal	Size	VF	EF	Unc
544F	ND	Silver	32mm	100.	150.	200.

Obverse as reverse of Baker 24 (eagle reverse of Idler's imitation Washington half dollar). Rv: As reverse of 544. Plain edge. Rarity 9. (Miller Pa 213)

Baker	Date	Metal	Size	VF	EF	Unc
544G	ND	Copper	32mm	35.00	55.00	100.

As 544F. Plain edge. Rarity 7.

Baker	Date	Metal	Size	VF	EF	Unc
544H	ND	Brass	32mm	35.00	55.00	100.

As 544F. Plain edge. Rarity 7.

Baker	Date	Metal	Size	VF	EF	Unc
544J	ND	WM	32mm	35.00	55.00	100.

As 544F. Plain edge. Rarity 7. (Miller Pa 215A)

Baker	Date	Metal	Size	VF	EF	Unc
545	ND	Silver	20mm	75.00	200.	350.

Undraped bust right, LOVETT under bust, GEORGE WASHINGTON around. Rv: W. IDLER / DEALER IN / COINS, / MINERALS, / SHELLS, / ANTIQUES &C. / 111 N. 9TH. ST. PHILADA. Plain edge. Rarity 8. (Miller Pa 229A)

Baker	Date	Metal	Size	VF	EF	Unc
545A	ND	Copper	20mm	—	20.00	45.00

As 545. Plain edge. Rarity 6. (Miller Pa 229)

Baker	Date	Metal	Size	VF	EF	Unc
545B	ND	Brass	20mm	—	20.00	45.00

As 545. Plain edge. Rarity 6.

Baker	Date	Metal	Size	VF	EF	Unc
545C	ND	Nickel	20mm	—	30.00	60.00

As 545. Plain edge. Magnetic. Rarity 6.

Baker	Date	Metal	Size	VF	EF	Unc
545D	ND	Wm	20mm	—	20.00	45.00

As 545. Plain edge. Rarity 6. (Miller Pa 230)
All Idler cards were struck by Robert Lovett Jr.

E. IVINS
Philadelphia, Pa.
Struck ca. 1860

Baker	Date	Metal	Size	VF	EF	Unc
546	1789	Silver	25mm	—	800.	1000.

Roman-mantled bust right, R L on truncation. Around: GEN. GEORGE WASHINGTON. / FIRST PRES. U.S. 1789 (same obverse as Baker 336). Rv: U.S. Shield within circle of 25 stars. Around: E. IVINS, MANUFACTURER OF METALLIC TRIMMINGS. / FIFTH & COLUMBIA AV. / PHILADELPHIA. in three concentric lines. Plain edge. Rarity 8. (Miller Pa 233A)

Baker	Date	Metal	Size	VF	EF	Unc
546A	1789	Copper	25mm	125.	175.	225.

As 546. Plain edge. Rarity 6. (Miller Pa 231)

Baker	Date	Metal	Size	VF	EF	Unc
546B	1789	Brass	25mm	100.	150.	200.

As 546. Plain edge. Rarity 6. (Miller Pa 232)

Baker	Date	Metal	Size	VF	EF	Unc
546C	1789	Nickel	25mm		200.	250.

As 546. Plain edge. Rarity 6. Magnetic.

Baker	Date	Metal	Size	VF	EF	Unc
546D	1789	CN	25mm		200.	250.

As 546. Plain edge. (Miller Pa 231A)

Baker	Date	Metal	Size	VF	EF	Unc
546E	1789	WM	25mm	150.	200.	250.

As 546. Plain edge, Rarity 6. (Miller Pa 233)

All struck by Robert Lovett Jr. of Philadelphia.

F. C. KEY & SONS

Baker	Date	Metal	Size	VF	EF	Unc
548	ND	WM	28mm	20.00	45.00	60.00

Obverse as Baker 210 (undraped bust left, KEY under bust, PATRIAE PATER around. Rv: F. C. KEY & SONS / DIE SINKERS & / MEDALISTS / 123 / ARCH ST. / PHILADELPHIA in six lines. Plain edge. Rarity 7.

Baker	Date	Metal	Size	VF	EF	Unc
549	1732	Silver	28mm	—	175.	275.

Obverse as Baker 211 (Undraped bust left in an arched frame, KEY under bust, PATRIAE PATER1732 around). Rv: F. C. KEY & SONS / DIE SINKERS & MEDALISTS / 123 / ARCH ST. / PHILADA. in five lines. Plain edge. Rarity 9.

Baker	Date	Metal	Size	VF	EF	Unc
549A	1732	Copper	28mm	—	—	50.00

As 549. Plain edge. Rarity 7.

Baker	Date	Metal	Size	VF	EF	Unc
549B	1732	Brass	28mm	—	—	50.00

As 549. Plain edge. Rarity 7.

Baker	Date	Metal	Size	VF	EF	Unc
549C	1732	WM	28mm	—	—	50.00

As 549. Plain edge. Rarity 7.

Baker	Date	Metal	Size	VF	EF	Unc
550	1732	Silver	28mm	—	—	—

Obverse as 549. Rv: ORNAMENTAL MEDAL & SEAL / DIE SINKERS / &C &C / 329 ARCH ST. PHILA., all within large open letters K E Y. Around all are 33 stars. Plain edge. Rarity 9.

Baker	Date	Metal	Size	VF	EF	Unc
550A	1732	Copper	28mm	—	—	32.50

As 550. Plain edge. Rarity 7.

Baker	Date	Metal	Size	VF	EF	Unc
550B	1732	Brass	28mm	—	—	32.50

As 550. Plain edge. Rarity 7. (Miller Pa 271-; Rulau Pa-Ph 173A)

Baker	Date	Metal	Size	VF	EF	Unc
550C	1732	WM	28mm	—	—	32.50

As 550. Plain edge. Rarity 7. (Miller Pa 271A; Rulau Pa-Ph 173)

Baker	Date	Metal	Size	VF	EF	Unc
551	ND	Silver	28mm	—	—	—

Obverse as Baker 219 (head right, resting on clouds dotted with stars, at each side two U.S. flags, rays above the head. Around: THE UNION

MUST AND SHALL BE PRESERVED). Rv: As reverse of 550. Plain edge. Rarity 9.

Baker	Date	Metal	Size	VF	EF	Unc
551A	ND	Copper	28mm	—	—	60.00

As 551. Plain edge. Rarity 7.

Baker	Date	Metal	Size	VF	EF	Unc
551B	ND	Brass	28mm	—	—	32.50

As 551. Plain edge. Rarity 7.

Baker	Date	Metal	Size	VF	EF	Unc
551C	ND	WM	28mm	—	—	32.50

As 551. Plain edge. Rarity 7.

F. C. Key & Sons apparently was located at 123 Arch Street from about 1849 until 1861 or 1862. The firm appears in the 1863 city directory 329 Arch Street. They appear in the 1850 Philadelphia directory at the 123 Arch Street address.

Thus Baker 548 and 549 were struck, most likely, in the 1859-61 period and 550 and 551 after the Civil War. The firm was striking tokens at 329 Arch Street dated at least to 1872.

LINGG
Philadelphia, Pa. ?

Baker	Date	Metal	Size	F	VF	Unc
S-551	ND	—	31mm	—	—	Unique

Equestrian figure in uniform left, on an eminence, head facing, a city and American army in background (central device of Baker 50). There is no legend. Rv: (All lettering incused) LINGG / 37 (in circle) / 1602 MAR-KET. Plain edge. (H. Joseph Levine sale of May 14, 1983, lot 53)

This item offered in the 1983 Levine sale was the first ever for publication of this piece, this merchant and this Washington effigy without inscription. Probably the work of Robert Lovett Jr. of Philadelphia.

The "Lingg" may be connected with the later Linggs who produced Centennial cards in the 1870s.

R. LOVETT JR.

Baker	Date	Metal	Size	VF	EF	Unc
556	1776	Silver	32mm	—	100.	350.

Obverse as Baker 50 (uniformed equestrian figure left, on an eminence, head facing, city, battery and camp in background, GEO: WASHINGTON 1776 around). Rv: R. LOVETT. JR: DIE SINKER, PHILADELPHIA. PA: / DIES FOR / AGRICULTURAL (on scroll) / (plow left) / SOCIETIES (on scroll) / COLLEGES &C. / MEDALS STRUCK IN / -GOLD,- SILVER AND BRONZE / (branch). Reeded edge. Rarity 8.

Baker	Date	Metal	Size	VF	EF	Unc
556A	1776	Copper	32mm	—	—	50.00

As 556. Reeded edge. Rarity 6. (Miller Pa 342)

Baker	Date	Metal	Size	VF	EF	Unc
556B	1776	Brass	32mm	—	—	50.00

AS 556. Reeded edge. Rarity 6. (Miller Pa 339)

Baker	Date	Metal	Size	VF	EF	Unc
556C	1776	Brass	32mm	—	—	50.00

As 556. Plain edge. Rarity 6. (Miller Pa 337)

Baker	Date	Metal	Size	VF	EF	Unc
556D	1776	Nickel	32mm	—	—	50.00

As 556. Reeded edge. Rarity 6. (Miller Pa 343)

Baker	Date	Metal	Size	VF	EF	Unc
556E	1776	WM	32mm	—	—	50.00

As 556. Reeded edge. Rarity 6. (Miller Pa 340)

Baker	Date	Metal	Size	VF	EF	Unc
556F	1776	WM	32mm	—	—	40.00

As 556. Plain edge. Rarity 6. (Miller Pa 341)

MASON & CO.
Philadelphia, Pa.

Baker	Date	Metal	Size	VF	EF	Unc
559	1870	Silver	19mm	—	—	280.

Bust in civil dress facing three-quarters left, BORN FEB. 22, 1732 above, DIED DEC. 14, 1799 below (same obverse as Baker 76). Rv: MASON & CO. / 1870 / COIN & STAMP / DEALERS. / 189 / NO. 9TH ST. PHILA. Plain edge. Only 2 struck. (Rulau Pa-Ph 290A)

Baker	Date	Metal	Size	VF	EF	Unc
559A	1870	Copper	19mm	—	50.00	130.

As 559. Plain edge. Rarity 6. (Rulau Pa-Ph 291; Wright 671; Fuld NC-16a). 100 pieces struck.

Baker	Date	Metal	Size	VF	EF	Unc
559B	1870	Brass	19mm	—	50.00	100.

As 559. Plain edge. Rarity 6. (Rulau Pa-Ph 292; Fuld NC-16b; Miller Pa 365). 100 pieces struck.

Baker	Date	Metal	Size	VF	EF	Unc
559C	1870	Nickel	19mm	—	—	150.

As 559. Plain edge. Rarity 7. (Rulau Pa-Ph 293; Miller Pa 366). Only 20 struck.

Baker	Date	Metal	Size	VF	EF	Unc
559D	1870	WM	19mm	10.00	25.00	50.00

As 559. Plain edge. Rarity 6. (Rulau Pa-Ph 290; Fuld NC-16e; Miller Pa 363). 100 pieces struck.

Mason listed the mintages for his store cards in his journal. The order was executed by Charles Warner and the dies cut by William Key. By 1872 Mason had moved his operation to 907 Chestnut Street.

N. & G. TAYLOR CO.

Baker	Date	Metal	Size	VF	EF	Unc
577	1862	Brass	37mm	—	200.	

Undraped bust left,1862 under bust. Above: N & G. TAYLOR CO. (Gothic letters) / 303 BRANCH ST. Below: PHILADELPHIA. Rv: TIN PLATE (Gothic letters) / WIRE STREET IRON FILES / METALS (Gothic letters) / STAMPED / & JAPANNED WARE / COPPER &C. &C. Reeded edge. Rarity 7. (Fuld Pa 750V-3b; Miller Pa 516: H-G not listed)

Baker	Date	Metal	Size	VF	EF	Unc
578	1862	Brass	37mm	—	200.	

Obverse similar to 577, but 303 BRANCH ST. in much smaller letters, beginning at G of N & G. TAYLOR. Rv: Similar to reverse of 577, but different spacing. Wider border on each side. Reeded edge. Rarity 7. (Fuld Pa 750V-4b; Miller Pa 517; H-G not listed)

Baker	Date	Metal	Size	VF	EF	Unc
579	ND	Brass	37mm	—	200.	—

Obverse similar to 577, but N & G TAYLOR CO. is in normal Roman lettering. Rv: TIN PLATE / STAMPED / & / JAPANNED WARE / METALS / WIRE STREET IRON / FILES / COPPER &C. &C. (not Gothic lettering). Reeded edge. Rarity 8 (Fuld Pa 750V-5b; Miller Pa 514; H-G not listed)

Baker	Date	Metal	Size	VF	EF	Unc
579A	ND	WM	37mm	—	300.	—

As 579. Reeded edge. Rarity 7. (Fuld Pa 750V-5e; Miller Pa 515)

Baker	Date	Metal	Size	VF	EF	Unc
579E	ND	Brass	37mm	—	75.00	—

Obverse as 579. Rv: Similar to reverse of 579, but letters are spaced differently. The last period after &C. is further away from N of IRON; word FILES is longer than word SHEET. Reeded edge. Rarity 7. (Fuld Pa 750V-6b; Miller Pa 513)

Baker	Date	Metal	Size	VF	EF	Unc
580	1863	Copper	25mm	9.00	15.00	40.00

Undraped bust right, N. & G. TAYLOR CO / 1863 above, 303 / BRANCH ST. / PHILADELPHIA. below. Rv: TIN PLATE, / FILES, / METALS, / STEEL, / WIRE, COPPER &C. Plain edge. Rarity 4. (Fuld Pa 750V-1a; Miller 513A; H-G 9368)

Baker	Date	Metal	Size	VF	EF	Unc
580A	1863	WM	25mm	—	—	150.

As 580. Plain edge. Rarity 9. (Fuld Pa 750V-1e)

Baker	Date	Metal	Size	VF	EF	Unc
580B	1863	Silver	25mm	—	—	325.

As 580. Plain edge. Rarity 9. (Fuld Pa 750V-1f)

| 580F | 1863 | Copper | 25mm | — | — | Unique |

Obverse similar to 580, but Washington bust is in a frame which divides 18 - 63. Rv: As reverse of 580. Plain edge. Rarity 10. (Fuld Pa 750V-2a)

Fuld says 580F is probably a rejected die trial for 580.

Though classed as Civil War tokens, the Taylor cards have always been desired by collectors of other series as well and thus are priced much higher than similarly rare CWT's.

CHAS. K. WARNER
Philadelphia, Pa.
Issued 1861-63

Baker	Date	Metal	Size	VF	EF	Unc
582	ND	Copper	27mm	17.50	25.00	50.00

Obverse as Baker 551 (head right resting on clouds, THE UNION MUST AND SHALL BE PRESERVED, etc.). Rv: C. K. WARNER. / (eagle) / NUMISMATIST, / 326 / CHESTNUT ST. / PHILADELPHIA. in six lines. Plain edge. Rarity 8. (Rulau Pa-Ph 450; Miller Pa 557)

| 582A | ND | Brass | 27mm | 17.50 | 25.00 | 50.00 |

As 582. Plain edge. Rarity 8. (Rulau Pa-Ph 450A; Miller Pa 558)

| 582B | ND | WM | 27mm | 17.50 | 25.00 | 37.50 |

As 582. Plain edge. Rarity 6. (Rulau Pa-Ph 450B; Miller Pa 559)

| 583 | ND | Copper | 27mm | — | — | 35.00 |

Head right. Around, in two concentric lines: CHAS. K. WARNER, DEALER IN AMERICAN & FOREIGN MEDALS 728 CHESTNUT ST. * PHILADA: *. Plain edge. (Rulau Pa-Ph 440; Miller Pa 539)

| 583A | ND | Brass | 27mm | — | — | 35.00 |

As 583. Plain edge. (Rulau Pa-Ph 440A; Miller Pa 540)

| 583B | ND | WM | 27mm | — | — | 35.00 |

As 583. Plain edge. (Rulau Pa-Ph 4408; Miller Pa 541)

| 583E | 1860 | Copper | 27mm | — | 50.00 | 85.00 |

Obverse as 583. Rv: Beardless Lincoln bust right, tiny R L PHILA under bust. ABM: LINCOLN, REP. CANDIDATE FOR PRESIDENT around, 1860 below. Plain edge. (King 601; DeWitt AL 1860-51 (B); Rulau Pa-Ph 448; Miller Pa 554). Only 15 struck.

| 583F | 1860 | Brass | 27mm | — | 50.00 | 85.00 |

As 583E. Plain edge. (Miller Pa 555)

| 583G | 1860 | WM | 27mm | — | 50.00 | 85.00 |

As 583E. Plain edge. (Miller Pa 556)

Struck 1869

| 583J | 1864 | Copper | 27mm | — | 50.00 | 85.00 |

Obverse as 583. Rv: Bearded Lincoln bust left, W. H. KEY under bust, ABRAHAM LINCOLN PREST. OF THE U.S. / 1864 below. Circle of stars at rim. Plain edge. (Rulau Pa-Ph 458; King 591; Miller Pa 800)

| 583K | 1864 | Brass | 27mm | — | 50.00 | 85.00 |

As 583J. Plain edge. (Miller Pa 801)

Baker	Date	Metal	Size	VF	EF	Unc
583L	1864	WM	27mm	—	50.00	85.00

As 583J. Plain edge. (Rulau Pa-Ph 458B; Miller Pa 802)

| 583N | 1864 | Copper | 27mm | — | 50.00 | 85.00 |

Obverse as 583. Rv: Lincoln bust left within circle of 31 stars, ABRAHAM LINCOLN PRESIDENT OF THE U.S. **** around, 1864 below. Under Lincoln's bust: W. H. KEY. Plain edge. (Rulau Pa-Ph 461 B; King 596; Miller 809)

Struck 1863-65

| 583P | ND | Copper | 27mm | — | 50.00 | 85.00 |

Obverse as 583. Rv: Military bust of Grant left, W.H.K. below bust. Around: LIEUT. GEN. U. S. GRANT. Plain edge. (Rulau Pa-Ph 442; Miller Pa 542). Only 15 pieces struck.

Type 583P also in Brass and White Metal.

Struck 1864

Baker	Date	Metal	Size	VF	EF	Unc
583R	ND	Copper	27mm	—	50.00	100.

Obverse as 583. Rv: Uniformed McClellan bust left, MAJ. GEN. GEO. B. McCLELLAN around. Plain edge. (Rulau Pa-Ph 451; Miller Pa 560). Only 15 pieces struck.

Type 583R also in Brass and White Metal, 15 of each struck.

| 583T | 1864 | Copper | 27mm | — | 50.00 | 100. |

Obverse as 583. Rv: Uniformed McClellan bust left, W. H. KEY F. under bust. Around: MAJ. GEN. GEO. B. McCLELLAN. 1864. Plain edge. (Rulau Pa-Ph 452; Miller Pa 563)

Type 583T also in Brass and White Metal.

Struck 1868

| 583U | ND | Copper | 27mm | — | 50.00 | 100. |

Obverse as 583. Rv: Seymour bust right, HORATIO SEYMOUR around. Plain edge. (Rulau Pa-Ph 445; Miller Pa 548)

Type 583U also struck in Brass and White Metal.

Struck 1865-69

Baker	Date	Metal	Size	VF	EF	Unc
583V	ND	Copper	27mm	—	50.00	100.

Obverse as 583. Rv: Lyle bust left. Around: FOR SHERIFF GEN. PETER LYLE. Plain edge. (Rulau Pa-Ph 439; Miller Pa 536)

Type 583V also struck in Brass and White Metal.

| 583W | ND | Copper | 27mm | — | 50.00 | 100. |

Obverse as 583. Rv: Accolated heads of Victoria and Albert of England left. Around: VICTORIA . ALBERTUS . Plain edge. (Rulau Pa-Ph 454; Miller Pa 566)

Type 583W also struck in Brass and White Metal.

| 583X | ND | Copper | 27mm | — | 50.00 | 100. |

Obverse as 583. Rv: FREE HOMES FOR FREE MEN Plain edge.

Baker	Date	Metal	Size	VF	EF	Unc
583Y	1862	Copper	27mm	—	65.00	150.

Obverse as 583. Rv: Monitor at center, MONITOR above, 1862 below. Plain edge. (Rulau Pa-Ph 446: Miller Pa 551)

Type 583Y also struck in Brass and White Metal.

| 583Z | ND | Copper | 27mm | — | 50.00 | 100. |

Obverse as 583. Rv: CEDAR MOUNTAIN TO REAMS STATION 28 BATTLES. Plain edge. (Rulau Pa-Ph 435; Miller Pa 533)

Type 583Z also struck in Brass and White Metal.

Baker	Date	Metal	Size	VF	EF	Unc
583AC	ND	Copper	27mm	—	—	—

Obverse as 583. Rv: As obverse of Baker 219 (Washington bust resting on clouds, etc.). Plain edge.

| 583AA | 1865 | Copper | 27mm | — | 50.00 | 100. |

Obverse as 583. Rv: SURRENDER OF GEN. LEE TO GEN. GRANT APRIL 9TH 1865. Plain edge. (Rulau Pa-Ph 443; Miller Pa 545)

Type 583AA also struck in Brass and White Metal.

Baker	Date	Metal	Size	VF	EF	Unc
583AC	ND	Copper	27mm	—	—	—

Obverse as 583. Rv: As obverse of Baker 219 (Washington bust resting on clouds, etc.). Plain edge.

Type 583AC also struck in Silver, Brass and White Metal.

As can be noted by the diesinker initials appearing in several pieces in the Warner series, some were designed by Robert Lovett Jr., others by William H. Key.

Charles K. Warner was born March 29, 1845, the son of medalist John S. Warner. Charles Warner established his coin and medal business at 326 Chestnut St., Philadelphia, in 1861. During 1862-63 he commissioned W. H. Key to strike a series of patriotic store cards bearing portraits of Van Buren, Lincoln, McClellan, Washington, etc., with his store card on the other side. Only 15 of each were struck and these were not sold, but presented to friends. In 1869 he moved to 728 Chestnut St. where he continued issuing special store cards until 1871.

The extensive mulings listed here under Baker 583 exhibit the extremes to which muling of dies was carried by Warner.

R. CHAMBERLAINE
Norfolk, Va.
Circa 1860-70

Baker	Date	Metal	Size	EF	Unc	Proof
525	ND	Wm	28mm	—	300.	500.

Head right within olive wreath, tiny M below bow, WASHINGTON above. Rv: Star within circular wreath at center. R. CHAMBERLAINE / * NORFOLK. * around. Plain edge. Rarity 9. (Miller Va 10A; Schenkman 3680X)

TOKLAS SINGERMAN & CO.
Seattle, Wash.

| | | | | 526 | ND | WM | 28mm | — | 300. | 500. |

Uniformed bust left, BOLEN under the bust. THE FATHER OF OUR COUNTRY around. Rv: As reverse of 525. Plain edge. Rarity 9. (Miller Va IOA; Schenkman 3680Ya)

| 526A | ND | Copper | 28mm | — | 375. | — |

As 526. Plain edge. Rarity 9; possibly unique. (Miller Va 10B; Schenkman 3680Yb)

Richard Chamberlaine entered business about 1860, at 93 East Main Street. He was a merchant and oyster packer. It is believed that Baker 525 was struck for him by Merriam of Boston before the Civil War broke out. Most likely Baker 526 - and other mulings using the Chamberlaine reverse - were made about 1870 by Merriam's successors.

Baker	Date	Metal	Size	F	VF	EF
697	1888	Copper	35mm	150.	170.	200.

Undraped bust left, COR. FRONT & COLUMBIA ST. above, 1888 below, all within beaded central circle. Around: COMPLIMENTS OF TOKLAS SINGERMAN & CO. / * SEATTLE. W. T. Rv: Within laurel and oak wreath: STRICTLY / ONE PRICE / & - / LOWEST / FIGURES. Around: CLOTHIERS & GENTS FURNISHERS. Issued with loop for use as a fob. Plain edge. (B. P. Wright 1087; Rulau Wa-Se 8; Clark sale, lot 2149)

W.T. - Washington Territory.

Chapter 36

20TH CENTURY STORE CARDS

ALBERTS SAMUELS CO
San Francisco, Calif.

Baker	Date	Metal	Size	VF	EF	Unc
AA700	1932	Bronze	Rect 32x80mm	—	10.00	14.00

Flag at center. In lower fob: View of San Francisco at top in enamel. To left is red NSBW and to right California bear with a star. Attached to a red-white-blue ribbon with imprint: SAN FRANCISCO / (civil Washington bust 3/4 right) / 1932. Ribbon is attached to a bar. At top, a bear in bars. TWIN PEAKS PARLOR / 214 (in shield) / ADMISSION DAY. Rv: THE ALBERTS / SAMUELS CO. / JEWELERS / S.F. (Fuld NLH115-Bo)

Badge, manufactured by the Alberts Samuels Co.

ERADICANE (&) FUSILADE
Wilmington, Del.

Baker	Date	Metal	Size	EF	AU	Unc
AB700	1991	CN	25.4mm	15.00	20.00	25.00

Washington bust left, modeled closely from that on U.S. quarter dollar coins of 1932-1990, even to the font of type used, is 1.1mm larger in diameter and .1mm thicker. Above: ERADICANE. At left: IN GOD WE / TRUST. Below: 1991. Rv: Same as obverse, except FUSILADE replaces ERADICANE along upper rim. Reeded edge. 1.7mm thick at edge.

This "double-head quarter" in direct imitation of the circulating Washington quarter, even to the font of type used, is 1.1mm larger in diameter and .1mm thicker at the rim. Theoretically, it should not activate vending or toll-collecting machines, but experience in 1991 showed that in fact it could. These pieces could, and did, pass easily as change as people (even bank tellers) glance casually at quarters.

Eradicane and Fusilade are pesticides useful to farmers in ridding their fields of problems. Currently (1998) these pesticides are made by Zeneca Ag. Inc. of Wilmington, Del., but Wisconsin Zeneca representative Dave Piogoria says the producers have changed frequently since he began selling the products in 1978. In 1978 Stauffer Chemical Co. owned the rights, followed in order by Chesebrough-Ponds, Unilever NV and Imperial Chemical Industries (ICI) of Great Britain.

The U.S. Secret Service halted production and distribution of these tokens soon after they were given away to farmers in the Midwest, and most copies have long since been confiscated, or destroyed. They are now very difficult to locate, though it is believed some farm families have one or two pieces tucked away, forgotten. There are very few tokens in numismatic hands.

EQUITABLE LIFE INSURANCE CO.
Washington, D.C.

B780	1932	Gilt/Copper	33mm	—	10.00	15.00

Same obverse as Baker 907A. Rv: United States Capitol dome surrounded by a glory of rays within a round panel, inscribed halfway around above. AT THE HEAD OF THE NATION, EQUITABLE on a scroll in exergue; +HOME OFFICE...WASHINGTON, D.C. + / LIFE INSURANCE CO. around periphery. (Collins 510)

FIRST FEDERAL SAVINGS AND LOAN
Broward County, Fla.

Baker	Date	Metal	Size	VF	EF	Unc
AC 700	1958	A & S *	39mm	—	15.00	—

* Aluminum ring-encased silver U.S. 1958 quarter. FIRST FEDERAL SAVINGS AND LOAN ASSOCIATION / OF / . BROWARD COUNTY. Rv: 25 YEARS OF SERVICE / 1933 - 1958. Issued holed. (Slawsky 335)

Fort Lauderdale is the Broward County seat.

HARVEY'S RESTAURANT
Miami, Fla.

Baker	Date	Metal	Size	VF	EF	Unc
AE 700	1961	A&S*	39mm	—	15.00	—

* Aluminum ring-encased silver U.S. 1953 quarter. HARVEY'S RESTAURANT MIAMI, FLA. / SILVER ANNIVERSARY / 1936 - 1961. Rv: Blank. (Slawsky 336)

MAX M. SCHWARTZ
Miami, Florida

Struck late 1960's

Baker	Date	Metal	Size	VF	EF	Unc
A700	ND	Aluminum	38.3mm	—	—	12.50

GEORGE WASHINGTON / EXONUMIA / BUY SELL / OR / TRADE / TRANSPORTATION TOKENS / MARDI GRAS DOUBLOONS. Rv: ANA L80 - AVA L3 - TAMS 105 / -*- / MAX M. / SCHWARTZ / 2920 / POINT EAST DR. / . MIAMI, FLA. 33160. Plain edge. (Neil Shafer coll.)

Attorney Max M. Schwartz was a lifelong collector of tokens and medals. Before his retirement from his law business in the New York area and removal to retirement in Florida, he had been chairman of the Token committee of the American Numismatic Society. His other affiliations are given on his personal card - ANA (American Numismatic Association), AVA (American Vecturist Association), TAMS (Token and Medal Society). This piece reportedly was also struck in several off metals, but we have no record of these.

THE FLAMINGO
Miami Beach, Florida

Baker	Date	Metal	Size	VF	EF	Unc
B700	1932	Yellow Bronze*	Rect 48x68mm	—	30.00	75.00

* Antiqued finish.
Civilian bust in high relief facing left. 1972 -- 1932 on scrolls at left and right opposite top of head. Facsimile signature in exergue on raised cartouche. Rv: COMPLIMENTS / THE FLAMINGO / MIAMI BEACH in three lines. Rarity 7. (Levine 31; Collins 544)

GEORGIA MARBLE COMPANY
Tate, Georgia

Baker	Date	Metal	Size	VF	EF	Unc
C700	1932	Svd/Copper	38.2mm	—	50.00	65.00

Nude bust right, THE GEORGIA MARBLE CO./ TATE, GEORGIA around. Rv: 27TH / ANNUAL / DESIGN SHOW / AUGUST 16-19-1932 / WASHINGTON / D.C. in six lines. GEORGE WASHINGTON BICENTENNIAL. / 1732-1932 around all. Rarity 8. (Fuld NLH81-1-Ag; Collins 467)

Baker	Date	Metal	Size	VF	EF	Unc
CA700	1932	Silver	32mm	—	—	35.00

Obv. of Baker 925. Rv: In eight lines 27TH ANNUAL / DESIGN SHOW / WASHINGTON, D.C. / AUG. 16 TO 19, 1932 / THE / GEORGIA MARBLE COMPANY / TATE, GA. In exergue, METAL ARTS CO., ROCH., N.Y. (Fuld NLH81-Ag)

IDAHO SAVINGS & LOAN ASSN.
Boise, Idaho (etc.)

Baker	Date	Metal	Size	VF	EF	Unc
D700	1959	B & S*	39mm	—	—	15.00

* Brass ring-encased silver U.S. 1959 quarter.
IDAHO SAVINGS & LOAN ASSN. / BOISE. TWIN FALLS. / POCA-

TELLO. IDAHO FALLS. Rv: EARN MORE WITH SAFETY / AT YOUR FRIENDLY SAVINGS INSTITUTION. Issued holed. (Slawsky 337)

DAVE & DICK
Canton, Ill.

Baker	Date	Metal	Size	VF	EF	Unc
E700	ND	Brass	32mm	20.00	25.00	30.00

Washington civil bust facing three-quarters right, DAVE & DICK above, CANTON, ILLS. / (tiny) W. & H. CO. NEWARK, N.J. Rv: ONE / OF THESE IS WORTH / 25 ¢/ ON EVERY $5 PURCHASE / AT / DAVE & DICK'S. Plain edge. R5. (Vacketta Can 03)

B.B.B. LUNCH ROOM
Chicago, Ill.

Baker	Date	Metal	Size	VF	EF	Unc
F700	ND	Brass	30mm	—	15.00	—

Obverse as Tri-Angle Mfg. Co, Baker 707. Rv: GOOD FOR 5¢ IN TRADE / B.B.B. / LUNCH ROOM / 1008 MADISON ST. / CHICAGO / (tiny) GREENDUCK CO. CHICAGO. Plain edge. R7. (Vacketta Chi B24)

CARMACK
Chicago, Ill.

Baker	Date	Metal	Size	VF	EF	Unc
G700	ND	Brass	32mm	—	25.00	—

Washington bust facing 3/4 right, on plain field. Rv: TALK WITH / CARMACK / ABOUT / STATE MUTUAL / GOLD BONDS / 85 DEARBORN ST. / CHICAGO / (tiny) W. & H. CO. NEWARK N.J.

DEARBORN CLUB

Baker	Date	Metal	Size	VF	EF	Unc
K700	1911	Gilt Brass	28.5mm	—	15.00	25.00

Washington head left, GEORGE **** WASHINGTON **** around. Rv: DEARBORN CLUB / MASQUERADE / WASHINGTON'S / BIRTHDAY / FEBRUARY 22, 1911 / CLARK & ILLINOIS STS. / CHICAGO / (tiny) THE GREENDUCK CO. CHICAGO.

S. D. CHILDS & CO.

Baker	Date	Metal	Size	VF	EF	Unc
701	1932	Gilt Bronze	32mm	—	20.00	25.00

Bust to left in field surrounded by two concentric circles, within grating lines, to left, 1732 and to right 1932. Around: GEORGE WASHINGTON CENTENNIAL Rv: In the field in seven lines, COMPLIMENTS / OF THE / MAKERS / S.D. CHILDS & CO. / 136 S. CLARK ST. / DEPT 2 / CHICAGO (Fuld NLH116-BoGf)

GREENDUCK CO.
Circa 1908

Baker	Date	Metal	Size	VF	EF	Unc
702	ND	S/Brass	32mm	—	15.00	—

Washington bust right. Rv: IF FOUND RETURN TO GREENDUCK CO., CHICAGO. Plain edge.

Struck by the Greenduck Company, medal and token makers.

Baker	Date	Metal	Size	VF	EF	Unc
A702	ND	—	32mm	—	15.00	—

Obverse and reverse as 702 obverse (two-headed flipping coin). (Kirtley report). Legend: GREEN DUCK CO. / FLIPPIN' COIN.

Baker	Date	Metal	Size			Unc
B702	ND	Brass	28.5mm	—	30.00	—

Obverse as Baker K700. Rv: Blank, except tiny THE GREENDUCK CO. CHICAGO at bottom. Sample piece made ca. 1911? (Kirtley May 6, 1997 sale, lot AD04)

Struck 1911

Baker	Date	Metal	Size	VF	EF	Unc
C702	ND	Nic/Brz	29mm	15.00	20.00	—

Obverse as K700. Rv: Blank. (Kirtley March 1998 sale, lot Q6; realized $12.10 in VF-plus)

Baker	Date	Metal	Size	EF	AU	Unc
D702	1932	Gilt/Brass	32mm	—	65.00	—

Nude bust left, 1732 at left, 1932 at right. Around: GEORGE WASHING-TON / BI-CENTENNIAL. Rv: Blank, except at bottom are three pseudohallmarks above GREENDUCK CO. (Kirtley March 31, 1998 sale, lot Q80; brought $66 in AU)

Interesting, and scarce, Greenduck sample piece of the 1932 era. Issued holed.

F. H. NOBLE & CO.

Baker	Date	Metal	Size	VF	EF	Unc
704	1932	Bronze	32mm	—	30.00	65.00

Undraped bust right, 1732 / 1932 below. Around: GEORGE WASHING-TON / BI-CENTENNIAL. Rv: In 11 lines: WHY NOT DISTRIBUTE THIS WASHINGTON BI-CENTENNIAL COIN AMONG YOUR CUSTOMERS WITH YOUR ADVERTISEMENT ON THIS SIDE / * / F.H. NOBLE & CO CHICAGO. Plain edge. (Hansen 10)

| 704A | 1932 | Copper/Brz | 32mm | — | — | 65.00 |

As 704. Plain edge. (Hansen 10)

| 704B | 1932 | Nickel/Brz | 32mm | — | — | 135. |

As 704. Plain edge. (Hansen 10; Kirtley sale 158, lot P27)

| 704C | 1932 | Gilt/Brz | 32mm | — | — | 65.00 |

As 704. (Kirtley sale 158, lot P28)

Struck by F. H. Noble & Co.. Chicago, who also made Baker 762, which uses the same obverse die.

NUMISMATIC SCRAPBOOK MAGAZINE

Baker	Date	Metal	Size	VF	EF	Unc
705	1797	Gilt/B	28mm	—	—	25.00

Nude bust right, 1789 1ST PRESIDENT U.S.A. 1797 / . GEORGE WASHINGTON . around. Rv: THE NUMISMATIC SCRAPBOOK MAG-AZINE / TO A / CONTRIBUTOR / - / FOR YOUR EFFORTS / IN THE / ADVANCEMENT OF / NUMISMATICS / CHICAGO. Plain edge.

Baker 705 was used by Lee F. Hewitt. the founding editor of *Numismatic Scrapbook Magazine*, as a form of thank you token for literary contributors. Hewitt was editor of this famous old magazine January 1935 through April 1968; he was succeeded by Russell Rulau April 1968 through April 1974 and then Courtney L. Coffing April 1974 through May 1976, when the magazine ceased publication after more than 41 years of service to the hobby. It was published in Chicago 1935-1968 and in Sidney, Ohio 1968-1976.

TIME
Chicago, Ill.

Baker	Date	Metal	Size	VF	EF	Unc
706	1948	N & S*	40mm	—	40.00	—

* Nickel ring-encased silver U.S. 1948 quarter. REPRESENTATIVES SILVER AWARD TIME (large) THE WEEKLY NEWS MAGAZINE / 1923 - 1948. Rv: TIME means MONEY / A QUAR-TER CENTURY OF NEWS REPORTING. (Slawsky 341)

Issued holed, with suspension ring. Presented in custom-made box labeled TIME, 115 East Ohio Street, Chicago, Ill. Recipient's name was placed on a label on the box, mailed with a U.S. 6-cent stamp.

Encased silver Washington quarters are a very small, unusual group within a super-crowded field of encased coins. Most encased pieces are Indian head cents 1901-1909, with Lincoln cents 1909-1980, with occasional nickels, and other coins. The March 30, 1995 Bob Slawsky sale in Windermere, Fla. contained seven Washington pieces ranging in issue-date 1948-1961, the largest such grouping we've noticed in recent years.

Prices above include original mailing box. Reduce by 20% for token alone. (See Numismatic News for May 19, 1998, page 23)

TRI-ANGLE MFG. CO.
Freeport, Ill.

| 707 | ND | Brass | 31mm | 20.00 | — | — |

Nude Washington bust left, with laurel sprays at either side. Rv: THIS COIN WILL PAY / 5 % / OFF YOUR NEXT / SILVER-NICKLE (sic!) / COPPER OR BRASS / PLATING / AT / THE TRI-ANGLE MFG. CO. / FREEPORT, ILL. / (tiny) GREENDUCK CO. CHICAGO. Plain edge. R6. (Vacketta Fpt 10)

GOULD INC.
Rolling Meadow, Ill. and Fort Lauderdale, Fla.

Struck 1976-78

Baker	Date	Metal	Size	EF	AU	Unc
B707	ND	Titanium*	26.5mm	—	—	150.

* Sintered titanium, golden colored. Washington bust right, Washington monument at left behind him, Gould logo below. Above: Gould Inc. Rv: Presidential eagle seal. Weight 65.6 grains. Rarity 7. (Type of Pollock 5425; Slawsky Dec. 26, 1997 sale, lot 945)

Auctioneer Bob Slawsky refered to this piece as an "unofficial pattern dollar" and says these have been sold in the $200-$700 range. It would be easy to assume this is a brass piece, except for its light weight.

Titanium, silver-white in pure form, has strength, light weight and is somewhat brittle. Not a precious metal, it is plentiful in nature, occuring in its oxides and nitrides. It is used in aircraft for firewalls, for fans in jet engines, and in missiles and space capsules. Specific gravity is only 4.5. It is unusual to find titanium in numismatics, as it is too hard and brittle for normal striking methods; without sintering it would oxidize in air.

Gould Inc. manufactures computer and electronics systems. Using titanium for its advertising pattern dollar would have captured public attention. Though recent, this token must be considered scarce and desirable.

Baker	Date	Metal	Size	F	VF	Unc
B707A	ND	Titanium x	26.5mm	—	—	200.

x Pure titanium, lead-gray color.
As B707. Rarity 7. (Pollock 5430)

Baker	Date	Metal	Size	F	VF	Unc
B707B	ND	Pure nickel	26.5mm	—	—	100.

As B707, but word TITANIUM below Gould Incorporated on obverse. Rarity 7? (Smithsonian Inst. coll; Pollock 5440). Magnetic.

Pollock lists a total of 11 so-called pattern dollars of this type in silver, copper, brass, iron, aluminum, nickel and titanium.

SOUVENIR COIN
Glasgow, Ky.

Baker	Date	Metal	Size	VF	EF	Unc
708	1909	Brass	33mm	—	37.50	—

Washington bust, TWENTIETH CENTURY above, 1909 below. Rv: SOUVENIR COIN. GLASGOW, KY. (Kirtley May 6, 1997 sale, lot AD 20; realized $33 in EF)

ALFRED JONES SONS
Bangor, Maine

Struck ca. 1912?

Baker	Date	Metal	Size	VF	EF	Unc
710	ND	Copper	29mm	15.00	25.00	—

Houdon bust left, GEORGE **** WASHINGTON **** around. Rv: Headless fish, on which is lettered: TRY / JONES' CELEBRATED / FINNAN / HADDIE / CURED BY / ALFRED JONES / SONS. / BANGOR / ME. (Fuld H53-4-Cu; Springfield 4093; Collins 570)

Baker	Date	Metal	Size	VF	EF	Unc
711	ND	Copper	29mm	—	20.00	—

Similar to Baker 710, but no fish outline around the legend. (Fuld H53-5-Cu)

Baker	Date	Metal	Size	VG	VF	Unc
A711	ND	Brass	29mm	15.00	—	—

As 710, but Jones' name not on fish. (Kirtley March 31, 1998 sale, lot M11)

J. WATERMAN CO.
Bangor, Maine

Baker	Date	Metal	Size	F	VF	Unc
715	1908	Gilt/Brass	30mm	10.00	30.00	40.00

Washington bust, 1908 below; FORTIETH ANNIVERSARY above. Rv: GOOD FOR / $1.00 / J. WATERMAN CO. / BANGOR, ME. / ON A $10.00 / PURCHASE / DURING 1908. Plain edge.

THE GREAT AGRICULTURAL FAIR
Lewiston, Maine

Baker	Date	Metal	Size	F	VF	Unc
C715	1908	Gilt/Brass	30mm	—	30.00	40.00

Similar to Baker 716. (Kirtley report)

MAINE STATE FAIR
Lewiston, Maine

Baker	Date	Metal	Size	VF	EF	Unc
716	1908	Brass	29mm	—	30.00	40.00

Undraped bust right, THE GREAT AGRICULTURAL FAIR OF MAINE around. Rv: MAINE STATE FAIR / (bow and arrows) / LEWISTON / (bow and arrows) / SEPT. 7, 8, 9 & 10, 1908. Plain edge.

FRANK M. LOW & CO.
Portland, Maine

Baker	Date	Metal	Size	EF	Unc	Proof
C716	1908	Brass	31mm	20.00	30.00	—

Nude bust right, FRANK M. LOW & CO. above, 1908 below. Rv: GOOD FOR / 50 ¢ AT / FRANK M. LOW & CO.'S (in a rectangle) / ON A / $5oo / PURCHASE. Plain edge. (Dr. Irving Schuster coll; formerly Baker 781)

PEAVY CLO. CO.
Waterville, Maine

Baker	Date	Metal	Size	F	VF	Unc
717	1908	Brass	32mm	—	—	30.00

Washington bust right, 1908 below. Rv: PEAVY CLO. CO. / GOOD FOR / $1.00 / WATERVILLE, ME. Plain edge.

AUSTIN BISCUIT CORPORATION
Baltimore, Md.

Baker	Date	Metal	Size	VF	EF	Unc
A717	1960	N & S *	39mm	—	15.00	—

* Nickel ring-encased silver 1959 U.S. quarter.
AUSTIN BISCUIT CORPORATION / BALTIMORE, MD. Rv: 25TH ANNIVERSARY / 1935-1960.

MELVIN (&) GEORGE FULD
Baltimore, Md.

Made 1968

Baker	Date	Metal	Size	EF	AU	Unc
D717	ND	Plastic*	31.7mm	—	—	10.00

* White incused lettering on bright red plastic.
M. FULD / BALTIMORE, MD. / COLLECTOR OF / TOKENS. Rv: ANA -
RO 11932 / MEMBER / A.N.A. - A.N.S. / T.A.M.S. - A.V.A. / C.W.T.S. -
N.L.G. Smooth edge.

Made ca. 1970

Baker	Date	Metal	Size	EF	AU	Unc
E717	ND	Plastic x	31.7mm	—	—	7.00

x White incused lettering on bright red or on bright blue plastic, both
types issued. Prices equal.
MELVIN FULD / BALTIMORE, MD. /ANA 11932. Rv: COLLECTOR OF
/ CIVIL WAR TOKENS / WASHINGTON, / FRANKLIN & / LAFAYETTE
/ MEDALS. Smooth edge.

Baker	Date	Metal	Size	EF	AU	Unc
F717	ND	Plastic x	31.7mm	—	—	7.00

GEORGE FULD / BALTIMORE, MD. / ANA LM 434. Rv: Same as E717
reverse.

All the Fuld tokens were molded at a Baltimore commercial sign house. Melvin
Fuld (1901-1987) and George Fuld (born 1932) were a father-son collector-author
team for about 35 years until the father's death in 1987. Fuld Bros. Chemical Co.
in Baltimore supplied the family's income for its dedication to exonumia.

George J. Fuld has been associated with Bowers & Ruddy Galleries, Kagin's
of San Francisco, Dorge' Inc. and other numismatic firms, and also employed in
biochemical research in Ohio and California. Now a self-employed retiree, George
resides in Owings Mills, Md.

The name Fuld has become so intertwined with Washingtonia that their tokens
are included in this section. Those of co-author Russell Rulau appear under Wisconsin in this section. George Fuld has authored 12 major studies on numismatic
Washingtonia in addition to the 1985 and 1998 editions of *Medallic Portraits of
Washington* .

ROBBINS CO.
Attleboro, Mass.

Baker	Date	Metal	Size	VF	EF	Unc
718	(1932)	Gilt-Cop	32mm	—	10.00	—

Obv. Civilian bust facing one-quarter left. Rv: COMPLIMENTS OF THE
ROBBINS CO. ATTLEBORO MASSACHUSETTS BADGES * MEDALS
& SOUVENIRS ADVERTISING SPECIALTIES in nine lines. (Hansen
36; Collins 536)

Baker	Date	Metal	Size	VF	EF	Unc
718A	(1932)	Copper	32mm	—	10.00	—

Identical to preceding, but antique copper finish (Hansen 36)

BOSTON AMERICAN
Boston, Mass.

Baker	Date	Metal	Size	VF	EF	Unc
B718	(1912?)	Gilt/Cop	29mm	15.00	25.00	—

Obverse as Baker 710 in smaller size. Rv: COMPLIMENTS / OF THE /
BOSTON / AMERICAN / A HUSTLER / IS ALWAYS / LUCKY / LUCKY
PIECE in eight lines. (Fuld H53-1-BoGf; Collins 568; Kirtley March 31,
1998 Sale, lot M59)

Struck by the Greenduck Co., Chicago.

S.M. SPENCER MFG. CO.
Boston, Mass

Baker	Date	Metal	Size	VF	EF	Unc
C718	ND	Gilt	31mm	—	30.00	55.00

Same obverse die as B-904Q. Rv. S. M. SPENCER / MFG. CO. / 3
CORNHILL / BOSTON, MASS. in four lines, * MEDALS, CHECKS,
BADGES, NAME PLATES, STAMPS, STENCILS around periphery.
Rarity 7. (Fuld NLH94-BoGf; Collins 590)

CAPE COD PROFIT SHARING CLUB
Cape Cod, Mass.

Baker	Date	Metal	Size	VF	EF	Unc
D718	1932	Gilt/Brz	30mm	—	10.00	—

Obv. of Baker 904Q. Rv: Around, CAPE COD PROFIT SHARING
CLUB. In center in four lines, APRIL 1.1932 / DISCOUNT / COIN / TO
JULY 1.1932 (Fuld NL-H95-BoGf)

RING & WELCH'S
Milford, Mass.

Baker	Date	Metal	Size	VF	EF	Unc
785	1907	Brass	30mm	15.00	25.00	—

Washington bust, 1907. Rv: RING & WELCH'S (etc.). Plain edge.
(Bullowa-Lessin sale, lot 5)

MONARCH LIFE INSURANCE COMPANY
Springfield, Mass.

Baker	Date	Metal	Size	VF	EF	Unc
E718	1932	Copper	32mm	—	20.00	—

Obverse as 910. Rv: WASHINGTON / BICENTENNIAL / CELEBRA-
TION / 1932 / MONARCH / LIFE INSURANCE / COMPANY / SPRING-
FIELD, MASSACHUSETTS. (Fuld H40-3-Bo; Collins 547)

HENDERSONS
Worcester, Mass.

Baker	Date	Metal	Size	F	VF	Unc
780	1907	Brass	31mm	—	20.00	25.00

Washington bust right, TWENTY-FIFTH ANNIVERSARY / 1907 around. Rv: GOOD FOR / 50 ¢ / AT / HENDERSONS / ON A / $5.00 / PURCHASE. Plain edge. (Storer 1796)

This piece appeared in the PCAC sale of Dec. 14, 1981, lot 760.

Baker	Date	Metal	Size	VF	EF	Unc
A780	1907	Brass	31mm	—	—	25.00

As 780, but bust in laurel wreath. (PCAC Dec. 1995 sale, lot 1645)

MICHIGAN MUTUAL LIABILITY COMPANY

Michigan

Baker	Date	Metal	Size	VF	EF	Unc
A719	1932	Brass/Cop	32mm	—	15.00	—

Periwigged nude bust facing left, flanked on either side by birth and death years, GEORGE WASHINGTON / BI-CENTENNIAL around the periphery. Rv: Clasped hands in a glory of rays within shield, outer shield inscribed MICHIGAN MUTUAL / LIABILITY / COMPANY; at top in two lines, PREFERRED PROTECTION FOR, around bottom, MAN AND MOTOR. (Fuld NLH88-Bri; Collins 586)

AMERICAN SAVINGS

Detroit, Mich.

Baker	Date	Metal	Size	VF	EF	Unc
876	1955	B & S*	39mm	—	20.00	—

* Brass ring-encased silver U.S. 1954 quarter.
AMERICAN SAVINGS / SAVE THE AMERICAN WAY. Rv: AMERICAN SAVINGS / 8th ANNIVERSARY 1955 DETROIT, MICH.

Baker	Date	Metal	Size	VF	EF	Unc
A876	1956	B & S	39mm	—	22.50	—

* Brass ring-encased silver 1956 U.S. quarter.
Obverse as 876. Rv: AMERICAN SAVINGS / DETROIT, MICHIGAN.

LUTHERAN CHURCHES

Baker	Date	Metal	Size	EF	AU	Unc
B719	1932	Brass	Rect 21x35mm	—	—	25.00

Military bust right, signature below. Rv: WASHINGTON / BICENTENNI-AL / NOV. 8. 1932 / LUTHERAN CHURCHES / DETROIT / (tiny) THE ROBBINS CO. ATTLEBORO. (Renumbered from Baker E799)

VAN SICKLE

Detroit, Mich.

Baker	Date	Metal	Size	VF	EF	Unc
719	ND	Brass	32mm	—	25.00	30.00

Civil bust facing three-quarters right on plain field. Rv: TALK WITH / ... / VAN SICKLE / ABOUT / HOME LIFE OF N.Y. / ENDOWMENT & / GOLD BONDS / ... / MAJESTIC BLDG. DETROIT. Plain edge. (Rich Hartzog coll.)

ROYAL FURNITURE CO.

Grand Rapids, Mich.

Baker	Date	Metal	Size	VF	EF	Unc
719K	ND	Tin ?	45mm	—	10.00	—

Washington bust three-quarters left. Around: ROYAL FURNITURE CO. / GRAND RAPIDS, MICH. Rv: Intaglio of obverse.

Baker	Date	Metal	Size	VF	EF	Unc
719L	ND	Copper*	45mm	—	10.00	—

* Antiqued copper.
As 719K. (Ex-Fuld coll.)

LUFT-BICE CO.

Monroe, Mich.

Baker	Date	Metal	Size	F	VF	Unc
719M	1908	Gilt/B	32mm	15.00	20.00	30.00

Bust of Washington right, 15 stars around, 1908 below. Rv: GOOD FOR 50 ¢ / *** / HATTERS / LUFT-BICE CO. / CLOTHIERS / MONROE / MICH. / ON A $10oo CASH PURCHASE. Plain edge. (Paul A. Cunningham coll.)

ELLIOTT'S

St. Louis, Mo.

Circa 1908

Baker	Date	Metal	Size	F	VF	Unc
720	ND	Brass	32mm	16.50	25.00	—

Washington bust left. Rv: WE PAY THE DIFFERENCE IF YOU BUY THE SAME ARTICLE FOR LESS ELSEWHERE ON THE SAME DAY. ELLIOTT'S. WASHINGTON AT 4TH ST. LOUIS. Plain edge.

W. A. SCHABEL

Goldfield, Nevada

Baker	Date	Metal	Size	VF	EF	Unc
720F	ND	Brass	32mm	—	32.50	40.00

Facing civil bust after the Stuart portrait on a plain field. Rv: REBATE CHECK / 2 1/2 ¢ / THE DEN (Gothic letters) / W. A. SCHABEL / PROP. / GOLDFIELD. NEVADA. Plain edge. (Dr. I. Schuster coll.)

FIRST WESTERN SAVINGS

Las Vegas, Nev.

Baker	Date	Metal	Size	VF	EF	Unc
720J	1954	B & S*	39mm	—	15.00	—

* Brass ring-encased silver U.S. 1954 quarter.
EARN MORE WITH SAFETY / (eagle) FIRST WESTERN SAVINGS (eagle). Rv: FIRST WESTERN SAVINGS LAS VEGAS, NEVADA/ MULTI-MILLION DOLLAR INSTITUTION. (Slawsky 338)

TALBOT'S CLOTHING
Nashua, N.H.

Circa 1908

Baker	Date	Metal	Size	VF	EF	Unc
790	ND	Brass	30mm	20.00	25.00	—

Undraped bust right. TALBOT'S CLOTHING IS BEST. around. Rv: GOOD / FOR / 50 ¢ / AT / TALBOT'S (script) / ON A / $10.00 / PURCHASE. Plain edge. (Kurt Krueger Aug. 13-20, 1983 sale, lot 1985)

THE SHERMAN OUTFITTING CO.
Newark, N.J.

Baker	Date	Metal	Size	F	VF	Unc
720T	ND	Brass	26.5mm	25.00	35.00	—

Stuart bust of Washington 3/4 right. Around: THE SHERMAN OUTFITTING CO. / NEWARK N. J. Rv: WORTH 50 ¢ / ON ALL / PURCHASES / OVER / CLOTHING $10 FURNITURE / CASH OR CREDIT / THE / SHERMAN OUTFITTING (curved) / 199 - 205 / MARKET ST. / NEWARK, N. J. (Kirtley report)

This token fetched $31.90 in VF in a 1990 sale.

WHITEHEAD & HOAG CO.
Newark, N.J.

Baker	Date	Metal	Size	VF	EF	Unc
721	1932	Bronze	Oct.25mm	—	—	12.50

Obverse same as Baker 787 and 932 (octagonal). Rv; In nine lines: TO / COMMEMORATE / THE BICENTENNIAL / OF THE BIRTH OF GEORGE WASHINGTON / (horizontal fasces) / DESIGNED AND MADE BY / THE WHITEHEAD / & HOAG CO. / NEWARK N.J. Plain edge. (Hansen 29; Collins 524)

COLUMBIAN PROTECTIVE ASSOCIATION
Binghamton, N.Y.

A721	1932	Gilt	32mm	—	15.00	—

Obv. Of Baker 925. Rv: 50 / ANNIVERSARY / 1882-1932 / LIFE, HEALTH / AND ACCIDENT / INSURANCE in six lines. COLUMBIAN * PROTECTIVE * ASS'N around periphery. (Fuld NLH80-BoGfDf; Collins 482)

KELLY
Brooklyn, N.Y.

Baker	Date	Metal	Size	VF	EF	Unc
C721	1933	Gilt/Brz	32mm	—	18.00	25.00

In field, Houdon bust to right. Under chin in two lines: 1863 / 1933. Around: CREDIT WITH CONFIDENCE - KELLY - 287 LIVINGSTON ST. BROOKLYN. Rv: Shield in center, KELLY at top above, WORTH / $2.50. Lettering around below. (Fuld NLH87-BoGF)

JOHN A. SCHWARZ
Brooklyn, N.Y.

Baker	Date	Metal	Size	VF	EF	Unc
722	1932	Bronze	32mm	—	—	30.00

Undraped bust by Houdon right, 1876 / 1932 at lower right. Entirely around: JOHN A SCHWARZ, JAMAICA FINE FURNITURE, BROOKLYN. Rv: in seven lines: WORTH $5 / JOHN A SCHWARZ / INC. ON ANY / PURCHASE / OF $50 OR / OVER. At bottom, in tiny letters: WHITEHEAD-HOAG. Plain edge. (Hansen 24; Collins 506)

Schwarz' firm was founded in 1876. Struck for Schwarz by Whitehead & Hoag Co., Newark, N.J. in connection with the Washington Bicentennial in 1932.

A.C. GIBSON CO. INC.
Buffalo, N.Y.

723	1932	Bronze	32mm	—	15.00	—

Obv. of Baker 925. Rv: in ten lines, A.C. GIBSON CO., INC / 70 OAK ST. / BUFFALO, N.Y. / MANUFACTURERS RUBBER STAMPS / STEEL LETTERING DIES STENCILS, / METAL TOKENS AND COINS / BRONZE TABLETS AND / MEMORIAL PLATES (Levine 2)

ELMIRA WATER, LIGHT & RAILROAD CO.
Elmira, N.Y.

Baker	Date	Metal	Size	VF	EF	Unc
A723	ND	Copper	29mm	—	17.50	25.00

Same obverse as Baker 919l. Rv: LUCKY NUMBERS / WORTH / $10.00 / WATCH ADVERTISEMENTS / "WIRE YOUR / HOME NOW" / NO. 5691 in seven lines, ELMIRA WATER, LIGHT & RAILROAD CO. around below. (Fuld H53-3-Cu; Collins 569)

Other numbers than 5691 are known.

DREAMLAND DINER

Central Islip, N.Y.

Baker	Date	Metal	Size	EF	AU	Unc
875	1932	Brass	32mm	15.00	—	—

Bust left between 1732 -- 1932. Around: GEORGE WASHINGTON / BI-CENTENNIAL. Rv: DREAMLAND DINER / EXCELLENT FOOD / GOOD / LUCK / QUICK SERVICE / 2950 W. 8th ST. C.I., N.Y. / (tiny) GREENDUCK CO CHI. (Kirtley May 26, 1998 sale, lot C28)

HERRIEFF'S

Cooperstown, N.Y.

Baker	Date	Metal	Size	VF	EF	Unc
AA723	ND	Brass	31mm	—	20.00	25.00

Washington bust right. Above / SPEND YOUR MONEY IN COOPER-STOWN / HELP BOOM THE BEST TOWN IN THE STATE. Rv: GOOD / FOR / 50¢ / AT / HERRIEFF'S / CLOTHES SHOP / ON A / $5.00 / PURCHASE. (PCAC sale 55, Dec. 1993, lot 912)

BOYERTOWN BURIAL CASKET CO.

Jamaica, N.Y.

Baker	Date	Metal	Size	VF	EF	Unc
E723	1932	Bronze	32mm	—	15.00	—

Obv. of Baker 905. Rv: In nine lines, 1932 / BOYERTOWN / BURIAL CASKET CO / JAMAICA, N.Y. / ---- / PHONES / JAMAICA / 6-0450 / 6-0451. In exergue: BASTIAN BROS. CO., ROCHESTER, N.Y. (Fuld H40-2-BoDf)

BRISTOL

New York, N.Y.

Baker	Date	Metal	Size	VF	EF	Unc
K723	ND	Brass	32mm	15.00	20.00	—

Washington bust facing three-quarters right. Rv: TALK WITH / BRIS-TOL / ABOUT / HOME LIFE OF N.Y. / ENDOWMENT & / GOLD BONDS / 286 BROADWAY. NEW YORK. (Renumbered from Baker 719)

THOMAS L. ELDER

New York, N.Y.

Baker	Date	Metal	Size	EF	Unc	Proof
724	1889	Silver	31mm	—	40.00	—

Undraped bust right. Around: 1789 1889/ GEORGE WASHINGTON / INAUGURAL CENTENNIAL IN NEW YORK. Rv: MORE ENDURING THAN BOOKS, OR / CUSTOMS, / OR NATIONS: / - A COIN. - / ..-.-. / THOMAS L. ELDER. / COIN DEALER. / 32 EAST 23RD ST., / NEW YORK CITY. Plain edge. (DeLorey 5)

Baker	Date	Metal	Size	EF	Unc	Proof
724A	1889	Copper	31mm	—	20.00	

As 724. Plain edge. (Bullowa-Lessin 19)

| 724B | 1889 | Brass | 31mm | — | 20.00 | |

As 724.Plain edge. 50 struck.

| 724C | 1889 | Alum | 31mm | — | 35.00 | |

As 724. Plain edge. 261 struck. (Bullowa-Lessin 19)

| 724D | 1889 | WM | 31mm | — | 20.00 | |

As 724. Plain edge.

| 724E | 1889 | GS | 31mm | — | 50.00 | |

As 724. Plain edge. Only 11 struck.

Baker	Date	Metal	Size	EF	Unc	Proof
725	1907	Silver	31mm	—	30.00	—

Obverse as 724. Rv: Within central circle: ROBERT FULTON / -*- / b 1785 d 1815 / THOMAS L. ELDER / NUMISMATIST / 32 E. 23D. ST. / NEW YORK / CITY. Around: STEAM NAVIGATION CENTENNIAL / -*-1807-1907 -*-.Plain edge.

| 725A | 1907 | Copper | 31mm | | 9.00 | |

As 725. Plain edge.

| 725B | 1907 | Brass | 31mm | | 9.00 | |

As 725. Plain edge.

| 725C | 1907 | Aluminum | 31mm | | 9.00 | |

As 725. Plain edge.

| 725D | 1907 | WM | 31mm | | 9.00 | |

As 725. Plain edge.

| 725E | 1907 | Lead | 31mm | | 15.00 | |

As 725. Plain edge. Only 10 struck. (DeLorey 8)

Baker	Date	Metal	Size	EF	Unc	Proof
726	1907	Silver	31mm	—	40.00	—

Obverse as 724. Rv: COMMEMORATING / JAMESTOWN / TER-CEN-TENNIAL / EXPOSITION / 1607-1907 / THOMAS L. ELDER / COIN DEALER / 32 E. 23D. ST. / N.Y. CITY. Plain edge. (DeLorey 7)

| 726A | 1907 | Copper | 31mm | — | — | — |

As 726. Plain edge.

| 726B | 1907 | Brass | 31mm | | 35.00 | |

As 726. Plain edge.

| 726C | 1907 | Aluminum | 31mm | | 20.00 | |

As 726. Plain edge. (Bullowa-Lessin 6)

| 726D | 1907 | WM | 31mm | — | — | — |

As 726. Plain edge.

| 726E | 1907 | Lead | 31mm | | 20.00 | |

As 726. Plain edge. (Bullowa-Lessin 6)

Baker	Date	Metal	Size	EF	Unc	Proof
A726	1910	CN	30mm	—	50.00	—

Obverse as 724. Rv: * / STRUCK TO COMMEMORATE / SALE OF / THE MOUGEY COLLECTION / OF COINS, / SEPT. 1, 2, & 3. / AND A.N.A. CONVENTION, / NEW YORK 1910. / THOMAS L. ELDER / NUMISMATIST / -.- / 32 E. 23RD STREET. Plain edge.

| A726A | 1910 | Aluminum | 30mm | — | 35.00 | — |

As A726. (Collins 675)

Baker	Date	Metal	Size	EF	Unc	Proof
728	1916	Silver	32mm	—	60.00	—

Undraped bust right, tiny R L under truncation. Around: GEORGE WASHINGTON / * SECURITY * (obverse of Baker 102). Rv: THIS MEDAL WAS STRUCK / * BY * / THOMAS L. ELDER / * IN THE * / INTEREST OF A MORE / ARTISTIC SILVER COINAGE / -FOR THE UNITED STATES / 1916. Plain edge. (DeLorey 12)

| 728A | 1916 | Copper | 32mm | 30.00 | 40.00 | — |

As 728. Plain edge. Only 10 struck. (Leon Hendrickson coll.)

| 728B | 1916 | Aluminum | 32mm | 30.00 | 40.00 | — |

As 728. Plain edge. Only 10 struck. (Springfield sale, lot 4093)

| 728C | 1916 | Red Fiber | 32mm | — | 60.00 | — |

As 728. Plain edge. Only 9 struck. (Springfield 4093)

Elder resurrected the old Robert Lovett Jr. die for Baker 621, a Civil War dog tag of about 1861, to create this appeal for a better coinage in America. The United States did adopt new coinage in 1916 - the Mercury dime. Standing Liberty quarter and Walking Liberty half dollar - in silver.

GUTTAG BROS.

Baker	Date	Metal	size	VF	EF	Unc
730	1926	Bronze	29.5mm	—	—	30.00

Busts of Lincoln and Washington facing each other, INTERNATIONAL PHILATELIC EXHIBITION around, NEW YORK 1926 below. Rv: GUTTAG BROS. / COINS / SEND FOR SELLING LIST / NEW YORK. Plain edge. (King 932)

| 730A | 1926 | Silver | 29.5mm | — | — | 50.00 |

As 730. Edge lettered.

| 730B | 1926 | S/Brass | 29.5mm | — | 24.00 | 30.00 |

As 730. Plain edge. (Dr. I. N. Schuster coll.)

Type 730 is also known in Aluminum, Antiqued Brass, Yellow Brass and Lead. These appeared in the Kirtley March 31, 1998 sale, lots M29-M32. In Unc. the Aluminum and Lead fetched $16.50 in 1998, the others $11 in Unc.

Engraved by Jonathan M. Swanson. Struck by Medallic Art Co., New York.

(Washington in Ring of 35 Stars)

(Martinka Co.)

Struck Ca 1900

Baker	Date	Metal	Size	VF	EF	Unc
731	ND	CN	39mm	15.00	20.00	—

Nude bust right. Around: * GEORGE WASHINGTON * BORN 22 FEBY 1732 DIED 14. DECR 1799. Around all, a ring of 35 stars. Rv: Almost identical to obverse, from different die. (*TAMS Journal* for Oct., 1978, cataloged as MT 241)

A magician's two-headed "silver dollar" made circa 1900 by the Martinka Co. of New York City, suppliers of magical apparatus.

NEW YORK WORLDS FAIR

Baker	Date	Metal	Size	VF	EF	Unc
734	1939	Aluminum	31mm	—	—	7.50

Four men, one of them Washington with his hand on a Bible, stand on a terrace enacting the oath of office. Around: SOUVENIR OF THE 150TH ANNIVERSARY. In exergue: GEORGE WASHINGTON'S / INAUGURATION. Plain edge. (Bullowa-Lessin sale, lot 1)

ROSENBAUM'S

Baker	Date	Metal	Size	VF	EF	Unc
735	ND	Gilt/Bs	29mm	—	—	10.00

Washington bust facing 3/4 right, LUCKY POCKET COIN FROM ROSENBAUM'S around. Rv: Within oak wreath: ROSENBAUM'S / 3 STORES / GENTS FURNISHERS / 128 - 1362 - 2008 / 3rd. AVE. / N.Y. At bottom: (tiny) W & H NEWARK N.J.

MAX M. SCHWARTZ

Struck ca 1962

Baker	Date	Metal	Size	EF	AU	Unc
736	1799	Bronze	32mm	—	—	40.00

Nude periwigged bust left, GEORGE WASHINGTON (spray) 1732. 1799 (spray) around. Rv: At center: MAX M. SCHWARTZ / NEW YORK / CITY. Around: I NUMISMATIST. A.N.A.-L80 I VECTURIST. A.V.A.-L3 I EXONUMIST. T.A.M.S.-105. Plain edge. Thick flan. Mintage: 100 pcs. (ANS coll.; Slabaugh coll.)

See Max M. Schwartz under Miami, Florida (Baker A700).

Baker 736 was superbly executed by Medallic Art Co., New York, more in the medallic than the tokenlike fashion. According to Arlie R. Slabaugh, MACO also struck 100 bronze medals with an Abraham Lincoln portrait and the same reverse for Schwartz.

In 1947 Schwartz' New York City office was used to found American Vecturist Association. His AVA, ANA and TAMS membership numbers appear on his personal card (L = Life). He was, until his move to Florida, chairman of the American Numismatic Society's token committee, and an enthusiast for medallic art. Your authors George Fuld and Russ Rulau counted the late Max Schwartz both friend and fellow Washingtonia devotee.

STACK'S
New York, NY

Baker	Date	Metal	Size	VF	EF	Unc
737	1939	Aluminum	28.5mm	—	2.50	5.50

Undraped bust right. Around: 1789 1st PRESIDENT U.S.A. 1797 / . GEORGE WASHINGTON. Rv: VISIT THE / WORLDS FAIR / NEW YORK 1939 / STACKS (script) / DEALERS IN COINS (script) / 32 W. 46TH ST / NEW YORK. N.Y. Plain edge.

Struck by Osborne Coinage Co., Cincinnati.

BASTIAN BROS.
Rochester, N.Y.

Baker	Date	Metal	Size	EF	AU	Unc
G737	1932	Brass	31mm	—	—	25.00

Head right, GEORGE WASHINGTON / * 1732 (signature) 1932 * around. Rv: WASHINGTON / BICENTENNIAL / CELEBRATION / 1932 / BASTIAN BROS. / CO. / ROCHESTER, N.Y. (Renumbered from Baker G799)

Struck by Bastian Brothers, diesinkers and tokenmakers active 1917-1949.

METAL ARTS CO. INC.
Rochester, N.Y.

Baker	Date	Metal	Size	VF	EF	Unc
877	1955	B & S*	39mm	—	20.00	—

* Brass ring-encased silver 1955-D U.S. quarter.

METAL ARTS CO., INC. / BRONZE CRAFT LINE. Rv: KEEP ME AND NEVER GO BROKE.

TARRYTOWN NATIONAL BANK
Tarrytown, N.Y.

Baker	Date	Metal	Size	VF	EF	Unc
A738	1932	Bronze*	25mm	—	—	15.00

Obv. of Baker 947. Rv: In eleven lines: CELEBRATING THE / 200TH ANNIVERSARY OF / WASHINGTON'S BIRTH / AND THE / 50TH AN-NIVERSARY OF / THE TARRYTOWN NATIONAL / BANK AND TRUST COMPANY'S / SERVICE TO THE COMMUNITY / -.- / TARRYTOWN, N.Y. / 1932. In exergue: WHITEHEAD-HOAG CO. (Fuld H27-2-BoBf)

| A738A | 1932 | Bronze* | Oct. 25mm | — | — | 15.00 |

Very similar to preceding, but larger lettering. No manufacturers name. (Fuld H27-3-Bo.)

| A738B | 1932 | Bronze* | Oct.24.5mm | — | — | 15.00 |

Very similar to preceding, but lettering is smaller. (Fuld H27-4-BoGf.)

The bronze on 738-738B is copper-finished.

SOUTHERN TEXTILE ASS'N.
Hendersonville, N.C.

Baker	Date	Metal	Size	F	VF	Unc
738	1932	Bronze	32mm	35.00	45.00	—

Nude bust right in circle. Border includes two laurel sprays and two un-inscribed scrolls. Rv: COMMEMORATING / THE BICENTENNIAL / OF THE / BIRTH OF / GEORGE WASHINGTON / (ornament) / SOUTH-ERN TEXTILE ASS'N / HENDERSONVILLE,N. C. / 1932. Unpub-lished. (Kirtley March 1998 sale, lot Q78; fetched $36.30 in stained Abt. Fine)

DIMKE & ROETHER
Archbold, Ohio

Baker	Date	Metal	Size	F	VF	Unc
739	1908	Brass	32mm	30.00	35.00	45.00

Washington bust, 1908 below. Rv: ONE CHECK GOOD FOR / 25 ¢ / ON A / $5oo CASH / PURCHASE AT DIMKE & ROETHER / THE QUALITY / CLOTHIERS / ARCHBOLD, O. Plain edge. (Lipscomb AR5010)

GEIGERS CLOTHING STORE
Bucyrus, Ohio

Baker	Date	Metal	Size	F	VF	Unc
745	1908	Brass	32mm	—	25.00	—

Washington head. WASHINGTON above, 1908 below. Rv: ONE CHECK GOOD 50 ¢ AT / GEIGERS / CLOTHING / STORE / BUCYRUS O. ON A / $15.00 CASH PURCHASE. Plain edge.

W. J. Geiger, clothing and furnishings, were still in business in 1918.

WASHINGTON SAVINGS BANK
Cleveland, Ohio

Baker	Date	Metal	Size	F	VF	Unc
739M	1920	Brass	28mm	—	25.00	35.00

THE WASHINGTON SAVINGS BANK / (Washington bust) 1920 / CLEVELAND. Rv: Legend in Polish. Plain edge. (Lipscomb CL4810; Kirtley March 31, 1998 sale, lot P9)

BANNER SHOE STORE
Columbus Grove, Ohio

| 740 | 1908 | Brass | 31mm | — | — | 12.00 |

Washington bust right, 15 stars around, 1908 below. Rv: ONE CHECK GOOD FOR / . 50 ¢ . / ON CASH / PURCHASES / OF $20.00 AT / THE BANNER SHOE / STORE / COL. GROVE, O. Plain edge. (Lipscomb CO6010)

G. M.
(General Motors)
Dayton, Ohio

Struck 1960's

Baker	Date	Metal	Size	VF	EF	Unc
747	1797	Gilt/B	28.5mm	—	—	15.00

Obverse as Baker 737. Rv: G. M. (large open letters) / DAYTON. Plain edge.

Struck by Osborne Coinage Co.. Cincinnati, Ohio (formerly Osborne Register Co., maker of the Orco series of tokens).

SMITH CLOTHING CO.

Delaware, Ohio

Baker	Date	Metal	Size	VF	EF	Unc
741	1908	Brass	32mm	—	37.50	45.00

Washington bust, 1908 below. Rv: ONE CHECK GOOD FOR / 50 ¢ AT THE / SMITH / CLOTHING CO / DELAWARE - O. / ON A $15.00 CASH / PURCHASE / SIGN OF THE BEAR. Plain edge. (Lipscomb DE3630)

JETTINGHOFF BROS.

Delphos, Ohio

Baker	Date	Metal	Size	F	VF	Unc
742	1908	Brass	32mm	—	—	30.00

Washington bust, 1908 below. Rv: ONE CHECK GOOD FOR / 50 ¢ AT / JETTINGHOFF / BROS THE / CLOTHIERS / DELPHOS, O. / ON A / $15.00 CASH PURCHASE. Plain edge. (Lipscomb DE4100)

GEHRING & HUIT

Delta, Ohio

Baker	Date	Metal	Size	F	VF	Unc
743	1908	Brass	32mm	—	25.00	35.00

Washington bust, 1908 below. Rv: GEHRING & HUIT / DELTA, O. / 5% / CASH DISCOUNT / ON EVERYTHING / A MAN WEARS. Plain edge. (Lipscomb DE4520)

FEDDERS SUPPLY CO.

Franklin, Ohio

Baker	Date	Metal	Size	VF	EF	Unc
A745	1952	B & S*	39mm	—	15.00	—

* Brass ring-encased silver U.S. 1952 quarter. fedders supply co (slanting letters) / * FRANKLIN-OHIO *. Rv: SOUVENIR OF FEDDERS 25TH ANNIVERSARY. (Slawsky 339)

W. J. WAGNER

Fostoria, Ohio

Baker	Date	Metal	Size	VF	EF	Unc
744	1908	Brass	32mm	—	25.00	35.00

Washington bust, 1908 below. Rv: ONE CHECK GOOD FOR / 50 ¢ ON A $15.00 CASH / PURCHASE / W. J. WAGNER / CLOTHIER FOSTORIA - O. Plain edge. (Lipscomb F08170)

BABIONE

Fremont, Ohio

Baker	Date	Metal	Size	F	VF	Unc
746	1908	Brass	31mm	—	25.00	35.00

Washington bust, 1908 below. Rv: WORTH 50 ¢ / IF PRESENTED / WHEN MAKING A / $10.00 / CASH PURCHASE / BABIONE / CLOTHIER / HABERDASHER / FREMONT, O. Plain edge. (Lipscomb FR7010)

E. C. JOBES

Greenville, Ohio

Baker	Date	Metal	Size		VF	EF	Unc
748	1908	Aluminum	32mm			30.00	40.00

Washington bust, 1908 below. Rv: ONE COIN RECEIVED / AS / $20.00 / IN PART / PAYMENT ON ANY / PIANO IN MY STOCK / E. C. JOBES / GREENVILLE O. Plain edge. (Lipscomb GR6240)

LEWIS & ALFORD

Leipsic, Ohio

Baker	Date	Metal	Size		VF	EF	Unc
749	1908	Brass	32mm			40.00	50.00

Washington bust, 1908 below. GOOD FOR $2.00 ON A NEW BUGGY around. Rv: ONE CHECK GOOD FOR $20.00 / ON ANY / PIANO / AT / LEWIS / & ALFORD / LEIPSIC, OHIO / UNTIL JAN 1, 1909 / Plain edge. (Lipscomb LE5020)

HENRY ACKERMAN

Marion and Galion, Ohio

Baker	Date	Metal	Size	F	VF	Unc
751	1908	Brass	32mm	—	—	25.00

Washington bust, 1908 below. Rv: THIS COIN GOOD FOR / $20.00 / ON DATE OF / PURCHASE ON / ANY PIANO AT / H. ACKERMAN's / MARION & / GALION, O. / GOOD UNTIL JAN. 1, 1909 / HENRY ACKERMAN's SPECIAL SALE COINS. Plain edge. (Lipscomb GA2010 and MA5530; the descriptions vary slightly)

FREUNDLICH

Marion Ohio

Baker	Date	Metal	Size	F	VF	Unc
751F	1908	Brass	32mm	—	25.00	35.00

Washington bust, 1908 below. Rv: ONE CHECK GOOD FOR / 50 ¢ ON / A $15oo / CASH PURCHASE / FREUNDLICH / CLOTHIER / CORNER / OF PUBLIC SQUARE. Plain edge. (Lipscomb MA3320)

RUSSELL & SMITH

Mt. Gilead, Ohio

Baker	Date	Metal	Size	F	VF	Unc
752	1908	Brass	32mm	—	—	50.00

Washington bust. 1908 below. Rv: ONE CHECK GOOD FOR / 50 ¢ AT / RUSSELL / & SMITH / CLOTHIERS / MT. GILEAD / O. / ON A $10.00 CASH PURCHASE. Plain edge. (Lipscomb MT2050)

NORWALK PIANO CO.

Norwalk, Ohio

Baker	Date	Metal	Size	F	VF	Unc
752F	1908	Brass	32mm	—	25.00	35.00

Washington bust, 1908 below. Rv: NORWALK PIANO CO. / THE GREATEST / PIANO / BARGAIN / HOUSE IN NORTHERN OHIO / M. C. PRICE, MGR / C. F. CAMBY VICE PRES. Plain edge. (Lipscomb NO7060)

WISE CLOTHING & SHOE CO.

Ottawa, Ohio

752J	1908	Brass	32mm	20.00	30.00	—

Washington bust, 1908 below. Rv: ONE CHECK GOOD FOR / 50¢/ AT WISE / CLOTHING & / SHOE CO / OTTAWA. O. / ON A $10.00 CASH PURCHASE. Plain edge. (Lipscomb OT2110)

BURGNEL BROS.

Paulding, Ohio

752L	1908	Brass	32mm	20.00	—	35.00

Washington bust, 1908 below. Rv: ONE CHECK GOOD FOR / 50 ¢ AT / BURGNEL BROS / CLOTHING / & SHOE STORE / PAULDING, O. / ON A / $10.00 CASH PURCHASE. Plain edge. (Lipscomb PA6510)

752M	1908	Copper	32mm	—	—	35.00

As 752L. Plain edge. (Lipscomb PA6520)

GEO. M. BAUER

Piqua, Ohio

Baker	Date	Metal	Size	F	VF	Unc
755	1908	Brass	32mm	—	25.00	35.00

Washington bust, 1908 below. Rv: ONE COIN GOOD FOR / $20.00 / ON THE PURCHASE / PRICE ON ANY PIANO / IN MY STOCK UNTIL / APRIL 1, 1909 / GEO. M. BAUER / MAYS OPERA / HOUSE / PIQUA, OHIO. Plain edge. (Lipscomb P15020)

MONTANUS THE SHOE MAN

Sidney, Ohio

Baker	Date	Metal	Size	F	VF	Unc
750	1908	Brass	32mm	30.00	45.00	75.00

Washington bust, 1908 below. Rv: ONE CHECK GOOD FOR / 25¢ ON A / $5.00 CASH / PURCHASE / MONTANUS / THE SHOE MAN / SIDNEY, O. Plain edge. Rarity 7. (Lipscomb SI1260; Kirtley May 6, 1997 sale, lot AD 46; *Numismatic Scrapbook Magazine* for Jan. 1970)

SIDNEY PRINTING & PUBLISHING CO.

Sidney, Ohio

Issued ca. 1963

Baker	Date	Metal	Size	VF	EF	Unc
753	1797	Aluminum	28.5mm	—	—	9.50

Obverse as Baker 737. Rv: Products of Sidney Printing & Publishing Co. are mentioned, COIN WORLD, SIDNEY DAILY NEWS. Plain edge. Rarity 1. (Kirtley May 6, 1997 sale, lot AD47)

Issued ca. 1965

Baker	Date	Metal	Size			Unc
754	1797	Aluminum	28.5mm	—	—	9.50

Obverse as Baker 737. Rv: As reverse of 753, but more products are added: WORLD COINS, LINN'S WEEKLY STAMP NEWS. Plain edge. Rarity 1.

The owners of Sidney Printing & Publishing Co. (now called Amos Press Inc.) commissioned the Osborne Coinage Co. of Cincinnati, Ohio to strike these tokens for mass distribution as a circulation-builder, using the old die utilized by Stack's Inc. for their New York World's Fair card of 1939 (Baker 737). Recent auctions demonstrate these are now quite desirable.

MILLER'S MUSIC STORE

Springfield, Ohio

756	1908	Brass	32mm	—	20.00	30.00

Washington bust, 1908 below. Rv: ONE CHECK GOOD FOR / $20.00 / ON ANY PIANO / AT MILLERS MUSIC STORE / 31 S. LIMESTONE / SPRINGFIELD, / OHIO / GOOD UNTIL JAN. 1, 1909. Plain edge. (Lipscomb SP6470)

GEO. N. HENKE

Tipp City, Ohio

757	1908	Brass	32mm	—	20.00	30.00

Washington bust. 1908 below. Rv: ONE COIN GOOD FOR 50¢ / ON A / $10.00 CASH / PURCHASE AT GEO. N. HENKE / PALACE CLOTHING / & SHOE / HOUSE / TIPP CITY, OHIO. Plain edge. (Lipscomb T16130)

NOTE: This merchant also issued a token with the same reverse and the swastika, DON'T WORRY CLUB motif on the obverse, at about the same period.

WILLYS-OVERLAND

Toledo, Ohio

A757	1932	Svd/Cop	32mm	—	15.00	25.00

Same obverse as Baker 925. Rv: Silver / Anniversary in italics in center, WILLYS-OVERLAND / 1907-1932 around periphery. (Fuld NLH84-Bo-Agf; Collins 487)

Struck by Whitehead & Hoag Co., Newark, N.J.

HERMAN MARX

Troy, Ohio

Baker	Date	Metal	Size	F	VF	Unc
758	1908	Brass	31.5mm	—	25.00	35.00

Washington bust right, 17 stars around, 1908 below. Rv: GOOD FOR 50¢ / ON A $5.00 / PURCHASE AT THE / CUT / PRICE / CLOTHING / STORE / HERMAN MARX, PROP / CUT PRICE / ON EVERYTHING / TROY, OHIO. Plain edge.

H. A. GOODMAN

Upper Sandusky, Ohio

Baker	Date	Metal	Size	F	VF	Unc
759	1908	Brass	31mm	—	25.00	35.00

Washington bust, 1908 below. Rv: ONE CHECK GOOD / FOR 50¢ / ON A $10.00 CASH / PURCHASE / H. A. GOODMAN / DRY GOODS / CLOAKS ETC / UPPER SANDUSKY O. Plain edge. (Lipscomb UP5090)

STAMM CLOTHING CO.

Van Wert, Ohio

759M	1909	Brass	31mm	18.00	—	30.00

Washington bust, 1909 below. Rv: STAMM CLOTHING CO. / THE MEN'S / VAN WERT / O. / STYLE LEADERS / VALUE GIVERS / EVERYTHING / ALWAYS THE BEST / FOR THE PRICE. Plain edge. (Lipscomb VA3170)

CRAIG BROTHERS

West Liberty, Ohio

Baker	Date	Metal	Size		VF	Unc
759P	1908	Brass	32mm	—	25.00	40.00

Washington bust, 1908 below. Rv: ONE CHECK GOOD FOR / 50¢ AT / CRAIG / BROTHERS / CLOTHING, SHOES, & RUBBERS / WEST / LIBERTY / O. / ON A $10.00 PURCHASE. Plain edge. (Lipscomb WE5010)

WILGUS BROS.

West Mansfield, Ohio

Baker	Date	Metal	Size	F	VF	Unc
759S	1908	Brass	31mm		18.00	25.00

Washington bust, 1908 below. Rv: ONE CHECK GOOD FOR / 50¢ / WILGUS BROS. / CLOTHING, SHOES / & FURNISHINGS / WEST MANSFIELD, 0 / ON A $10 CASH / PURCHASE. Plain edge. (Lipscomb WE6020)

NOTE: Special gratitude is extended for the use of data from Gaylor Lipscomb's catalog of Ohio trade tokens, included in this chapter, and to Hank Spangenberger for his tireless efforts to improve this chapter.

ROSE AND SONS

Youngstown, Ohio

Baker	Date	Metal	Size		VF	Unc
759T	(1912)	Bronze	30mm	—	15.00	

Naked bust of Washington left in field. Wreath on left and right. Rv: Above ROSE AND SONS; around at bottom WE SAVE YOU MONEY. In field in three lines: YOUNGSTOWN, O. / THE WORKINGMAN'S STORE. In exergue: GREENDUCK, CHI. (Fuld NLH79-Bo)

WASHINGTON HOSE CO. NO. 1

Coatesville, Pa.

Baker	Date	Metal	Size	VF	EF	Unc
759W	1971	Silver	32mm	—	—	30.00

Head right, INCORPORATED AUGUST 17, 1871, all within beaded central circle. Around: WASHINGTON HOSE CO. NO. 1 / COATESVILLE, PA. / (tiny) AUG. C. FRANK CO. Rv: Antique fire engine, below: "THE DANGER OF OUR CITIZENS / PROMPTS US TO ACTION" / COATESVILLE, PA. / 1871-1971. Above: 100 YEARS OF VOLUNTEER FIRE FIGHTING. Plain edge.

759X	1971	Goldine	32mm	—	17.50	22.50

As 759W. Plain edge.

GREAT EASTERN CLOTHING HOUSE

Johnstown, Pa.

Baker	Date	Metal	Size	VF	EF	Unc
759Z	(1908-09)	Brass	30mm	25.00	30.00	35.00

Nude bust left, flanked by oak branches at either side. Rv: GOOD FOR / 50¢ / AT THE / GREAT EASTERN / CLOTHING HOUSE /

JOHNSTOWN, PA. / ON A / $500 / PURCHASE. Plain edge. (Hartzog coll.)

There are two die varieties, H of HOUSE directly below S, the other with H slightly right of S.

FIRST NATIONAL BANK

McDonald, Pa.

Baker	Date	Metal	Size	VF	EF	Unc
760	1932	Bronze	32mm	—	—	27.50

Obverse as Baker 925 (undraped bust right, GEORGE WASHINGTON BICENTENNIAL around, 1732 / 1932 to right). Rv: Bank building, FORTIETH ANNIVERSARY 1892-1932 around. THE / FIRST NATIONAL BANK / McDONALD, PA. / WHITEHEAD-HOAG below. Plain edge. (Hansen 20)

Struck by Whitehead & Hoag Co., Newark, N.J.

CENTRAL CIGAR STORE

Norristown, Pa.

Baker	Date	Metal	Size	VF	EF	Unc
761	1912	Bronze	28mm	—	25.00	

Obv as Baker 717B. Around: 100 ANNIVERSARY NORRISTOWN, PA. MAY 5-11, 1912. Rv: Central inscription in six lines, CENTRAL / CIGAR STORE / AND POOL PARLOR / 14 W. MAIN ST. / C.E. FREY / PROP. In exergue: GREENDUCK CO. CHI. (Levine 15; Kirtley March 31, 1998 sale, lot M49)

The date of 1912 on this token is assumed to be accurate, and thus others of this type may well precede the 1932 issues by some decades.

CENTRAL CIGAR STORE AND POOL PARLOR

Norristown, Pa.

761A	(1932?)	Gilt/Brz	32mm	—	15.00	

Obv. of Baker 919I. Rev. CENTRAL CIGAR STORE AND POOL PARLOR, 14 W. MAIN STREET, NORRISTOWN, PENNA. Made by Greenduck, Chicago. (Fuld H53-2-BoGf)

VARIETY CLUB

Philadelphia, Pa.

Baker	Date	Metal	Size	VF	EF	Unc
761S	1960	N & S *	40mm	—	35.00	—

* Nickel ring-encased silver U.S. 1959 quarter. VARIETY CLUB / * OF PHILADELPHIA *. Rv: THE HEART OF SHOW BUSINESS / JAN. 11, 1960, 25TH ANNIVERSARY. Issued holed. (Slawsky 340)

This is a very attractive encased coin, and most likely quite scarce.

WOLFE PRINTING & PUBLISHING CO.

Pittsburgh, Pa.

Baker	Date	Metal	Size	VF	EF	Unc
878	1957	B & S *	39mm	—	30.00	—

* Brass ring-encased silver 1956 U.S. quarter.
1932 1957 / WOLFE PRINTING & PUBLISHING CO. Rv: 1932 1957 / GREETING FROM MAY DILLON CARD CO.

FIRST NATIONAL BANK

Plymouth, Pa.

Baker	Date	Metal	Size	VF	EF	Unc
B761	1932	Brass	32mm	12.50	—	20.00

Washington bust right, 1732 / 1932 at right. Rv: DO YOUR BANKING WITH THE / FIRST / NATIONAL BANK / PLYMOUTH, PA. SAFETY / STRENGTH / SERVICE / ORGANIZED 1864. (Fuld NLH96-BoGf)

Probably a Whitehead & Hoag striking. Scarce.

PAUL KALDES

Scranton, Pa.

Baker	Date	Metal	Size	VF	EF	Unc
762	1932	Bronze	32mm	—	30.00	—

Undraped bust right, 1732 / 1932 below. Around: GEORGE WASHING-TON / BI-CENTENNIAL. Rv: In nine lines: COMMEMORATING / THE BIRTHDAYS / OF CANDYLAND / 1911-1932 / OASIS / 1922-1932 / PAUL KALDES SCRANTON, PA. Plain edge. (Hansen 9)

Struck by F. H. Noble & Co., Chicago, Ill. to the order of Paul Kaldes, proprietor of the establishments known as Candyland and Oasis. Kaldes was not in business in 1918, according to the R. G. Dun Register for that year.

NYCE MANUFACTURING COMPANY

Vernfield, Pa.

Baker	Date	Metal	Size	VF	EF	Unc
763	1932	Gilt/Cop	33mm	—	12.50	—

Obverse as Baker 903B. Rev. Corner view of building., GREETING CARDS, BUSINESS CALENDARS around above, AND COMMERCIAL PRINTING in three lines below, ESTABLISHED 1908 in two lines in exergue, within a round panel; * NYCE MANUFACTURING COMPANY * / VERNFIELD, PA. around periphery.

AUTOMOBILE MUTUAL INSURANCE COMPANY OF AMERICA

Providence, R.I.

765	1932	Copper Shell	204mm	—	20.00	30.00

Plaque, periwigged civilian bust facing left within a round medallion, FIRST IN THE HEARTS OF HIS COUNTRYMEN / 1732 * 1932 around the raised peripheral borders. Rev. Incuse impression of the obverse, manufacturer's signature in two lines at lower right, COPYRIGHT 1931 BY AUTOMOBILE MUTUAL INSURANCE COMPANY OF AMERICA PAT. AP'D FOR / PROVIDENCE R.I. around the upper periphery of the portrait frame. (Levine 33)

This firm still in business 1998, now called Amica.

G. & D. HDW. CO.

(Gray & Dudley Hardware Co.)

Nashville, Tenn.

Circa 1908

Baker	Date	Metal	Size	F	VF	Unc
770	ND	Brass	30mm	30.00	55.00	110.00

Washington bust left within laurel wreath. Rv: BUY / "WASHINGTON" / HARDWARE / HARNESS / SADDLERY / STOVES / G. & D. HDW. CO. / NASHVILLE. Along bottom rim (tiny): THE GREENDUCK CO. CHICA-GO. Plain edge.

Gray and Dudley Hardware Co. by 1918 was a very large firm in the wholesale hardware business. The token was struck by the Greenduck Co. token and medal makers in Chicago.

KIRBYVILLE MERCANTILE CO.

Kirbyville, Texas

Baker	Date	Metal	Size	VF	EF	Unc
771	1909	Alum	34mm	—	42.50	55.00

Bust left, KIRBYVILLE MERCANTILE CO. / 1909 around. Rv: GOOD FOR / 50 ¢ / ON YOUR NEXT / $5.oo / PURCHASE. (Kirtley May 6, 1997 sale, lot AD53; the AU specimen fetched $39.55)

Very few aluminum Washington store cards are dated 1908-1912, and only three issuers in all of Washington cards are reported from Texas in this period.

PACIFIC NATIONAL LIFE ASSURANCE COMPANY

Salt Lake City, Utah

Baker	Date	Metal	Size	VF	EF	Unc
772	1953	B & S *	39mm	—	25.00	—

* Brass ring-encased silver 1952-D U.S. quarter.
* PACIFIC NATIONAL LIFE ASSURANCE COMPANY * / MAIN OF-FICE / SALT LAKE CITY. Rv: A QUARTER CENTURY OF PROGRESS / 25TH ANNIVERSARY YEAR 1953.

VAN DYK TEAS & COFFEES

Virginia

Baker	Date	Metal	Size	VF	EF	Unc
775	1932	Bronze	32mm	—	—	22.50

Undraped bust right, 1732 / 1932 to lower right. Around: GEORGE WASHINGTON BICENTENNIAL. Rv: In upper half a view of Wakefield, WASHINGTON'S BIRTHPLACE WAKEFIELD WESTMORELAND COUNTY VIRGINIA. In lower half, between percolators in four lines: VAN DYK / TEAS & COFFEES / FAMOUS / SINCE 1760. Plain edge. (Hansen 19)

Struck by Whitehead & Hoag Co., Newark, N.J. Also occurs gilt, $17.50 in Unc.

HOTEL JOHN MARSHALL

Richmond, Va.

Baker	Date	Metal	Size	EF	AU	Unc
A775	1932	Brass	32mm	—	—	25.00

Obverse as G737. Rv: HOTEL / JOHN MARSHALL / RICHMOND, VIRGINIA / HOSTS FOR EVERY OCCASION / (tiny) BASTIAN BROS. CO. ROCHESTER. N.Y. (Kirtley May 26, 1998 sale, lot C34)

HOTEL RICHMOND

Richmond, Va.

Baker	Date	Metal	Size	EF	AU	Unc
B775	1932	Brass	32mm	—	—	25.00

Obverse as A775. Rv: HOTEL / RICHMOND / RICHMOND, VIRGINIA / IN THE / CENTRE OF EVERYTHING / (tiny) BASTIAN BROS. CO. ROCHESTER. N.Y.

SHENANDOAH VALLEY NATIONAL BANK

Winchester, Va.

Baker	Date	Metal	Size	EF	AU	Unc
C775	1932	Gilt/Cop	32mm	—	12.50	—

Same obverse as Baker 775. Rv: Corner elevation of a colonial farmhouse, CELEBRATING / THE 200TH ANNIVERSARY OF / WASHINGTON'S BIRTH / AND THE 66TH ANNIVERSARY / OF THE SHENANDOAH VALLEY / NATIONAL BANKS SERVICE / TO THE COMMUNITY / WINCHESTER, VA. / 1932 in nine lines. (Levine 3; Collins 496)

WEIN'S CLOTHING STORE

Spokane, Wash.

Baker	Date	Metal	Size	VF	EF	Unc
879	1906	Brass	33mm	25.00	35.00	60.00

Bust three-quarters right. Above: IN GOD WE TRUST. Below: (Three hearts) 1906 (three hearts). Rv: SOUVENIR / OF / WEIN's / CLOTHING STORE / 515 SPRAGUE AVE. / SPOKANE / (tiny) WHITEHEAD & HOAG CO NEWARK NJ.

RUSSELL RULAU

Iola, Wisconsin

Baker	Date	Metal	Size	EF	Unc	Proof
A776	1990	CN	38.6mm	—	25.00	17.50

Viking ship sailing toward viewer's right, its sail bearing a shield featuring demi-unicorn left. Small PM mintmark above right waterline. Legend: RUSSELL RULAU / 50 YEARS IN NUMISMATICS / AUTHOR / 1939 -- 1989 / JOURNALIST / COINED 'EXONUMIST' 1960. Rv: Within modernistic wreath: AUTHOR / OF / 'HARD TIMES TOKENS' / 'LATIN AMERICAN TOKENS' / 'U.S. MERCHANT TOKENS' / 'DISCOVERING AMERICA'. Around rim: EDITOR 'WORLD COINS' 1964-74 - 'WORLD COIN NEWS' 1974-84 / - POBJOY MINT REP. IN U.S. 1985-90 - U.S. ASSAY COMMISSIONER 1973 -. Plain edge. Mintage: 1000 in Proof; 6 test strikes in Unc., beginning May 19, 1990.

Baker	Date	Metal	Size	EF	Unc	Proof
A776A	1990	Silver	38.6mm	—	—	50.00

As A776, struck in .999 fine silver. Plain edge. Mintage: 20 pieces.

Baker	Date	Metal	Size	EF	Unc	Proof
A776B	1990	Yellow bronze	38.6mm	—	—	60.00

As A766, struck in yellowish bronze. Plain edge. Mintage: Only 2 pieces.

Baker	Date	Metal	Size	EF	Unc	Proof
A776C	1990	Gold	38.6mm	—	—	850.

As A766, struck in .999 fine gold. Plain edge. Weight 31.1 grams. Mintage: Only 2 pieces.

All struck at Pobjoy Mint, Sutton, Surrey, England. The cupronickel blanks (75% copper, 25% nickel) were used from stock intended for 1990 Isle of Man and Gibraltar legal tender crowns, before edge-reeding was applied. Initially 500 pieces were to be struck and passed out without charge to hobby personalities at the August 1990 conventions of the Canadian Numismatic Association in Vancouver and American Numismatic Association in Seattle. A second striking of 500 off the dies was made in July, 1990 and Rulau has occasionally given these as mementos to persons within and outside numismatics, including about 20 medical personnel at Mayo Clinic, Rochester, Minn. who saved his life following heart surgery in August, 1995.

The 20 silver pieces were presented to Rulau family members, Chester Krause, Clifford Mishler, ANA museum, ANS and Smithsonian Institution.

Rulau kept one gold and one bronze specimen, giving the others to his eldest son, Lance Eric Rulau of Elida, Ohio.

By the end of 1998 virtually all the medallions had been distributed. They are included in the Washington catalog because Rulau's name has become inextricably linked to numismatic Washingtonia.

The first edition of *Medallic Portraits of Washington* won for authors George Fuld and Russell Rulau the "Best Specialized Book" award of the Numismatic Literary Guild for 1985.

COLONIAL INN

Milwaukee, Wis.

Baker	Date	Metal	Size	F	VF	Unc
776	ND	Brass	32mm	—	22.00	30.00

Obverse as Baker 719 (civil bust facing on plain field). Rv: REBATE CHECK / 2 1/2 ¢ / COLONIAL INN (Gothic letters) / 171 . 2ND ST. / O. J. HERRMANN PROP. Plain edge. Rarity 7.

Baker	Date	Metal	Size	F	VF	Unc
776A	ND	Brass	32mm	—	22.00	30.00

As 776. Reeded edge.

| 776F | ND | Brass | 32mm | — | 22.00 | 30.00 |

Nude bust right on plain field. Rv: REBATE CHECK / 2 1/2 ¢ / COLONIAL INN (Gothic letters) / O. J. HERRMANN PROP. / 171 - 2ND ST. / MILWAUKEE, WIS. Plain edge. Rarity 7.

Baker 776 and 776F are in the collection of Rich Hartzog, Rockford, Ill.

MARATHON COUNTY HOME COMING

Wausau, Wis.

Baker	Date	Metal	Size	VF	EF	Unc
777	1932	Gilt/Bs	35.5mm	—	25.00	—

Small Washington head right, 1932 below. Around: (In semi-script lettering) MARATHON COUNTY HOME COMING WASHINGTON BI-CENTENNIAL. Rv: Hills in background, plain in foreground. Around: RIB MOUNTAIN / HIGHEST POINT IN THE STATE / WAUSAU, WIS. (formerly Baker 939)

Wisconsin being devoid of mountains, Rib Mountain near Wausau qualifies as the state's highest hill. Struck by F. H. Noble Co.

CARPENTER

Location Not Known

Baker	Date	Metal	Size	EF	Unc	Proof
778	ND	Aluminum	20mm	—	7.00	—

Nude bust right, 2 STEELS FOR 95% OF YOUR ALLOY NEEDS above. CARPENTER / NO. 158 below. Rv: As obverse, except CARPENTER / NO. 5-317 below bust instead of two-line inscription on obverse. Plain edge, (Dr. Schuster coll.)

INDIAN MOTOR CYCLE

| 780C | 1932 | Bronze | 32mm | — | 15.00 | — |

Obv. of Baker 905. Rv: At top, INDIAN MOTOR CYCLE in scroll. In field is Indian to right. Below, 1901 WORLD'S FINEST 1932. (Fuld NLH40-8-Bo)

LOOS SHAFFER GOLADEK ADV. INC.

Baker	Date	Metal	Size	EF	Unc	Proof
780F	1972	CN	39mm	—	7.00	—

Washington bust facing within large O of two-line inscription: THINK / MORE. Rv: KNOW MORE ABOUT YOUR MONEY / $1... George

Washington / $2 ... Thomas Jefferson / $5... Abraham Lincoln / $10... Alexander Hamilton / $20... Andrew Jackson / $50... Ulysses S. Grant / $100... Benjamin Franklin / $500... William McKinley / $1,000... Grover Cleveland / $5,000... James Madison / $10,000... Salmon P. Chase / $100,000... Woodrow Wilson / (tiny) SO1-c 1972 Loos Shaffer Goladek Adv. Inc. Reeded edge.

QUIGLEY'S

Baker	Date	Metal	Size	VF	EF	Unc
783	1908	Brass	30mm	11.00	20.00	32.50

Washington bust, 1908. Rv: GOOD FOR / 50 ¢ / QUIGLEY'S. Plain edge. Two die varieties. (Springfield 4092)

REMEMBER THE YELLOW FLAG

Baker	Date	Metal	Size	VF	EF	Unc
882	1958	B & S *	39mm	—	20.00	—

* Brass ring-encased silver 1958-D U.S. quarter. REMEMBER THE YELLOW FLAG. Rv: CONGRATULATIONS / - ACCIDENT FREE ANNIVERSARY -. (Fuld coll.)

SHELL (OIL CO.)

Non-local

Baker	Date	Metal	Size	EF	Unc	Proof
799	ND	Aluminum	25.5mm	—	.75	—

Facing civil bust, GEORGE WASHINGTON above. Rv: Within ornate border at rim: SHELL'S / FAMOUS / FACTS / & FACES / GAME. Plain edge.

Distributed in the United States in the 1970's by the Shell Oil Company as a business builder for its gasoline stations. Part of a lengthy series featuring famous men and women. Struck by the Franklin Mint, Franklin Center, Pa.

Home office is in Houston, Texas. Associated with Royal Dutch Shell.

SHIPSTEADS & JOHNSON ICE FOLLIES

Location not known

Baker	Date	Metal	Size	VF	EF	Unc
881	1960	N & S *	39mm	—	25.00	—

* Nickel ring-encased silver 1960-D U.S. quarter. EDDIE SHIPSTEAD . OSCAR JOHNSON . ROY SHIPSTEAD . 25TH YEAR. Rv: SHIPSTEADS & JOHNSON ICE FOLLIES SILVER JUBILEE EDITION.

SILVER-MARSHALL

Baker	Date	Metal	Size	VF	EF	Unc
787	1932	Bronze	Oct.25.4mm	—	—	Very Rare

Undraped bust right, 1732 / 1932 at right, GEORGE WASHINGTON in arc below. Rv: SUPERHETERODYNE / BY / SILVER-MARSHALL / PRESIDENTIAL / MODEL / BICENTENNIAL / SPECIAL / WHITE-HEAD-HOAG. Plain edge. Issued holed. Rarity 9. (Hansen 27)

Struck by Whitehead & Hoag Co., Newark, N.J. Silver-Marshall was a radio manufacturer 1929-1934, when it became bankrupt. It's "Presidential Model" honored Washington.

STAR CLOTHING COMPANY

Baker	Date	Metal	Size	VF	EF	Unc
788	1932	Copper	32mm	—	15.00	25.00

Same obverse as 792. Rv: THIS COIN / WORTH $1.00 ON THE PUR-CHASE OF / ANY SUIT / AT THE / STAR CLOTHING / CO. in seven lines. (Fuld NLH H9-2-Bo; Collins 462)

Baker	Date	Metal	Size	VF	EF	Unc
788B	1932	Copper	32mm	—	—	35.00

Same obverse as 788. Rv: Blank. (Levine 3)

WASHINGTON NATIONAL INSURANCE CO.

Baker	Date	Metal	Size	VF	EF	Unc
792	1932	Bronze	32mm	—	—	20.00

Obverse as Baker 704. Rv: PRESENTED TO / OUR / ROLL OF HON-OR / POLICYHOLDER / WASHINGTON NATIONAL / INSURANCE CO. / "LUCKY COIN" / F. H. NOBLE CO. CHICAGO (tiny) Plain edge. (Leon Hendrickson coll.)

Baker	Date	Metal	Size	VF	EF	Unc
792A	1932	CN	32mm	—	—	30.00

As 792.

WEISFIELD & GOLDBERG

Baker	Date	Metal	Size	VF	EF	Unc
794	ND	Gilt/Cop	32mm	—	7.50	11.00

Nude bust right. In exergue in four lines: THIS LUCKY COIN ALWAYS GOOD FOR $1.50 TO $50 ON THE DIAMOND RING OF YOUR CHOICE BRING IT TO [Vertical arrow] WEISFIELD; & GOLDBERG / GOLDEN JUBILEE *GROW-A-DIAMOND-PLAN* around the periph-ery. Rv: Similar design as obverse, though with a large diamond super-imposed on a tree in place of Washington's portrait.

A. J. WILLS OPTICIAN

Location Not Known

Baker	Date	Metal	Size	VF	EF	Unc
795	1909	Brass	30mm	—	30.00	

Undraped bust right, TWENTIETH CENTURY above, 1909 below. Rv: GOOD FOR / 50 ¢ AT / A. J. WILLS (script) / OPTICIAN / ON A / $5.00 / PURCHASE. Plain edge. (Bullowa-Lessin sale, lot 5)

OTHER 20TH CENTURY STORE CARDS

Other 20th century store cards have been reported, for which the authors have only partial descriptions. They are listed here as a reader service. Where prices are given, they are based upon 1997-98 auction records.

Baker	Description
800	Washington Savings, Hollywood, CA (modern)
A800	Boyertown Burial Casket Co., Oakland, CA, 1932, 32mm
801	Bethlehems Gemeinde 1883-1908, Chicago, IL, 1907, 31 mm (AU $17.50)
802	The Chicago Daily News, Chicago, IL, 1932
803	The Play Clubs of Chicago, Chicago, IL, 1932
804	Waller's, Albany, IN, 50c (Wagaman A890)
805	The Boston Store, Alexandria, IN, 50c, 1909 (Wagaman A1280)
806	The New York Store, Cicero, IN, 50c. Rare. (Wagaman C2330)
807	Stewart Bros., Dunkirk, IN, 50c, 1908. R8 (EF $25)
808	Washington Bank & Trust, Indianapolis, IN, $1, 1927
808a	as 808, ctsp S (VF $20, AU $25)
808b	as 808, ctsp A (AU $20)
808c	as 808, ctsp E (VF $10, AU $20)
808d	as 808, ctsp V (AU $20)

(A set of 808a thru d was worth $1 in trade if customer could get ctsps spelling S-A-V-E. A few non-ctsp pieces exist)

809	Downing the Shoe Man, Union City, IN, 25c, 1908 (Wag U440)(VF $17)
810	U. S. Brumer Jewelry and Gift Shop, DeWift, IA, $1
811	First State Bank, Mapleton, IA (VF $25)
812	Pearl Theatre, Newton, KS, 5c (EF $25)
813	City National Bank, Paducah, KY, 1911 (VF $37.50)
814	Massachusetts School Children Memorial, 1932
815	Boston Badge Co., Boston, MA, 50c (VF $16.50)
816	Rome Bros., Gardner, MA, $1, 32mm, ca 1908 (VF $17)
821	American General Casualty, Baltimore, GW mounted (1950-60)(EF $7)
817	Talk with Grieg about Home Life, Detroit, MI
A817	Talk with Moore about Home Life, Detroit, MI (EF $20)
818	Talk with Wiesinger about Home Life, Detroit, MI
819	Talk with Kimes about Home Life, Grand Rapids, MI
820	Talk with Van Tuyl about State Mutual, Minneapolis, MN, 1906 (VF $20)
A820	Union Coffee Co. Limited, New York, NY, brown vulcanite, 40mm (VF $25)
B820	Union Coffee Co. Limited, black vulcanite, 40mm (VF $25)
C820	Union Coffee Co. Limited, dark blue vulcanite, 40mm (VF $25)

A820-C820 are part of a series of all presidents issued under the Alaroma & Bunola trade names by Union Coffee Co. circa 1900.

823	Wanamaker's Christmas, New York, NY, 1913 (WM 38mm)(VF $16.50)
824	J. LaRock Grocery, Ogdensburg, NY, (alum)(VF $21)
825	Herrieff's Clothes Shop, Oneonta City, NY, 50c, 1908 (VG $16.50; EF $30)
826	Emil Geiger's Clothing & Shoe Store, Bellefontaine, OH, 1908 (EF $25)
827	D. L. Yake's Clothier, Cardington, OH, 50c, 1908 (VF $22)
822	Osborne Register Co., Cincinnati, OH, 29mm (1939)(Unc $40)
828	Rotary Club, Eaton, OH, 1932
830	Pri... Piano. C. W... , Shelby, OH, $20 on piano, 1908 (only reported specimen very worn; realized $18.70 in May 1997)
831	Tucker Furniture Co., Oklahoma City, OK, $1 (VF $20)
832	Diamond Jewelry Co., Tulsa, OK, $1 (EF $20)
833	First National Bank of Dunmore, PA, 1910-1930
834	Grand View Hospital, Sellersville, Pa., 1932
835	Alamo Jewelry Co., San Antonio, TX, $1
836	Dr. Pepper Co., Waco, TX, a drink (Sil pl brass)(EF $45)
837	Zale Jewelry Co. Inc., Wichita Falls, TX, $1 (VF $26)
838	Bank of Hampton, VA, Cornwallis 1781-1931 (AU $16)
839	Washington Trust Co., Spokane, WA, 50c (EF $11)
841	Westside Clothing Co., Green Bay, WI, 50c, 1908 (VF $20)
842	Rock County Savings & Trust Co., WI, 50c, ca 1912 (VF $25; EF $40)

Maverick Pieces

Baker	Description
843	The Cash Clothing Store, 50c, 1908
844	Crown Gasoline (modern, 28mm)
845	Cumberland Gardens, $1 (modern, 28mm)
A845	Dicalite, brass-ringed 1954 silver quarter, 1930-1955 (EF $20)
846	Essay Contest Charm, rectangular copper, 1932
847	Gardner Lodge No. 1426, B.P.O.E., (Elks), 1932
848	General Electric, Electric Coffee Maker, 25mm
A848	Genung's, 1932, gilt/brass, 32mm
849	K. of P. National Encampment (Knights of Pythias), octag., 1932
850	E. S. Levy & Co.'s Boys Shop, premium token
851	Little Dutchess Laundry Blue, 25mm
A851	Lunday-Thagard Oil Co., nickel-ringed 1962 silver quarter, 1937-1962
852	The C. & S. Newman Bank, 1957, 28mm
853	Nutone Ventilating Fans, 39mm (modern)
854	Pied Piper Ice Cream Money, 20mm (modern)
856	Rook Bros., 506 Broadway, 25c
A856	Royal Union Life, 1932, bronze, 32mm
857	J. S. & Co. (monogram), WM, 26mm (EF $10)
857a	J. S. & Co. (monogram), Brass, 26mm (EF $10)
A857	Silverberg's Clothes, 1932, gilt/brass, 31 mm
858	Swiss Cleaners & Dyers, 25c
859	Syndicate Clothing Co., 1908, brass, 31 mm (EF $25)
860	Upson Singleton & Co., 1908 (AU $25)
861	Washington Shirt Co., half dollar, 1891-1939 (VF $3, AU $8)
862	Your advertisement can appear, No. 124 (oval 22x33mm)(VF $18)

NOTE: In this chapter, special thanks are due to the late Gaylor Lipscomb and the late Jack Collins, each of whom generously shared information after the 1985 edition of this catalog was released. Gratitude is expressed to Henry Spangenberger for material input. A special debt is owed to Charles E. Kirtley, whose auctions in the 1990s have been strong in Washington store cards, most notably those of May 6, 1997 and March 31, 1998, which had remarkable offerings of 1907-1912 pieces in choice condition. Each token in this chapter features an effigy of George Washington.

There are three basic periods in which Washington tokens appeared: 1907-12, which were generally not collected at the time and thus seldom can be found Unc.; 1932, for the Bicentennial of Birth, much more common; and modern (post-WWII).

Though these Washington tokens of the 20th century are not well publicized or priced high, they constitute one of the collecting opportunities for the 21st century.

TOKENS

Under this heading, William S. Baker in 1885 listed the relatively few tokens known to him as numbers 465 through 505. These were primarily Civil War patriotic tokens, the cent-sized type of token without redeemer's name which passed current at one cent in the 1862-1864 period.

The advances in knowledge obtained in the century-plus since that time by Civil War token collectors has greatly expanded this segment of the subject of Washingtonia -- so much so that complete treatment of the subject here would add endless detail to this catalog -- and merely duplicate the magnificent M. & G. Fuld opus on *Patriotic Civil War Tokens*.

Pricing also is volatile in the patriotic CWT field, so volatile and upward in direction that there is now need for at least biennial updating, and any prices listed in this reference (which we believe may remain in print many years) might be more of a dis-

service than a service.

Prices of patriotic CWT's are fully covered in the $7.50 4th edition of the Fuld work, available through the Civil War Token Society. This is a modest and worthwhile investment.

In addition, a new pricing factor has been introduced, the inclusion of both Civil War store cards and tokens (commonest varieties only) in the three editions of the huge new catalog, *Standard Catalog of United States Tokens 1700-1900*. The catalog, authored by Russell Rulau, had its first edition in late 1994, its second in early 1997, and the third due out in mid-1999.

Civil War buffs will find extensive treatment of Civil War store cards in Chapter 35, 19th Century Store Cards, and many other CWT's are scattered thoughout this catalog in chapters such as those on Carnivals and Fairs, Masonic pieces, etc.

CALIFORNIA GOLD

(All photos shown double normal size)

Baker	Date	Metal	Size	EF	AU	Unc
503	1872	Gold	9mm	660.	770.	1200.

Washington head left, 13 stars around, 1872 below. Rv: In olive wreath: 1/4 / DOLLAR/ CAL. Plain edge. Rarity 4. (Lee 63; BG-722; Norweb 1060-1061)

Baker	Date	Metal	Size	EF	AU	Unc
503A	1872	Gold	9mm	—	700.	1100.

As 503, period after CAL. Rarity 6. (BG-723; Norweb 1062)

Baker 503-503A were minted by Frontier & Bellemere of San Francisco

A perfect Unc. specimen of Baker 503, rated "Mint State 66" by Professional Coin Grading Service (PCGS), fetched $1650 in Superior Auction Galleries sale in 1997 (lot 2852).

Baker	Date	Metal	Size	EF	AU	Unc
504	1872	Gold	Oct,9mm	150.	180.	325.

Washington head left, 13 stars around, 1872 below (same as 503). Rv: CALIFORNIA / * CHARM. */ 1/4 GOLD. Plain edge. Rarity 7. (Lee 62)

Baker	Date	Metal	Size	EF	AU	Unc
504A	1872	Gold	Oct, 9mm	—	—	450.

Obverse as 54. Rv: CALIFORNIA GOLD / 1/4 / * CHARM. *. Plain edge. Rarity 8.

Baker	Date	Metal	Size	EF	AU	Unc
504B	1872	Gold	Oct, 9mm	—	—	400.

Obverse as 504. Rv: 1/4 / DOLLAR / CAL within open-end wreath. Plain edge. Rarity 8.

Baker	Date	Metal	Size	EF	AU	Unc
A504	1872	Gold	10mm	425.	700.	1100.

Similar to Baker 503, on round flan, period after CAL. Plain edge. Rarity 5. (BG-818; Norweb 1077-1078)

Baker	Date	Metal	Size	EF	AU	Unc
505	1872	Gold	Oct, 11mm	—	600.	—

Obverse similar to 503. Rv: CALIFORNIA / * CHARM. */ 1/2 GOLD. Plain edge. Rarity 8.

NOTE: There are other California gold pieces, old and modern imitations as well, with Washington effigies. Consult the references by Lee or Burnie or Breen-Gillio for full details (see Bibliography).

GW WITH PLOW

Struck ca. 1842

Baker	Date	Metal	Size	VF	EF	Unc
T-505	ND	GS	18mm	300.	700.	—

Plow right, initials G W above its beam, and a small eagle displayed, head turned right, above. Around the rim are curiously-shaped shield designs. Rv: Blank. Plain edge. Rarity 7. (Garrett 1905; ex-W.W.C. Wilson sale; Chester Krause coll.; Rulau HT E420)

This token, of apparent early 19th century provenance, is a numismatic mystery. Nothing was known of its background in the early-20th century Wilson sale, or the recent Garrett sales by Bowers & Ruddy Galleries.

It had long been thought the "G W" was associated with George Washington. Stephen Tanenbaum more recently attributed it to Philadelphia, circa 1842.

WILSON'S MEDAL

Baker	Date	Metal	Size	VF	EF	Unc
587	1863	Copper	19.8mm	7.00	10.00	20.00

Head right, six stars at either side, 1863 below. Rv: WILSON'S MEDAL curves around figure 1 within olive wreath, small letter H in wreath opening at top. Plain edge. Rarity 1. (Fuld 112/396; H-G 635; Collins 670-671)

Struck by Charles D. Horter.

PROCESE

Issued ca. 1863

Baker	Date	Metal	Size	VF	EF	Unc
637	1799	WM	19mm	—	200.	—

Obverse as Baker 76 (Bust three-quarters left, BORN FEB. 22 1732. DIED DEC 14 1799. around). Rv: PROCESE across the field. Plain edge. Rarity 9. (Fulk 116/477)

PERSEVERANCE 5

Issued ca. 1867

Baker	Date	Metal	Size	VF	EF	Unc
638	ND	Copper	18mm	125.	175.	275.

Undraped bust right (Fuld CW die 122). Rv: In four lines: PERSEVER-ANCE / 5 / * EXTENDS * / A HEARTY / WELCOME. Plain edge. Rarity 8. (Fuld 122/462; Collins 624)

Baker	Date	Metal	Size	VF	EF	Unc
638A	ND	Nickel	18mm	—	—	375.

As 638. Plain edge. Magnetic. Rarity 9.

GRADE HEADINGS

Three grade (condition) columns appear in this catalog. Coins and tokens, which circulate, are graded down to VG (Very Good), but medals, which do not circulate, usually are graded no less than VF (Very Fine). Other abbreviations used are F (Fine), EF (Extremely Fine), AU (About Uncirculated), Unc (Uncirculated), and P-L (Prooflike). Proof is spelled out.

Chapter 38

ODDS AND ENDS

In this chapter are listed a representative selection of such quasi-numismatic oddments as pillboxes, broaches, pins, etc., and numismatic items which never quite seem to fit anywhere else - plaques, plates and the like. No attempt at completeness is intended - just a selection to show what is available.

PATENT MEDICINE PILLBOX

Baker	Date	Metal	Size	VF	EF	Unc
Y-1	ND	Brass	40mm	—	500.	—

Undraped bust left, WASHINGTON above, PREPARED ONLY BY G. ARNAUD / CACHOU & CARDAMOM AROMATISE below. Rv: Underside of pillbox. Plain edge. (Storer's *Medicina in Nummis* 7436; Mitchell-Rulau B-65; Garrett 1907)

This is a patent medicine pillbox. The piece in the Garrett collection was obtained from the W. Elliot Woodward sale of Feb. 1884, lot 553.

Sarah E. Freeman in *Medals Relating to Medicine and Allied Sciences* (Baltimore, 1964) reported that the Garrett specimen had been in the personal collection of Isaac F. Wood and that Woodward described it as having been designed by Key. It is 7mm thick.

MEDALLIC PAPERWEIGHT

Illustration reduced 50%

Baker	Date	Metal	Size	VF	EF	Unc
Y-2	1936	Brass	89mm	—	27.50	—

Military bust left on plain field. Rv: Liberty Bell. * 1936 *. NORTH PENN REPORTER. Washington quotation. Thick flan. (Kirtley Aug. 5, 1997 sale, lot Y020)

North Penn Reporter was a newspaper.

WATCHES

John Halifax

John Halifax, the well-known watchmaker and jeweler of London, England, who was active 1759-1781, made a watch to the order of George Washington which the general presented to his aide, Maj. Gen. Lafayette, after the Battle of Yorktown, Virginia. It was inscribed: "G. Washington to Gilbert Motier de Lafayette, Lord Cornwallis' Capitulation, December 17th, 1781."

An army of 4500 Americans under Maj. Gens. Lafayette, Anthony Wayne and Baron von Steuben was among the 20,000 French and Americans investing the Yorktown defenses. Lt. Gen. Lord Cornwallis' British-Hessian force, having suffered 600 casualties in the siege which commenced Sept. 26, surrendered his army of 8080 survivors on Oct. 20, 1781.

John Knox

This Belfast, Ireland watchmaker engraved a portrait of George Washington for a watchface paper. Knox was active in Larne for a time, then in Belfast on High Street 1783-1816.

Peter Litherland

The New York museum of the Patriotic Order of Sons of the Revolution had a lever watch patented and created by Peter Litherland of Liverpool, England which had belonged to Col. Benjamin Tallmadge, an intimate friend of George Washington. Litherland obtained his patents 1791-92. In 1816 the watchmakers became Litherland Davies & Co.

RECTANGULAR SILVER INGOTS

In the period 1965 to 1980, virtually every stamping works and even some one-coining press shops styled themselves a "mint" and produced one troy ounce .999 fine silver ingots, generally rectangular with rounded corners measuring 48-50 by 26-32 millimeters. Thicknesses varied. Many portrayed George Washington.

We have examined dozens of such "collector ingots" made by Madison Mint (1976), Washington Mint, Lombardo Mint, U.S. Coinage Corp. (1973), World Mint, Silver Towne, Hamilton Mint (1975), Franklin Mint (1974) and other minting entities -- most of which are of indifferent workmanship. They were produced to sell to the silver-crazed public of the Sixties and Seventies and many were remelted during the Great Silver Blowoff of 1979-1980 (silver reached $50 an ounce one day in January, 1980, then plunged).

These ingots are still being produced today, sometimes in multi-ounce versions and sometimes 24-karat gold plated or enameled in various colors. Taken as a group, they add almost nothing but bulk quantity to Washingtonia, and none is cataloged in this reference. When offered on the secondary market, they usually bring only melt value and frequently one to five per cent less than that.

SOUVENIR PENNIES

A great many copper-coated lead "souvenir pennies" have been produced commercially in the 20th century. Most depict on obverse an Indian Head or Lincoln Head to simulate the current U.S. one-cent piece. They are usually very broad and heavy and make ideal tourist souvenirs for places they visit. A few 73 millimeter "pennies" depict a Washington head left within a circle of 14 stars and are signed K. & O. CO. / MADE IN U.S.A. They are 4.9mm thick.

These copper-coated lead pieces include: "Home of Barbara Fritchie;" "Steamer Alexander Hamilton;" "High Water Mark Monument, Gettysburg," and "Terminal Tower, Cleveland." A very similar 13-star version is signed "J P" and reads "Souvenir Penny of Washington."

Antique shops, flea markets and some numismatic bourse areas see these pieces offered on occasion, but there are no set values, anything from $5 to $25 being the usual ask price. In our opinion, these Washington-head pieces are rather scarce in the numismatic marketplace, though they may well clutter many an attic, barn or garage.

PORCELAIN PORTRAIT

Baker	Date	Metal	Size	VF	EF	Unc
			Made after 1850?			
Y-3	ND	**	**	—	Rare	—

Colored transfer portrait onto porcelain, contained in ornate brass frame arranged diamond-shaped. Measures 91mm across corners. Looped for suspension.

Civil portrait three-quarters left after Gilbert Stuart painting; white periwig and collar, ruffles and shirtfront, deep purple coat. Rv: Blank but wide toothed border around.

WASHINGTON BROOCH

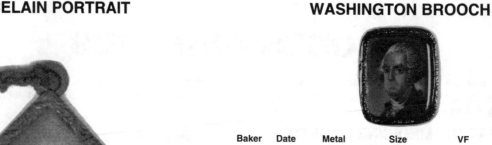

Baker	Date	Metal	Size	VF	EF	Unc
Y-5	1807	Ivory & Gold	Rect	22x26mm	—	1500.

Washington civil dress bust after Stuart facing three-quarters left, the portrait in full natural color on the ivory inset, framed by gold. Rv: Gold field, plain, engraved.: T. KEITH / 1807. Plain edge.

Timothy Keith the Younger, silversmith, jeweler and spectacle maker, was in partnership with his brother William in Boston from about 1805. Later (1825-29) they conducted business in Worcester, Mass.

Both were sons of Timothy Keith the Elder (1774-1806), gold and silversmith of Boston. The Keith brothers seem to have maintained a New York City outlet.

SHELL CAMEO

Created circa 1810

Baker	Date	Metal	Size	VF	EF	Unc
Y-6	ND	xx	Oval,	41.7x52.5mm	—	Ex. Rare

xx White and cream cameo cut from Mediterranean conch, measures 35.8x46mm. Background is pink-orange. Bezel is gold, fitted to sheet-gold by 4 set-screws; hinged pin on back. Specimen fitted with gold chain for alternative suspension in lieu of pinning.

Naked Houdon bust of Washington left, in peruke. (Stack's Inc. January 1998 auction, lot 223)

STICKPIN

Made before 1855

Baker	Date	Metal	Size	F	VF	EF
Y-7	ND	Iron & Gold	Oval 12x15mm	—	—	250.

Head in high relief right, struck on blackened iron oval, which has been attached to a gold stickpin. Pin length 80mm. (Massamore sale of June 11, 1884, lot 453; Clark sale of Feb 17, 1984, lot 2138)

Supposedly presented by Czar Nicholas I of Russia to the officers of a U.S. warship visiting St. Petersburg. Specially engraved in St. Petersburg.

IVORY CAMEO

Baker	Date	Metal	Size	VF	EF	Unc
Y-7A	ND	**	Oval 39x51mm	200.	—	—

** Hand-carved bust of Washington left in high relief on ivory. Frame is gilt brass. Only reported specimen is cracked at lower edge. (Kirtley May 26, 1998 sale, lot AD111)

The three-dimensional engraving is superb, Charles Kirtley commented. Unsigned; probably 19th century work.

SALT GLAZED PITCHER

Illustration reduced!!

Baker	Date	Metal	Size	VF	EF	Unc
Y-8	ND	xx	xx	—	2000.	—

xx Salt glazed pitcher, 9 1/4 inches in height.

Brown salt glazed ware made in either Lambeth or Nottingham. The side panel on the right bears a bust of Washington that is almost identical to the Thomas Webb portrait that appears on the 1805 Eccleston medal (Baker 85). The side panel on the left bears a depiction of a displayed American Eagle perched on a triangular shield. The rest of the pitcher is decorated with an intricate geometric design. Mint condition with no chips. Made ca. 1820-1840. (PCAC June 21, 1996 sale, lot 161)

FIELD MIRROR

Baker	Date	Metal	Size	VF	EF	Unc
Y-9	1844	S/WM Shell	67mm	—	300.	—

Undraped bust left, GEORGIVS WASHINGTON around, all within ornate circular frame. Rv: BREVETE / 1844 on cartouche at center of beaded field surrounded by irregular floreate border. Hanger at top. The two shells open to reveal a mirror. (Rich Hartzog sale of Sept. 4, 1984, lot 2593)

EMBOSSED SHELL CARD

FRENCH REMEDY

Issued ca. 1868

Baker	Date	Metal	Size	F	VF	EF
Y-10	ND	Brass shell	39mm	—	—	100.

Roman-mantled bust left, 13 stars around. Rv: (Paper label, printed): FRENCH REMEDY, / THE / MEDICAL / WONDER! / FOR NEURALGIA / HEADACHE, & C. / PREPARED BY / G. FLACK, (Two illegible lines). Plain edge. (Garrett 1908)

SQUARED QUARTER

Baker	Date	Metal	Size	VF	EF	Proof
Y-11	1984	Silver	Sq 22.4mm	—	—	45.00

Distorted version of Washington quarter design resulting from computerized rearrangement of normal design to enlarge to fill a square, rather than a round, format. The photo speaks for itself. LIBERTY / IN GOD WE / TRUST / 1984 are in normal positions, but "stretched" as though they were rubber. Rv: Stylized eagle displayed (squarish version of the coin's eagle); tiny .999 SILVER above the bundle of arrows. Above: UNITED STATES OF AMERICA / E PLURIBUS / UNUM. Below: SQUARED QUARTER. Reeded edge. (Rulau coll.)

Baker	Date	Metal	Size	VF	EF	Proof
Y-11A	1984	Silver	Sq 25.2mm	—	—	50.00

As Y-11 in larger size. Reeded edge. Weight 15.55 grams (1/2 troy ounce).

The issuers advertised these in periodicals in 1984, but the timing was wrong and they sold poorly. Only a small number was purchased; it is believed much of the issue was remelted.

Y-11 weighs 7.78 grams (1/4 troy ounce). In autumn, 1984, advertisements appeared in daily newspapers in New York, Dallas, Houston, San Juan (P.R.) and in certain selected numismatic and arts periodicals for these items.

A firm styling itself Square Deal Productions Inc. with a post office box address in New York City sold Y-11 at $39 and Y-11A at $49 (postpaid). Medallic Art Co., Danbury, Conn., now out of business, struck the pieces.

Some press comments at the time are poignant: "Coining a solution to squaring the circle." Money Maker Magazine.

"Was George a square?" Hustler Magazine.

"Should be a hit in financial corners." Houston Post.

Our own comment today: "Time tends to homogenize mistakes into realities. These computerized oddities today are actually worth what they cost 15 years ago, but because of scarcity, not hyped demand."

WASHINGTON HATCHET

Chicago, Ill.

Illustration reduced

Baker	Date	Metal	Size	VF	EF	Unc
Y-12	1900	xx	xx	—	Scarce	

xx Hatchet shape, 13 by 5 1/2 inches. Nickel-plated steel. Large enough to use as a hatchet, though intended only as a souvenir.
On hatchet blade: Periwigged nude bust left in high relief within oval depression. Below: G.A.R. / CHICAGO 1900. On handle: Washington / Inaugurated / President Of The / Apr. 30. 1789. / US (monogram form). (Bob Slawsky March 25, 1998 sale, lot 1762)

G.A.R. = Grand Army of the Republic, the principal veterans organization of Union soldiers, formed in 1866. Encampments were held annually into the 20th Century. By 1905 even the youngest soldiers who enlisted at 17 in 1865 were 57 years of age, and most veterans were aged 65 or older, and the G.A.R. was dying out.

Veterans of the Spanish-American War formed the V.F.W. (Veterans of Foreign Wars) in 1899, and veterans of World War I founded the American Legion in 1920. By the latter year, the G.A.R. was mostly just a memory.

INAUGURATION HATCHET

Specialist David Hirsch reports he possesses a Washington hatchet bearing the inaugural date 1789, possibly issued as part of the 1889 Centenial Celebrations. The item is said to be valued at about $60.

LIBBY GLASS HATCHET

Baker	Date	Metal	Size	VF	EF	New
Y-A12	1893	Clear glass	—	—	150.	—

Clear glass hatchet, LIBBY GLASS CO., 1893, WORLDS COLUMBIAN EXPOSITION. (David Hirsch coll.)

The various Washington hatchets refer to the fable about young George chopping down a cherry tree and, when asked by his father who had done this, responded: "I cannot tell a lie. I did it."

The story might be true, but is suspect because it first appeared in a 19th Century book written by a person whose own honesty was questioned. The story was repeated so often it has become legend.

UNIFACE DIE TRIAL

Baker	Date	Metal	Size	EF	AU	Unc
Y-13	ND	WM	Irreg oval 64.1x68.5mm		Unique	—

Nude periwigged bust left in 35mm circle, all struck on large dish-shaped white metal splasher. Rv: Blank. No signature. (Schuster coll., ex-H.I.M. Inc.'s M.B. Phillips sale on Feb. 11-12, 1983, lot 1187)

BOWERS-MERENA GRIFFIN ROUNDS

Baker	Date	Metal	Size	EF	AU	Proof
Y-16	1987	Silver	41mm	—	—	25.00

Civil bust left, small FG at lower right. Around: FIRST PRESIDENT OF THE UNITED STATES OF AMERICA 1789-1797 / .GEORGE WASHINGTON. Rv: Griffin trademark of the numismatic firm, tiny 1 OZ / .999 SILVER / FG at lower right. Around: BOWERS AND MERENA GALLERIES INC. (maker's mark) / 1987. Reeded edge.

Baker	Date	Metal	Size	EF	AU	Proof
Y-17	1988	Silver	41mm	—	—	25.00

As Y-16, dated 1988. Reeded edge.

Baker	Date	Metal	Size	EF	AU	Proof
Y-18	1989	Silver	41mm	—	—	25.00

As Y-16, dated 1989. Reeded edge.

FG = Frank Gasparro, then retired chief engraver of the U.S. Mint. These were sold by Bowers & Merena Galleries of Wolfeboro, New Hampshire, as commemorative medals. The portraiture is quite different than other civil busts of the Pater Patriae, reflecting Gasparro's talent.

WANAMAKER DRAWING COMPETITION

Baker	Date	Metal	Size	VF	EF	Unc
Y-20	1905	WM	38mm	17.50	25.00	—

Nude bust left, with tiny AUG. C. FRANK S.C. under truncation. GEORGE WASHINGTON FIRST PRESIDENT around; all within sunken circle. On raised border: 3rd ANNUAL DRAWING COMPETITION / (scroll) JOHN WANAMAKER (scroll). Rv: Within open-top oak wreath: 3rd ANNUAL / CHILDRENS CHRISTMAS / DRAWING COMPETITION / 1905 / JOHN WANAMAKER / PHILADELPHIA NEW YORK PARIS. Plain edge. (H.J. Levine report)

August C. Frank Co. of Philadelphia struck this unpublished piece.

METALLIC PRIVATE POSTAGE STAMP

Baker	Date	Metal	Size	EF	AU	Proof
Y-21	1978	Gold/Silver*	Rect 20x25mm	—	—	20.00

* Pure gold plate on sterling silver.
Imitation of City Dispatch Post stamp of 1842, Scott Local number 40L1, Scott type L106a. Facing Washington civil bust within oval frame, UNITED STATES CITY DISPATCH POST / (rosette) THREE CENTS (rosette) around. Rv: UNITED STATES / 1842 / (eagle right) / POSTMASTERS OF AMERICA (on scroll) / 3c CITY DISPATCH POST / N.Y.C. CARRIERS' STAMP / 24KT GOLD ELECTROPLATE / ON STERLING SILVER / C-in-circle FM monogram 78 P-in-square. Plain edge.

The New York City Dispatch Post, 46 William Street, New York City, issued the first adhesive stamp used in the U.S., on Feb. 1, 1842, five years before the federal government issued its first adhesive postage stamp in 1847. The issuer, and likely designer, of the stamp was Alexander M. Greig.

Franklin Mint, Media, Pa., created its "Postmasters of America" series of metallic imitations of famous postage stamps in 1978, of which Baker Y-21 was one. The series had only limited appeal to either the numismatic or philatelic fraternity.

The four hallmarks on reverse mean: Copyright Franklin Mint 1978 Proof.

PAGE MILITARY ACADEMY

Baker	Date	Metal	Size	VF	EF	Unc
Y-25	ND	Pewter	35.2mm	—	Rare	

Periwigged bust right. Around: GEORGE WASHINGTON MEDAL PAGE MILITARY ACADEMY / (small) LOS ANGELES. Rv: Small U.S. shield above: MADE OF METAL / FROM A SERVER / USED IN . THE HOME OF / GEORGE WASHINGTON / (crossed olive branches). (H.J. Levine report)

Struck by the Robbins Co., Attleboro, Mass.

LIBERTY LOBBY

Baker	Date	Metal	Size	EF	AU	Unc
Y-26	1979	Silver	40mm	—	—	12.50

Nude bust right, small faint L on truncation. Around: INTEGRITY / 1979 / LIBERTY LOBBY. Rv: Eagle displayed with shield on its breast containing LL interlocked. ETERNAL / VIGILANCE on folds of scroll above eagle. ONE / OUNCE at left, .999 / FINE at right. Around: ONE SILVER EAGLE / GUARANTEED. Reeded edge. (H.J. Levine report)

The workmanship is better than mediocre, considering this piece's purpose was to cash in on the frenzied silver market of 1979, which crashed by Feb., 1980. The authors are not aware who diesinker "L" may be, nor what the "Liberty Lobby" may have been. The eagle's talons clutch a bundle of arrows (right) and a wrench-like tool (left); there is a single 5-pointed star above the LL monogram.

WASHINGTON & PAINE

Baker	Date	Metal	Size	EF	AU	Unc
Y-27	1976	Bronze	45mm	—	—	35.00

Jugate busts right of Washington and Paine, GEORGE / WASHINGTON at left, THOMAS / PAINE at right. In left field, in small script letters: Richard / Lantz / 1976. In two concentric circles of text around: 1776 NEW ROCHELLE +A+ BICENTENNIAL + CITY * 1976. THESE . ARE . THE . TIMES . THAT . TRY . MENS . SOULS / THE* CONSTITUTION IS + THE + GUIDE + WHICH + I + CAN + NEVER + ABANDON (horseman left). Rv: Standing military Washington with sword, head turned right, surrounded by scenes of land and sea battle. Plain edge, marked: C-in-circle MEDALLIC ART CO., DANBURY, CT. - BRONZE. (H.J. Levine inventory)

This medal, engraved by Richard Lantz and struck at Medallic Art Co., has very high relief and exceptional portraiture. Thomas Paine (1737-1809), a British reformer, wrote *The Rights of Man*, an eloquent defense of the aims and achievements of the French Revolution, and his later *Common Sense* influenced American political thought toward independence in 1775.

The symbol (+) in the medal's legend represents a small fleur used as a word separator.

JUSTICE IN AMERICA

Baker	Date	Metal	Size	EF	AU	Unc
Y-28	1981	Bronze	69mm	—	15.00	17.50

Large periwigged head right. Around: THE . LAWS . SHALL . BE . FAITHFULLY . EXECUTED. (each E in all legends is actually a large "e" and the A's have rounded tops). Rv: Female Justice holding balance scales, coins weighting down one side. She wears a half-blindfold covering her right (the viewer's left) eye. Around:… THE . CRIMINAL . IS . SET . FREE . WHILE . THE . VICTIM . IS . FORGOTTEN…In exergue: JUSTICE IN AMERICA / RWJ.D 1981 / CWW. F. Plain edge, with MACO markings. (Kirtley June 16, 1998 sale, lot B020)

Struck at Medallic Art Company; designer R.W. J.; engraver C.W.W.

The right-wing viewpoint regarding uneven justice in America was particularly strong in the U.S. in the 1977-1981 period, the Carter presidency. The anti-criminal feeling helped elevate Ronald Reagan to the presidency 1981-1989 and led to the appointment of federal judges more sympathetic to victims' rights.

BADGES

WASHINGTON ASSOCIATION OF NEW JERSEY

Baker	Date	Metal	Size	VF	EF	Unc
Y-100	1780	Silver Irreg.	32x29mm	—	—	—

Roman-mantled bust left, WASHINGTON ASSOCIATION / .OF NEW JERSEY. around, on oval portion of badge, attached to irregularly rectangular plate with loop for suspension. Rv: Spacious home, inscribed: MORRISTOWN / 1779 1780. Suspended from white and blue ribbon with hanger bar which has for a device a horsehead left dividing W.A. - N.J. (Clark sale, lot 2139)

WASHINGTON LEGION NO 3.

Made 1800-30

Baker	Date	Metal	Size	F	VF	EF
Y-105	ND	Silver	49mm	—	Ex.Rare	—

Uniformed figure standing, facing, holding staff with Phrygian cap in left hand and sword in right, WASHINGTON LEGION NO. 3. / K OF R. above, LABOR OMNIA VINCIT below. U C H on three lower points of flan. (All design details engraved). On 13-point star-shaped flan. Plain edge. Suspended by two chains from hanger pin, which is inscribed (in this case: JOHN TEMPLE.

An early membership badge in the "K" of "R" showing Washington trampling a British crown under his right foot.

Another example appeared in the PCAC Nov. 1994 sale, lot 200.

CONTINENTAL GUARD MEDAL

Struck 1889

Baker	Date	Metal	Size	F	VF	Unc
Y-110	ND	Silver	36mm	—	Ex.Rare	—

Undraped bust left, WASHINGTON CONTINENTAL GUARD around. Rv: Three colonists in 1600's garb engaged in battle with four indians in a forest. In exergue: WE LOVE OUR / COUNTRY. Plain edge. Suspended by ornate hanger from series of five pin-bars separated by acorns reading, respectively: 10 YEARS / INDIAN CAMPAIGN / LOUISBURG / LEXINGTON / LONG AND FAITHFUL SERVICE. (Fuld coll.)

The interesting background of this medal may be found in the writings of George Fuld appearing in the *TAMS Journal* for Dec. 1962 (pg. 105) and Aug. 1963 (pg. 87). It was struck by Tiffany's of New York and appears with "service bars" such as 10 YEARS, INDIAN CAMPAIGN, LOUISBURG, LEXINGTON and LONG AND FAITHFUL SERVICE. The medal is related to the Washington Honor Guard medal of 1889 (Douglas 8) by portraiture and letter-punch links (the Honor Guard piece is another Tiffany product). No history of the "Continental Guard" is known, but it may have been a hereditary patriotic order.

KNIGHTS TEMPLAR NO. 33

Baker	Date	Metal	Size	VF	EF	Unc
Y-112	ND	Brass	xx	—	25.00	—

xx Tree-shaped flan, 34x50mm, looped.
Radiant Washington bust right within triangle, on arms of which are: WASHINGTON / COMMANDERY / NO. 33 K.T. Below base of tree: SARATOGA SPRINGS. Rv: Blank, but incused in small letters near bottom: C.G. BRAXMAR / 10 / MAIDEN LANE / NEW YORK. (H.J. Levine inventory)

Struck by the C.G. Braxmar firm of badge, plaque and medal makers.

ESSEX STAMP CLUB

Baker	Date	Metal	Size	VF	EF	Unc
Y-113	1947	Bronze	32mm	—	30.00	—

Washington bust left on imitation postage stamp, joyous female holding up wreath at right, rays emanating from right. Around: ESSEX STAMP CLUB / (branch) STAMPEX (branch). Rv: Blank, for engraving of award. Issued looped for suspension from tan ribbon with pinback hanger. (H.J. Levine inventory)

The Levine specimen has incused on reverse: 1947 / 3 RD.

MEDALS

POSTAGE STAMP ANNIVERSARY

Baker	Date	Metal	Size	VF	EF	Unc
Y-115	1972	Bronze	39mm	—	—	10.00

Replicas of 1847 5-cent Franklin and 10-cent Washington stamps, Scotts numbers 1 and 2. Above: 125TH ANNIVERSARY / 1847-1972. BENJAMIN / FRANKLIN below 5c stamp, GEORGE / WASHINGTON below 10c stamp. On ribbon: FIRST UNITED STATES / POSTAGE STAMPS, with 1972 below. Rv: 1847-1972 / THE ADOPTION OF POSTAGE STAMPS / IN 1847 FOR USE IN PREPAYMENT OF POST - / AGE REPRESENTED ONE OF THE MOST IMPORTANT / SINGLE IMPROVEMENTS IN THE HISTORY OF THE POSTAL / SERVICE. STAMPS WERE ISSUED TO PROVIDE AN ACCURATE / AND AUTOMATIC CHECK ON POSTAGE REVENUES. PRIOR TO / THE ISSUANCE OF STAMPS, LETTERS ACCEPTED BY POST - / MASTERS WERE MARKED 'PAID' BY MEANS OF PEN AND / INK OR HAND STAMPS OF VARIOUS DESIGNS -- all below seal of U.S. Postal Service. (Greenslet GM-245)

Baker	Date	Metal	Size	VF	EF	Unc
Y-115A	1972	WM	39mm	—	—	10.00

As Y-115.

Issued by the U.S. Postal Service in unknown quantity, one of a three-medal set from the U.S. Post office at Memphis, Tenn. 38117.

GREAT SEAL OF THE U.S.

Baker	Date	Metal	Size	VF	EF	Unc
Y-116	1937	Bronze	40mm	—	15.00	—

Great Seal. Interleaved rings with names of 48 states and 8 territories. Rv: Independence Hall. Effigies of six patriots: Washington, Hamilton, Morris, Franklin, Madison and Pinckney at Constitution Convention. Plain edge, marked MACO, 1937. (Greenslet GM-168)

Engraved by Rudolph Freund. Struck by Medallic Art Co., New York.

GALLERY OF GREAT AMERICANS

Baker	Date	Metal	Size	EF	AU	Proof
Y-117	1971	Silver	39mm	—	—	15.00

Bust facing forward, GEORGE WASHINGTON. Rv: Around above, GALLERY OF GREAT AMERICANS. Above, an eagle atop shield, inscription on shield. A medal in the Franklin Mint Gallery of Great Americans. Sculpted by Anthony Jones. Struck in Proof.

SO FEW LEAD THE WAY

Baker	Date	Metal	Size	EF	AU	Proof
Y-125	1976	Gold/Silver	62mm *	—	—	30.00

* 13-sided flan, 62mm.
Bust of Washington, Franklin, Jefferson and Kennedy facing front. Above: AND SO FEW LEAD THE WAY FOR SO MANY. Revolutionary War soldiers in foreground, above busts, Independence Hall, eagle's head, drummers and fife player within a circle of star, stripes and rocket being launched / 200 YEARS OF FREEDOM below. Rv: Star in center, divided into 13 sections, in each an impression in the form of the state, name of the state and the month and year the state ratified the Constitution. Plain edge, marked: IM 24KT EGP (serial number). (Greenslet GM-287)

Struck by Hamilton Mint.

PLAQUES

Many are rectangular, arranged vertically, unless noted otherwise.

SOCIETY OF COLONIAL WARS

Baker	Date	Metal	Size	VF	EF	Unc
Y-200	1909	Bronze	92x130mm	—	150.	stet

Washington bust facing three-quarters left in three-cornered hat and garb of his surveyor days or militia period, "THE COLONIAL WASHINGTON" above, SOCIETY OF COLONIAL WARS / STATE OF NEW YORK NOV. 16. 1909 below. Signature to right of bust in three lines: KELL / A... / PEALE. Rv: Blank. Plain edge. (Clark sale, lot 2186)

ST. SCHWARTZ, SC.

(photo reduced)

Baker	Date	Metal	Size	VF	EF	Unc
Y-210	ND	Copper	181x231mm	—	200.	—

Civil bust of Washington facing three-quarters left, signed ST. SCHWARTZ. Framed. (Clark sale, lot 2190)

Stephan Schwartz, born in Austria 1851, was employed by and studied medallic art under J.C. Klinkosch until 1870. In 1876 he was appointed professor of sculpture and medallic engraving at Vienna's Kunstgewerbeschule. He won a gold medal in 1900 at the Paris exposition and another at Berlin Academy's jubilee exhibition. In 1912 his list of works appeared in Leonard Forrer's *Biographical Dictionary of Medallists*, volume V. His normal signature was ST. SCHWARTZ.

OVAL PLAQUE

Baker	Date	Metal	Size	VF	EF	Unc
Y-215	ND	Bronze	120x145mm	—	100.	—

Oval

Bust facing slightly left, after Gilbert Stuart portrait. Rv: Stamped S in solid bronze. (Clark sale, lot 2179)

WASHINGTON IN ROOM

(photo reduced)

Baker	Date	Metal	Size	VF	EF	Unc
Y-220	ND	Bronze	150x220mm	—	250.	

Full-length figure standing in civil dress, facing slightly left, right arm outstretched as though deferring to another who is unseen, left hand resting on his sword. He stands in a room with tiled floor, drapery and a cloth-covered table at viewer's left, ornate high-backed chair at right. No signature or inscription. (Clark sale, lot 2188)

WASHINGTON & LINCOLN

SIDE-BY-SIDE PLAQUES

(photo reduced)

Baker	Date	Metal	Size	VF	EF	Unc
Y-230	1799	Nickel/Lead	170x220mm	—	250.	

Washington bust right within wreathed circle, on U.S. flag and above crossed branches, 1732 - 1799 at upper corners, G Washington (script) / THE FIRST PRESIDENT / OF THE UNITED STATES. on panel below. Rv: Blank.

Baker	Date	Metal	Size	VF	EF	Unc
Y-230A	ND	Nickel/Lead	170x220mm	—	250.	—

Lincoln bust left in wreathed circle, above eagle perched on draped flag atop crossed branches. FEB.12TH on scroll above, A Lincoln (script) / "WITH MALICE TOWARD NONE. / WITH CHARITY FOR ALL." on panel below. Rv: Blank.

PATER PATRIAE

Certain Latin terms appear on medals pertaining to George Washington, the first "General of the Armies of the United States." Only one other man held this title until the 5-star rank was created in World War II, and that was John J. Pershing, U.S. commander in France in WWI.

Pater Patriae (father of his country) is the apt title frequently appearing. Many other Latin words and phrases appear on items in this catalog; in most cases we have translated these for users.

(photo reduced)

Baker	Date	Metal	Size	VF	EF	Unc
Y-240	1916	Bronze	Round, 315mm	—	—	200.

Uniformed bust left, with aged countenance, GEORGE WASHINGTON around, 1732 1799 below. Signed in small letters at rim at 4 o'clock: R. OSTRANDER SMITH. SC. 1916. Rv: Blank. On edge: (c) BY THE WILLIAN INC., N.Y. (Clark sale, lot 2196)

PROGRESSIVE BRASS CO.

Baker	Date	Metal	Size	VF	EF	Unc
Y-241	ND	Brass	117.5mm	—	60.00	—

High relief bust left. Incused below: MADE BY / PROGRESSIVE BRASS / CO. K.C. MO. (PCAC Nov. 1997 sale, lot 1187)

PATER PATRIAE PLAQUE

20th century

Baker	Date	Metal	Size	VF	EF	Unc
Y-242	1789	Steel*	74mm	—	30.00	—

* Blackened steel.
Washington standing, facing left. On scroll: DEC. OF INDEP / GEN. GEORGE WASHINGTON / PATER-PATRIAE / INAUGURATED AS THE / FIRST PRESIDENT / OF THE / UNITED STATES OF AMERICA / AT NEW YORK / 1789. Rv: Blank. Issued with two holes for mounting. (C. & D. Gale listing 35, 1998, pg. 26)

HOWARD C. CHRISTY

Struck 1937

Baker	Date	Metal	Size	EF	Unc	Proof
Y-243	1937	Bronze	84x71mm	—	200.	—

Washington stands at left of table as nine other men wait to sign the Constitution. Signature HOWARD CHANDLER CHRISTY beneath desk opening. On table below: WASHINGTON HAMILTON MADISON FRANKLIN / READ SHERMAN PINCKNEY LIVINGSTON MORRIS KING. Rv: Medallion seals of the 13 original states form an arc over the Capitol, Carpenters Hall, U.S. Seal and Independence Hall below. 1787 - 1937 at top, UNITED STATES CONSTITUTION SESQUICENTENNI-AL across bottom. Plain edge. (ANS collection; Greenslet GM-74)

CAST IRON PLAQUE IN BUST SHAPE

Baker	Date	Metal	Size	VF	EF	Unc
Y-242	ND	Iron	Irreg.150x192mm	—	—	75.00

Cast iron civil bust of Washington with body facing three-quarters left and head turned full left. No inscription, signature or other markings. Mounted on hardwood plaque. (Clark sale, lot 2194)

THIN OVAL "LW" PLAQUE

Baker	Date	Metal	Size	VF	EF	Unc
Y-244	ND	Brass	100x145mm	—	150.	—

Thin brass plaque 100x145mm with high-relief 123x84mm oval border. Civil bust against background of 13 scattered stars. Small signature L W under truncation. Facsimile of G Washington signature in faint letters under bust. The oval portion is gilded, while the surround is enameled black. Holed at top for suspension. (PCAC Dec. 1995 sale, lot 1673)

RICHMOND, VA. PLAQUE

Baker	Date	Metal	Size	VF	EF	Unc
Y-245	1928	Bronze	Irreg.	—	85.00	—
			159x70mm			

Standing figure of Washington on pedestal bearing his name. In uniform, his right hand leaning on a cane and left hand resting on his cloak, which is draped over fasces. Below: 39TH ANNUAL CONVENTION SUPREME COUNCIL / M.O.V.P.E.R. RICHMOND, VA / 1928 / (small bearded "prophet" face). Thin planchet. Holed for suspension. (PCAC Dec. 1995 sale, lot 1674)

LAURA FRASER/MEDALLIC ART PLAQUE

Baker	Date	Metal	Size	VF	EFUnc
Y-246	ND	Bronze	151x249mm	—	300.

Huge mounted plaque. Screw mounted on 8 3/4 by 13 13/16-inch slab of black onyx-like material; lock suspension.
Equestrian bas-relief of Washington in general's uniform at center. Above: GEORGE WASHINGTON / 1799. Below: HE WENT TO WAR / A COLONIAL VIRGINIAN / HE RETURNED A CITIZEN / OF THE UNITED STATES, flanked by fasces. Washington coat of arms separates OF THE -- UNITED STATES. (Hansen 58, design of Hansen 57; PCAC July 1993 sale, lot 202)

Engraved by Laura Gardin Fraser and struck at Medallic Art Co., New York.

OVAL FRENCH PLAQUE

Baker	Date	Metal	Size	VF	EF	Unc
Y-247	1859	Bronze	84x119mm	—	90.00	—

High relief civil bust of Washington, legend: GEORGES WASHING-TON. Incused in left field: (small) APHSE FOQUET (1859). High rim. Thick (10mm) planchet. Rv: Blank. (PCAC sale 55 of Dec. 1993, lot 85)

KATO UNIFACE PLAQUES

Cast circa 1900?

Baker	Date	Metal	Size	VF	EF	Unc
Y-248	ND	Svd/Bronze	108mm	75.00	125.	—

Bust left, GEN. WASHINGTON / 1782 - 1799 around. Rv: Blank, but K-within-oval logo appears. (Kirtley March 31, 1998 sale, lot N25)

Y-248A	ND	Gilt/Bronze	108mm	75.00	125.	—

As 248, golden colored. (Kirtley N26)
Y-248 and 248A are cast in bronze, not struck. G. P. Kato issued a quite similar portrait plaque honoring Christopher Columbus in 1892 (Rulau *Discovering America* B88-B88A; Eglit 301). All Kato's plaques were intended as hanging decorations.

Kirtley's N25 and N26 realized only $35 each in 1998 in EF, far less than their Columbian counterparts fetched years earlier. This may have been due in part to the wrong illustration accompanying the lots. All Kato plaques are scarce and desirable, as antiques as well as numismatica.

LUINI PLAQUE

Photo reduced 50%

Baker	Date	Metal	Size	EF	AU	Unc
Y-250	ND	Bronze	175x260mm	—	—	300.

Periwigged military bust left, with strong and exceptional portraiture. Tiny signature C. Luini at lower left corner. Rv: Blank, but loop for hanging attached. (Kirtley March 10, 1990 sale, lot 2610; estimated in 1990 at $300 to $450)

Artist C. Luini has not been traced. The plaque is cast in bronze, not struck. The workmanship is superb for this unpublished, little-known work.

Y-249	ND	Bronze	69mm	—	45.00	—

Bust left, G. Washington above: Rv: Blank, but K-within-oval logo. (Kirtley report)

Cast, possibly circa 1889.

Adams, E. H. & Woodin, W. H., "United States Pattern, Trial and Experimental Pieces." New York, 1913.

Albert, Alphaeus H., "Washington Historical Buttons." Hightstown, N.J., 1949.

Atkins, James, "The Tradesmens Tokens of the Eighteenth Century." London, 1892.

Bailey Banks & Biddle Co., "American Orders & Societies and their Decorations." Philadelphia, 1913.

Baker, William S., "Medallic Portraits of Washington." Philadelphia, 1885. Also, revision by George J. Fuld, Iola, Wis., 1965.

Belden, Bauman L., "Indian Peace Medals Issued in the United States." New York, 1927.

Belden, Louise Conway, "Marks of American Silversmiths in the Ineson-Bissell Collection." Winterthur, Del., 1980.

Betts, C. Wyllys, "American Colonial History Illustrated by Contemporary Medals." New York, 1894.

Bolen, James A., "An Accurate and Descriptive Catalog of the Medals, Cards & Facsimiles struck from Dies made by J. A. Bolen." Providence, R.I., 1905.

Bowers, Q. David, "The History of United States Coinage as Illustrated by the Garrett Collection." Los Angeles, 1979.

Breen, Walter, "United States Half Cents." New York, 1985.

Breen, Walter, "Walter Breen's Complete Encyclopedia of U.S. and Colonial Coins." New York, 1988.

Breen, W. & Gillio, R., "California Pioneer Fractional Gold." 1983.

Brunk, Gregory G., "Merchant Countermarked Coins." Copyright 1993; not published until 1999, Rockford, Ill. (Replaces a 1987 version)

Brunk, Gregory G., personal correspondence 1993-1998 with the authors.

Burnie, R. H., "Small California and Territorial Gold Coins." Pascagoula, Miss., 1955.

Bushnell, Charles I., "An Arrangement of Tradesmen's Cards, Political Tokens, also Election Medals." New York, 1858.

Calvert, M. and Young, P., "A Dictionary of Battles (1715-1815)." New York, 1979.

Contenson, Baron L. de, "La Societe des Cincinnati de France et la Guerre d/Amerique, 1778-1783." Paris, 1934.

Crosby, Sylvester S., "The Early Coin of America." Boston, 1875. (Reprint 1975)

Dalton, R. & Hamer, S. H., "The Provincial Token-Coinage of the 18th Century." Reprint, Lawrence, Mass., 1977.

Davidson, Marshall B., "The American Heritage History of American Antiques from the Revolution to the Civil War." 1968.

DeWitt, J. Doyle, "A Century of Campaign Buttons 1789-1889." Hartford, Conn., 1959.

Dickeson, Montroville W., "The American Numismatic Manual." Philadelphia, 1859-1865.

Dillon, Richard H., "North American Indian Wars." New York, 1983.

Douglas, Susan H., "The George Washington Medals of 1889." In The Numismatist for 1949.

Dubois, Patterson, "The Pattern Piece." In American Journal of Numismatics for Jan., 1883.

Forbes, Esther, "Paul Revere & the World He Lived In." Boston, 1942.

Ford, John J., "The Washington Before Boston Medal." In Spink's Numismatic Circular for May, 1969.

Fuld, George J., "The Washington Before Boston Medal." In TAMS Journal for 1963.

Fuld, George J., "Medallic Memorials to Franklin." In The Numismatist for 1956.

Fuld, George J., "A Group of Restruck Patterns." In The Numismatist for May, 1998.

Fuld, George J., "Coinage Featuring George Washington." In Coinage of the Americas Conference (COAC 95) by American Numismatic Society, New York, Oct. 28, 1995. (This 94-page monograph completely reexamines all cataloging of 1783-1820 Washington portrait coins, tokens and fantasies, and their mid-19th century restrikes and imitations. The Fuld numbering system, e.g. WA-1786-4, is cited under the Baker numbers.)

Fuld, George J., "Origin of Washington 1783 Cents." In The Numismatist for 1964, pgs. 1745-1781.

Fuld, George J., "Oval Washington Indian Peace Medals." In The Numismatist for March, 1996, pgs. 278-286.

Fuld, George & Melvin, "U.S. Civil War Store Cards." 2nd edition, Lawrence, Mass., 1975.

Fuld, George & Melvin, "Patriotic Civil War Tokens." Racine, Wis., 1960. 4th revised edition by Civil War Token Society, 1993.

Fuld, G. J. & Newman, E. P., "Rediscovery of the 1796 Getz Dollar." In Numismatic Scrapbook Magazine for 1961, pgs. 2802-2805.

Fuld, Melvin, "Hansen on Washington Bicentennial Medals Listed by Obverse." In TAMS Journal for Nov.-Dec., 1966.

Greenslet, Philip, "The Medals of Franklin." Token & Medal Society.

Hansen, Harvey L., "George Washington Bicentennial Celebration 1732-1932." In *The Numismatist* for Jan., 1934.

Hibler, Hal E. & Kappen, Charles, "So-Called Dollars." New York, 1963.

Holland, "Centennial Medals." In *American Journal of Numismatics* for Oct. 1878.

Hume, Edgar E., "George Washington's Eagle of the Society of the Cincinnati," in *The Numismatist* for March, 1934.

Hume, Edgar E., "The Medals of the Society of the Cincinnati." In T*he Numismatist* for April, 1934.

Johnson, Edwin L., "J. A. Bolen's Medals, Cards, and Facsimiles." 1882.

Judd, J. Hewitt, "United States Pattern, Experimental & Trial Pieces." Racine, Wis., 1962.

JK = Julian, R. W. and Kuesch, E. W., "Medals of the United States Assay Commission 1860-1977." In *TAMS Journal* for October, 1989.

Julian, Robert W., "The Medals of the United States Mint." (1792-1892). El Cajon, Calif., 1977.

Kenney, Richard D., "Struck Copies of Early American Coins." New York, 1952.

Kenney, Richard D., "Early American Medalists and Die-Sinkers Prior to the Civil War." New York, 1954.

King, Edward A., "Masonic Chapter Pennies." Pittsburgh, 1926.

King, Robert P., "Lincoln in Numismatics." In *The Numismatist* for 1924, 1927 and 1933.

Krause, C. & Mishler, C., "Standard Catalog of World Coins, 20th Century Issues." Iola, Wis., 1999.

Kurth, Howard, "American Game Counters." Chicago, 1952.

Langer, William L., "An Encyclopedia of World History." Boston, 1968.

Lee, Kenneth W., "California Gold Quarters - Halves - Dollars." Los Angeles, 1970.

Levine, H. Joseph, "George Washington Bicentennial Celebration, 1732-1932." In *The Numismatist* for April, 1979.

Lipscomb, Gaylor, "Ohio Merchant Tokens." Hamilton, Ohio, 1986.

Loewy, Benno, "Bibliography of Masonic Medals and Badges." 1905.

Loubat, Duke J. F., "The Medallic History of the United States of America, 1776-1876." New York, 1878.

Marvin, William T. R., "The Medals of the Masonic Fraternity." New York, 1880.

McCabe, James D., "Illustrated History of the Centennial Exhibition." Philadelphia, 1876.

Musante, Neil E., "A Supplement to Medallic Portraits of Washington, by William S. Baker." Transcribed with remarks in *TAMS Journal* for Aug., 1996.

Pessolano-Filos, Francis, "The Assay Medals, 1860-1977."

Pollock, Andrew W., "United States Patterns and Related Issues." Wolfeboro, N.H., 1994.

Prucha, Francis P., "Indian Peace Medals in American History." Lincoln, Neb., 1971.

Raiford, William Russell. Personal correspondence 1996-1998 between executive of the Society of the Cincinnati and the authors.

Raymond, Wayte, "The Early Medals of Washington 1776-1834." New York, 1941.

Roelofs, Reigh L. Personal correspondence 1997-1998 with the authors.

Rulau, Russell, "Standard Catalog of United States Tokens 1700-1900." 2nd edition, Iola, Wis., 1997.

Rulau, Russell, "Hard Times Tokens." 6th edition, Iola, Wis., 1996.

Rulau, R. and Fuld, G. J., "Medallic Portraits of Washington." Centennial edition, Iola, Wis., 1985.

Rulau, R. and Fuld, G. J., "American Game Counters." Iola, Wis., 1972.

Sipsey, E. T., "Dies by Wyon, an Exercise in Fact and Supposition." In *Colonial Newsletter* for 1965-66.

Snowden, James R., "A Description of the Medals of Washington; of National and Miscellaneous Medals." Philadelphia, 1861.

Stahl, Alan M., "Medals of the Comitia Americana Series in the Collections of the American Numismatic Society and Other Public Institutions." COAC 95, New York, 1996.

Taxay, Don, "The U.S. Mint and Coinage: An Illustrated History from 1776 to the Present." New York, 1966.

Vlack, Robert A., "Early American Coins." Johnson City, N.Y., 1965.

Waters, Arthur W., "Notes on Eighteenth Century Tokens." London, 1954.

Weidhaas, Ernest, "New York World's Fair Medals 1939-1940." In *The Numismatist* for March thru June 1963 and July 1966.

Witham, Stewart P. Personal correspondence 1984-1986 between the late Washington expert and the authors.

Wright, Benjamin P., "The American Store or Business Cards." Reprint, Lawrence, Mass., 1972.

Yeoman, Richard S., "A Guide Book of United States Coins." Racine, Wis., 1998.

NOTE: In addition to the references listed above, and the separate listing of Auction Catalogs referred to, occasional citations in the text of the catalog may refer to other books, catalogs or periodical articles.

INDEX

THE LATEST VALUES FOR COINS FROM AROUND THE WORLD

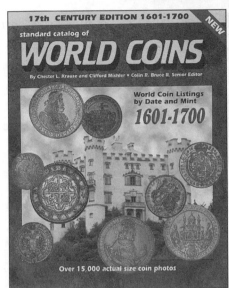

Standard Catalog of World Coins, 1601-1700
by Chester L. Krause and Clifford Mishler; Colin R. Bruce II, Senior Editor
Trace current values for all world coins minted between 1601-1700 in up to four grades of preservation. Buy or sell with inside information on mintages, types, rarity, value.

Softcover • 8-1/2 x 11 • 1,152 pages
15,000 b&w photos
C401 • $65.00

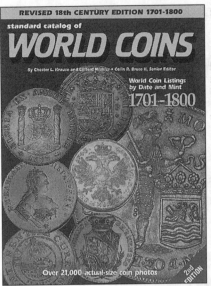

Standard Catalog of World Coins, 1701-1800
2nd Edition
by Chester L. Krause and Clifford Mishler, Colin R. Bruce II, Senior Editor
The latest values for coins from around the world dated 1701-1800 are conveniently listed by country and denomination in up to four grades of preservation. Includes more than 20,000 detailed photos for ease of identification. Companion volume to 17th, 19th, and 20th Century catalog/value guides.

Softcover • 8-1/2 x 11 • 1248 pages
20000 b&w photos
SE02 • $65.00

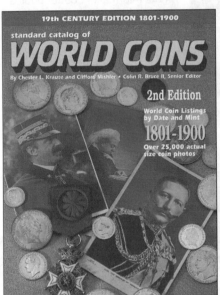

Standard Catalog of World Coins, 1801-1900
2nd Edition
by Chester Krause and Clifford Mishler. Edited by Colin Bruce
From the smallest developing nations to the most expansive monarchies, the record of the dynamic 19th century is captured forever in the coins of the world. Unearth tens of thousands of coins through detailed photographs, valuations in up to four grades of condition, mintage figures, precious metal weights, design details, identifying marks and much more. Fully updated market values for all listings and new illustrations give you the latest advantages on the previous century of coin collecting.
Softcover • 8-1/2 x 11 • 1,032 pages
24,000+ b&w photos • **SCN02 • $45.00**

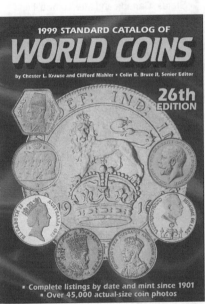

1999 Standard Catalog of World Coins
26th Edition
by Chester L. Krause and Clifford Mishler, Colin R. Bruce II
This sourcebook on 20th century coins contains more than 1 million prices covering every coin known to mankind. Completely updated and revised with world coins from 1901- early 1998. You'll find detailed photographs of obverses and reverses, valuations in up to 4 grades, accurate mintage figures, metallic composition and weight.

Softcover • 8-1/2 x 11 • 1,872 pages
46,000+ b&w photos
SC26 • $47.95

To order by credit card or to receive a FREE catalog, call

800-258-0929 Dept. NGB1

Mon-Fri, 7 a.m. - 8 p.m. • Sat, 8 a.m. - 2 p.m., CST
Krause Publications • 700 E. State Street • Iola, WI 54990-0001
web site: www.krause.com

Dealers call 888-457-2873 ext. 880, 8 a.m. - 5 p.m. M-F

THE MOST EXTENSIVE COIN AND PAPER MONEY SOURCES AVAILABLE

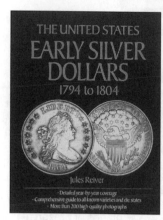

The United States Early Silver Dollars 1794 to 1804
by Jules Reiver
All-new volume based on M.H. Bolender's 1950 classic, sheds new light on one of the most treasured realms of American coin collecting. Covering the first decade of American silver dollars, from 1794-1804. This book explains how a fledging nation developed its currency and established its first mint.
Hardcover • 8-1/2 x 11 • 96 pages
200 b&w photos
ESD • $37.95

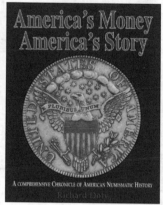

America's Money-America's Story
by Richard Doty
If you are a beginning or advanced collector, historian, or numismatic dealer, you will want the most comprehensive chronicle of American money ever published. This exhaustively researched volume traces American money's evolution from pre-European settlement to the present day. Included are chapters on the Revolutionary War, the California Gold Rush, America's Gilded Age, and more.
Softcover • 8-1/2 x 11 • 248 pages
250+ b&w photos
TPAN • $34.95

1999 North American Coins & Prices
8th Edition
Edited by David C. Harper
Sweep across one continent, three countries, hundred of years and thousands of great coin opportunities with the only updated book on North American coins that covers everything in the United States, Canada and Mexico. You'll find updated coin prices, commemoratives, varieties and errors, and the latest hot coin topics and controversies. More than 45,000 updated values help you know instantly the current value of a coin and more than 1,500 photos help you identify with certainty your treasures, rarities, and varieties.
Softcover • 6 x 9 • 544 pages
1,500 b&w photos • **NA08 • $16.95**

Standard Catalog of United States Tokens 1700-1900
2nd Edition
by Russell Rulau
The most extensive source available goes a step further in this new 2nd edition. You'll find 50% more information, better photos, updated pricing and carefully revised listings. Every token from colonial times to the dawn of the 20th century is cataloged and priced for beginning and veteran collectors.
Softcover • 8-1/2 x 11 • 944 pages
4000 b&w photos • **ST02 • $47.95**

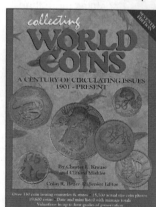

Collecting World Coins
Seventh Edition
by Chester L. Krause & Clifford Mishler, edited by Elizabeth Burgert
Find accurate values in up to the four most common grades of preservation for more than 19,750 popular world coins from 1901 to date. Represents 330 coin issuing countries. More than 15,000 crisp photos make coin identification easy.
Softcover • 8-1/2 x 11
752 pages
15,700 b&w photos
CC07 • $28.95

Standard Catalog of German Coins
1601-Present, 2nd Edition
by N. Douglas Nicol, edited by Fred J. Borgmann, Colin R. Bruce II, Senior Editor
Enjoy a 400-year symphony of rich art, diverse states and proud emperors through the comprehensive coverage of German coinage in this one volume. Here is your opportunity to amass a fortune of essential buying and selling power with tens of thousands of fully detailed coins - priced in up to four grades of preservation - from every dynasty, kingdom, and republic, within the German possessions since 1601. Crisp photos, historic maps and instant identifiers bring you the riches of the Empire.
Softcover • 8-1/2 x 11 • 1,064 pages
18,000 b&w photos
GE02 • $59.00

To order by credit card or to receive a FREE catalog, call

800-258-0929 Dept. NGB1

Mon-Fri, 7 a.m. - 8 p.m. • Sat, 8 a.m. - 2 p.m., CST
Krause Publications • 700 E. State Street • Iola, WI 54990-0001
web site: www.krause.com
Dealers call 888-457-2873 ext. 880, 8 a.m. - 5 p.m. M-F